KV-289-767

THE PRINCIPLES OF HEREDITY

WITHDRAWN
FROM
UNIVERSITY OF PLYMOUTH
LIBRARY

20. DEC 1982

90 0691446 6

Books are to be returned on or before
the last date below

25. OCT. 1983

14 MAR 1989

CANCELLED

-5. FEB. 1986

CANCELLED

12. JUN. 1986

25 JAN 1991

CANCELLED

CANCELLED

18. MAY 1994

- 1 MAY 2003

CANCELLED

CANCELLED

-1. Cancelled 1989

LIBREX—

PLYMOUTH POLYTECHNIC LIBRARY

LRC - 3 DEC 1981

Telephone
Ply. 21312
Ext. 219

Telex
45423

A book may be renewed by telephone or by personal visit
if it is not required by another reader.
CHARGES WILL BE MADE FOR OVERDUE BOOKS

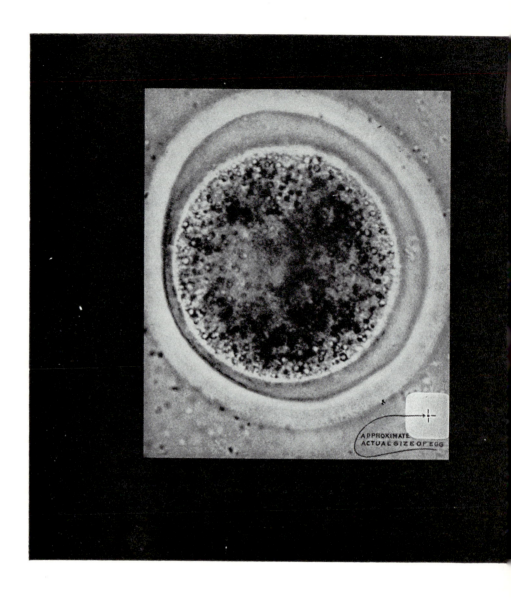

THE NARROW HEREDITARY BRIDGE. Through the microscopic egg and the even
smaller sperm are transmitted all the potentialities which can be
passed on from parents to offspring. Above, an egg, and at the
right, sperms, of cattle, magnified many hundred times. *From
Cook in the Journal of Heredity. Photomicrograph of egg by C. C.
Hartman and Warren H. Lewis. Photomicrograph of sperms by
Bureau of Dairy Industry.*

THE PRINCIPLES OF

HEREDITY

LAURENCE H. SNYDER, Sc.D.

Dean of the Graduate College
The University of Oklahoma

AND

PAUL R. DAVID, Ph.D.

Professor of Zoölogy
The University of Oklahoma

FIFTH EDITION

D. C. HEATH AND COMPANY · BOSTON

Library of Congress Catalog Card Number: 57-6312

PLYMOUTH POLYTECHNIC
LEARNING RESOURCES CENTRE

ACCN.
No.   69070

CLASS
No.   575·1 SNY

-0. SEP. 1977

Copyright 1957 by L. H. SNYDER AND PAUL R. DAVID

No part of the material covered by this copyright may be reproduced in any form
without written permission of the publisher. *Printed in the United States of America.*
D. C. HEATH AND COMPANY

To the memory of

CHARLES BENEDICT DAVENPORT
Who, in the midst of arduous administrative
duties, found time to teach and to befriend

PREFACE

Through its previous four editions this book has been designed to acquaint the beginning student of heredity with the facts and principles of inheritance. It has also been the purpose of the book to arouse and hold the interest of the student and to stimulate his thinking. To these ends human characters and other familiar examples have been chosen wherever feasible, and the discourse has been kept simple and straight-forward.

During each of the intervals between successive editions of the book, some new facet of genetics has developed to the point where it demanded inclusion in the text. Thus over the years there have been added, among others, discussions of giant chromosomes, of biochemical genetics, and of cytoplasmic inheritance. Such developments have not been lacking in the interval following the appearance of the fourth edition. The genetics of bacteria and viruses has now been brought to the point where a discussion of this topic seems imperative, and a chapter has been devoted to it. The new chapter has been correlated with the textual material on cytoplasmic inheritance and on genes and development, and these three chapters have been grouped together to form an integrated unit following the discussion of genes and mutations.

The phenomenon of pseudoallelism has become one of major interest, and a discussion of this topic is included in Chapter 26.

When the giant chromosomes were newly discovered, they were awarded a separate chapter in the text. It now appears that their study is so intimately concerned with the analysis of chromosomal aberrations that the material dealing with salivary chromosomes has been integrated with the treatment of aberrations. The discussion has been divided into two chapters, one dealing with variations in the numbers of chromosomes, and the other with rearrangements of chromosomal material. This division should provide a more effective teaching device.

The chemical structure of desoxyribose nucleic acid has now been elegantly determined by the British workers, and a discussion of the structure and genetic importance of this substance has been added to Chapter 24. Further discussions of the genetic implications of DNA appear in the new chapter on bacterial genetics.

The chapter on the physical background of Mendelian inheritance has been extensively rewritten, as have the chapters on sex-linked genes, on linkage and chromosome mapping, the cytological basis of crossing over, and the determination of sex. The presentation of the blood groups has been brought up to date, and the two systems of notation currently in use have been compared and explained. Since a clear understanding of the meaning of *locus* is helpful in grasping the idea of multiple allelism, the chapter on multiple alleles has been moved to follow the chapters on linkage and mapping.

Some additional rearrangement of chapters has been undertaken, largely on the advice of users of the text. A sampling of opinions of teachers who have adopted the book was made, and we are grateful for the many excellent suggestions we received. The chapter on lethal factors has been eliminated as such; its contents have in part been inserted into a new chapter (3) along with the discussion of lack of dominance, under the heading "Modifications of the 3:1 ratio," and in part included in the chapter on sex-linked genes. Sex-influenced and sex-limited characters have been combined into a single chapter.

Brief introductions to the production of enzymes by genes have been added to several of the early chapters, thus giving the student a feeling for biochemical genetics early in the course. The chapter on selection and breeding methods has been expanded, and almost every chapter has been revised to some degree.

In the discussion of evolution genetics (Chapter 28) improved continuity has been effected, we believe, by removing the greater part of the derivation of formulas to an appendix at the end of the chapter.

The general consensus of users of the fourth edition was that the final chapter, on the analysis of human pedigrees, was not assigned to students. In preparing manuscript for the fifth edition this chapter was therefore deleted, and some of the simpler concepts were discussed in other appropriate chapters.

Many new problems appear in this edition, and some of the problems of previous editions have been omitted. It should be re-emphasized that the problems provide valuable sources of factual and thought-provoking material supplementary to the discussion in the text. New illustrations have also been added to many of the chapters.

Although we cannot here mention them by name, we wish again to thank all those who gave advice and help with previous editions. For aid and advice in preparing manuscript for this edition, we wish to express our sincere thanks to our colleagues, Doctors H. L. Chance, J. B. Clark, K. E. Crook, B. B. Hyde, and S. H. Wender. We are grateful to Mr. and Mrs. R. C. Dragoo, Jr., who helped so effectively in the preparation of the manuscript and illustrations. The authors assume full responsibility for any errors which may appear and will always welcome suggestions and criticisms from those who may use the book.

LAURENCE H. SNYDER
PAUL R. DAVID

The University of Oklahoma

CONTENTS

THE PRINCIPLES OF HEREDITY

CHAPTER ONE

The study of heredity

One of the most interesting developments of the twentieth century has been the clarification of the basic principles underlying the production of characteristics, or traits, in successive generations of living organisms. Although from time immemorial man has speculated as to the causes of variation, it is only in comparatively recent years that any real understanding of the principles involved has been reached.

The most elementary observation will provide us with material for thought along these lines. Dogs, for example, produce puppies, never kittens. Yet the puppies in a litter may possess such individuality that a child can distinguish one from the others by looking at it or by listening to it squeal or even by touching it in the dark. The puppies themselves will be able to distinguish any person from any other by odor as well as in other ways.

No two individuals are exactly alike. Variability is a fundamental characteristic of living things. Although no two individuals are quite alike, we do recognize many similarities among organisms, and we soon come to realize that many of these similarities are obviously correlated with the closeness of the biological relationship between the individuals. We do not always so readily realize what is equally true, namely that the *differences* among individuals may also be correlated with the relationship between them.

Biological relationship, however, is only part of the cause of similarities and differences between individuals. Actually such individuality is the result of the interaction of hereditary and environmental influences. The relative contribution of each of these influences varies from trait to trait and from circumstance to circumstance. The science of **genetics** embodies the study of the contributions of biological make-up and environment and the analysis of the principles and laws underlying the action of the biological influences.

As a subject for thought and discussion genetics arouses our keenest interest because we ourselves are the products of innumerable hereditary traits, developing and interacting under the influence of the environment which is our world. As a science genetics is subject to certain natural laws, and although relatively young it already compares in exactness with such older sciences as physics and chemistry.

Genetics touches many fields, from each of which it has drawn material for its foundations and support and to some of which it has contributed definite principles or practical applications in return. Examples of such practical applications will be brought out in succeeding chapters.

The earlier work in genetics was largely evolved from the experimental study of plants and animals. One of the pleasing later results has been that the genetic principles thus evolved appear to be just as applicable to man as to the flies, corn, cows, or Jimson weeds from the study of which they were developed. It is possible, therefore, in a beginning study of genetics to use human beings to some extent as the subjects for discussion. This we shall endeavor to do as far as possible.

In developing principles, however, it is frequently valuable and sometimes quite necessary to illustrate by means of such plants and animals as are easily and quickly raised by investigators in the laboratory. In many instances, of course, the student of heredity is directly concerned with the improvement of domestic animals and cultivated plants. It is no uncommon procedure these days for the geneticist to make a new variety of plant to order. In animals the procedure is slower and more difficult, but the improved breeds of live stock, pets, and poultry owe their present-day perfection to man's increasing knowledge of the principles of genetics. And the end is not yet.

In the case of man himself we are just beginning to realize our opportunities. The vision of a day when more and more individuals will be like the best of our race, and fewer and fewer like the poorest, is dawning under the influence of the genetic viewpoint. Every day new facts about human inheritance are being discovered, and every day new possibilities present themselves. Genetics is a dynamic subject. Even during the progress of a semester's course the student may expect the opportunity of making a small but potentially valuable contribution to the subject by presenting for analysis family histories of his own taking.

The laws of heredity are well enough understood, however, for us not to expect to discover any new fundamental principles from the study of man. Rather we hope to analyze the human organism and relate its hereditary make-up to principles and laws already understood. This is necessarily a slow process, but the day-by-day advances make fascinating study.

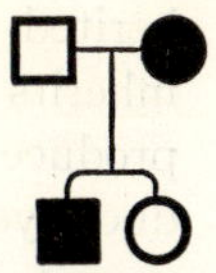

To develop a knowledge of heredity we must have variations. A species showing striking differences between individuals becomes for this reason valuable to us from the standpoint of genetics. If every person, for example, had brown eyes, we should know nothing as to the nature of the inheritance of eye color in man. But, when in the midst of a brown-eyed population we meet a blue-eyed person, we begin to collect data on the heredity of the color of eyes. Variations, especially striking variations, then, make a convenient introduction to genetics.

Fig. 1.1 A family history illustrating the inheritance of eye color in man. Solid symbols indicate blue eyes; hollow symbols indicate brown eyes. Squares indicate males, circles females.

Among our own families we find an available source of variations with which to begin our observations. Let us look about us at our own friends and relatives. Let us note some differences and resemblances in people and try to develop a few fundamental principles for ourselves before starting the more technical discussion of heredity.

The color of eyes makes a convenient and easily available beginning. Here is a family in which some of the members are blue-eyed and some brown-eyed. Let us illustrate such a family in the form of a chart, which is a very convenient aid to analysis. In illustrating families it is customary to indicate males by squares, females by circles. Matings are illustrated by horizontal lines connecting the appropriate squares and circles; offspring by vertical lines leading to other squares and circles. In the family under discussion are a son and a daughter. The father and daughter are brown-eyed, the mother and son blue-eyed. Let us represent brown eyes by hollow squares and circles, blue eyes by solid ones. Our family thus can be visualized as in Figure 1.1. This we speedily learn to recognize as a family consisting of two parents and two children, a boy and a girl. The hollow symbols denote one character, the solid ones a contrasting character; in this case brown and blue eyes, respectively.

Let us look a bit further in our search for eye color in families. Here is a family in which the parents are both brown-eyed (Fig. 1.2). But it is seen that some of the children are brown-eyed, like the parents, and some are blue-eyed, unlike either parent. Does this mean that the blue eyes are not a result of heredity? Not at all; we shall find many instances of heredity in which the offspring differ from both parents. We shall find that hereditary potentialities are the things that are in-

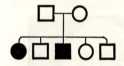

Fig. 1.2 Family history illustrating the inheritance of eye color in man. Brown eyes are represented by hollow symbols, blue eyes by solid symbols.

herited and not developed characters. We say that a certain child inherits his father's eyes. What the child inherits is the capacity to produce eyes like those of the father. Or the capacity may be to produce eyes like those of some other ancestor and not like those of either parent. Yet that capacity was inherited through the parents just as surely and in just as definite a manner as though the child's eyes were exactly like those of one of the parents.

Our attention is caught by an unusual eye color. Here is a family in which some of the individuals have pink eyes. The hair and skin are devoid of pigment, resulting in snow-white hair and a rosy-white skin, due to the fact that the circulating blood in the deeper layers shows through the semi-transparent outer layers. The pink color of

the iris of the eyes is likewise caused by the fact that the blood vessels are seen through it. People with these characters are called *albinos*. In Figure 1.3 are photographs of albinos, and Figure 1.4 shows a family history in which this character occurs.

Here again it is seen that a character in an offspring may be different from the corresponding character in either parent. This is true in certain conditions of heredity but not in others. Figure 1.5 shows a family history in which both parents are albinos and all their children are albinos. Try as we may we cannot find an instance where two albino parents have produced anything but albinos. We shall find in the progress of our study numerous characters which seem to "breed true" and do not ordinarily give rise to dissimilar traits.

Here is an interesting family in which a character appears with striking frequency. In this case it is an extra finger on each hand which attracts our attention. It is indicated by the black squares and circles in Figure 1.6. We note that this character does not seem to occur in an individual unless one of the parents had an extra finger. It seems to occur equally readily in both sexes. We shall find many characters of this nature.

A family in which many of the members are bald-headed next engages our attention. Here we note a new fact: The condition is largely confined

Fig. 1.3   Two albino parents and their albino child. *From Davenport in the Journal of Heredity*

to males and may pass directly from father to son (Fig. 1.7). Such conditions will require careful analysis later on.

In contrast to the above family is one in which hemophilia, or "bleeding," occurs. Here again we notice that the condition is apparently restricted to males. It seems, however, not to be passed from father to son, but rather to be transmitted from an afflicted man through his daughters to some of his grandsons. Many characters of this type of behavior will be met with as we proceed (Fig. 1.8).

One last family may be considered before we turn to the more detailed study of heredity. Here is a family in which for several generations the men have been stone-cutters. Their occupation brings them into close contact with fine stone-dust which they are forced to breathe to some extent. These men have frequently shown a lung disease which develops late in life. It was thought by the family that the constant breathing of stone-dust caused the lung trouble.

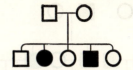

Fig. 1.4 Family history of albinism in man. The solid symbols indicate the albino individuals.

Fig. 1.5 A family where both parents are albinos. Note that all the children are albinos.

However, in the last two generations some of the members of the family have not been stone-cutters, yet have developed the lung trouble just the same. It likewise appeared in a woman in a late generation. And one of the stone-cutters did not develop the trouble. The lung disease is indicated by solid symbols, and the stone-cutters are shown by including the letter S in the symbols in Figure 1.9.

Several interesting questions present themselves. Was the lung trouble originally due to the continued inhalation of dust from stone cutting? If so, could the trouble become so firmly ingrained in the stock that finally it was transmitted to individuals who were not themselves stone-cutters? Or was the lung disease inherited and just

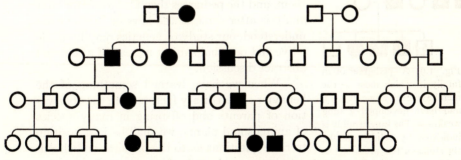

Fig. 1.6 A family history of polydactylism (an extra finger on each hand).

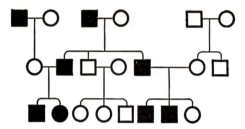

Fig. 1.7 A family history of baldness. The bald individuals are indicated by solid symbols.

happened to appear in those of the stone-cutting trade? If the condition was inherited could the irritation of the stone-dust hasten or aggravate its development? Why did not all the stonecutters develop the trouble if stone-dust caused it? Such questions will be discussed during the progress of our study.

Enough has been said to suggest the fascinating possibilities in searching for hereditary traits in families. Many

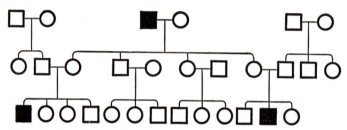

Fig. 1.8 A pedigree of hemophilia. The solid symbols indicate the hemophilic individuals.

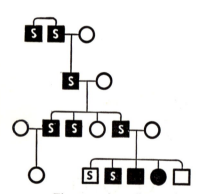

Fig. 1.9 A pedigree of a family in which most of the men have been stone-cutters, and have developed a lung weakness. The lung trouble is indicated by solid symbols; the stone-cutters are designated by an enclosed S.

more traits may readily be found and considered. Such characters as blindness, deafness, musical ability, disease susceptibility, stature, longevity, temperament, and many others make interesting material for study. If such pedigrees are examined at the very beginning of our study, a few apparently general principles drawn from them, and the pedigrees then filed away for later analysis after some of the laws of heredity are understood, our study of genetics may be made a live and personal subject instead of a cold and abstract discussion.

When we have learned something of the behavior of hereditary factors from the observation of parents and offspring in many species of animals and plants, we shall be in a position to raise questions as to the physical and chemical nature of such factors, their location within the organism, and their modes of action in producing characteristics.

We shall discover that hereditary factors are complex molecules, which we call **genes.** They appear to be composed of desoxyribose nucleic acids. Genes are located at definite points in microscopic structures called chromosomes, found within cells. The detailed chemical composition of chromosomes is rapidly becoming known. Although the overwhelming majority of hereditary differences within species are due to differences in genes, there are also materials in the cytoplasm which have a role in heredity, and these, too, we shall study.

Genes are capable of reproducing themselves exactly for many cell generations. Occasionally, however, the chemical arrangement of a gene may change, resulting in a different structure and action of the gene, and hence, under certain circumstances, in a new character. Such a change we call a **mutation.** We shall find that the mutated gene now reproduces itself in its changed form just as faithfully as it previously copied its original form. Thus mutations may be inherited.

Experimental studies of mutations show that the slow natural mutation rate may be greatly speeded up by various forms of radiation and by certain chemicals. In this way the whole problem of evolution is opened to experimental attack; and this problem is one of the major research interests of geneticists at the present time. The effects of radiation on mutations in human beings will be of interest to us, and we shall discuss them carefully.

During the course of our study of genetics, then, we shall establish the fact that many characters are the results of genes, working within the framework of their own environment and that of the organism. The question will logically arise as to the specific action of genes in producing characters. How, for instance, can a microscopic molecule of protein in the cell make a person an albino or cause him to have brown eyes or to be mentally deficient? Answers to problems such as these are rapidly coming to hand, and we shall learn what research workers in this area are discovering. Those of you who have studied organic or biological chemistry will be familiar with enzymes, the organic catalytic agents which facilitate chemical reactions in living bodies. The study of the production of enzymes by genes, along with the subsequent action of the enzymes in controlling metabolism and development, is one of the most interesting phases of the science of genetics.

Genetics will also prove to be of very practical value in agriculture and in furthering the health, welfare, and happiness of mankind. We shall discover that the application of our knowledge of the production by gene action of certain diseases and anomalies can result in the earlier diagnosis and treatment, and even in the prevention, of many of these illnesses and abnormalities.

In these and other ways genetics will unfold to us as a science which is of basic importance in the understanding of the phenomena of the growth and development of individuals and of the evolution of living organisms.

PROBLEMS

Make a record of a family known to you in which some interesting characteristic appears in several members. Record it in the form of a pedigree chart as was done in this chapter. Answer as many of the following questions about the character as you can:

1.1 Is the character clear-cut, so that a person either has it or does not have it, or are there various degrees of expression ranging from one extreme to the other?

1.2 Does it occur in both males and females, and if so, do both sexes show it with approximately the same frequency?

1.3 Does it ever appear in a son or daughter when neither parent showed it?

1.4 When both parents have the character, do all the children show it?

1.5 Would the expression of the character be easily influenced by changes in the environment?

1.6 If the character could be influenced by the environment, do you think it might still have a hereditary basis?

1.7 File away the pedigree you have recorded, and after you have completed the study of the first sixteen chapters, examine it again and determine what kind of hereditary behavior, if any, appears to be concerned in the transmission of the character.

1.8 List some human characters which might be readily influenced by changes in the environment. Suggest the environmental changes which might be expected to influence each.

1.9 List some human characters which would probably not be easily influenced by changes in the environment.

1.10 List some human characters which do not appear until late in life. Would such characters be relatively easy or difficult to study from the standpoint of heredity? Why?

1.11 List some human characters which vary considerably in the degree of their expression from person to person. In beginning the study of heredity, would such characters be the most favorable kind for study? Give reasons for your answer.

1.12 List some characters in domestic animals or pets which you have observed to be apparently dependent upon heredity. Why would it be easier to learn the fundamental principles of heredity from the study of animals and plants than from the study of human beings?

CHAPTER TWO

Simple Mendelian inheritance.
The 3:1 ratio

Among the dogs of certain breeds there occasionally appears one which is deaf (Fig. 2.1). This is an undesirable characteristic, as can be readily imagined, and breeders of dogs are desirous of getting rid of it. Yet, in spite of taking the precaution of not using deaf dogs for breeding, the character crops up again and again in the puppies born in certain kennels. It is obvious that some hereditary factor is causing the deafness, since in the same litter, raised under external conditions practically identical for each puppy, some will be deaf and others not.

Fig. 2.1 This spaniel would make an excellent pet were it not for the fact that she is completely deaf. The deafness is hereditary.

The study of the inheritance of this character makes an interesting story. In order to understand it fully certain matings should be made. We find that if a dog with normal hearing, from a strain in which there is no deafness, is bred to a deaf dog, all the puppies have normal hearing. If we allow these puppies to grow up and then mate two of them together, they will produce puppies in the ratio of three normal to one deaf. Moreover, when two deaf dogs are crossed they produce only deaf puppies.

The geneticist, seeing these results, knows immediately that deafness and normal hearing in dogs are dependent on a pair of unit genes, with deafness recessive. He knows this because of the laws and principles discovered in the eighteen-sixties by Gregor Mendel. Moreover, the geneticist can immediately predict what the results of other crosses involving deafness will be, such as crossing one of the dogs which had one normal and one deaf parent with a deaf dog. Further, the geneticist can tell the dog-breeder how to get rid entirely of deafness in his strain and how to do it easily and quickly. He can do this because of his knowledge of Mendel's laws.

Let us examine these laws of Mendel. Let us see why the three-to-one ratio is familiar to the geneticist, and let us find out how he is able to use this knowledge in a practical way.

Our present knowledge of heredity rests directly on certain principles and laws discovered through the painstaking research of Mendel. Others have added to and extended these principles, but he was the first to set forth clearly a logical explanation of the way in which genes behave during a cross. Johann Mendel was born in 1822, of German parentage, in the village of Heinzendorf, in Silesia. In 1843, at the age of twenty-one, he entered the Augustinian Monastery at Brünn, Moravia, as a novice. There he spent the remainder of his life, except for short periods of teaching in nearby high schools and a course of study at the University of Vienna. Upon entering the monastery he took the name of Gregor, and was thenceforth known as Gregor Johann Mendel. A fascinating account of the life of Mendel has been written by Iltis.

In a little strip of garden behind the monastery building Mendel conducted his experiments upon hybridization. Having a scientific turn of mind, he made investigations not only in biology but in meteorology and geology as well. In his rooms he hybridized mice, along the edge of the garden he experimented with bees, and in the garden itself he made numerous crosses with many kinds of plants.

Mendel entered the priesthood for economic reasons and to seek leisure for experimental work. There is a touch of humor in the result, for while at first he had leisure for his work, he was limited in the space available for him. Later, when elected prelate, all the space he desired was at his disposal, but his duties robbed him of the time he needed. Still later, when both time and space were available, he was handicapped by an excess of avoirdupois, having become too stout to make the long walks and hill-climbings so necessary in the collection of material. He smoked as many as twenty cigars a day in an effort to overcome this increasing weight.

Nevertheless, Mendel accomplished a tremendous amount of investigation. Moreover, it was exceedingly well planned and admirably carried out, so that the results form today the very basis of all studies on heredity.

Mendel's classic paper was written in 1865 and published in the following year. Considering that men have been vitally interested in the mysteries of heredity at least since the dawn of history, it may seem remarkable that the relatively simple rules of inheritance which Mendel discovered had not been recognized long before his time. Part of the explanation lies in the fact that every scientific discovery depends to an important degree on discoveries previously made. Mendel's laws, as we shall soon see, are essentially *statistical* laws, based on the proportions of different types of progeny produced from various kinds of matings. For anyone to recognize the constancy of these proportions, it was necessary to work with organisms which could be mated or crossed according to the investigator's plans, and from which very large numbers of progeny could easily be obtained.

Many common plants meet both of the requirements just mentioned, and Mendel's crucial discoveries were in fact made in the course of his plant-breeding experiments. But the possibility of making controlled crosses in plants depends on the knowledge that plants reproduce sexually, and that seeds are formed only as a result of the uniting of male and female germ cells. These facts were not discovered in modern Europe until nearly 1700 although, interestingly enough, they were in essence well known to growers of date palms in the Near East a thousand years or more before the Christian era.

The discovery of sexuality in plants has turned out to be one of the most revolutionary discoveries of the last three hundred years in its practical as well as its theoretical consequences, but it appears to have excited relatively little interest at the time it was made. It was not until the 1760's that the knowledge of sexual reproduction in plants was applied to scientific investigation, when the first systematic experiments in plant hybridization were undertaken by Koelreuter, a German professor of natural history. His studies laid the groundwork for most subsequent attempts to understand the mechanism of heredity.

Strong interest in the experimental hybridization of plants developed in the early 19th century. From the 1820's on, gaining momentum as the years passed, there was a surge of activity in Germany, in England, and in France, concerned with investigations of inheritance in plant crosses. The stimulus for this activity derived from two sources. First, there was a growing awareness of its practical importance, dating from Thomas Knight's demonstration, at the beginning of the century, that improved varieties of food plants could be developed by the use of artificial hybridization. Second, the idea of evolution was coming to the forefront in biological thinking. It had been shown much earlier that cross-fertilization in plants occurs not only through artificial interference, but is a common phenomenon in nature, and many biologists now thought they might find a key to evolutionary processes through the study of plant hybrids.

During the forty or fifty years immediately preceding the publication of Mendel's paper, more than a dozen experimenters, both professional biologists and practical plant-breeders, were working intensively on the same problems that Mendel was concerned with. Many of them were men of outstanding ability and several of them in their experiments used the same plant with which Mendel obtained his most illuminating results; even some of the very observations which Mendel made, and which served as major links in his chain of analysis, had been independently reported by other workers. Why then, was Mendel alone able to analyze successfully the phenomena he was studying?

The answer, we think, lies primarily in the fact that Mendel was the first to approach the problem *quantitatively*. It was essential to his success that he carefully select for his crosses plants which differed in clear-cut, readily distinguishable features. It was especially essential that he test each parent strain to be sure that it was true breeding. But others had also followed these procedures. Indeed, some of them had observed, as Mendel was to do, that the offspring of crosses between white- and purple-flowered plants, for example, were purple-flowered, and that seeds from these hybrid plants, in turn, produced *some* white- and *some* purple-flowered progeny. But Mendel alone kept careful records of seed sown from each individual plant, and *counted the numbers of each type of offspring*. He did this, moreover, on a large enough scale to satisfy himself that from a given kind of cross, the proportions of different types of progeny were always the same.

In his experiments with plants Mendel used garden peas, columbines, snapdragons, slipperworts, sedge, pumpkins, hawkweed, vetch, four-o'clocks, beans, cinquefoil, mullein, violets, maize, and others. It is especially the work with peas, however, which is remembered today and which has formed the basis for modern genetics. In garden peas Mendel observed seven pairs of contrasting characters. These included smooth seeds and wrinkled seeds, yellow cotyledons and green cotyledons, inflated pods and constricted pods, yellow pods when unripe and green pods when unripe, flowers in the axils of the leaves and flowers at the ends of the stems, transparent seed coats and brown seed coats, tall plants and dwarf plants.

Thus the first step towards analyzing inheritance was the observation of clear definite differences between individuals of the species. The next step was the crossing of individuals which differed one from the other in regard to these characters. Mendel crossed a plant having a certain character with one having the contrasting character. He was able to do this by removing the stamens from a flower, so that self-pollination and self-fertilization could not occur. He then by hand placed on the stigma of this flower pollen from another plant having the alternative character. A cross between the two was thus achieved. The artificially pollinated flower was carefully protected from any other pollen grains which might reach it by means of insects, wind, or other agencies.

The seeds produced by the cross-pollinated flower were planted, and the resulting hybrids were carefully observed. They were then crossed among themselves to obtain another generation. The careful observation of this second generation of hybrids resulted in the formulation of certain fundamental and important principles.

Let us follow one such cross. Among the pea plants Mendel noted some which were tall, acquiring a height of six feet or more, while others grown in the same soil were dwarf, reaching a height of only eighteen inches or less. He crossed a tall plant from a tall race (that is, with no dwarfness in its ancestry as far as he knew) with a dwarf plant from a dwarf race. The resulting plants were all tall, thus:

$$
\begin{array}{ccc}
\textit{Parents} & \text{Tall} \times \text{Dwarf} \\
& \downarrow \\
F_1 & \text{Tall}
\end{array}
$$

Mendel then took a very important step. He crossed two of these hybrid tall plants together. These hybrid tall plants form what we call the first filial generation, or as it is usually written, the F_1. He raised as many plants from this cross of two F_1 plants as possible, and found that among the offspring there were both tall and dwarf plants. Moreover, there were three times as many tall plants as dwarf ones, thus:

$$
\begin{array}{ccc}
\textit{Parents} & \text{Tall} \times \text{Dwarf} \\
& \downarrow \\
F_1 & \text{Tall} \times \text{Tall} \\
& \downarrow \\
F_2 & 3 \text{ Tall} \qquad 1 \text{ Dwarf}
\end{array}
$$

Counting the actual numbers of tall and dwarf plants in the second filial generation (the F_2) was a master stroke. Mendel then self-pollinated the F_2 plants; that is, he allowed the pollen from a flower to fall on the stigma of the same flower. He found that the dwarf plants when self-pollinated produced only dwarf, while of the tall plants in the F_2 one third bred true and two thirds produced both tall and dwarf in the ratio of three to one, as the F_1 plants did.

Thinking about these results brought Mendel to several conclusions. First, only one of the two characters concerned in the cross showed up in the F_1. In this case all the F_1 plants were tall, never dwarf. Second, the dwarf character, although it disappeared in the F_1, was not lost, since it appeared again in the F_2. Mendel reasoned therefore that the F_1 plants must have carried a "hidden" gene for dwarfness as indicated in the following diagram. (Although, as we shall see in Chapter 4, Mendel did not use the word "gene" and never saw a chromosome, his hypothetical "factors" behaved as today we know genes to behave. We shall, therefore, use "gene" in relating Mendel's work.)

Parents	Tall $\times$ Dwarf
F_1	Tall (dwarf)

If then the F_1 plants contain two genes for height (one for tallness which shows up and one for dwarfness which remains hidden), it is only logical to suppose that any plant of any generation must also contain two genes for height. A tall plant from a tall race might thus be supposed to have two genes for tallness, while a dwarf plant might be supposed to have two genes for dwarfness. Our cross could thus be visualized:

Parents		Tall (tall) $\times$ Dwarf (dwarf)		
F_1		Tall (dwarf) $\times$ Tall (dwarf)		
F_2	Tall (tall)	Tall (dwarf)	Tall (dwarf)	Dwarf (dwarf)

Mendel designated as **dominant** the character which appears in the F_1, masking the effect of the gene for the alternative character; the character which does not appear (although its gene is present) he called **recessive**. Today we apply these terms to the genes themselves as well as to the characters. Thus tallness is due to a dominant gene, dwarfness to a recessive. As long as the dominant gene is present, the recessive gene does not produce any obvious effect. A similar situation held in the other pairs of characters which Mendel studied. Thus, when a plant with axillary flowers was crossed with a plant having terminal flowers, all the F_1 plants had axillary flowers, but the F_2 generation showed some plants with axillary flowers and some with terminal flowers, again in the ratio of three to one.

One further point seems clear. If the genes are supposed to occur in pairs in each individual (as appears to be the most reasonable explanation), some method must exist which keeps the genes in pairs from generation to generation. Mendel suggested that to account for this we assume that only one of the two genes of a pair gets into each mature germ cell. Thus when two such germ cells unite we shall have two genes for each character brought back together in the new individual. Today we are very sure that this explanation is correct. This is known as the **law of segregation.**

Now let us find a more convenient method than the use of whole words for diagraming crosses. Symbols will be much simpler. It is customary in genetics to use pairs of letters to represent pairs of genes. A capital letter is generally used for the dominant gene and the corresponding small letter for the recessive gene of the pair. The first letter of the name of one of the characters is usually chosen. Thus *dwarfness* begins with "d," so we may let D (a capital letter) represent a dominant gene and d (the corresponding small letter) represent the alternative recessive gene. These genes act in such a way that the combinations DD and Dd produce tallness and dd results in dwarfness. Let us indicate mature germ cells (which we call gametes) by putting circles around them. We may then summarize our cross as follows:

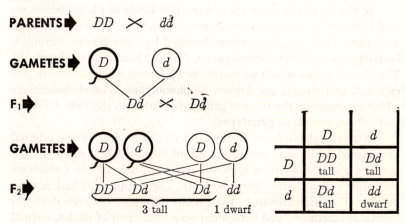

Let us designate male gametes by attaching a tail to the circle. This distinction will be found convenient in diagraming both plant and animal crosses.

Then, if each type of sperm has an equal opportunity of meeting each type of egg, we shall obtain by this method of symbols the results which were actually obtained by breeding. It is to be noted that genes segregate in the germ cells: that is, only one of a pair of genes is found in a gamete.

The checkerboard in the preceding diagram is a convenient method of recording all the possible combinations of gametes.

By reference to the above diagram we may derive a set of terms which will be of use to us in subsequent gene analyses. The character which shows up in the F_1 is, as stated earlier, due to a **dominant gene.** The one which remained hidden is due to a **recessive gene.** In the foregoing example D represents a dominant gene and d represents a recessive gene. Two such genes forming a contrasting pair are said to be **alleles.** The adjective formed from this word is **allelic.** When the difference between a given character and an alternative one is determined by a single pair of alleles, the character is said to be a **unit character.**

A mature germ cell is frequently called a **gamete;** the union of two gametes results in a **zygote.** A zygote is said to be a **homozygote** if the two members of the pair of genes are alike; a **heterozygote** if the two members are different. Thus the zygote DD is a homozygote or, as we often say, a plant of the genetic formula DD is **homozygous** for tallness. A plant of the formula dd is homozygous for dwarfness. A plant of the formula Dd, having the two genes of the pair different, is **heterozygous** for the genes for height. It will be seen later that an individual may be homozygous for one pair of genes, heterozygous for another pair, and so on.

In the F_2 of the cross there were two kinds of plants which we could discern by means of our senses: tall and dwarf. However, there were three kinds of plants when classified by their genetic formulas: homozygous tall, DD; heterozygous, Dd; and homozygous dwarf, dd. The classifications which we can make by means of our senses (in this case tall and dwarf) are known as **phenotypes.** The classifications which are made on the basis of genetic formulas (in this case DD, Dd, and dd) are known as **genotypes.**

With the above facts in mind, let us think again of the original problem of deafness in certain breeds of dogs. We first made a cross between a deaf dog and a normal one from a normal line (which we may now call a homozygous normal). The puppies all had normal hearing. This indicates to us that, if the difference between deaf and normal is hereditary and dependent on a single pair of alleles, normal hearing is dominant over deafness. If this is true, what should we expect in the F_2? Obviously the three-to-one ratio with which we have become familiar, that is, in this case, three times as many normal puppies as deaf puppies.

When we find that this ratio is actually obtained in the F_2, we are justified in assuming that deafness in dogs is a unit character, recessive to normal hearing, so that the gene for normal hearing and the gene for deafness are alleles. As such, only one of these genes could be in a gamete, and two (any two) in a zygote.

Assuming, then, from these results that the genes for deafness and for normal hearing are alleles, we may henceforth indicate them by symbols. Since the word *deafness* begins with "d," just as *dwarfness* did, we may again choose the same letters. Let D represent a dominant gene and d its recessive allele, acting so that DD and Dd produce normal hearing and dd produces deafness.

What will be expected, then, if we cross two deaf dogs? Obviously all the puppies should be deaf, since deafness must be homozygous to show up. Thus:

$$dd \times dd$$

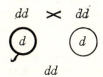

$$dd$$

Now can we tell the breeder how to get rid permanently of deafness in his strain? He is already eliminating the deaf dogs from his breeding stock as fast as they appear, but in spite of this, deafness continues to appear. How can deafness appear when no deaf dogs are used as parents? Obviously because the normal parents are in some cases heterozygous, thus:

$$Dd \times Dd$$

These will produce some deaf puppies. The kind of dogs the breeder should have are of the homozygous formula DD, but these cannot be told by external examination from the heterozygous dogs (Dd).

By breeding each normal dog to a deaf dog and observing the results separately, we may readily identify and eliminate the heterozygous individuals as well as the deaf ones, leaving only the homozygous normals. Work out a diagram of these matings for yourself and see that it is so. A strain composed only of dogs homozygous for normal hearing will thenceforth be expected to produce only normal puppies. Thus an undesirable recessive hereditary character, which could never be eliminated simply by culling out the individuals showing the character, may be quickly and permanently eliminated by simple genetic methods.

PROBLEMS

2.1 A brown mink crossed with a silver-blu mink produced all brown offspring. When these F_1 mink were crossed among themselves they produced forty-seven brown animals and fifteen silverblu animals. Which of these characters is dependent upon a dominant gene?

2.2 How many of the brown mink in the F_2 generation in the preceding problem would be expected to be homozygous? How many of the silverblu F_2 animals would be homozygous?

2.3 How could you determine which of the brown mink in the F_2 generation of problem 2.2 were homozygous and which were heterozygous?

2.4 In poultry rose comb is dependent upon a dominant gene (R), single comb upon its recessive allele (r). Birds of the Wyandotte breed are required to have rose combs. In certain strains of Wyandottes, however, single-combed birds occasionally appear. Why is this?

2.5 The Wyandotte breeders never use a single-combed bird for mating. When one appears in a flock it is immediately discarded. Will this practice be sufficient to eliminate the gene for single comb from the flock?

2.6 How can a breeder of Wyandottes eliminate the single-comb gene from his flock most efficiently?

2.7 A rose-combed male is mated with two rose-combed females. Female A produces fourteen chicks, all rose-combed. Female B produces nine chicks, seven of which are rose-combed and two single-combed. What are the genotypes of the three parent birds?

2.8 Broccoli ordinarily has dull green foliage. A recessive mutation results in glossy foliage, which is undesirable because the glossy leaves are highly susceptible to attack by insects. If glossy-foliaged plants appear in a nursery which produces broccoli seed for sale, how might this undesirable characteristic be eliminated?

2.9 In sheep white is due to a dominant gene (W), black to its recessive allele (w). A white ewe mated to a white ram produces a black lamb. If they produce another offspring, could it be white? If so, what are the chances of its being white? List genotypes of all the animals mentioned in this problem.

2.10 In dogs wire hair is due to a dominant gene, smooth hair to its recessive allele. Two wire-haired dogs produce a male pup which is wire-haired. To find out most quickly whether he carries the gene for smooth hair, he should be mated to what kind of female?

2.11 In guinea pigs the coat may be rough (rosetted) or smooth. Certain rough-coated guinea pigs when crossed with smooth-coated ones produce all rough-coated offspring. Other rough-coated guinea pigs when crossed with smooth-coated ones produce equal numbers of rough-coated and smooth-coated offspring. Smooth-coated guinea pigs crossed together always produce smooth-coated offspring. Explain these results. Write the genotypes for all animals concerned in the crosses.

2.12 In tomatoes the texture of the skin may be smooth or peach (hairy). The Ponderosa variety has fruits with smooth texture. The Red Peach variety has fruits with peach texture. Crosses between the two varieties produced all smooth fruits. Crosses between these smooth-fruited F_1 plants produced 174 peach-textured fruits and 520 smooth-textured fruits. How are these skin textures inherited?

2.13 What would be produced if the F_1 plants of the preceding problem were crossed to the Ponderosa variety? To the Red Peach variety?

2.14 In cattle a dominant gene (N) results in a deep notch in each ear. A recessive gene (*u*) results, when in the homozygous condition, in an udder abnormality. A farmer has a herd of cattle in which some of the individuals have notched ears and some have abnormal udders. He desires to rid his herd of these characters. Which would be the more easily eliminated from the herd? How should he go about eliminating each?

2.15 In man normal pigmentation is due to a dominant gene (*C*), albinism to its recessive allele (*c*). A normal man marries an albino woman. Their first child is an albino. What are the genotypes of these three persons? If there are more children, what would they probably be like?

2.16 An albino man marries a normally pigmented woman. They have nine children, all normally pigmented. What are the genotypes of the parents and of the children?

2.17 A normally pigmented man whose father was an albino marries an albino woman both of whose parents were normally pigmented. They have three children, two normally pigmented and one albino. List the genotypes of all these persons.

2.18 Albinism frequently skips generations in human pedigrees, while polydactyly (extra fingers) does not. How do you explain these facts?

REFERENCES

ILTIS, H., *The Life of Mendel*. New York, W. W. Norton and Co. (1932).

MENDEL, G., "Versuche über Pflanzen-Hybriden," *Verhandl. Naturf. Ver. Brünn* **4**:3 (1866). (Facsimile reprint in *Jour. Hered.* **42**:1 (1951); English translation published by Harvard Univ. Press, Cambridge, 1925).

ROBERTS, H. B., *Plant Hybridization before Mendel*. Princeton, Princeton Univ. Press, 1929.

ZIRKLE, C., *The Beginnings of Plant Hybridization*. Philadelphia, Univ. of Pennsylvania Press (1935); *The Knowledge of Heredity before 1900* (in *Genetics and the 20th Century*, edited by L. C. Dunn). New York, The Macmillan Co. (1951).

CHAPTER THREE

Simple Mendelian inheritance. Modifications of the 3:1 ratio

In crosses described in the last chapter between peas (Tall ✕ Dwarf) or dogs (Deaf ✕ Normal) which differed in a single character, the F_1 progeny were indistinguishable from one of the parental types; that is, one gene of a pair was dominant to its allele in each instance. This is by no means always the case. In poultry, when birds with splashed-white plumage (predominantly white feathers, with scattered slate-blue flecks) are mated to solid blacks, the offspring are "blue," having slate-blue feathers edged with black, as in the Blue Andalusian breed (Figure 3.1). In the F_2 the ratio observed is approximately one black, two blue, one splashed-white. Schematically:

Parents	Black ✕ Splashed-white
	↓
F_1	Blue ✕ Blue
	↓
F_2	Black Blue Blue Splashed-white

If you compare the above diagram with the similar one of the pea cross shown on page 16, an explanation of these results should occur to you at once. The blue chickens here correspond to the peas symbolized as "Tall (dwarf)" in the earlier diagram. That is, they are heterozygous for a pair of allelic genes; one of the alleles, when homozygous, produces black plumage, the other in homozygous state gives splashed white. To put this in symbols, we may represent the two alleles by the letters W and w. Neither allele is dominant to the other (so that the choice of which allele to symbolize by the capital letter is entirely arbitrary); instead, the heterozygote has an intermediate appearance. Thus the WW genotype produces black, Ww gives blue, and ww splashed-white.

If our theory is correct, mating two birds with black plumage together should give only black progeny, and the splashed-whites should likewise breed true, while blue × blue should always give the same 1:2:1 ratio found in the F_2 above; and this is in fact what happens. Using letter symbols, work out the results in F_1 and F_2 from the cross black × splashed-white in a diagram similar to that on page 17. What crosses involving still other combinations of genotypes are possible?

Another familiar example of lack of dominance is found in shorthorn cattle. We may designate the alleles involved as R and r. Homozygous RR animals are red, and rr homozygotes are white. The heterozygote, Rr, is *roan*, exhibiting a fine intermixture of red and white hairs which give it a pepper-and-salt effect. If you purchased a herd of roan shorthorns and consistently got rid of all red and all white calves as they were born, how many generations would it take to produce a true-breeding herd of roan shorthorns?

We shall encounter many instances of alleles which in heterozygous condition produce an effect that is readily distinguishable from both homozygous types, so that neither allele, strictly speaking, can be described as dominant to the other. On the other hand, even

Fig. 3.1 Blue Andalusian fowls. These birds are heterozygous. Their color is due to the blending effect of a pair of alleles. Birds homozygous for these alleles are either black or splashed-white. Blue Andalusian fowls are therefore not a true-breeding variety.

when the heterozygote *cannot* be distinguished from one of the homozygous types in superficial appearance, we frequently find that it is distinguishable by more critical examination or by the use of special techniques. One of the character pairs with which Mendel worked, *round* versus *wrinkled* peas belongs in this category, although the fact was unknown to Mendel himself.

When true-breeding pea plants with round seeds (RR) are crossed to wrinkled-seed plants (rr), the F_1 all have round seeds. In the F_2 we obtain a ratio of three round to one wrinkled. To the unaided eye the heterozygous Rr pea looks just as round and smooth as the homozygous RR, whereas the seed coats of the rr peas are distinctly wrinkled and shrunken. The cause of the difference in appearance between round and wrinkled has been traced to a difference in starch content. In both types of pea the seed when immature contains sugar. In the round pea, the sugar is almost wholly converted into starch as the seed matures, and this retains water, so that the ripe seed remains round and firm. In the rr pea, the conversion of sugar into starch is very incomplete, less water is retained during the ripening process, and the seed coat becomes wrinkled as its contents shrink.

Microscopic examination of the food reserves in RR and rr seeds reveals an abundance of well-formed starch grains in the former; in the rr peas, on the other hand, the number of starch grains is greatly diminished, and the individual grains that are found appear to be imperfectly formed or partly disintegrated. When now we examine microscopically the seed contents of the Rr heterozygotes, we find an intermediate condition: starch grains are distinctly less numerous than in RR seeds, but much more abundant than in the rr's, and the individual grains are imperfectly formed, though to a less degree than those of *wrinkled* homozygotes.

Thus while the R allele, judged by its most obvious effect (the development of a round, filled-out seed), appears to be dominant to r, the dominance is absent or incomplete in terms of the basic process for which the gene is responsible, the conversion of sugar into starch reserves in the seed.

If you will think a little about the case just described, it may give you a clue to a possible explanation of the phenomenon of dominance. We have seen that in RR plants there is practically complete conversion of sugar into starch within the ripening seeds, while in rr's the conversion takes place only to a very limited degree. We might plausibly suppose that an R gene is concerned with the production of some substance, X, (an enzyme, perhaps) which is necessary for the chemical transformation of sugar into starch, and that an r gene produces a much smaller quantity of this substance. The incomplete dominance of the R allele, then, would be explained, if two R genes produce sufficient of the substance X to convert all of the sugar, while the combination R plus r falls just short of providing enough. If the R gene were still a stronger producer of substance X than it is, it might well be that even the one R gene in the heterozygote would suffice for complete conversion of the sugar. Since two R alleles in the homozygous RR could do no more than this, RR and Rr would be altogether indistinguishable, and dominance would be complete. Similarly, if the R allele were appreciably "weaker" than it is, the Rr peas might even in gross appearance be intermediate between RR and rr peas, and there would be no dominance.

There are numerous other instances of close superficial resemblance of a heterozygote to one of the homozygous types, from which it can nevertheless be distinguished by special means. Let us examine an example from human genetics.

A gene, s, when homozygous, results in the development of sickle-cell disease, a condition which is characterized by severe chronic anemia, retarded physical development, and pains in the joints, muscles, and abdomen. It is fatal almost without exception. Microscopic examination of the blood in this disease reveals that a large proportion of the red blood cells are of grossly abnormal forms, of which the term "sickle-shaped" is very roughly descriptive. All of the red cells in a sample of blood from ss individuals will become "sickled" if the blood is deprived of access to oxygen. Heterozygous Ss individuals appear to be entirely healthy, exhibiting none of the disabling impairments listed above as characteristic of the disease. Nevertheless, if their blood is examined under the microscope, a small percentage of the red cells are seen to be sickled, and all of them can be induced to become so by oxygen deprivation, although a considerably greater reduction in oxygen tension is required than is needed to produce the same effect in blood from persons with the sickle-cell disease (Fig. 3.2.).

The student should recognize by now that dominance is a relative, not an absolute term; it applies to a phenomenon which varies greatly from case to case. At one extreme (as illustrated by roan cattle or Blue Andalusian poultry) the heterozygote shows the effect of each allele to about the same extent; dominance is absent. In other cases the effect of one member of a pair of genes in the heterozygote is much more apparent than is the effect of its allele. This is often called **incomplete dominance.** Sometimes, as in the case of the *round* allele in peas (which, in fact, is commonly referred to as dominant) the resemblance is almost, but not quite complete. And finally, we have **complete dominance** if the effect of an allele in heterozygous condition is identical with its effect in the homozygote. The terms "dom-

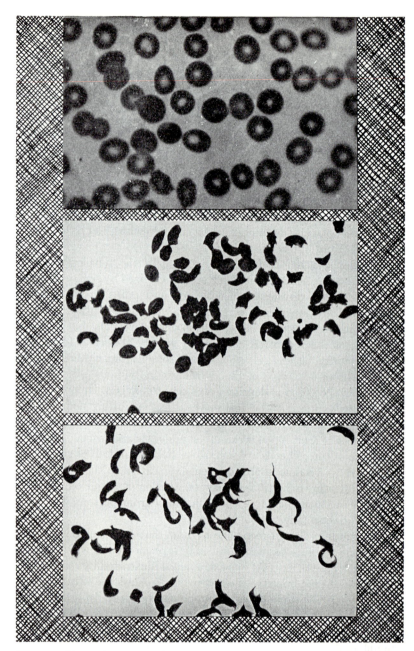

Fig. 3.2 Photomicrographs of human red blood cells. Upper, normal cells from a person of genotype *SS*. Center, cells from a heterozygous individual *Ss*, showing sickling of some of the cells. Lower, cells from a homozygote, *ss*, with complete sickling. *Courtesy of the University of Michigan Heredity Clinic, Dr. James V. Neel, Director*

inance" and "dominant" originally referred to the last-described situation only, but in the light of the preceding discussion, the student should not be surprised to find that there is some variation in the way they are used. In particular, when an allele produces a distinctly *abnormal* effect in the heterozygote, it is rather commonly referred to as dominant, without qualification, even when its effect in homozygotes is conspicuously more extreme or (especially in human genetics) when it has not been found in homozygous condition.

We have seen in the case of sickle-cell disease, a gene which when homozygous has effects so drastic as to result in death. Genes with regularly fatal effects are called **lethal genes,** and they have been found in every kind of plant and animal that has been studied genetically.

Some lethal genes are completely recessive, producing no discernible effect in the heterozygote, but killing the animals or plants that have them in homozygous condition. Other lethals, besides being fatal when homozygous, have recognizable but nonlethal effects in heterozygotes. Genes of this latter class, if they kill before birth or hatching (or before germination in plants) result in a modification of the 3:1 or 1:2:1 ratio that we have learned to expect in the offspring of two heterozygotes.

A good example of the modification of the 3:1 ratio by a gene which produces a conspicuous effect in the heterozygote and, when homozygous, kills during embryonic development is provided by the Creeper fowl. In this animal wings and legs are considerably shortened and deformed, giving it a squatty appearance (Fig. 3.3). When Creepers are mated to normal birds, we obtain equal numbers of Creeper and normal progeny. When Creepers are crossed together the offspring always show a ratio of two Creepers to one normal. Normal birds crossed together never produce Creepers. The actual results obtained by Landauer and Dunn in crosses of this nature are given in Table 3.1.

Since two normal parents never produce Creeper offspring, but two Creeper parents frequently produce some normal offspring, it is obvious that Creeper cannot be due to a recessive gene. It can be due to a dominant gene, however, since Creeper is inherited directly from one generation to the next, a Creeper bird

Fig. 3.3 A Creeper fowl. In the heterozygous condition the gene produces the squatty appearance shown above; in the homozygous state it is lethal. *From Landauer in Bull. 193 of the Conn. Agr. Exp. Station*

Table 3.1. Results of Various Crosses Involving Creeper and Normal Fowls. (*From Landauer and Dunn*)

MATING	OFFSPRING	
	CREEPER	NORMAL
Creeper $\times$ Creeper	775	388
Creeper $\times$ Normal	1676	1661
Normal $\times$ Normal	none	all

always having at least one Creeper parent. If Creeper *is* due to a dominant gene, however, Creeper birds must always be heterozygous, since Creeper crossed with normal always gives a one-to-one ratio. This, it will be remembered, is the ratio obtained by crossing a heterozygous individual with a recessive individual. Further indication that Creepers are always heterozygous is found in the fact that they never "breed true" when crossed among themselves, but always produce some normal offspring.

The explanation of the fact that Creepers are always heterozygous is found in the ratio of two Creeper to one normal that is always obtained among the offspring when both parents are Creepers. That this ratio is simply a modification of the 1:2:1 ratio we have already discussed is readily seen when we discover that about a quarter of the developing embryos from Creeper $\times$ Creeper matings die in the shell, most frequently around the fourth day of incubation. The product of the mating, then, really includes three classes of progeny, in the ratio of *one* nonviable embryo : *two* Creepers : *one* normal. After hatching we see only the last two classes, and the ratio then observed is, of course, two Creepers to one normal. Letting C represent the gene for Creeper and c its normal allele, and remembering that the Creeper gene produces its lethal effect only in homozygous condition, we may diagram the cross between two Creepers and the cross between Creeper and normal as shown. Thus crosses of Creeper $\times$ normal always result in the 1:1 ratio, because all Creepers are heterozygotes.

Lethal genes which have an obvious effect in heterozygous condition, as in the case just described, are relatively easy to recognize because of the abnormal ratios they produce. It is not always easy to find the nonviable homozygotes, however, because some lethals kill early in development. Thus, the *Yellow* gene in mice has long been recognized as lethal in homozygous condition, because crosses of Yellow $\times$ nonyellow always produce Yellow and nonyellow progeny in a 1:1 ratio, and Yellow $\times$ Yellow crosses produce Yellows and nonyellows in a 2:1 ratio. But it was many years before the homozygotes were identified: they die at a very early stage (shortly after the

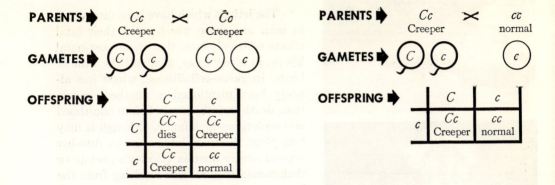

fertilized egg has passed down the oviduct into the uterus) because they do not become properly attached to the uterine lining.

Lethal genes which produce no discernible effect in heterozygous condition are somewhat harder to distinguish. They may be identified, however, by various methods.

In cattle, for example, calves which are homozygous for a certain lethal gene have an abnormal lower jaw with impacted molar teeth. They never live more than a few hours after birth and they may even be born dead (Fig. 3.4). Calves heterozygous for the gene are perfectly normal and show no detectable sign of the gene's presence. The existence of this gene, which has been named "parrot beak," was easily discovered because the homozygotes do not die until they have developed sufficiently to be readily found and recognized as abnormal. If the lethal killed the embryos very early in embryonic life (as does the Yellow lethal in mice), the homozygotes very likely would have escaped detection, and the existence of the gene would not have been discovered.

Several other lethals of the same general nature as "parrot-beak" have been described in cattle by various investigators, particularly Mohr and Wriedt. These include "amputated," in which the calves are born dead with legs and lower jaw missing, "short-spine," a condition of fused and compacted vertebrae, "hairless," and others (Fig. 3.5). The "bull-dog" lethal, on the other hand, is more like the Creeper condition in fowls, the heterozygotes being the short-legged "Dexter" cattle, while the homozygous lethal genotype produces dead calves with bashed-in faces, ridiculously short legs, and other peculiarities (Figs. 3.6 and 3.7). More than 25 lethal genes have been reported in cattle, 7 in horses, 14 in swine, 6 in sheep, 21 in chickens, and 1 in ducks.

Since lethal genes may be carried along from generation to generation by heterozygotes, their elimination requires a breeding test of all normal individuals, as outlined in Chapter 2.

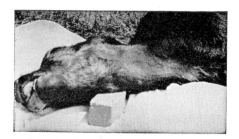

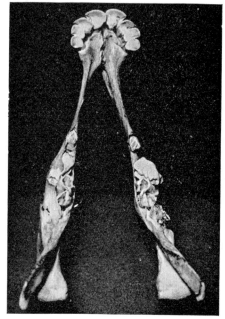

Fig. 3.4 The result of a lethal gene in cattle which has no visible effect in the heterozygous condition. When in the homozygous recessive state, the gene produces a "parrot-beak" calf (above), which never lives more than a few hours. Below is shown the lower jaw of a "parrot-beak" calf, with molars impacted and jaw-bone fractured.

The lethals which have been discovered in man are those which exert their fatal effects relatively late, that is, in post-natal life or, in a few cases, at about the time of birth. In sickle-cell disease, which has already been mentioned in another connection, death usually occurs before adulthood and sometimes in infancy, although it may take place, rarely, as late as age 30. Another type of severe anemia (Cooley's anemia or thalassemia major), also resulting from the homozygous condition of a lethal gene, is usually fatal during childhood or early youth. There are two forms of amaurotic idiocy, a condition characterized by striking mental and physical deterioration, abnormal lipoid metabolism, and rapidly progressive degeneration of the retina leading to total blindness. The two forms are distinguished by differences in age of onset and of death; each is caused by a different recessive gene in homozygous condition. In one form (called juvenile), the onset takes place about age 6 or 7 and death occurs rather regularly in the middle teens. The other form (infantile), is usually noticed in the first 6 or 8 months after birth, and ends in death during the second or third year.

A few lethals are known in man which are fatal during the first few days of life or even just prior to birth; among these is the gene responsible for one of the recessive types of epidermolysis bullosa, a condition in which spontaneous blisters and other severe lesions develop in the skin. Numerous other lethals in man cause death during childhood or adolescence. Lethals which kill in the first stages of embryonic life doubtless exist in man also, but you can perhaps see that they would be extremely difficult to recognize. It is quite possible that at least a portion of the miscarriages that occur in early pregnancy are consequences of the action of lethal genes.

Several of the lethals in man which are mentioned above (juvenile and infantile amaurotic idiocy, and the severe type of epidermolysis) resemble the "parrot-beak" lethal in cattle, in that the genes respon-

Fig. 3.5 The results of lethal genes in cattle which have no visible effect in the heterozygous condition. Above, a "short-spine" calf; below, an "amputated" calf. *From Mohr and Wriedt in the Journal of Genetics, courtesy of the Cambridge University Press*

sible have no effect, as far as we can discover, in heterozygous state. The sickle-cell and thalassemia lethals, on the other hand, are more comparable to the Creeper lethal in poultry or to Yellow in mice because effects of these genes can be detected in heterozygotes (by microscopic examination of the blood) as we have already noted in the case of the sickle-cell gene. Perhaps even more closely comparable is a gene for brachyphalangy which in heterozygous

condition causes a shortening of the middle joints of one or more fingers. The condition is so rare that it is excessively unlikely to be found in both of two parents, and therefore there is little chance of discovering what the gene does when homozygous. One family, however, has been reported in which both parents (close relatives of each other) had the abnormality. Of their two children one had the shortened fingers characteristic of persons heterozygous for the brachyphalangy gene. The other was born without fingers or toes; the child had, moreover, a variety of severe deformities

Fig. 3.6 The results of a lethal gene in cattle which has a visible effect in the heterozygous condition. Above, a short-legged Dexter cow, the result of the heterozygous state of the gene, which in the homozygous state produces still-born "bull-dog" calves similar to that shown in Figure 3.7. Below, a normal Kerry cow.

Fig. 3.7 A "bull-dog" calf, the result of a lethal gene in the homozygous condition. *From Wriedt, Heredity in Live Stock, by permission of The Macmillan Co.*

throughout the skeleton, and it survived for only a year after birth. It is reasonable to suspect (though we of course cannot accept it as proved) that the severely deformed child was homozygous for the brachyphalangy gene, and that the effect of this gene in the homozygote is lethal.

In plants, albinism is a good example of a lethal gene which has no effect in the heterozygous condition; but homozygous albino plants, because they have no chlorophyll, are unable to manufacture sugar, and although they live long enough to be recognized, they die as soon as the food material in the seed is exhausted. On the campus of a large Southern university there is a row of maple trees beneath which large numbers of seedlings start to grow each year. Regularly one quarter of these seedlings are albino, indicating that the parent trees are heterozygous for albinism. Many lethals of various types are known in plants.

The lethal genes discussed in this chapter were discoverable, as we have already noted, either because they produce a discernible effect in the heterozygous condition, as in the Creeper case in fowls, or because they do not kill until a relatively late stage of embryonic or seedling development, as in the case of "parrot beak" in cattle or albinism in plants. When a lethal produces no noticeable effect in heterozygous condition and kills at an *early* stage of development, it is much more difficult to identify. The recognition of lethals of this kind is often possible by the use of special genetic techniques, but since these methods involve the analysis of *linkage* relations, we shall defer consideration of them until the subject of linkage has been discussed (Chapter 10).

We may summarize this chapter by reminding you that the 3:1 ratio found in the F_2 of crosses involving a dominant and a recessive allele is really a 1:2:1 ratio in which the first two classes appear alike. Where dominance is lacking, the true ratio of 1:2:1 may be readily observed. In some cases, one allele of a pair may be lethal in the homozygous state and produce a visible effect in the heterozygous state, so that the observed ratio among the living offspring will include only two of the classes, and will be 2:1 instead of 3:1 or 1:2:1.

PROBLEMS

3.1 Yellow guinea pigs crossed with white ones always produce cream-colored offspring. Two cream guinea pigs when crossed produce yellow, cream, and white offspring in the ratio of 1 yellow : 2 cream : 1 white. How are these colors inherited?

3.2 In radishes the shape may be long or round or oval. Crosses between long and oval gave 159 long, 156 oval. Crosses between round and oval gave 199 round, 203 oval. Crosses between long and round gave 576 oval. Crosses between oval and oval gave 121 long, 243 oval, 119 round. What type of inheritance is involved?

3.3 From the material given in the preceding problem, what would be expected from the cross of long with long? Of round with round?

3.4 Using the facts given in this chapter, what kinds of offspring would be expected and in what proportions if a Blue Andalusian male bird were mated to a black female? A blue female? A splashed-white female?

3.5 In foxes, a pair of alleles P and p interact as follows: PP is lethal, usually killing during embryonic life; Pp results in platinum color, and pp produces silver foxes. Could a fox breeder establish a true-breeding variety of platinum foxes?

3.6 When platinum foxes are crossed together, the offspring usually appear in the ratio of 2 platinum : 1 silver. Occasionally, however, a pure white pup appears from such matings, but invariably dies after a few hours or days. What is the probable explanation of the white pups?

3.7 In mink, a popular new color is blufrost. When standard brown mink are crossed with blufrost, the offspring appear in the ratio of one brown to one blufrost. Brown crossed with brown never produces blufrost. What would you predict among the offspring from a cross of blufrost with blufrost?

3.8 Albinism is lethal in plants, yet many species of plants produce albinos among their offspring. If albinos always die before reproducing, why does the character not become eliminated?

3.9 Gallus, a famous Holstein bull, was heterozygous for the recessive lethal gene responsible for absence of legs ("amputated"). Such famous sires may have many hundreds of offspring, and through Gallus the gene for amputated was widely spread among the Holstein breed. What problems of importance to the Holstein breeders does this fact create?

3.10 Outline a breeding program by means of which this character might be eliminated from the Holstein breed.

3.11 There are many characters in man which never skip generations, but which occur so rarely that two affected persons seldom if ever marry. Hence we know such a character (*hypotrichosis*, or the complete absence of hair, for example) only in the heterozygous state. Would it be possible for the homozygous state of the gene for such a character to be lethal?

3.12 In a certain series of matings between normal pigs, 38 offspring were born. Of these, 29 were normal and 9 had greatly swollen forelegs. The latter lived only a few hours. How could these results be explained genetically?

3.13 In the Tzourcana sheep of Roumania gray individuals and black individuals are found. The black animals when bred together give all black offspring. Black mated to gray results in approximately equal ratios of black and gray lambs. When grays are bred together, approximately two thirds of the offspring are gray and one third black. How are these colors inherited?

3.14 Certain breeds of dogs, such as the Mexican Hairless, have very little hair and few teeth. Crosses of hairless with normal dogs produce equal numbers of hairless and normal offspring. Crosses between hairless dogs produce only half as many normal offspring as hairless offspring. In addition a proportion of the puppies is born dead. These stillborn puppies lack external ears and show abnormalities of the buccal cavity. Account for these results genetically.

3.15 In crosses between two crested ducks, only about three quarters of the eggs hatch. The embryos of the remaining quarter develop nearly to hatching, and then die. Of the ducks which do hatch, about two thirds are crested and one third have no crest. What would you expect from the cross of a crested with a noncrested duck?

3.16 A breeder of Shorthorn cattle has cows which are white and a bull which is roan. What proportion of the calves produced in his herd will be white? Roan? Red?

3.17 Which of the calves in the preceding problem would be homozygous? Which would be heterozygous?

3.18 Starting with a roan bull and white cows, as in Problem 3.16, could you eventually establish a true-breeding red herd? How?

3.19 Would it be easier from a genetic standpoint to establish a true-breeding herd of red Shorthorns than to establish a true-breeding flock of rose-combed Wyandottes? If so, why? (See Problem 2.4.)

REFERENCES

LANDAUER, W., *Storrs Agr. Exper. Sta. Bull.* **193** (1934).

LANDAUER, W., and DUNN, L. C., *Jour. Genetics* **23**:397 (1930).

LERNER, I. M., *Jour. Heredity* **35**:219 (1944).

MOHR, O. L., and WRIEDT, C., *Carnegie Inst. Wash. Publ.* **295** (1919); *Jour. Genetics* **22**:279 (1930).

SHRODE, R. R., and LUSH, J. L., *Advances in Genetics* **1**:209. New York, Academic Press, Inc. (1947).

SORSBY, A., editor, *Clinical Genetics.* St. Louis, C. V. Mosby Co. (1953).

WRIEDT, C., *Heredity in Live Stock.* London, The Macmillan Co. (1930).

CHAPTER FOUR

The physical background
of Mendelian inheritance

In the preceding chapter we learned that genes are transmitted from parents to offspring in a manner that is statistically predictable. We also noted that genes are parts of chromosomes. In this chapter we shall consider some of the details of the transmission of genes from parents to offspring. We shall learn how genes occur in pairs in the somatic cells of an organism, and segregate in the germ cells.

Although Mendel's work was published in 1866 and seems to us, when we read it to-day, a masterpiece of clear and convincing exposition, none of Mendel's own contemporaries recognized its significance. For more than thirty years his contributions to our understanding of heredity were entirely neglected. Then, near the close of the last century, DeVries in Holland, Correns in Germany, von Tschermak in Austria, and Spillman in the United States, working independently of one another and in ignorance of the writings of Mendel, reached conclusions which were essentially identical with his. A search through the literature brought Mendel's paper to light, and in the year 1900 the results of his work, verified by workers of a later generation, were made known to the scientific world. This event marks the beginning of modern genetics.

The questions of why Mendel's discoveries made no impression at the time they were published, nor for nearly thirty-five years afterward, have aroused much speculation. Perhaps, as Glass suggests, the biologists of the time, as a result of the tremendous impact of Darwin's *Origin of Species*, were so intent upon problems relating to differences *between* species that their interest was not excited by reports of crosses *within* species. How many scientists read Mendel's paper in the years before it was disinterred we do not know but references to it in other works indicate that it was not understood by those who cited it, and make plausible the contention of Iltis that the time simply was not ripe for an understanding of Mendel's analysis. In a period when quantitative methods were unheard of in most areas of biology, a paper on plant hybridization which bristled with numerical ratios and with letter symbols in what looked like algebraic formulas could well have been brushed aside by many a reader as apparently irrelevant to its subject, or even as incomprehensible gibberish.

The fact that the Mendelian laws were almost simultaneously rediscovered by at least four independent investigators near the end of the century was, of course, no mere coincidence. Interest in problems of evolution was as intense as it had been earlier. But serious doubts had been cast upon the validity of the Lamarckian idea (accepted by Darwin) that variations produced in organisms by the direct action of the environment are causes of evolutionary change. This led to the focusing of attention on variations which are *not* traceable to environmental differences, and other considerations caused particular interest to center upon *discontinuous* variations — i.e., precisely such contrasting "unit character" differences as those which Mendel had studied. In the meantime, developments in statistics and biometry had received wide recognition, so that *quantitative* analysis of the progenies of segregating crosses was now a natural thing to attempt. Once this was undertaken by competent investigators, the rediscovery of the laws of Mendel was practically inevitable.

Mendel's laws are essentially a description of *what* happens when we make various kinds of crosses or matings. Having found this out, the next question we are likely to ask is *how* or *why* it happens. The answer, as was seen almost immediately upon the rediscovery of the Mendelian laws, is to be found in the behavior of the **chromosomes** (Fig. 4.1). These are deeply-staining structures found in the nuclei of cells, and we now know that they are the basis for segregation and other phenomena of heredity. But Mendel knew nothing of the behavior of chromosomes, nor even of their existence, for knowledge of the intimate details of cell structure had to await certain critical improvements in the microscope which were not accomplished until the nineteenth century was well under way. The basic facts of chromosome behavior were just becoming known in the last two decades of the century. But the more essential of these facts had been learned by the time Mendel's laws were rediscovered in 1900, and several biologists almost at once saw that there was a striking series of parallels between the behavior of genes on the one hand and the behavior of chromosomes on the other. This led them to suggest that the genes are located on the chromosomes. Let us

Fig. 4.1 Chromosomes in a cell of Ascaris (a worm).

look into the behavior of chromosomes and see how it parallels the behavior of genes. We shall thus come to some conclusions about what genes actually are.

First of all we can readily see by microscopic examination that living organisms are composed of minute structural units. These we call **cells.** All parts of the organism seem to be made up of these cells, arranged in various ways. When we examine them closely we find that, while they apparently differ considerably in shape and appearance, practically all of them possess one characteristic in common: a more or less spherical **nucleus** somewhere in the interior of the cell.

The material of which cells are composed is known as **protoplasm.** It is the living material of our world. Part of the protoplasm forms the nucleus in each cell. The rest of the protoplasm, different in appearance and structure, is known as **cytoplasm.** We find this part to be the basis of the differences in general appearance of cells. Muscle cells, nerve cells, epithelial cells, and others differ from each other in the shape and construction of the cytoplasmic part of the cell. The nuclei of all the cells of an organism, however, are surprisingly alike. It is to the nucleus that we must turn our attention for the analysis of the physical basis of Mendelian heredity.

All the millions of cells in our bodies have come into existence by division and subsequent growth from other cells, originally tracing back to the single fertilized egg cell from which each individual arises. Every cell, if we could watch it long enough, would be seen either to die or to divide. The knowledge of what happens when a cell divides is of fundamental importance in understanding heredity.

Mitosis

Many years devoted to the development and application of careful techniques lie behind our knowledge of what happens when cells divide. New techniques are currently adding to that knowledge at a rapid rate. The use of the phase microscope, for example, makes it possible to see, in living and unstained cells, structures which cannot be distinguished with the ordinary miscroscope because they have the same degree of transparency as their surroundings. Electron microscopy is contributing information about details of chromosome structure that are far below the limits of visibility under the highest magnifications afforded by conventional microscopes. Special methods have been devised to permit the study of isolated chromosomes, and through the use of these methods much has been learned about the chemical composition of chromosomal material.

When a cell is not dividing, we speak of it as being in the **interphase.** At this time, in most living cells, little or no structural detail can be seen in the nucleus with an ordinary light microscope. Cells that are killed and stained present a variety of appearances, depending on the method by which the cells are killed and on the stains that are used. Quite commonly, however, the stained interphase nucleus has a finely granular appearance and contains what looks like a loose skein or network of delicate fibrils. Careful study has shown that there is no actual "network," but instead, a number of very long, loosely coiled filaments. These are the **chromonemata** (singular, *chromonema*); chemically they appear to be composed chiefly, if not altogether, of protein. The granular material has long been called **chromatin,** because of the readiness with which it is colored or stained by certain dyes. We now know that it is composed of nucleoproteins, substances of very complex chemical composition whose molecules consist of protein combined with nucleic acids (see p. 363).

If we examine cells in successive stages as they approach division, we find that the chromonemata appear to become progressively shorter and thicker. The shortening is largely a consequence of their becoming more tightly coiled. The apparent thickening is also in some degree a result of the tighter coiling, but it is chiefly accounted for by the fact that DNA (desoxyribose nucleic acid), or DNA-containing nucleoprotein, condenses about the chromonemal filaments. The condensation of the DNA is not a mere deposition of this material on the chromonemata; rather, it appears to result from the contraction of a colloidal mass of nucleoprotein in gel form which has previously been in a diffuse or extended state. As the condensation of the deeply staining DNA proceeds, the coiled chromonemata within it are usually obscured, although they still can be made visible by special treatments which cause the coils to relax before the cells are killed.

The condensed masses of nucleoprotein, together with the chromonemata within them, are the **chromosomes.** When they have attained their final thickened condition, we can observe several interesting and important facts. First, in favorable material, each chromosome is seen to be a *double* structure as is clearly shown in Figure 4.2; the two halves are called **chromatids.** Second, if we examine numerous cells from the same animal or plant, or from other individuals of the same species, we find in general that *the number of chromosomes is the same from cell to cell and that it is constant for the species*. Third, individual chromosomes are often distinguishably different in size or in shape and we are able to see (with certain exceptions to be discussed later) that *the chromosomes occur in pairs;* that is, for each chromosome we identify there is another which matches it in shape and

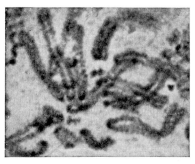

Fig. 4.2 Prophase chromosomes in a cell of a grasshopper. *Courtesy of Dr. G. H. Mickey*

size. Thus, in each body cell of a human being there are 48 chromosomes (24 pairs), in each cell of a mosquito there are 6 (3 pairs), in each cell of a corn plant 20 (10 pairs), in each cell of a certain species of crayfish 200 (100 pairs), and so on. The two members of each pair of chromosomes, which are with rare exceptions indistinguishable from each other in size and shape, are referred to as **homologous** chromosomes.

While the chromosomes have been attaining their final condensed form, a spindle-shaped structure composed of fine, non-staining fibers has made its appearance. In the cells of animals and of some lower plants, the fibers of the spindle body radiate from a pair of granules called **centrioles.** During interphase, the centrioles lie at one side of the nucleus as shown in Figure 4.3, A; or there may be only a single centriole which divides into two as mitosis begins. As the chromosomes condense, the centrioles migrate toward opposite poles of the cell (Fig. 4.3, B, C), and at the same time the nuclear membrane begins to disappear.

The cell changes so far described occur during what is called the **prophase** of mitosis. We conventionally regard the prophase as completed when (1) the nuclear membrane has altogether disappeared and (2) the centrioles have reached opposite poles of the cell. In the meantime the chromosomes (which during their condensation have been rather irregularly scattered in the nucleus) have become shifted in position so that they lie in a single plane (the **equatorial plate**) across the center of the spindle. The stage during which the chromosomes lie in the equatorial plate is known as **metaphase** (Figs. 4.3, D; 4.4). It can now be seen that some of the fibers of the spindle extend from pole to pole without interruption, whereas others are attached to the chromosomes — typically, one to each chromosome. At the point where the spindle fiber is attached, there is a constricted region which is not colored by the usual chromosomal stains, although it may contain one or more stainable granules. This is the **centromere** (Fig. 4.5). We can now see that the shape of the chromosome depends on the point of spindle-fiber attachment: if the centromere is practically at the end of a chromosome, the chromosome tends to be straight or rod-shaped. If the centromere is at an appreciable distance from the end, the chromosome is J-shaped; chromosomes which have their centromeres near the middle are V-shaped.

A cell may remain in metaphase for only a fraction of a minute, or for ten minutes or more, depending on the nature of the cell and on physiological conditions; characteristically it is the briefest phase of mitosis.

At the beginning of the next stage of mitosis, the **anaphase,** we see that each centromere has divided into two, and the chromatids

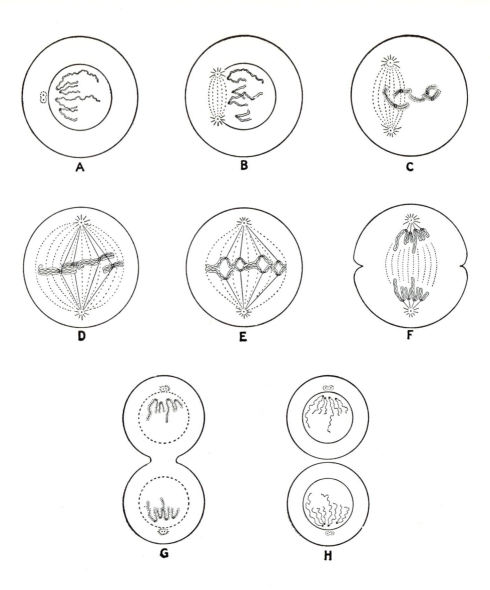

Fig. 4.3 Diagrammatic illustration of mitosis. Two pairs of chromosomes are shown. A, resting phase or interphase. B–C, prophase, showing the formation of the spindle extending from the centrioles, the disappearance of the nuclear membrane, and the condensation of the chromosomes. D, metaphase, showing the equatorial arrangement of the chromosomes and the attachment of spindle fibers to the centromeres of the chromosomes. E, early anaphase, showing the two chromatids of each chromosome separating and moving toward opposite poles. F–G, telophase, showing the reorganization of the nuclei and the splitting apart of the two halves of the original cell to form H, two daughter cells, each with the same number and types of chromosomes as in the original cell.

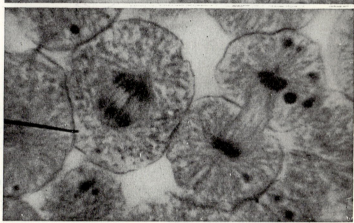

Fig. 4.4 Photomicrographs of various stages of mitosis in the whitefish. The upper pointer designates a metaphase. The lower pointer indicates an anaphase, with a telophase just to the right of it.

of each chromosome begin to move apart, apparently pulled by the attached spindle fibers (Figs. 4.3, E, F; 4.4). At the same time (in animal cells) a constriction can be seen around the equatorial region of the cell itself: the cytoplasm has begun to divide.

The two chromatids of each chromosome continue to move apart until they reach opposite poles of the spindle. This marks the end of the anaphase. It is followed by the **telophase** during which a nuclear membrane forms around the chromatids which are grouped at each pole, the nucleoprotein material of the chromatids or "daughter chromosomes" becomes diffuse, exposing once again the coiled chromonemata; the coils of the latter loosen, and there is a gradual return to the interphase condition. Meanwhile, division of the cytoplasm is completed, and the spindle disappears. There are thus two new cells, each containing one of the new nuclei, *and each of the cells has the same number of chromosomes as the original parent cell.*

At some time during the latter stages of mitosis each daughter chromosome duplicates itself, so that there are again two chromatids making up each chromosome when it appears in the next prophase. The details of this duplication will be further considered in Chapter 24.

The division of the cytoplasm in the formation of the daughter cells is not necessarily equal, although it is often approximately so. But the division of the chromosomal material appears to be precisely equal from a quantitative standpoint, and we shall see later that it is also qualitatively equal. Thus, as the result of a mitotic cell division, we have two cells each containing a set of chromosomes identical with that contained in the other, and both sets identical with that which was present in the parent cell.

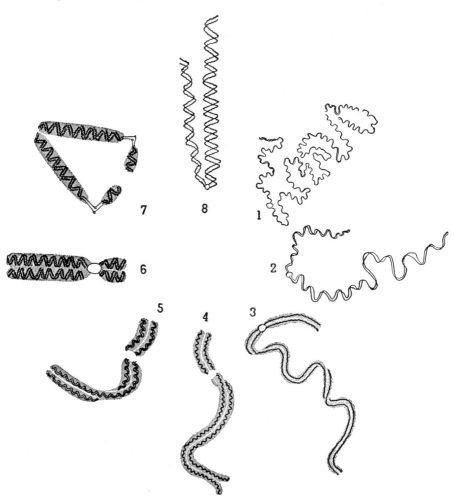

Fig. 4.5 Diagram of successive stages of chromosome condensation during mitosis. 1, interphase; 2–5, prophase; 6, metaphase; 7, anaphase; 8, telophase. The centromere has been indicated by a clear circle. *From DeRobertis, Nowinski and Saez, GENERAL CYTOLOGY, courtesy of W. B. Saunders Co.*

The Maturation of the Germ Cells

As we have just seen, before a somatic cell divides by mitosis, each chromosome has become duplicated, so that from one cell generation to the next the chromosomes remain constant in number and in kind. At one phase in the life history of animals and plants which reproduce sexually, however, a modification of this process is found: duplication of the chromosomes takes place only once *in the course of two successive cell divisions*. These are the **meiotic** divisions. The net result of **meiosis,** as the two meiotic divisions together are called, is that cells are produced which have just half the number of chromosomes present in somatic cells. We should recall that in somatic cells the chromosomes are found in homologous pairs. The cells resulting from meiosis receive one chromosome from each of these pairs.

In animals meiosis occurs in the formation of the germ cells or gametes. The whole process of the formation of the gametes, including the meiotic divisions as well as changes in size and form, is known as **maturation.**

We know that among sexually reproducing organisms each new individual is started by the union of two gametes: a sperm cell from the father and an egg cell from the mother. All of the somatic cells of the new individual are produced by repeated mitotic divisions of cells tracing back to the zygote formed by this union. Since the number of chromosomes in the somatic cells of any one species remains constant from generation to generation, it is clear that there must be some mechanism that keeps the number from doubling at each fertilization. Under the microscope, we can see how the process of meiosis provides this mechanism. We shall now examine the meiotic process as it occurs during the maturation of the germ cells in animals. In a later chapter we shall consider the same process in plants, where it is in all essential respects the same.

In the testes, or sex glands of a male animal, will be found many cells in all stages of development from potential spermatozoa to fully formed spermatozoa. We may speak of spermatozoa as **sperms** for short: they are the gametes, or sex cells, produced by a male. We may follow their development, which includes two cell divisions, again by using the microscope and techniques of staining.

The potential sex cells in the testis are **spermatogonia.** They divide frequently by mitosis, forming more spermatogonia. Every so often groups of spermatogonia undergo a series of events leading to the formation of mature sperms. Let us follow one spermatogonium through such a transformation (Figs. 4.6 and 4.7).

The first visible sign of maturation is the rapid enlargement of the spermatogonium. When this is accomplished it is definitely on the road to becoming a sperm. After it enlarges it is called a **primary**

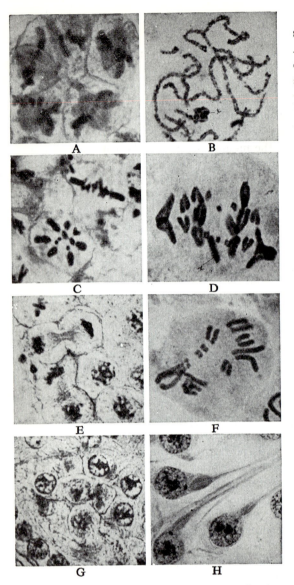

A   **B**

C   **D**

E   **F**

G   **H**

Fig. 4.6 Photomicrographs of various stages in the spermatogenesis of the grasshopper, *Romalea microptera*. A, spermatogonia in metaphase. B, primary spermatocyte in prophase. C, metaphase of the first maturation division. D, anaphase of the first maturation division. E, telophase of the first maturation division. F, metaphase of the second maturation division (secondary spermatocyte). G, spermatids. H, spermatids elongating during transformation into spermatozoa. *Photomicrographs by courtesy of Dr. G. H. Mickey*

spermatocyte (Figs. 4.6, B; 4.7, A). After a brief resting period, the chromosomes begin to appear as slender coiled filaments, as in the prophase of mitosis (Fig. 4.7, A, B). Now, however, the chromonemata which represent the homologous chromosomes of each pair, instead of retaining independent positions in the nucleus, become closely applied to each other throughout their lengths (Fig. 4.7, C, D). This is known as **synapsis.** While the homologous filaments are in synapsis, condensation of the chromosomal material proceeds, the chromosomes shorten and thicken, and the two members of each pair become coiled about each other. When the homologous chromosomes of each pair are thus intimately associated, it becomes evident that each chromosome of every pair has become duplicated and hence is now composed of two **chromatids,** held together by a single centromere. Consequently, for each chromosome pair there are now four chromatids in close association. The four-stranded structure formed in this way is called a **tetrad** (Fig. 4.7, E).

While the changes just described have been taking place, a spindle has been forming, and now the two centromeres of the tetrad, each with its two attached chromatids, begin to move toward opposite poles. At the beginning of this anaphase movement, the four chromatids of each tetrad tend to loop out in pairs in a twisted formation which we shall soon describe more fully (Fig. 4.7, F, G).

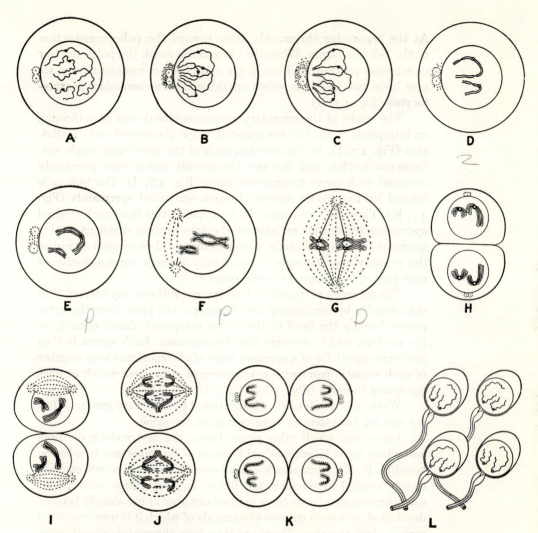

Fig. 4.7 Diagrammatic illustration of the maturation of the germ cells (meiosis) in the male. Two pairs of chromosomes are shown. A, primary spermatocyte, with chromosomes beginning to show orientation. B, chromosomes oriented with free ends toward centrioles. C, synapsis beginning at free ends of chromosomes. D, synapsis complete. E, each chromosome has split lengthwise, forming two chromatids. The four chromatids thus closely associated comprise the tetrad. The two pairs of chromatids have partially separated, showing chiasmata. F, the chromatids have shortened and thickened. The asters are migrating toward the poles of the cell, and a spindle is forming between them. G, spindle complete, fibers attached to centromeres of chromatid pairs (dyads), which are now equatorially located. H, the dyads have separated and two secondary spermatocytes have been formed. I–K, division of the two secondary spermatocytes to form four spermatids. L, the four spermatids have transformed into four spermatozoa, each with the haploid number of chromosomes, i.e., one chromosome of each pair. The tetrads (E–G) would actually appear, in cross-section or end view, like this : : However, for clarity in flat-plane representation, to which printing is restricted, they are drawn as if they appear thus . . . . in end view.

As the separating chromatids move toward the poles, constriction of the cell has begun. When the chromatids reach the poles, nuclear membranes re-form, division of the cytoplasm is completed, and we now have two new cells which are designated as **secondary spermatocytes** (Fig. 4.7, H).

The nuclei of the secondary spermatocytes do not pass through an interphase stage, but immediately begin the second meiotic division (Fig. 4.7, I). In this division each of the previously single centromeres divides, and the two chromatids which were previously attached to it move to opposite poles (Fig. 4.7, J). The new cells formed by the second meiotic division are called **spermatids** (Fig. 4.7, K). There will, of course, be four spermatids from each original spermatogonium that underwent the two meiotic divisions, and a spermatid will contain only a single chromatid from each tetrad of the primary spermatocyte — hence only a single representative of each pair of homologous chromosomes.

The spermatids transform into sperms without any further division, usually by condensing and forming a tail piece from the cytoplasm, leaving the head of the sperm composed almost entirely of the nucleus, which contains the chromosomes. Each sperm is thus made up essentially of a compact mass of chromosomes (one member of each somatic pair) with a tail piece of cytoplasm which enables the sperm to move (Figs. 4.6, H; 4.7, L).

While the details of the maturational process vary among different species, the essential features remain the same.

One event which takes place during the first meiotic division, and which must be emphasized because of its important bearing on heredity, is this: while the two members of a pair of chromosomes are closely applied in synapsis and before any separation takes place, each chromosome (as we have pointed out above) has already become duplicated, although the two chromatids of which it is now composed remain close together. There are thus four chromatids closely associated in each pair of chromosomes (the tetrad). When the two members of a pair of chromosomes separate after synapsis, it is seen that they separate in a peculiar crossed manner (Fig. 4.7, G). Each cross is called a **chiasma.** It is interpreted to be the result of the exchange of segments between two of the chromatids belonging to different members of the pair. We thus see that the two chromosomes of a pair may exchange material with each other before separating, and two of the four sperms from a primary spermatocyte may each contain a chromosome which is not identical with the corresponding chromosome in each of the other two sperms. This point will be enlarged upon later in connection with genetic linkage (Chapters 10 and 11).

In the formation of mature **ova,** or eggs, from potential egg cells in the ovary of an animal, a similar series of events takes place. The maturation divisions, including the formation of tetrads and chiasmata, go on as in the formation of sperms. The only difference is that instead of the process yielding four mature gametes, as it did in the case of males, three of the four cells resulting from the divisions are small, and disintegrate. We speak of them as **polar bodies.** The fourth cell gets all the cytoplasm and becomes a mature ovum, larger than most cells of the body.

The terminology of the maturation process and structures in the female is similar to that used in the male: an **oögonium,** or potential egg cell, enlarges to become a **primary oöcyte;** this divides to produce a **secondary oöcyte** and a polar body; these by dividing form an **oötid** and three polar bodies; and finally the oötid without further division becomes a mature **ovum.**

As a result of maturation, then, we have in males the production of sperms, each containing half the number of chromosomes which the body cells possess; and in females, we have the production of egg cells, likewise containing half the number of chromosomes which the other cells possess. This half number of chromosomes for any species we call the **haploid,** or **n,** number of chromosomes. The number found in the other cells of the species we call the **diploid,** or **2n,** number of chromosomes.

We cannot too strongly emphasize that the haploid number of chromosomes does not consist of *any* half of the diploid number, but always consists of *one of each pair* of chromosomes.

Each chromosome of a haploid set, moreover, may be *either* member of the pair that was present in the spermatogonium. That is, it may be the one that the individual received from its mother (the "maternal" chromosome of the pair) or it may be the one which was received from its father (the "paternal" chromosome). *And whether a sperm receives a maternal or a paternal member of one chromosome pair is entirely independent of which member of any other pair it receives.* We cannot usually prove this by direct observation, since as we have learned, the maternal and paternal members of a pair of homologous chromosomes are, with rare exceptions, indistinguishable in appearance. But direct evidence on this point can be obtained in certain exceptional cases (that is, cases in which more than one pair of chromosomes that synapse during meiosis are composed of visibly distinguishable maternal and paternal elements) and in all of these, independent assortment of the pairs has been shown to occur.

We find, then, several facts about chromosomes that will remind us of similar facts which we have previously observed about genes. First, chromosomes occur in pairs in the zygote and the somatic cells of the body. *So do genes.* Mendel came to the same conclusion with respect to the determinants of alternative characteristics: determinants which we now call allelic genes. Second, chromosomes segregate in the germ cells. That is, only one member of each pair of chromosomes normally enters a gamete. *So do genes segregate in the germ cells.* Again this latter conclusion was reached before chromosomes were known.

Chromosomes retain their individuality from generation to generation. In the prophase stage, when they do not appear as visible formed chromosomes, they are still entities. Under careful observation through the microscope, the chromatin material of each chromosome is seen to be intact and independent of other chromosomes. *Genes, too, retain their individuality.* A pair of genes for dwarfness in the F_2 generation produces a plant just as dwarf as though its effect had not been hidden while being carried through the tall F_1 generation. Of course the exchange of material by homologous chromosomes is an exception to the statement that chromosomes keep their individuality, but later we shall find a comparable exception for groups of genes.

Thus we already have three parallels between the behavior of chromosomes and the behavior of genes. We have just seen that either chromosome of a pair may occur in a gamete with either chromosome of any other pair, the only requisite being that there be one of each pair in every gamete. In other words, chromosomes *assort at random*. In the next chapter we shall see that genes also assort at random.

These parallels, along with many others which we shall learn about in later chapters, indicate that genes are actually integral parts of chromosomes. This hypothesis will be developed and elaborated as we proceed with our study of genetics.

PROBLEMS

4.1 In each somatic cell of a human being there are forty-eight chromosomes. How many chromosomes will be found in a mature human egg? In a polar body? In a sperm? In a spermatid? In a primary spermatocyte?

4.2 Observation and experiment show that an individual receives its genes through the sperm as well as through the egg. What part of a cell would thus appear to be chiefly concerned in the transmission of genes?

4.3 If a certain character were always inherited through the egg, never through the sperm, what part of the gamete would probably be responsible for the transmission of the genetic basis for the character?

4.4 Each somatic cell of *Drosophila melanogaster* (fruit fly) contains four pairs of chromosomes. In any individual Drosophila what relation do these four pairs of chromosomes bear to the chromosomes of the two parents of the fly?

4.5 When a Drosophila forms gametes, what proportion of the gametes will be expected to carry all the chromosomes of maternal origin? Can you derive a simple formula to give this proportion for any number of pairs of chromosomes?

4.6 Using the formula derived in the preceding problem, what proportion of human sperms would contain twenty-four maternal chromosomes?

4.7 How many human sperms will result from fifty primary spermatocytes? From fifty spermatids?

4.8 How many human eggs will result from two primary oöcytes? From two secondary oöcytes?

4.9 The dog has 39 pairs of chromosomes, the wolf also has 39 pairs, but the red fox has only 17 pairs. What would you predict as to the relative probability of finding dog-wolf hybrids as compared with the probability of finding dog-fox hybrids?

4.10 As a matter of fact, dog-wolf hybrids are well known. How many chromosomes would you expect the hybrid to have? Dog-fox hybrids have occasionally been claimed to occur, but none has ever been confirmed. If such a hybrid should ever be found, how many chromosomes would it have? Would these chromosomes be in pairs?

4.11 Although the red fox has 17 pairs of chromosomes, the arctic fox has 26 pairs. Occasional hybrids between these two species are known. How many chromosomes would be found in a gamete of the red fox? In a gamete of the arctic fox?

4.12 How many chromosomes would be found in each somatic cell of the hybrid fox? Will these chromosomes all be in pairs? Might any of them show pairing?

4.13 The hybrid foxes have always proved to be sterile. Do the facts on chromosomal numbers give any clue to the reason for the sterility?

4.14 Suppose you examined the cells of a species of plant and found 12 chromosomes: a long straight pair, a short straight pair, a medium-length straight pair, a long bent pair, a short bent pair, and a medium-length bent pair. You then breed plants of this species for several generations. At the end of this time would you expect to find some plants with all the straight chromosomes and none of the bent ones? Would you expect any of the plants to have all of the bent chromosomes and none of the straight ones? Explain.

4.15 In plants like those described in Problem 4.14 what proportion of the gametes should have three straight chromosomes and three bent ones? Four straight chromosomes and two bent ones? Six bent chromosomes?

4.16 In what respects are the maturation processes in males and females similar?

4.17 In what respects are the maturation processes in males and females different?

4.18 How would the chromosome content of the cell of the eye of a man compare with the chromosome content of the fertilized egg from which he developed?

4.19 Would you expect the cytoplasm of the eye cell to be as similar to the cytoplasm of the fertilized egg as the chromosomes of the eye cell are to the chromosomes of the fertilized egg? Give reasons for your answer.

4.20 How does the chromosome content of a secondary spermatocyte compare with that of a spermatogonium? Of a sperm with that of a spermatid? Of an oötid with that of a secondary oöcyte? Of an ovum with that of a somatic cell?

REFERENCES

DE ROBERTIS, E. D. P., NOWINSKI, W. W., and SAEZ, F. A., *General Cytology*, 2nd ed. Philadelphia, W. B. Saunders Co. (1954).

GLASS, BENTLEY, In *Studies in Intellectual History*. Baltimore, The Johns Hopkins Press (1953).

HUGHES, A., *The Mitotic Cycle*. New York, Academic Press, Inc. (1952).

MANTON, I., *Biol. Rev.* **25**:486 (1950).

RILEY, H. P., *An Introduction to Genetics and Cytogenetics*. New York, John Wiley and Sons (1948).

RIS, H., *Cell Division*. (Chapter 3 in WILLIER, B. H., WEISS, P. A., and HAMBURGER, V., eds., *Analysis of Development*). Philadelphia, W. B. Saunders Co. (1955).

SERRA, J. A., *Cold Spring Harbor Symp. on Quant. Biol.* **12**:192 (1947).

WHITE, M. J. D., *The Chromosomes,* 3rd ed. London, Methuen and Co., Ltd. (1947).

WILSON, E. B., *The Cell in Development and Heredity*, 3rd ed. New York, The Macmillan Co. (1925).

CHAPTER FIVE

Crosses involving two pairs of genes

We are now familiar with the way in which one pair of genes behaves in inheritance, and we have seen the physical basis for such behavior. Let us next find out what occurs when we watch the behavior of two pairs of genes in the same cross.

Mendel made such crosses. We recall that in peas tallness is due to a dominant gene, dwarfness to a recessive, and the two genes are allelic. Likewise, axillary flowers (that is, flowers appearing in the axils of the leaves) are due to a dominant gene, while terminal flowers (flowers appearing at the ends of the stems) are due to its recessive allele (Fig. 5.1).

When a homozygous tall axillary-flowered plant is crossed with a dwarf terminal-flowered plant, the F_1 are all tall with axillary flowers. We can readily see why this should be so, on the basis of our previous work.

Let D and d represent a pair of alleles such that $D-$ results in tall plants and dd results in dwarf plants.

And let T and t represent another pair of alleles, such that $T-$ results in plants with axillary flowers and tt results in plants with terminal flowers.

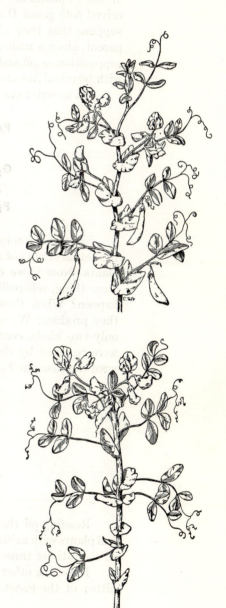

Fig. 5.1 Contrasting types of flowering in garden peas. Above, axillary flowers; below, terminal flowers.

It is customary in genetic terminology to use a dash following one allele to indicate that the other allele could be either the dominant or the recessive gene. Thus $D-$ indicates either DD or Dd.

Then a homozygous tall axillary-flowered plant would be represented by $DDTT$ and a dwarf terminal-flowered plant by $ddtt$. Since all the F_1 plants are tall with axillary flowers, we know that they received *both* genes D and T from one parent. To be logical we must suppose that they also received the genes d and t from the other parent, since a male and female gamete united at fertilization. This supposition is proved by the F_2, which contains some dwarf plants with terminal flowers.

Let us write our cross thus far:

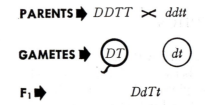

PARENTS ▶ $DDTT \times ddtt$

GAMETES ▶ DT dt

F_1 ▶ $DdTt$

Since D is dominant to d and T to t, our theoretical results satisfy the actual results of an F_1 composed entirely of tall axillary-flowered plants. Now if we cross two F_1 plants (or, what amounts to the same thing, self-pollinate an F_1 plant) to obtain an F_2, what could happen? When these F_1 plants produce gametes, what kinds will they produce? We might suppose at first that they would produce only two kinds, containing DT and dt respectively, since the genes were received by the F_1 from its parents in that way. But if this were the case our F_2 should be as follows:

	DT	dt
DT	$DDTT$	$DdTt$
dt	$DdTt$	$ddtt$

Reading off the checkerboard would give us an F_2 composed of tall plants with axillary flowers and dwarf plants with terminal flowers in the ratio of three to one.

If, on the other hand, the F_1 plants could produce gametes with either of the genes for height contained in the same gamete with either of the genes for flower-position, there would be four kinds of male gametes and four kinds of female gametes: *DT, Dt, dT, dt.* Our F_2 would then be as follows:

	DT	*Dt*	*dT*	*dt*
DT	*DDTT*	*DDTt*	*DdTT*	*DdTt*
Dt	*DDTt*	*DDtt*	*DdTt*	*Ddtt*
dT	*DdTT*	*DdTt*	*ddTT*	*ddTt*
dt	*DdTt*	*Ddtt*	*ddTt*	*ddtt*

Reading off the checkerboard would then give us the following kinds of plants in the F_2: tall axillary-flowered, tall terminal-flowered, dwarf axillary-flowered, and dwarf terminal-flowered, in the ratio of 9:3:3:1.

This is the ratio which is actually obtained when the cross is made. It indicates to us that all four types of gametes were possible in the F_1. Either one of the genes for height may occur in a gamete with either one of the genes for flower-position. In other words, *genes assort at random.* This makes another parallel between the behavior of chromosomes and the behavior of genes, since it will be recalled from the last chapter that chromosomes also assort at random. This cross likewise offers additional proof that gametes may unite at random.

Further proof of the random assortment of genes is found in the results of the cross involving the opposite arrangement of genes. When a homozygous tall terminal-flowered plant is crossed with a homozygous dwarf axillary-flowered plant, the F_1 and F_2 results are exactly the same as in the previous cross, although the genes entered the cross in opposite combinations. There seems to be no doubt that genes assort at random. Later we will find certain exceptions to this principle, but for the present we may content ourselves with the principle itself.

Thus the typical F_2 ratio in a cross involving two pairs of genes is 9:3:3:1. Similar analyses may be made of crosses involving three, four, or more genes, and typical F_2 ratios may be evolved for them. Work out for yourself a diagram of a cross involving three independent pairs of genes, and prove that the results will give a ratio in the F_2 of 27:9:9:9:3:3:3:1.

The Interaction of Genes

The number and kinds of genes involved in any cross are determined from the breeding results. Often we are completely unable to predict these results for newly discovered characters before the crosses are made. Once the breeding results are obtained, however, definite conclusions may be drawn as to the nature of the inheritance involved. Remembering what we have already learned as to dominance, recessiveness, blending, and similar phenomena, let us take a case in point and attempt to analyze it.

Let us make a cross involving coat colors in rats. In the laboratory we may find two kinds which will serve our purpose: jet-black rats and yellow rats. Let us cross a black rat with a yellow one. What might we expect in the F_1? From our previous work we will immediately be able to say that the F_1 may all be yellow, in which case we would suspect that yellow was due to a dominant gene. Or we might expect the F_1 to be all black, in which case we would suspect that black was due to a dominant gene. Or, as another possibility, we might expect the F_1 to be intermediate between the parents in color, due to a blend.

When we actually make the cross, all the F_1 are gray. This appears to be a blend between the black and yellow, and on this basis we would expect the F_2 to give the typical blending ratio: one black, two gray, one yellow. But when we cross two F_1 individuals and obtain an F_2 generation, it does not give the blending ratio, but produces *four* colors of rats in the following proportions: nine gray, three black, three yellow, one cream. The cream-colored rats, occurring in one sixteenth of the F_2 individuals, are a new variety, different from anything previously involved in the cross.

Obviously this is a two-pair ratio, and the coat colors under discussion must be dependent, not upon the transmission of a single pair of genes, but of *two* pairs.

Referring back to the two-pair cross at the beginning of this chapter, it will be recalled that the F_1 individuals showed the characters due to both dominant genes. The "nine-sixteenths" group of the F_2 also showed the characters due to both dominant genes.

In the rats, then, we should expect the F_1 to show the result produced by the presence of a dominant gene of each pair. The F_1 rats are, it will be remembered, gray. Gray must therefore represent the combined effect of a dominant gene of each pair. Likewise cream, occurring on the average in only one out of sixteen F_2 individuals, must represent the effect of both pairs of recessive genes. Black must be produced by the dominant gene of one pair and the homozygous recessive gene of the other, while the reverse condition produces yellow.

We may therefore assume two pairs of alleles, *A* and *a*, *R* and *r*, affecting coat color and interacting as follows:

A–R– results in gray
A–rr results in yellow
aaR– results in black
aarr results in cream

Again keep in mind that when a dash follows one allele, as in the above scheme, it means that the other allele of the pair could be either the dominant or the recessive gene.

Our cross between a homozygous black rat and a homozygous yellow rat must have been as follows:

$$aaRR \times AArr$$

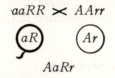

AaRr

Since each parent brought in the dominant which the other one lacked, the F_1 are gray, like the ancestral wild rats, due to the combined effect of both dominants. This effect is sometimes spoken of as **atavism,** or **reversion.** It merely represents the formation of a genotype similar to one which existed at some time in the past.

The gray F_1 rats would each produce four kinds of germ cells, as follows:

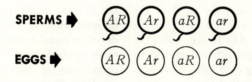

A checkerboard giving all possible unions of sperms and eggs may be made:

	AR	*Ar*	*aR*	*ar*
AR	*AARR* gray	*AARr* gray	*AaRR* gray	*AaRr* gray
Ar	*AARr* gray	*AArr* yellow	*AaRr* gray	*Aarr* yellow
aR	*AaRR* gray	*AaRr* gray	*aaRR* black	*aaRr* black
ar	*AaRr* gray	*Aarr* yellow	*aaRr* black	*aarr* cream

Thus, although we could not have predicted it before the matings were made, our cross between a black rat and a yellow rat involves *two* pairs of genes. The F_2 ratio of 9:3:3:1 which we obtain shows us clearly that changes in coat color cannot depend in this cross on changes in a single pair of alleles, as deafness did in dogs in a preceding chapter. We shall find many examples of characters which depend upon the interaction of more than one pair of alleles. As a matter of fact, the modern genetic belief is that no single gene is solely responsible for the production of any one character. Every character results from the interaction of all the genes. A change in a particular gene may influence one character more than it does another, and conversely a change in one gene may influence a particular character more than a change in another gene does. This viewpoint of "genic interaction" will be elaborated in Chapter 17.

Some shortcuts in solving problems

The alert student will recognize that the checkerboard diagrams used in this and earlier chapters are essentially devices for the combining of ratios or proportions, and he will be able to take advantage of short-cut procedures that will both save time and reduce chances of error in working many types of problems. Thus, in the mating diagramed on page 55, $\frac{1}{4}$ of the sperms carry the genes AR and $\frac{1}{4}$ of the eggs likewise carry AR. Hence, $\frac{1}{4} \times \frac{1}{4}$, or $\frac{1}{16}$, of all sperm-egg combinations will be AR sperm $\times$ AR egg or $AARR$ zygotes, as indicated by the fact that this genotype is entered in one square out of 16. Similarly, $\frac{1}{4} \times \frac{1}{4}$, or $\frac{1}{16}$, of the sperm-egg combinations will be AR sperm $\times$ Ar egg, or $AARr$ zygotes, and another $\frac{1}{16}$ will be Ar sperm $\times$ AR egg combinations, which are also $AARr$

zygotes. Zygotes of genotype $AARr$ will therefore constitute $\frac{2}{16}$ of the total progeny of the cross, and correspondingly we find this genotype entered in two of the sixteen squares.

In this fashion we have worked out the ratios of various combinations of *gametes*. This was done to emphasize the fact that the F_2 ratios result from the combining of different kinds of gametes which are produced in equal numbers. We can use the same method to work out the expected proportions of various combinations of *genotypes*. Thus, a zygote of the constitution $AARR$ can be thought of as a combination of AA and RR genotypes.

In the progeny of the cross $AaRr \times AaRr$, if we look at each pair of alleles separately, we note that with respect to the

A,a Genotypes

R,r Genotypes		1 AA	2 Aa	1 aa
	1 RR	1 AARR	2 AaRR	1 aaRR
	2 Rr	2 AARr	4 AaRr	2 aaRr
	1 rr	1 AArr	2 Aarr	1 aarr

A,a pair, the genotypes should occur in the ratio $1\ AA : 2\ Aa : 1\ aa$, and similarly for the R,r pair. We may use a checkerboard p. 56 to combine these ratios.

The number in each square of the above checkerboard is obtained by multiplying the number at the head of the column in which the square is found by the number at the left of the row. The results, of course, are identical with those in the diagram on page 55, but we have reduced the number of squares from sixteen to nine, and there are no duplications of genotypes.

Even further economy can be achieved in a problem in which we are required to obtain only the *phenotype* ratios. In this example, our checkerboard would become

A,a Phenotypes

		3 *A-*	1 *aa*
R,r Phenotypes	3 *R-*	9 *A-R-* gray	3 *aaR-* black
	1 *rr*	3 *A-rr* yellow	1 *aarr* cream

If we recognize that in all our checkerboard diagrams the checkerboard itself has been used only as a framework for performing multiplications, we can dispense with it altogether and simply write in place of the diagram above:

A,a phenotypes　(3 *A-* + 1 *aa*)
R,r phenotypes × (3 *R-* + 1 *rr*)

Combinations:
9 *A-R-* + 3 *aaR-* + 3 *A-rr* + 1 *aarr*
　gray　　black　　yellow　　cream

Alternatively, we may express our proportions in fractional form:

A,a phenotypes　($\frac{3}{4}$ *A-* + $\frac{1}{4}$ *aa*)
R,r phenotypes × ($\frac{3}{4}$ *R-* + $\frac{1}{4}$ *rr*)

Combinations:
$\frac{9}{16}$ *A-R-* + $\frac{3}{16}$ *aaR-* + $\frac{3}{16}$ *A-rr* + $\frac{1}{16}$ *aarr*
　gray　　　black　　　yellow　　　cream

The student should try to develop facility in the combining of proportions when they are expressed as fractions as well as when they are given in whole-number ratios, because the combination of proportions in fractional form will be important in connection with later topics.

To obtain genotype or phenotype ratios in crosses which involve *three* pairs of alleles (as is required in problems 5.23, 5.24, and 5.25 below) we merely perform an additional multiplication. Thus, instead of the original two-pair cross in the example we have just worked out, suppose we had started with a three-pair cross, $AARRCC \times aarrcc$, where the gene interactions are such that

A-R-C- results in gray
A-rrC- results in yellow
aaR-C- results in black
aarrC- results in cream
A-R-cc ⎫
A-rrcc ⎬ result in albino
aaR-cc ⎪
aarrcc ⎭

If we are asked the phenotype proportions in the F_2, we note that with respect to the A,a pair we should get the ratio 3 *A-* : 1 *aa;* for the R,r pair the ratio would similarly be 3 *R-* : 1 *rr;* and for the C,c pair, 3 *C-* : 1 *cc*. Multiplying the first ratio by the second, just as was done above, we get

9 *A-R-* + 3 *aaR-* + 3 *A-rr* + 1 *aarr*

We now perform a second multiplication:

(9 *A-R-* + 3 *aaR-* + 3 *A-rr* + 1 *aarr*)
× (3 *C-* + 1 *cc*)

27 *A-R-C-* + 9 *aaR-C-* + 9 *A-rrC-* + 3 *aarrC-*
　gray　　　black　　　yellow　　　cream
+9 *A-R-cc* + 3 *aaR-cc* + 3 *A-rrcc* + 1 *aarrcc*
albino　　　albino　　　albino　　　albino

Would the F_2 results be any different if the parents of the F_1 had been $AArrCC \times aaRRcc$ or $aaRRCC \times AArrcc$? If you should attempt the three-pair problem we have just completed by the usual checkerboard method, how many squares would you have to fill in?

PROBLEMS

5.1 In turkeys a dominant gene, R, produces the familiar bronze color; its recessive allele, r, results in red. Another dominant gene, H, results in normal feathers; its recessive allele, h, produces feathers without webbing, so that they resemble tufts of hairs. Two bronze turkeys with normal feathers were mated, and their offspring consisted of eight bronze with normal feathers, three bronze with hairy feathers, two red with normal feathers, and one red with hairy feathers. What were the genotypes of the parents?

5.2 Assuming that the red bird with hairy feathers is a female, what kinds of offspring would you expect, and in what proportions, if it were mated to its male parent?

5.3 In horses black is dependent upon a dominant gene, B, and chestnut upon its recessive allele, b. The trotting gait is due to a dominant gene, T, the pacing gait to its recessive allele, t. If a homozygous black pacer is mated to a homozygous chestnut trotter, what will be the appearance of the F_1 generation?

5.4 If two F_1 individuals from the preceding problem were mated, what kinds of offspring could they have and in what proportions?

5.5 If an F_1 male from Problem 5.3 were mated to a homozygous female black pacer, what kinds of offspring could be produced and in what proportions?

5.6 In rabbits black is due to a dominant gene, B, brown to its recessive allele, b. Short hair is due to a dominant gene, L, long hair to its recessive allele, l. In a cross between a homozygous black short-haired male and a homozygous brown long-haired female, what would be the genetic constitution and the appearance of the F_1 generation? Of the F_2 generation?

5.7 How would the F_1 and F_2 of Problem 5.6 compare with the F_1 and the F_2 from a cross between a homozygous black long-haired male and a homozygous brown short-haired female?

5.8 In the F_2 generation of Problem 5.6 what proportion of the black short-haired rabbits would be homozygous for both pairs of genes?

5.9 Suppose you had a black short-haired male rabbit and a brown long-haired female rabbit and wished to develop a homozygous strain of black long-haired rabbits from them. Outline the breeding procedure necessary to establish such a strain.

5.10 In tomatoes red fruit color is dependent upon a dominant gene, R, yellow is dependent upon its recessive allele, r; tallness is due to a dominant gene, D, dwarfness to its recessive allele, d. The Golden Beauty variety has yellow fruit and is tall. The Dwarf Giant is dwarf with red fruit. Using these two varieties to start with, could you eventually obtain a homozygous variety which was tall with red fruit? Could you obtain a homozygous variety which was dwarf with yellow fruit? Which would be more readily obtained? Outline the procedure in each case.

5.11 In summer squashes white fruit is due to a dominant gene, W, and colored fruit to its recessive allele, w. Disk-shaped fruit is due to a dominant gene, S, sphere-shaped fruit to its recessive allele, s. How many different genotypes may squash plants have in regard to color and shape of fruit? How many phenotypes result from these genotypes? How many different homozygous genotypes are possible?

5.12 Using data contained in this chapter, what would be the result of a cross between two cream rats? Could a black race be developed, starting with two cream rats as parents?

5.13 If a homozygous gray rat were crossed with a homozygous cream rat, what would be the genotype and phenotype of the F_1? If one of the F_1 animals were crossed with a cream rat, what kinds of offspring could they produce?

5.14 If an F_1 animal from Problem 5.13 were crossed with a homozygous gray rat, what kinds of offspring could they produce? What proportion of these offspring would be expected to be homozygous?

5.15 In poultry black color is due to a dominant gene, E, red to its recessive allele, e. Crested head is due to a dominant gene, C, plain head to its recessive allele, c. A red, crested male bird is mated to a black, plain female. They produce many offspring, half of which are black, crested and half red, crested. What were the genotypes of the parents?

5.16 Two black, crested birds are mated. They produce thirteen offspring, as follows: 7 black, crested; 3 red, crested; 2 black, plain; and 1 red, plain. What were the genotypes of the parents?

5.17 In the garden phlox white flower color is due to a dominant gene, W, cream to its recessive allele, w. Salver-shaped flowers are due to a dominant gene, S, funnel-shaped flowers to its recessive allele, s. A plant producing white funnel-shaped flowers is crossed to one producing cream salver-shaped flowers. Of the offspring, one quarter produced white salver-shaped flowers, one quarter produced white funnel-shaped flowers, one quarter produced cream salver-shaped flowers, and one quarter produced cream funnel-shaped flowers. What were the genotypes of the parents?

5.18 A plant producing white salver-shaped flowers is crossed with one producing cream funnel-shaped flowers. Of the 76 offspring 37 produce white salver-shaped flowers, and 39 produce cream salver-shaped flowers. What were the genotypes of the parents?

5.19 A plant producing white funnel-shaped flowers is crossed with one producing cream salver-shaped flowers. Ninety-six offspring are produced, all having white salver-shaped flowers. What are the genotypes of the parents? What would result in the F_2 generation of this cross?

5.20 In guinea pigs rough (rosetted) coat is due to a dominant gene, R, smooth to its recessive allele, r. Short hair is dependent upon a dominant gene, L, long hair upon its recessive allele, l. Black is due to a dominant gene, B, white to its recessive allele, b. A homozygous rough short-haired black guinea pig is crossed to a smooth long-haired white one. What would be the appearance of the F_1? Of the F_2?

5.21 What kinds of offspring would be expected and in what proportions, if the F_1 animals from Problem 5.20 were mated to smooth long-haired white guinea pigs?

5.22 A rough long-haired black male guinea pig is mated to a rough short-haired white female. After they have produced several litters, their offspring are found to be as follows: 15 rough short-haired black, 13 rough long-haired black, 4 smooth short-haired black, and 5 smooth long-haired black. What were the genotypes of the parents?

5.23 In addition to the three pairs of genes previously mentioned in guinea pigs, there is another pair in which S is a gene for solid color, s for spotting. How many different kinds of gametes will a guinea pig of the formula $BBLlrrSs$ produce?

5.24 How many different kinds of gametes could be produced by a guinea pig of the formula $bbLlRrSs$?

5.25 If a male guinea pig of the formula $BbLlRrSs$ were mated to a female of the formula $bbllrrss$, how many different kinds of sperms would be produced by the male? How many different kinds of eggs would be produced by the female?

5.26 In man aniridia (a type of blindness) is due to a dominant gene. Migraine (a type of sick headache) is the result of a different dominant gene. A man with aniridia whose mother was not blind marries a woman who suffers from migraine but whose father did not. In what proportion of their children would both aniridia and migraine be expected to occur?

5.27 Suppose a woman who was not blind, but both of whose parents have aniridia, comes to you for advice. She suffers from migraine, which her father also had. She wants to know what the chances are of her children having aniridia or migraine. What would you tell her?

5.28 In watermelons the skin color may be green or striped, the fruit shape may be long or short. A plant of a homozygous long green variety was crossed to one of a homozygous short striped variety. The F_1 plants all bore short green melons. The F_2 plants from this cross were of four types in regard to the melons they produced, occurring in the ratio 9 short green : 3 short striped : 3 long green : 1 long striped. How many pairs of genes are concerned in the cross? Which genes are allelic? Which are dominant?

5.29 What results would be expected if the F_1 plants of Problem 5.28 were crossed to plants of a long striped variety?

5.30 What results would be expected in the F_1 and F_2 from a cross between watermelon plants of a homozygous short green variety and of a homozygous long green variety?

5.31 In cocker spaniels black is due to a dominant gene, B, red to its recessive allele, b. Solid color is dependent upon a dominant gene, S, white spotting upon its recessive allele, s. A red male was mated to a black-and-white female. They had five puppies, as follows: one black, one red, one black-and-white, and two red-and-white. What were the genotypes of the parents?

5.32 A black male was mated to a black female. They had six puppies, all black. What were the probable genotypes of the parents? Why can the genotypes in this case not be given with the same accuracy as those in the Problem 5.31?

CHAPTER SIX

Modified two-pair ratios

Although the classical F_2 ratio for a cross involving two pairs of genes is $9:3:3:1$, this ratio may be modified in various ways. Since the student of heredity frequently meets with such modified ratios in practical genetic work, it is important that they be thoroughly understood and readily recognized.

In the $9:3:3:1$ ratio there are, of course, four phenotypes. Modifications of this ratio are of two general sorts: those in which there are more than four phenotypes, and those in which certain of the classes cannot be told apart by the senses, so that there are fewer than four phenotypes. Let us take up first the modifications in which there are more than four phenotypes.

In shorthorn cattle the polled, or hornless, condition is found to be due to a dominant gene, P, while the horned condition is brought about by the homozygous state of its allele, p. Another pair of alleles, R and r, affect the color of the coat, but R is not dominant to r, so that the genes act as follows: RR produces red coat, Rr produces roan coat, and rr produces white coat. If now we undertake a two-pair cross in which a homozygous polled red male is mated to a horned white female, we shall obtain an F_1 consisting of polled roan animals (Fig. 6.1). Since calves are normally born one at a time, we must make the mating several times in order to produce several F_1 individuals, or else make several similar matings at the same time.

Producing an F_2 will give us a modification of the $9:3:3:1$ ratio. As seen from the checkerboard (p. 62), the ratio will be $3:6:3:1:2:1$. Here due to the lack of dominance there will be more than four phenotypes.

In a similar manner we shall obtain an F_2 ratio with even more phenotypes if we make a two-pair cross in which dominance is lacking in both pairs of genes. For example, in snapdragons there is a pair of alleles, R and r, acting on flower color in such a way that

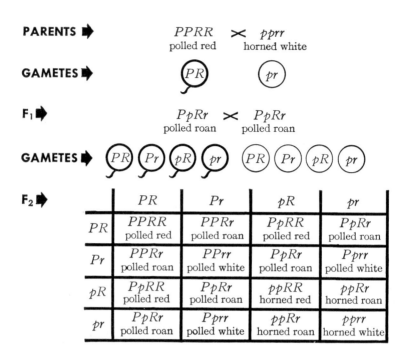

PARENTS ➡ PPRR ✕ pprr
            polled red   horned white

GAMETES ➡ PR   pr

F₁ ➡ PpRr ✕ PpRr
      polled roan   polled roan

GAMETES ➡ PR Pr pR pr   PR Pr pR pr

F₂ ➡

	PR	Pr	pR	pr
PR	PPRR polled red	PPRr polled roan	PpRR polled red	PpRr polled roan
Pr	PPRr polled roan	PPrr polled white	PpRr polled roan	Pprr polled white
pR	PpRR polled red	PpRr polled roan	ppRR horned red	ppRr horned roan
pr	PpRr polled roan	Pprr polled white	ppRr horned roan	pprr horned white

RR produces red, *Rr* produces pink, and *rr* produces white. Similarly another pair of alleles, *B* and *b*, affect leaf shape in such a manner that *BB* produces broad leaves, *Bb* intermediate leaves, and *bb* narrow leaves like those of grass.

A red-flowered, broad-leaved plant when crossed with a white-flowered, narrow-leaved one will produce an *F₁* consisting of all pink-flowered, intermediate-leaved plants. Work out a diagram of the *F₂* from such a cross and see for yourself that the ratio will be 1:2:2:4:1:2:1:2:1. This is again a modification of the 9:3:3:1 ratio, as may readily be seen from the diagram at the end of this chapter. In this case each genotype produces a different phenotype.

It sometimes happens that two or more pairs of alleles, in which there are no dominant genes, act on the same character. Under such conditions we get *cumulative effects* of the genes, giving various grades of the character ranging from one extreme to the other. Such groups of genes are known as "multiple genes." Since they are of especial importance in genetics their discussion will be reserved for a later chapter (Chapter 14).

Turning now to cases in which the 9:3:3:1 ratio is modified so as to produce fewer than four phenotypes, we find that this frequently occurs where two pairs of genes with dominance affect the same character. Of course two pairs of genes acting on the same character may give the characteristic 9:3:3:1 ratio, as we saw in the previous chapter, where two pairs of genes affecting coat colors in rats produced in the F_2 a ratio of 9 gray:3 black:3 yellow:1 cream. Sometimes, however, an allele of one pair shows the same characteristic effect in the presence of *either* allele of the other pair.

Thus we find in rats (and many other animals) a pair of alleles, C and c, acting on color in such a way that the genotypes CC and Cc allow the production of pigment, while the genotype cc prevents any pigment at all from being produced. Thus cc individuals are albinos, pure white with pink eyes. The gene C is thought to determine the production of an enzyme which, by oxidizing chromogen, produces color. The particular color produced will depend upon other genes for specific colors. The gene c when in the homozygous state determines the absence of the enzyme, so that no color at all is produced, although the genes for specific colors may be present.

It will be remembered from the last chapter that black rats are of the formula $aaR-$, while cream ones are $aarr$. Since both these types of rats are colored, they must also contain the gene C. All colored rats, whatever the color, must contain at least one C, while all albinos contain cc, whatever other genes they may carry.

At this point let us get one idea clearly in mind. With certain exceptions to be discussed later, *every animal or plant carries two genes of each set which is found in the species*. This means that if we wrote out the entire genetic formula of an individual it would contain

Fig. 6.1 A cross in shorthorn cattle involving two pairs of genes, one showing dominance and the other not. Top, a polled red male and, center, a horned white female. Bottom, their polled roan offspring.

hundreds, perhaps thousands, of pairs of genes. When we make a cross, we consider only the gene pairs in which the individuals in the cross *differ*, and we leave out all other pairs in order to save space.

Again, each gamete carries *one of each set* of genes which is found in the species. But again we only write down those genes in which the individuals differ, leaving out all others, although we know them to be there.

Continuing this point, the only way we have of knowing that a certain pair of genes exists is to find an allele of a normal gene. For example, as long as all the rats we see are colored, we could know nothing of the genes producing pigment. But when we see an albino rat (without any pigment) and find by breeding tests that albinism is due to a simple recessive gene, we immediately discover the existence of a pair of alleles, *C* and *c*, affecting the production of pigment.

Returning now to modified two-pair ratios, let us cross a homozygous black rat with an albino which carries the recessives *aarr*. Our black rat will be of the formula *aaRRCC*, and the albino will be of the formula *aarrcc*. Since the genes *aa* are identical in the two individuals, we may omit them from the diagram and show it as we would show a two-pair cross, as below.

Reading the F_2 ratio from the checkerboard, and remembering that all the rats in this particular cross contain *aa*, we find that there will be black, cream, and albino rats in the ratio of 9:3:4. The 9:3:3:1 ratio has been modified because two classes which are normally phenotypically distinct cannot in this case be told apart. That is, any rat which contains the genes *cc* is albino, whether it contains *R–* or *rr*. When a gene of one pair masks the expression of the genes of another pair, it is said to be **epistatic** to the other pair. Thus in this case *c* is epistatic to *R* and *r*. The noun formed from the adjective epistatic is **epistasis.** Epistasis is

PARENTS ➡

$RRCC$ ✕ $rrcc$
black   albino

GAMETES ➡

(RC) (rc)

F₁ ➡

$RrCc$ ✕ $RrCc$
black   black

GAMETES ➡ $(RC)(Rc)(rC)(rc)$ $(RC)(Rc)(rC)(rc)$

F₂ ➡

	RC	Rc	rC	rc
RC	RRCC black	RRCc black	RrCC black	RrCc black
Rc	RRCc black	RRcc albino	RrCc black	Rrcc albino
rC	RrCC black	RrCc black	rrCC cream	rrCc cream
rc	RrCc black	Rrcc albino	rrCc cream	rrcc albino

thus the same effect between genes of two different pairs that dominance is between two alleles of the same pair. Since the epistatic gene, c, in the case just described is recessive to its own allele, C, we may speak of this two-pair cross as involving **recessive epistasis.**

Another type of modified two-pair ratio may be illustrated by an example in dogs. In these animals we know a pair of genes, B and b, acting on coat color in such a way that B results in black, bb in brown. We also know a pair of genes, I and i, which control the production of pigment in such a way that animals containing I are prevented from developing pigment in the fur, even though specific genes for color be present. The result of a dominant white gene can be told from the albino white produced by the recessive albino gene because animals which are white due to a dominant color-inhibiting gene always have pigmented eyes, while those which are white due to the albino gene always have unpigmented eyes which look pink because of the blood showing through. There are, as it happens, some recessive white genes other than albinism, which result in white with pigmented eyes. Such genes occur, for example, in certain white breeds of poultry to be described later in this chapter.

In regard to the genes I and i an individual must be of the genotype ii to have any pigment developed. Animals of the genotype I– are white. Let us, then, cross a homozygous brown dog with a homozygous white one which has black but no brown among its ancestors. The cross would be diagramed as follows:

PARENTS ➡ $bbii$ $\times$ $BBII$
                 brown   white

GAMETES ➡ (bi) (BI)

F₁ ➡ $BbIi$ $\times$ $BbIi$
            white   white

GAMETES ➡ (BI) (Bi) (bI) (bi) (BI) (Bi) (bI) (bi)

F₂ ➡

	BI	Bi	bI	bi
BI	$BBII$ white	$BBIi$ white	$BbII$ white	$BbIi$ white
Bi	$BBIi$ white	$BBii$ black	$BbIi$ white	$Bbii$ black
bI	$BbII$ white	$BbIi$ white	$bbII$ white	$bbIi$ white
bi	$BbIi$ white	$Bbii$ black	$bbIi$ white	$bbii$ brown

The resulting ratio is 12:3:1, another modification of the 9:3:3:1 ratio. Since the epistatic gene, I, is dominant to its allele, i, this case is one of **dominant epistasis.**

Sometimes dominant epistasis and recessive epistasis occur in the same cross. The White Leghorn breed is white because of the dominant gene I, although this breed carries color genes which cannot be expressed in the presence of I. On the other hand the White Silkie is white because of the presence of a recessive gene, c, which conditions the absence of a chromogen necessary for color. Birds of the formula cc are white even though they carry color genes, for the color genes cannot be expressed in the absence of the chromogen (Fig. 6.2).

If we should cross White Leghorns with White Silkies, the F_1 would all be white because they would inherit the dominant gene I from the White Leghorn parent. In the F_2, however, colored individuals would appear in a peculiar ratio. See the diagram on page 67.

In the F_2 it may be seen that, out of every sixteen birds, twelve will inherit the dominant epistatic gene, I, and will thus be white. The other four will lack this gene, but one of these will also be white because of the homozygous condition of the recessive epistatic gene, c. Only three out of every sixteen have the requisite genotype ($iiC-$)

Fig. 6.2 White Leghorn rooster (top), white because of a dominant color-inhibiting gene. White Silkie hen (bottom), white because of a recessive gene preventing color. The F₁ from these parents is white; the F₂ contains white and colored in the ratio 13:3.

for the production of color. The resulting ratio of white to colored is 13:3, a peculiar modification of the two-pair ratio, due in this case to **dominant and recessive epistasis.** The actual color of the colored birds will, of course, depend on whatever genes for particular pigments they may have inherited.

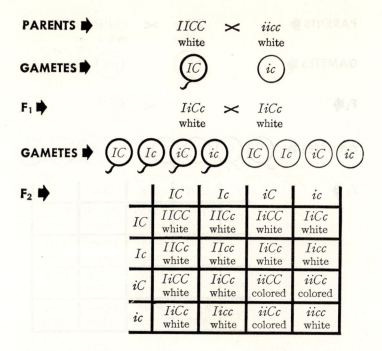

PARENTS ➡				*IICC* white	✕	*iicc* white		
GAMETES ➡				Ⓘ*C*		ⓘ*c*		
F₁ ➡				*IiCc* white	✕	*IiCc* white		
GAMETES ➡	Ⓘ*C*	Ⓘ*c*	ⓘ*C*	ⓘ*c*	Ⓘ*C*	Ⓘ*c*	ⓘ*C*	ⓘ*c*

F₂ ➡

	IC	*Ic*	*iC*	*ic*
IC	*IICC* white	*IICc* white	*IiCC* white	*IiCc* white
Ic	*IICc* white	*IIcc* white	*IiCc* white	*Iicc* white
iC	*IiCC* white	*IiCc* white	*iiCC* colored	*iiCc* colored
ic	*IiCc* white	*Iicc* white	*iiCc* colored	*iicc* white

Another modification of the 9:3:3:1 ratio occurs when *each* of the two pairs of alleles contains a recessive epistatic gene. For example, in the common yellow daisy the flowers typically have purple centers. A yellow-centered variety was discovered, however, which when crossed with the purple-centered type gave all purple-centered in the F₁ and three purple to one yellow in the F₂. The yellows bred true. Later more yellow-centered flowers were discovered in another locality, and these behaved in the same way when crossed with purple. The yellow-centered flowers from the two localities were thought, of course, to be the same variety, but when they were crossed with each other they surprisingly produced all purple-centered offspring. The F₂ gave a ratio of nine purples to seven yellows. Obviously the two yellow-centered varieties were genetically different, the yellow in each case being due to a different recessive gene. Apparently two pairs of genes are concerned in the cross, the dominant gene of each pair being necessary for the production of purple.

Let *P* and *p*, *R* and *r* represent two pairs of alleles, acting on flower color in such a way that when both *P* and *R* are present the flowers have purple centers, all other combinations of these genes producing yellow centers. A cross between two yellow-centered varieties differing in two pairs of genes would be written as diagramed on the next page.

Here the 9:3:3:1 ratio is modified because the recessive *p* is

| | PARENTS ➡ | | 𝑃𝑃𝑟𝑟 ✕ 𝑝𝑝𝑅𝑅 |
| yellow | yellow |

PARENTS ➡   𝑃𝑃𝑟𝑟 ✕ 𝑝𝑝𝑅𝑅
                 yellow   yellow

GAMETES ➡   (𝑃𝑟)   (𝑝𝑅)

F₁ ➡   𝑃𝑝𝑅𝑟 ✕ 𝑃𝑝𝑅𝑟
                 purple   purple

GAMETES ➡   (𝑃𝑅)(𝑃𝑟)(𝑝𝑅)(𝑝𝑟)   (𝑃𝑅)(𝑃𝑟)(𝑝𝑅)(𝑝𝑟)

F₂ ➡

	PR	Pr	pR	pr
PR	$PPRR$ purple	$PPRr$ purple	$PpRR$ purple	$PpRr$ purple
Pr	$PPRr$ purple	$PPrr$ yellow	$PpRr$ purple	$Pprr$ yellow
pR	$PpRR$ purple	$PpRr$ purple	$ppRR$ yellow	$ppRr$ yellow
pr	$PpRr$ purple	$Pprr$ yellow	$ppRr$ yellow	$pprr$ yellow

epistatic to R and r, and in addition the recessive r is similarly epistatic to P and p. Consequently the 3, the 3, and the 1 cannot be told apart phenotypically, resulting in a ratio of 9:7, a familiar modification. This case is therefore one of **duplicate recessive epistasis.** A similar situation occurs in stocks, where single flowers depend upon the simultaneous presence of two different dominant genes, the absence of either or both resulting in double flowers (Fig. 6.3).

Another example of this type of gene interaction occurs in human beings, where deaf-mutism appears to be inherited in the same manner. We find that in man two pairs of genes, D and d, E and e, interact in such a way that $D–E–$ produces normal hearing, while any other combination of these genes produces children who are deaf at birth. They are not truly "mute," but they do not speak without special training simply because they have never heard words. Figure 6.4 illustrates a typical family history of deaf-mutism.

Of course the knowledge that a human character depends on this type or any other type of hereditary behavior is not obtained from the study of F_2 generations, as is the case in animals or plants. It will be noted, however, that a character dependent on this type of inheritance behaves in a manner that precludes the assumption of a single pair of genes, even in human beings. If deaf-mutism were dependent upon the recessive of a single pair of genes, it would be impossible for two deaf parents to produce anything but deaf children.

Fig. 6.3 Single- and double-flowered stocks. The center plant is single-flowered, the others are double-flowered.

However, not only do two normal parents sometimes produce deaf children, but two deaf parents sometimes produce normal children, as seen in Figure 6.4. This is explainable on the basis of two pairs of genes acting as outlined above. In the case of deaf-mutism in man, the two recessives are relatively rare, so that most people carry at least one dominant of each pair and so have normal hearing. Those individuals heterozygous for one or the other recessive or for both cannot be told from homozygous individuals except when they happen to produce a deaf child. Deaf-mutism should not be confused with otosclerosis, which is a type of deafness occurring later in life, and is inherited in quite another manner.

In addition to duplicate recessive epistasis, we may have **duplicate dominant epistasis,** when each of the two pairs of alleles contains a dominant epistatic gene.

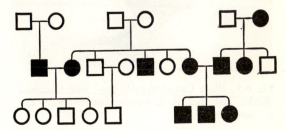

Fig. 6.4 Pedigree of a family in which many of the members were born deaf. Note the two cases where both parents were deaf, and the difference between the offspring in the two cases. Black squares and circles indicate deaf mutes.

We may illustrate such a case by another example from poultry. Certain breeds have feathers on the shanks, while others have none. The Black Langshans have feathered shanks, while the shanks of the Buff Rocks are unfeathered (Fig. 6.5). A cross between these breeds results in an F_1 with feathered shanks and an F_2 with a ratio of fifteen feathered-shanked birds to one with no feathers on the shanks. The cross may be diagramed as on page 71, assuming two pairs of genes, F and f, S and s.

Considering merely the presence or absence of feathering we find that only the double recessive *ffss*, that is, one out of every sixteen of the F_2 generation, has unfeathered shanks. These genes have in addition a partial cumulative effect, which we need not consider here. Duplicate dominant epistasis is more common in plants than in animals.

One last modification of the 9:3:3:1 ratio may be discussed, choosing an example from pigs. Duroc Jersey pigs are usually red in color. A mutation to sandy color was discovered, and it proved to be due to a recessive gene, so that the cross between red and sandy produced all red in the F_1 and three red to one sandy in the F_2. Sandy pigs, of course, bred true and produced only sandy offspring.

Fig. 6.5 Black Langshan male (top) with feathered shanks, and Buff Rock female (bottom) with unfeathered shanks.

On one occasion, however, two sandy animals from different localities were crossed, and the F_1, to the surprise of the investigators, were all red. Obviously the two sandy parents were not of the same genotype. Such an occurrence would immediately cause us to suspect more than one pair of genes to be involved. This case looks similar

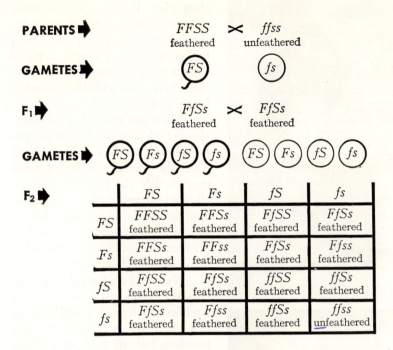

PARENTS ➡   *FFSS* ✕ *ffss*
                feathered   unfeathered

GAMETES ➡   (*FS*)   (*fs*)

F₁ ➡   *FfSs* ✕ *FfSs*
             feathered   feathered

GAMETES ➡   (*FS*) (*Fs*) (*fS*) (*fs*)   (*FS*) (*Fs*) (*fS*) (*fs*)

F₂ ➡

	FS	*Fs*	*fS*	*fs*
FS	*FFSS* feathered	*FFSs* feathered	*FfSS* feathered	*FfSs* feathered
Fs	*FFSs* feathered	*FFss* feathered	*FfSs* feathered	*Ffss* feathered
fS	*FfSS* feathered	*FfSs* feathered	*ffSS* feathered	*ffSs* feathered
fs	*FfSs* feathered	*Ffss* feathered	*ffSs* feathered	*ffss* unfeathered

to the one in which two yellow varieties of daisies produced a purple F_1, and we might predict that the F_2 would give the 9:7 ratio, that is, 9 red:7 sandy. However, when the F_2 were raised, they were found to be in the proportion of 9 red:6 sandy:1 white. Obviously this is a modified two-pair ratio, and the white animals apparently represent the double recessive (Fig. 6.6). The genes must interact as follows, allowing R and r, S and s to represent the two pairs of alleles.

         R–S– produces red
         R–ss produces sandy
         rrS– produces sandy
         rrss   produces white

No one could have predicted before the cross was made that the genotype *rrss* would produce a white animal. The logical prediction would have been sandy. It is never possible to predict with certainty what the phenotypic expression of an unknown genotype will be. The cross in pigs just discussed may be diagramed as on page 73.

The 9:6:1 ratio is therefore another modification of the 9:3:3:1. Again we are dealing with duplicate genes. Here the *r* and *s* genes interact (in this instance cumulatively) so that the *rrss* phenotype is different from that produced by either *RRss* or *rrSS*. Hence, we may designate this as a case of **duplicate genes with interaction.** This modification is not common, but is known in some organisms other

Fig. 6.6 Duroc Jersey pigs. Top, red; center, sandy; bottom, white.

than pigs. It may be considered either as a special case of the duplicate epistatic ratio 9:7 with the 7 broken into 6 and 1 or as a special case of the duplicate dominant epistatic ratio 15:1 with the 15 broken into 9 and 6.

There are still other modifications which because of their complications will not be considered here. Thus the presence of lethal genes may modify the two-pair ratio by eliminating certain classes. Linkage, another special case, may also result in peculiar modifications. This phenomenon will also be treated in detail later on (Chapter 10).

We see, then, that the classical two-pair ratio may be variously modified. Such modified ratios when first seen by investigators were puzzling, but are now well understood. The student of genetics should familiarize himself with them and be able to recognize them when met with. Three-pair ratios and others involving still more pairs of genes may also be variously modified. For instance, the normal three-pair ratio of 27:9:9:9:3:3:3:1 may appear as 27:37, 48:15:1, etc.

Table 6.1 summarizes the various two-pair modified ratios dealt with in this chapter.

We are now ready to make our acquaintance with a principle which is rapidly coming to pervade all genetic theory. The principle is that a gene apparently functions by producing a specific substance which determines the effect of the gene on the organism. In many, if not in most instances, this substance is an enzyme. An enzyme is an organic catalytic agent which functions by bringing about a biochemical reaction without being itself used up in the process. Each enzyme is responsible for the catalysis of a specific step in metabolism.

Through the action of an enzyme one compound is converted to another. In symbolizing such changes, we commonly indicate the

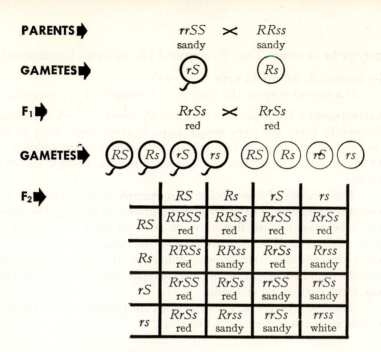

Table 6.1. Summary of the Modifications of the Two-Pair Ratio

	AABB	AABb	AaBB	AaBb	AAbb	Aabb	aaBB	aaBb	aabb	TYPE OF RATIO	EXAMPLE ON PAGE
Number of phenotypes increased because of lack of dominance	1	2	2	4	1	2	1	2	1	dominance lacking in both pairs	61
	3		6		1	2	3		1	dominance lacking in one pair	61
Classical ratio	9				3		3		1	dominance in both pairs no epistasis	51
Number of phenotypes decreased because of dominance and various types of epistasis	9				3		4			recessive epistasis *aa* epistatic to *B, b*	64
	12						3		1	dominant epistasis *A* epistatic to *B, b*	65
	13						3			dominant and recessive epistasis *A* epistatic to *B, b* *bb* epistatic to *A, a*	66
	9				7					duplicate recessive epistasis *aa* epistatic to *B, b* *bb* epistatic to *A, a*	67
	15								1	duplicate dominant epistasis *A* epistatic to *B, b* *B* epistatic to *A, a*	69
	9				6				1	duplicate genes with interaction *A–bb* and *aaB–* identical as to phenotype; *A–B–* and *aabb* independently distinguishable	70

enzyme by an arrow. Thus, if compound 1 is converted to compound 2 by enzyme A, we would write $C_1 \xrightarrow{A} C_2$.

If a second enzyme (B) then acts on compound 2, converting it to compound 3, the sequence would read $C_1 \xrightarrow{A} C_2 \xrightarrow{B} C_3$. Enzymes frequently carry out very simple steps in conversion, such as hydroxylation (adding an OH group) or methoxylation (adding an OCH_3 group). The reverse conversions, removing groups, also may occur.

The genetics of flower color is an example of this principle. The chemical composition of many flower pigments is known. The differences between diverse flower colors are ordinarily determined by gene differences. When the presence of one pigment rather than another depends on a single gene difference, the two pigments are usually found to be chemically very similar, often differing in only one small part of the molecule.

Thus, red flowers may depend upon the presence of the pigment cyanidin, which is chemically like this

For those not acquainted with chemistry we should point out that a basic part of many biochemical compounds is the benzene ring, a hexagon of six carbon atoms with six attached hydrogen atoms, as follows

This basic structure occurs so frequently that it is commonly symbolized by a simple hexagon, thus

In this symbol the carbon atoms and their attached hydrogen atoms are not specifically indicated, but where other atoms or groups of atoms are substituted, these are indicated by the appropriate letters.

A single pair of genes, P and p, is responsible in many plants for the difference between purple flowers and red flowers, $P-$ resulting in purple, and pp in red. The chemical difference between the pigments is also very simple, cyanidin (red) being merely hydroxylated, forming a purple pigment, delphinidin. The gene for purple apparently produces an enzyme which will hydroxylate cyanidin, as follows

cyanidin (red)   delphinidin (purple)

Note that delphinidin differs from cyanidin only in having one more OH group substituted in the right-hand ring.

Many other pigments differ one from the other in correspondingly simple chemical variations. Each biochemical change appears to be controlled by an enzyme, and each enzyme appears to be produced as a result of the activity of a gene. Note how the following pigments, each a different color, differ one from the other and from those already discussed in simple biochemical ways.

pelargonidin (light red)   apigenin (ivory)

peonidin (magenta)   luteolin (pale yellow)

malvidin (blue)   quercetin (intense yellow)

These are but a few of the many plant pigments known, but they will serve the purpose of indicating how an enzyme may convert one of them to another in a simple biochemical step. They are presented here as a brief introduction to the problem of how genes act, a problem which will be considered in further detail in chapters 24 and 26. Many questions concerning dominance and epistasis may be clarified by thinking in biochemical terms. Remember that an enzyme may accomplish a conversion all out of proportion to the amount of enzyme present, since it is not used up in the process. Thus one dose of gene P may provide enough enzyme to convert cyanidin to delphinidin, and therefore a plant of the genotype Pp will have flowers just as purple as will one of PP.

When two pigments are present, the darker one may obscure the lighter, thus resulting in epistasis. For example, cotton may have brown, green, or white lint. Brown and green are both dominant to white, but brown is epistatic to green, resulting in the dominant epistatic ratio of 12 brown : 3 green : 1 white. Of the browns, some also have green, and some do not. These cannot be differentiated on simple inspection, but the hidden green in the former can easily be demonstrated by fluorescence in ultraviolet light.

We see, therefore, that geneticists and biochemists are more and more often finding themselves working together on common problems, and that the ultimate solution of many genetical phenomena depends on the cooperation of these two groups of workers.

PROBLEMS

6.1 A variety of pepper having brown fruits was crossed with a variety having yellow fruits. The F_1 plants all had red fruits. With only this information, devise two possible explanations for the inheritance of fruit colors in peppers. What further information would you need to decide between these?

6.2 When the red-fruited F_1 plants of Problem 6.1 were crossed, the F_2 consisted of 182 plants with red fruits, 59 with brown fruits, 61 with yellow fruits, and 20 with green fruits. What now appears to be the genetic basis of these fruit colors in peppers?

6.3 In mink, two different recessive genes, p and i, are known, either or both of which in homozygous form results in platinum coat color. The presence of both of the dominant alleles results in the wild-type brown color. Will platinum mink necessarily breed true? Set up a cross between two platinum minks which will result in all brown offspring. What would be expected in the F_2 from this cross?

6.4 In onions, a recessive gene c results in the lack of an enzyme necessary for color production; in the presence of C, the enzyme is produced. Another gene, I, results in the inhibition of the enzyme so that it does not function in color production; the allele i does not inhibit the enzyme. Both C and ii are therefore necessary for the production of color. A true-breeding colored variety was crossed with a white variety having the genotype $ccII$. What would be the expectation in the F_1? The F_2?

6.5 It has been discovered that the scales of a white onion will react differently to ammonia fumes, depending on the genotype. If the genes cc are present, ammonia fumes will not color the scales, but if the gene I is present in the absence of cc, ammonia fumes will turn the scales yellow in a matter of seconds. Applying this test, what change in the observable F_2 ratio of Problem 6.4 would occur?

6.6 In poultry white may be the result of the homozygous state of the recessive gene o or it may be the result of the homozygous state of the recessive gene c. The presence of both dominants, C and O, is necessary for color. The Silkie breed is white, of the formula $ccOO$. The White Wyandotte breed has the formula $CCoo$. What would be the appearance of the F_1 and F_2 in a cross between these two breeds?

6.7 In the F_2 generation from Problem 6.6, what proportion of the birds would be of the genotype of the Silkie breed? What proportion would be of the genotype of the White Wyandotte breed?

6.8 In cultivated stocks (a flower) a cross was made between a red-flowered plant and a white-flowered plant. The F_1 plants were all red-flowered. In the F_2 the flower colors were as follows: ninety-two red, thirty cream, forty-one white. Explain these results.

6.9 In crossing the white-flowered plants of the F_2 generation of Problem 6.8 among themselves, what proportion of the offspring would be red-flowered? Cream-flowered? White-flowered?

6.10 In wheat red kernel color is dependent upon the presence of two dominant genes, R and B, white kernel color upon the presence of both recessives in the homozygous state. Other combinations result in brown. Two brown varieties, $rrBB$ and $RRbb$, are crossed. What is the appearance of the F_1? Of the F_2?

6.11 If you had a large number of F_2 kernels from the cross of Problem 6.10 available, how would you go about developing a homozygous red variety? Remember that wheat is normally self-fertilized.

6.12 In summer squashes white fruit color is dependent upon a dominant gene, W, colored fruit upon its recessive allele, w. In the presence of ww, the color may be yellow, due to a dominant gene, G, or green, due to its recessive allele, g. How many different genotypes may be involved in the production of white fruits?

6.13 If a white-fruited squash plant of the formula $WWGG$ is crossed with a green-fruited plant, what will be the appearance of the F_1? Of the F_2? (See Problem 6.12.)

6.14 In the shepherd's purse (a plant) the form of the seed capsule may be either triangular- or top-shaped. A cross between a triangular-capsuled plant and one with top-shaped capsules gave an F_1 all of which had triangular-shaped capsules. In the F_2 only one out of every sixteen plants had top-shaped capsules. How many pairs of genes are concerned in the cross and how do they interact?

6.15 In the F_2 generation of Problem 6.14, what proportion of the triangular-capsuled plants is homozygous?

6.16 In human beings two right-handed parents sometimes produce a left-handed child. Also two left-handed parents sometimes produce a right-handed child. If left-handedness is hereditary, could the above facts be explained on the basis of a single pair of genes? Discuss reasons for your answer.

6.17 In radishes the shape may be long or round or oval. The color may be red or white or purple. A long red variety was crossed with a round white variety. The F_1 were all oval purple. In the F_2 the following results were obtained: 8 long red, 15 long purple, 17 oval red, 31 oval purple, 7 long white, 15 oval white, 8 round red, 16 round purple, 9 round white. What is the genetic basis for these characters?

6.18 How many true-breeding varieties of radishes in regard to shape and color could be established?

6.19 If you wanted to develop for commercial purposes seed that would all result in long purple radishes, how could you obtain such seed?

6.20 How could you obtain seed which would all develop into oval red radishes?

6.21 In summer squash disk fruit shape has been shown to be dominant to spherical fruit shape. On one occasion, however, two spherical races from different localities were crossed and the F_1 fruits were all disk-shaped. The F_2 from this cross resulted as follows: 35 with disk fruits, 25 with spherical fruits, and 4 with elongate fruits. Explain these results.

6.22 What offspring would be expected if the elongated-fruit plants of Problem 6.21 were crossed among themselves?

6.23 What kinds of offspring would be produced, and in what proportions, if elongated-fruit plants were crossed to the F_1 plants from Problem 6.21?

6.24 In poultry a gene, C, produces Creeper in the heterozygous state but is lethal in the homozygous state. A gene for frizzled feathers, F, is dominant to its allele, f, for plain feathers. What kinds of offspring and in what proportions would result from the following matings? *CcFf* × *CcFf; CcFf* × *ccff; Ccff* × *ccFf; Ccff* × *ccFF; ccFf* × *ccFf*.

6.25 A frizzled-feathered Creeper male is crossed to a plain-feathered Creeper female. They produce eleven frizzled Creeper offspring and five frizzled normal offspring. What are the probable genotypes of the parents?

6.26 In cattle the polled condition is dependent upon a dominant gene, P, the horned condition upon its recessive allele, p. In Dexter-Kerry cattle a gene, D, results in short legs (Dexter) in heterozygous state, but is lethal in homozygous state. Its allele, d, in homozygous state results in the long-legged Kerry animals. Suppose a Dexter bull homozygous for polled were mated to a horned Kerry cow. What kinds of calves could they produce, and in what proportions?

6.27 Suppose two polled Dexter animals (see Problem 6.26) were mated and produced a horned Kerry calf. What would be the genotypes of the parents?

6.28 A yellow short-haired guinea pig was crossed with a white long-haired guinea pig. The F_1 were all cream short-haired. The F_1 animals were repeatedly crossed among themselves. The total F_2 from many litters was as follows: 15 yellow short-haired, 29 cream short-haired, 14 white short-haired, 5 yellow long-haired, 9 cream long-haired, 5 white long-haired. Explain these results.

6.29 Considering the data of Problem 6.28 what kinds of offspring would be expected and in what proportions from a cross of two cream long-haired guinea pigs?

6.30 Considering the data of Problem 6.28 what kind of mating should be made in order to obtain all cream long-haired offspring? All cream short-haired offspring?

6.31 In the peach family there are varieties with downy skins (peaches) and other varieties with smooth skins (nectarines). The difference between them is due to a single pair of alleles, D and d, the gene for peach being dominant to that for nectarine. Some varieties of peaches and nectarines have oval glands at the leaf bases, others have round glands, and still others have no glands. This difference is also due to a single pair of alleles, G being a gene for oval glands and g its allele for no glands. Neither is dominant, however, the heterozygote resulting in round glands. A homozygous peach with oval glands was crossed with a nectarine having no glands. What would be expected in the F_1 of this cross? The F_2?

6.32 Congenital deafness in man is due to the homozygous condition of either or both of the recessive genes d and e. Both dominant genes D and E are necessary for normal hearing. A deaf man marries a deaf woman and all the seven children have normal hearing. What are the genotypes of the parents and children?

6.33 A deaf man marries a deaf woman and their four children are deaf. Contrast the genotypes of this family with those of Problem 6.32.

6.34 Would it be of any advantage to the human race if we had some way of knowing which of the two genes for deafness a particular deaf person had? Can you suggest any way for finding this out?

6.35 In foxes nine coat colors are known, as follows: Red, Standard Silver, Alaskan

Silver, Double-black, Smoky Red, Cross-red, Blended-cross, Substandard Silver, and Sub-Alaskan Silver. A Red fox was crossed to a Double-black fox. The F_1 were all Blended-cross in color (reddish above, black below). The F_2 showed a ratio as follows: 1 Red : 2 Smoky Red : 2 Cross-red: 4 Blended-cross : 1 Standard Silver : 2 Substandard Silver : 1 Alaskan Silver : 2 Sub-Alaskan Silver : 1 Double-black. How many pairs of genes are concerned in the cross and is there any dominance?

6.36 Which of the above varieties of foxes of Problem 6.35 will breed true?

REFERENCES

Babcock, E. B., and Clausen, R. E., *Genetics in Relation to Agriculture.* New York, The McGraw-Hill Book Co. (1927).

Blakeslee, A.F., *Zeitschr. f. ind. Abstamm- und Vererbungsl.* 25:211 (1921).

Jull, M. A., *Poultry Breeding.* 3rd ed. New York, John Wiley and Sons (1952).

Saunders, E. R., *Jour. Genetics* 22:53 (1928).

CHAPTER SEVEN

Probability

The results which follow the Mendelian laws of segregation, random assortment, and random union of gametes are illustrations of the laws of **probability.** A brief introduction to probability will be of considerable aid in the interpretation of breeding results, particularly of family histories in man.

Consider the human family history shown in Figure 7.1. In this family the character under discussion is represented by the usual solid squares and circles. The parents do not show the character; three out of four offspring do. Let us ask ourselves some questions about this character. Could it be due to a dominant gene? Obviously not, since it appeared in the children when neither parent had it. Could it be due to a recessive gene? A character due to a recessive gene can, as we have seen, show up in the offspring without showing in either parent, provided the parents carry the gene, that is, are heterozygous for it. But should not the ratio of the dominant character to the recessive be 3:1? Yet in the family under discussion there are not three individuals showing the dominant to one showing the recessive, but quite the other way around, three recessives to one dominant. Could the character then be due to a recessive gene? Does the 3:1 ratio have to show up in each individual family?

The answer to all this is, of course, that the character represented by the solid square and circles in Figure 7.1 could certainly be due to a recessive gene. In the long run, taking a large number of such families, there would be three times as many individuals showing the dominant as those showing the recessive. But in any particular family the laws of probability make it possible for any combination of dominants and recessives to occur. It could happen, then,

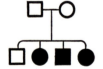

Fig. 7.1   A human family history in which a certain character is represented by solid symbols. Questions about the genetic nature of the character are discussed in this chapter.

that a recessive would show up in three out of four children in a particular family, as it did in this one. Not only *could* it happen, but the laws of probability show that it *will* happen in a certain number of cases. Let us ask a more specific question. When both parents are heterozygous for a pair of alleles, how many times in families of four will three of the children show the recessive character and one the dominant? To answer this, let us take up probability itself.

Let us toss a penny. It has an equal chance of falling heads or tails. We should expect heads in half the tosses, tails in half the tosses. Now let us toss two pennies together. Each penny has an equal chance of falling heads or tails. What will happen in a series of tosses of two pennies? We find that about one fourth of the results are two heads, one fourth are two tails, and one half consist of a head and a tail. This is because the chance of two independent things happening together is the product of the chances of each of them happening separately. The chance of each penny falling heads is one half. The chance of both of them falling heads together is therefore one out of four ($\frac{1}{2} \times \frac{1}{2} = \frac{1}{4}$). Similarly, the chance of both falling tails is one fourth. The chance of one falling heads and the other tails is one fourth, but the chance of one falling tails and the other heads is also one fourth, the total probability for one head and one tail thus being $\frac{1}{4} + \frac{1}{4} = \frac{1}{2}$.

If we toss four pennies together, we shall find that all four fall heads in about one toss out of sixteen, three heads and one tail appear in about four out of sixteen, two heads and two tails in about six out of sixteen, one head and three tails in about four out of sixteen, and finally four tails in about one out of sixteen tosses. These chances are again the products of the separate probabilities for each penny falling a head or a tail.

There is a convenient mathematical method for rapidly computing such chances. It consists of expanding the binomial $(a + b)$ to the nth power, where a and b are the chances for the possible results (in this case heads and tails) and n is the number of individuals concerned in the event (in these cases two pennies, or four pennies, as the case may be).

Suppose we let a stand for the chances of a penny falling heads and b stand for the chances of its falling tails. We know that the chance of each penny falling heads is one half, of falling tails is also one half. Then we may compute how often in tossing four pennies we should expect four heads or three heads and a tail or any other combination, as follows:

Let a = chances for heads = $\frac{1}{2}$
and b = chances for tails = $\frac{1}{2}$

In tossing four pennies we should use the expression $(a + b)^4$.

$$(a + b)^4 = a^4 + 4a^3b + 6a^2b^2 + 4ab^3 + b^4$$

From the above expansion we may pick out the appropriate term for any combination of heads and tails and substitute the values of a and b. Suppose we ask how many times in tosses of four pennies we should expect four heads. Since a stands for heads, we must choose the term a^4, which is four a's, or four heads ($a^4 = a \cdot a \cdot a \cdot a$). Substituting $\frac{1}{2}$ for a, we find that

$$a^4 = (\tfrac{1}{2})^4 = \tfrac{1}{16}$$

Therefore, we should expect four heads in one toss out of sixteen.

Again, suppose we ask how many times in tosses of four pennies we should expect two heads and two tails. The term containing two a's and two b's (standing for two heads and two tails) is $6a^2b^2$. Substituting the values of a and b, we find that

$$6a^2b^2 = 6(\tfrac{1}{2})^2(\tfrac{1}{2})^2 = \tfrac{6}{16}$$

Therefore we should expect two heads and two tails in six tosses out of every sixteen. Similarly we can find the probability for any other combination of four pennies.

If we were tossing five pennies at a time we should use the expansion $(a + b)^5$, and so on.

Let us now transfer this mathematical application to a case in human beings. How many times in families of three would you expect two boys and a girl? We may answer this just as we did the question about the pennies.

Let a = chances for boys = $\frac{1}{2}$
and b = chances for girls = $\frac{1}{2}$
$$(a + b)^3 = a^3 + 3a^2b + 3ab^2 + b^3$$

The term $3a^2b$ contains two a's and one b, that is, two boys and a girl. Substituting, we find that

$$3a^2b = 3(\tfrac{1}{2})^2(\tfrac{1}{2}) = \tfrac{3}{8}$$

Therefore, in three out of every eight families of three children we should expect two boys and a girl. This, of course, is on the assumption that the chances of boys and girls being born are equal. This assumption is accurate enough for ordinary determinations. To be very specific, however, there are about 105 boys born to every 100 girls. Therefore we might be extremely accurate by using proportions as follows:

Let a = chances for boys = $\frac{105}{205}$
and b = chances for girls = $\frac{100}{205}$

In this case the term $3a^2b$ would be equal to $\dfrac{3,307,500}{8,615,125}$ which reduces to approximately $\frac{3}{8}$.

In maternity wards at hospitals it sometimes happens that out of, let us say, eight newly born babies seven are girls, or perhaps all eight are girls. This is cause for newspaper comment, but the laws of probability tell us that not only *can* this happen, but that every so often it *will* happen. Compute how often in a group of eight newly born infants seven should be girls and how often all eight should be girls. Use probabilities of one half and one half.

Let us apply these methods to the first question raised in this chapter. Could the character represented in Figure 7.1 be due to a recessive gene? The figure represents a family of human beings, and the solid squares and circles represent *albinos*. Obviously if the parents were heterozygous for albinism they could produce some albino children. But in families of four where both parents are heterozygous, how many times will there be one normal child and three albinos?

We can let a represent the chances for normal pigment and b the chances for albinism. What are the chances of any one child being normal? Obviously three out of four. Likewise the chances of its being an albino are one out of four. That is because where the parents are heterozygous the genetic cross would be as shown in the diagram on this page letting C represent the gene for pigment and c the gene for albinism.

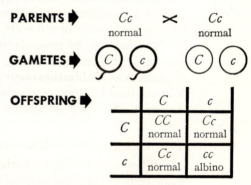

It is seen that there are three normal children produced to every albino, in the long run. However, the $3:1$ ratio would not have to hold in each family. To go back to our question, how many times in families of four, where both parents are heterozygous, would you expect one normal child and three albino children?

Let a = chances for normal individual = $\frac{3}{4}$
and b = chances for albino individual = $\frac{1}{4}$
$(a + b)^4 = a^4 + 4a^3b + 6a^2b^2 + 4ab^3 + b^4$

The term representing one normal child and three albino children is $4ab^3$. Substituting, $4ab^3 = 4(\frac{3}{4})(\frac{1}{4})^3 = \frac{12}{256}$. Therefore in twelve out of every 256 families of four, where the parents are heterozygous, we should expect to find one child showing the dominant character (in this case normal pigment) and three children showing the recessive character (in this case albinism).

Answering our original question as to the character illustrated in Figure 7.1, it could be due to a recessive gene, even though in this family the ratio of dominants to recessives was not 3:1. As a matter of fact, in a certain number of families of four where the parents are similar genetically to these parents, we must *expect* more children showing the recessive than those showing the dominant.

This method may be applied to other ratios than the 3:1. In the case of the feathered shanks and unfeathered shanks of poultry, the ratio of offspring of heterozygous parents is 15:1, as was seen in the last chapter. Here we would set up our probabilities as follows:

$$\text{Let } a = \text{chances for feathered} = \tfrac{15}{16}$$
$$\text{and } b = \text{chances for unfeathered} = \tfrac{1}{16}$$

Work out a problem as to how many times in families of five offspring, when the parents are both double heterozygotes, you would expect all five chicks to have unfeathered shanks.

This method may also be applied to cases in which there are more than two possibilities. In such cases more terms would be added to the binomial, using $(a+b+c)^n$, $(a+b+c+d)^n$, and so on.

The point to be remembered is that the random assortment of genes and chromosomes during segregation and the random union of gametes at fertilization occur according to the laws of probability. Various combinations of characters among the offspring can and do occur, and their occurrence in the long run may be predicted.

The Chi-Square Test of Mendelian Progenies

When new hereditary variations are discovered and crosses are made to determine the mode of inheritance, it becomes necessary to ascertain whether the observed data are in agreement with the proposed genetic explanation. We have seen in this chapter that chance will often produce a set of occurrences which do not conform exactly to the expected ratio. The problem then arises as to how large these discrepancies may become before we are forced to abandon the hypothesis, or what amounts to the same thing, how small they must be in order that they may reasonably be ascribed to chance. Such problems can be solved by application of a very simple statistical test known as **chi-square** (χ^2), which will now be illustrated for the convenience of students who may wish to analyze data arising from their own laboratory experiments or those of others whose experiments are quoted at various places throughout the book.

In searching for hereditary variations in the garden plant *Coleus*, Boye and Rife (1938) employed self-pollination of plants which for many years had been propagated vegetatively. Under the latter circumstance no variation due to segregation and recombination could be observed, but by selfing we produce an F_2 generation with regard to all genes for which the selfed plant happens to be heterozygous. In one case a number of plants with solid purple leaves produced, upon selfing, a total of 787 offspring, of which 207 bore leaves with a green-purple pattern. This would suggest that the original purple plants were heterozygous for a recessive gene for the pattern, since the latter type of plant comprised somewhere near a quarter of the total progeny. The observed *frequencies* (numbers) are not exactly in the ratio 3:1, however, and when compared with the expected frequencies we see in the fourth column of Table 7.1 that there is a deviation of 10.25 plants in each class.

Table 7.1. COMPUTATION OF χ^2 FOR A 3:1 EXPECTATION

CLASS	OBSERVED FREQUENCY o	EXPECTED FREQUENCY c	DEVIATION $o - c$	$\dfrac{(o - c)^2}{c}$
Purple	580	590.25	-10.25	0.178
Pattern	207	196.75	$+10.25$	0.534
Totals	787	787.00	0	$\chi^2 = 0.712$

The question which we now propose is this: how often by chance alone should one expect deviations as large as or larger than 10.25? If this probability is quite small, then we shall be willing to assume that chance alone did in fact *not* produce the discrepancy, that other agencies were at work, and that our genetic hypothesis is therefore false or, at least, incomplete. Note that we are not asking for the probability that we should obtain exactly 580 purple and 207 pattern plants under this situation. This would be given by

$$\frac{787!}{580!\,207!}\left(\frac{3}{4}\right)^{580}\left(\frac{1}{4}\right)^{207} = 0.023$$

which is the appropriate term in the expansion of $(\frac{3}{4} + \frac{1}{4})^{787}$. This must necessarily be a very small value, since there are so many results which may occur by chance — in this case, 788. Even the most likely event, under the 3:1 hypothesis, namely that of obtaining 590 purple and 197 pattern, is highly unlikely, which is another way of saying that we usually expect to obtain some deviation from the "expected" ratio, particularly when the progeny is quite large.

To repeat, then, we wish the probability of obtaining equally large or larger deviations from the expected 3:1 ratio, and, although a solution might be obtained by summing the appropriate terms of the binomial, $(\frac{3}{4} + \frac{1}{4})^{787}$, this would be much too laborious and a simpler procedure consists in the use of the chi-square (χ^2) test.

The general formula for chi-square is

$$\chi^2 = \sum \left\{ \frac{(o - c)^2}{c} \right\}$$

where o stands for any observed frequency, c for the corresponding calculated value, and Σ instructs us to sum the bracketed quantity for all classes. The procedure is very simply accomplished as is shown in the last column of Table 7.1, and we arrive at a value of 0.712 for χ^2.

Table 7.2. COMPUTATION OF χ^2 FOR A 9:3:3:1 EXPECTATION

CLASS	OBSERVED FREQUENCY o	EXPECTED FREQUENCY c	DEVIATION $o - c$	$\dfrac{(o - c)^2}{c}$
Bright, tendril	847	840.375	+6.625	0.052
Bright, acacia	298	280.125	+17.875	1.141
Dull, tendril	300	280.125	+19.875	1.410
Dull, acacia	49	93.375	−44.375	21.089
Totals	1494	1494.000	0	$\chi^2 = 23.692$

We see from the way in which χ^2 is computed that the larger the deviations relative to the expected values the larger will be the value of χ^2. It therefore constitutes a logical measure of deviation between observation and hypothesis, so that our original question will be answered if we can obtain an answer to the question: how often by chance alone should one obtain χ^2 values as large as or larger than 0.712? This is determined by reference to the Table of Chi-Square (Table 7.3), which gives the values of χ^2 which are exceeded by

Table 7.3. TABLE OF CHI-SQUARE *

In the body of the table are given, for various numbers of degrees of freedom, the values of χ^2 which are exceeded by chance in various percentages of trials as indicated at the top.

DEGREES OF FREEDOM	.99	.95	.70	.50	.30	.05	.01
1	.00016	.00393	.148	.455	1.074	3.841	6.635
2	.0201	.103	.713	1.386	2.408	5.991	9.210
3	.115	.352	1.424	2.366	3.665	7.815	11.341
4	.297	.711	2.195	3.357	4.878	9.488	13.277
5	.554	1.145	3.000	4.351	6.064	11.070	15.086
6	.872	1.635	3.828	5.348	7.231	12.592	16.812
7	1.239	2.167	4.671	6.346	8.383	14.067	18.475
8	1.646	2.733	5.527	7.344	9.524	15.507	20.090
9	2.088	3.325	6.393	8.343	10.656	16.919	21.666
10	2.558	3.940	7.267	9.342	11.781	18.307	23.209

* This table is taken by consent from *Statistical Methods for Research Workers* by Prof. R. A. Fisher, published by Oliver and Boyd Ltd., Edinburgh; and attention is drawn to the larger collection in *Statistical Tables* by Prof. R. A. Fisher and F. Yates, published by Oliver and Boyd Ltd., Edinburgh.

chance in various indicated percentages of trials. Glancing across the first row of the table we see that our value of χ^2 (0.712) falls between the tabulated values for the probabilities .50 and .30. This means that a deviation from the expected ratio of 10.25 or more plants will occur in somewhat over 30% of trials by chance alone when the true ratio is actually 3:1! Certainly, then, there is no reason for supposing that anything other than chance was responsible for our discrepancy, and we may therefore say that the data are in accordance with the proposed theory of recessive inheritance of the pattern leaf; in other words, there is no significant evidence against the hypothesis.

One of the many advantages of the chi-square method is the fact that it may be applied to cases where there are more than two classes. To illustrate the method once more, we now apply it to a dihybrid cross in sweet peas, reported by Punnett (1923). Crosses between true-breeding, bright-flowered, acacia-leaved (tendrilless) plants and true-breeding, dull-flowered, tendril plants produced an F_1 all of which had bright flowers and tendrils. From this one might suspect that acacia leaves and dull flowers are each dependent upon single recessive factors; in which case, if the F_1 plants are selfed, we should expect a ratio of 9 bright, tendril : 3 bright, acacia : 3 dull, tendril : 1 dull, acacia among the F_2 plants. The actual frequencies observed by Punnett among 1494 F_2 offspring are shown in the second column of Table 7.2. As might be anticipated, they do not agree precisely with the expected frequencies, c, which are, respectively, $\frac{9}{16}$, $\frac{3}{16}$, $\frac{3}{16}$, and $\frac{1}{16}$ of the total, 1494. Could the deviations be attributed to chance? To decide this, we square the deviations, divide each by the expected value, c, and sum, obtaining a value of 23.692 for χ^2.

In determining the probability of chance occurrence of such a χ^2 value we now enter the chi-square table in the row for 3 "degrees of freedom." In general, for simple Mendelian problems of the sort described here, it may be taken as a rule that the number of degrees of freedom associated with any chi-square value is always one less than the number of classes. Thus, in the first example there were 2 classes and 1 degree of freedom; here there are 4 classes and 3 degrees of freedom. We see from the table that our value for χ^2 (23.692) is considerably larger than the value tabulated for the .01 probability (11.341). The observed chi-square value should, therefore, be exceeded in much fewer than one trial in a hundred by chance alone, so that we are willing to assume that chance was, in fact, not solely responsible for the discrepancies between the observed and expected numbers. Our hypothesis as to the mode of inheritance is, therefore, inconsistent with the data. Those who are interested in a possible reason for the discrepancy will find the appropriate explanation in the phenomenon of genetic linkage to be described in Chapter 10.

As a matter of convention biologists and statisticians refer to any statistical constant such as χ^2 as a "significant" value when it exceeds the value corresponding to a probability of .05. A value exceeding the .01 value is labeled "highly significant." This means that there is significant, or highly significant, evidence *against* the hypothesis under test. Thus we might say, concerning the first example, that the χ^2 value of 0.712 is nonsignificant, that the hypothesis of recessive inheritance is therefore not disproved by the data. In the second example, we say that there is highly significant evidence against the hypothesis of independent two-pair inheritance. In Table 7.3 the last two columns thus have special importance, since they define the levels at which scientific hypotheses are accepted or rejected.

For those who may wish to employ the chi-square test of "goodness of fit" to simple genetic problems, we may now add the following precaution. The chi-square method is only approximate but furnishes a very good approximation so long as the expected frequency in any class is not less than 5. Where such small numbers are involved the binomial theorem should be used as a mathematically exact procedure. Other useful properties and extensions of the method to genetic problems may be found in the statistical manuals included among the references at the end of this chapter.

PROBLEMS

7.1 How many times in families of five would you expect four boys and a girl? Four girls and a boy? Five girls?

7.2 In man polydactyly (an extra finger on each hand) is due to a dominant gene. When one parent is polydactylous, but heterozygous, and the other parent is normal, how many times in families of three would you expect all normal children? One polydactylous and two normal?

7.3 In man albinism is due to a recessive gene. Two normal parents produce an albino child. If they produce another child what are the chances of its being albino?

7.4 Where parents are genetically similar to those in Problem 7.3, how many times in families of three would you expect three albino children? Three normal children?

7.5 In families like those in Problem 7.4, how many times in families of three would you expect one albino boy and two normal girls?

7.6 In a certain family there are six girls. What are the chances of the next child being a boy?

7.7 In human beings deaf-mutism may be the result of the homozygous state of either or both of two recessive genes d and e. Normal hearing results only when both dominants D and E are present. Where both parents are $DdEe$, how many times in families of two would you expect two deaf children?

7.8 Where both parents are $DdEe$ (see Problem 7.7), how many times in families of four would you expect three normal children and one deaf child?

7.9 Where one parent is $DdEe$ and the other parent is $ddEE$ (see Problem 7.7), how many times in families of three would you expect one normal child and two deaf children?

7.10 Two normal parents produce an albino son. What are the chances that their next child will be a normal girl?

7.11 In shorthorn cattle the genes for red and for white are alleles but neither is dominant, the heterozygous condition resulting in roan. Twins are sometimes born in cattle. If twins are born in crosses between red bulls and roan cows, how often should both twins be roan?

7.12 In crosses such as described in Problem 7.11, how often should one twin be roan and one red?

7.13 In a man keratosis (a skin abnormality) is due to a dominant gene. A man with keratosis whose father did not show the abnormality marries a woman with keratosis whose mother was free from it. If they have three children what are the chances that all three children will show the condition?

7.14 If the parents in Problem 7.13 have another child, what are the chances of its being a girl who will not have keratosis?

7.15 In corn dwarfism is due to a recessive gene. A farmer has seed corn which happened to come from normal plants which were heterozygous for dwarfism. He plants these seeds four to a hill. How often would you expect four normal plants in a hill? Two normal and two dwarf plants?

7.16 If the corn from Problem 7.15 were planted three seeds to the hill, how often would you expect three dwarf plants to a hill? How often would you expect two dwarf plants and one normal plant?

7.17 In poultry feathered shanks are the result of either or both of the dominant genes F and S. Unfeathered shanks are the result of the double recessive condition. In crosses where both parents are $FfSs$, how many times in families of three offspring would all be expected to have feathered shanks? All three unfeathered shanks?

7.18 If one parent were $FfSs$ and the other $ffss$ (see Problem 7.17), how many times in families of four offspring would you expect one feathered-shanked bird and three unfeathered-shanked birds?

7.19 In poultry the genes for black and for splashed-white are alleles but neither is dominant, the heterozygous condition resulting in blue (the Blue Andalusian). A pair of Blue Andalusians are mated, and the female lays two eggs. What are the chances that both eggs will hatch out Blue Andalusians?

7.20 If three eggs are laid by the bird mentioned in Problem 7.19 what are the chances that all three eggs will hatch out Blue Andalusians?

7.21 A certain plant when self-pollinated produced 400 offspring, 317 of which had white flowers and 83 of which had colored flowers. Using chi-square determine whether this segregation fits better a ratio of 3 : 1 or one of 13 : 3.

7.22 When a black rooster was mated to a splashed-white hen, the resulting offspring were blue. From many crosses among these F_1 individuals, the results in the F_2 were 93 black, 219 blue, 88 splashed-white. Using chi-square and remembering that in this case there are two degrees of freedom, determine whether there is significant evidence against the hypothesis of one pair of genes with blending as an explanation of these results.

REFERENCES

Boye, C.L., and Rife, D. C., *Jour. Heredity* **29**:55 (1938).

Fisher, R. A., *Statistical Methods for Research Workers*, 12th Ed. Edinburgh, Oliver and Boyd (1954).

Mather, K., *Statistical Analysis in Biology*, 2nd. Ed. New York, Interscience Publishers (1947)

Punnett, R. C., *Jour. Genetics* **13**:101 (1923).

Snedecor, G. W., *Statistical Methods Applied to Experiments in Agriculture and Biology*, 4th Ed. Ames, Ia., Collegiate Press, Inc. (1946).

Tippett, L. H. C., *The Methods of Statistics*, 4th Ed. New York, John Wiley and Sons (1952).

CHAPTER EIGHT

Sex-linked genes

In earlier chapters, we have seen that certain parallelisms between the behavior of allelic genes and of homologous chromosomes led early to the theory that the genes are parts of chromosomes or, as sometimes stated, that the genes are carried on the chromosomes. The observations that have been described up to this point could hardly be regarded as sufficient to prove the theory convincingly. But the history of genetics during the first fifteen or twenty years of this century is to a very great extent a history of accumulating fact upon fact in confirmation of the chromosome theory of heredity.

A disproportionately large share of the facts which proved beyond any shadow of a doubt the correctness of the chromosome theory was discovered through the study of a rather unimpressive little insect that we have all frequently encountered. This is the tiny midgelike *fruit fly*, so-called because it is so commonly found hovering about wherever there is fruit; more particularly, wherever fruit is beginning to show the slightest signs of fermentation. The scientific name of the species that has been most widely studied is *Drosophila melanogaster*.

About 1910, T. H. Morgan and a brilliant group of younger men (then barely in their twenties) who were associated with him at Columbia University began to use Drosophila in genetic experiments. Morgan in 1933 was awarded the Nobel Prize in Medicine and Physiology for his work with this animal, and we shall frequently have occasion to mention the contributions of his younger colleagues, among whom were H. J. Muller, also recipient of a Nobel Prize (1946), A. H. Sturtevant, and Calvin Bridges. Drosophila was shown by these men to be such a valuable genetic tool that laboratories in all parts of the world soon began to experiment with it, and to-day more is known about the genetics of this little insect than is known about that of any other organism. Drosophila is easily raised, it reproduces rapidly, and it exhibits many hundreds of heritable variations. In addition, it is favorable material for cytological study; its chromosomes are few in number (four pairs) and the homologous pairs are readily distinguished from one another. It is thus easier in this animal than in many others to study the parallel behavior of chromosomes and genes. The discovery some twenty years ago of the relatively gigantic salivary-gland chromosomes of Drosophila, in which a great deal of minute structural detail can be seen (see Chapter 21), has greatly facilitated this study.

Among the many millions — literally — of Drosophila that have been examined in genetics laboratories, occasional individuals have been found to differ in certain respects from the wild type. Many differences in the color of the eyes, which in the normal Drosophila are dull red, have been observed; variations in wing length and wing form, in body color and body shape, in bristles and in other structures have been found and tested genetically. Not all of these variations have proved to be heritable, but a genetic basis has been demonstrated for many of them.

Each heritable variation is now known to be due to a new gene or a new arrangement of genes. A "new" gene is not new in the sense of something that has been added to the genes normally present, but is rather a change in a gene already there. Changes of this kind are called **mutations,** and their nature will be discussed in some detail in Chapter 24.

The changes in the genes that we call mutations are expressed phenotypically as variations in structure or function. Most of the heritable variations found in the early studies on Drosophila, when tested genetically, conformed to the laws of Mendel in the manner with which we are already familiar. That is, breeding tests of hybrids between the mutant form and the wild type showed that each gamete of the heterozygotes carried either the mutated gene or its wild type allele, but never both (law of segregation); that the two types of gametes were produced in approximately equal numbers, and that when an individual was heterozygous for each of two different mutated genes, each mutant gene and its normal allele segregated independently of the other mutant-and-normal gene pair (law of independent assortment). Insofar as observations on the genetic behavior of the Drosophila mutations revealed conformity with the Mendelian laws, they of course added to the evidence, already obtained from peas and other organisms, that the distribution of pairs of alleles, in the formation of the gametes, corresponds precisely to the way in which pairs of homologous chromosomes are distributed. That is to say, they provided fresh confirmation of the chromosome theory of heredity. A crucial test of a scientific theory, however, is the extent to which it can account for *exceptions* to the laws it was originally designed to explain.

The first exception to the laws of Mendel found in the early Drosophila studies was noticed in breeding tests of a white-eyed Drosophila. In a culture of red-eyed Drosophila a single white-eyed individual was found. It was a male, and was promptly mated with a red-eyed sister (Fig. 8.1). The F_1 were all red-eyed, and the F_2 consisted of red-eyed and white-eyed flies in the ratio of three red-eyed to one white-eyed. This looks like the result to be expected from a pair of genes, with the red-eyed allele dominant; but it was noticed further that in the F_2 generation *all of the white-eyed flies were males.* No white-eyed females at all appeared in this generation, although very large numbers were raised.

Here indeed was a striking exception to the familiar sort of behavior, for hitherto (except for a single puzzling case in a moth, and another in poultry) in all crosses involving contrasting characters each variety of offspring had consisted of approximately equal numbers of males and females. Yet in this cross the white-eyed character, apparently recessive, occurred only in males.

Morgan and his associates discussed these unexpected results and rather quickly saw that the chromosome theory of heredity would fully explain them. To understand how this could be, the student should recall that when we stated that the chromosomes of somatic cells regularly occur in matched pairs (page 38), we mentioned that we would later discuss exceptions to this rule. Perhaps the most important of these exceptions had been discovered some years before the Drosophila work began. In the *male* somatic cells of several species of animals it was found that all the chromosomes are present in pairs *except one*, which is without a matching counterpart. The single chromosome that is unmatched in the somatic cells of the male, however, is found as a member of a pair in female cells. Because the significance of this peculiarly distributed chromosome was not at first understood, it was called the **X-chromosome,** a designation still in use. In the animals we are talking about, then, the males have one X-chromosome, the females have two. When the gametes are formed, every egg receives an X-chromosome, as well as one member of each of the other pairs of chromosomes, which we now call **autosomes.** In the maturation of the sperms, however, when a primary spermatocyte divides, only one of the secondary spermatocytes derived from it receives the X-chromosome. Consequently, half of the sperms possess an X-chromosome (in addition to a haploid set of autosomes) and half do not.

When an egg (each of which, you will remember, has an X-chromosome) is fertilized by a sperm that possesses an X-chromosome, the resulting zygote (**XX**) develops into a female. If an egg is fertilized by a sperm without an X-chromosome, the resulting zygote (conven-

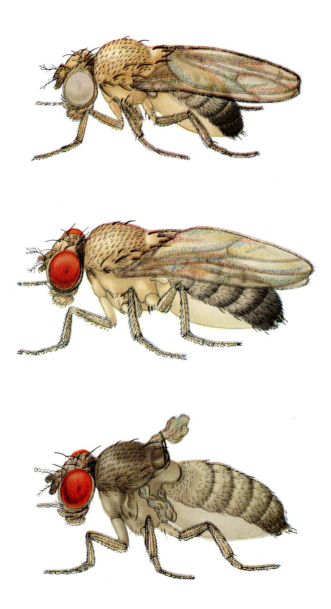

Fig. 8.1 *Drosophila melanogaster*. Top, white-eyed, long-winged, gray-bodied, male Drosophila. Middle, red-eyed, long-winged, gray-bodied, female Drosophila. Bottom, red-eyed, vestigial-winged, black-bodied, female Drosophila.

iently symbolized as **XO**) becomes a male. You will readily see that we have in fact been describing *a chromosomal basis of sex determination*.

The type of sex determination just described may be referred to as the **XX–XO** or, simply, as the **XO type.** This is not, however, the only mechanism of sex determination. In many animals, including man, the chromosomes in the somatic cells of both males and females occur in pairs, but in the males the chromosomes of one pair are *not matched*, that is, they are distinguishably different from each other. This is the case in Drosophila, as you will see in Figure 8.2. Here there are three pairs of autosomes in both the female and the male, but the remaining pair of chromosomes, the sex chromosomes, is composed of two identical-looking members in the female only. In the male, one member of the odd pair looks like the matched members of the corresponding pair in the female, but the other is clearly dissimilar, having a peculiar hook on one end. The odd-shaped sex chromosome found in the male is known as the Y-chromosome; the other one is the X-chromosome. Thus, in this type of sex determination, known as the **XX–XY** or, simply, the **XY type,** the female has two X-chromosomes, the male one X- and a Y-chromosome.

Fig. 8.2 The chromosomes of *Drosophila melanogaster*. Female on the left, male on the right. *From Bridges in Genetics*

In the XY type of sex determination, we can readily see that the sperms should be of two kinds with respect to the sex chromosomes they carry. Half the sperms will contain an X-chromosome, and half a Y, since at the first meiotic division of each primary spermatocyte the X will go into one secondary spermatocyte and the Y into the other. Each sperm will, of course, contain a haploid set of autosomes in addition to its X- or Y-chromosome. The eggs, obviously, will each contain an X-chromosome. Fertilization of an egg by an X-carrying sperm produces a female, fertilization by a Y-sperm gives a male.

At the time Morgan made his first observations on the peculiar genetic behavior of the white-eye character in Drosophila, the cytology of that insect had not been adequately studied, and it was believed to have the XO type of sex determination. As we have seen above, we now know that it has the XY type. Nevertheless, the knowledge that there was an X-chromosome associated with sex, being paired in the female and single in the male, was enough to suggest to Morgan and his collaborators a possible explanation for the genetic peculiarities of the white-eyed trait, since it also was plainly in some way associated with sex. They saw, in fact, that the odd behavior of white eye would be accounted for if the alleles for white and red eyes, respectively, are located on the X-chromosome.

If we let W represent a gene for red eyes, dominant to w, the gene for white eyes, the white-eyed mutant male in the cross described on page 92 would necessarily carry a w gene on his single X-chromosome. On the basis of Morgan's belief that Drosophila males were XO, the white-eyed male would, of course, have *only* the w allele of this pair. All of his daughters would receive this gene, together with a W gene from their mother, and hence would be Ww and phenotypically red-eyed. But the male offspring of the cross would get their X-chromosomes from the mother and would therefore be $W-$, producing sperm of which half (female determining) would carry an X-chromosome with the W gene, and half (male determining) would have no X-chromosome and therefore no W gene. The subsequent discovery that Drosophila males are XY does not affect this interpretation, because it has turned out that most of the Y-chromosome is genetically "blank;" that is, for the most part, it does not carry an allele of any gene found in the X-chromosome. With this fact in mind, we may diagram the cross between a white-eyed male and a red-eyed female as follows:

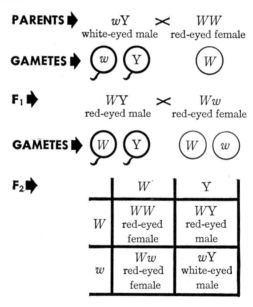

As you can see from the above, the hypothesis that the W,w alleles are carried on the X-chromosome, and on the X-chromosome alone, would lead us to expect in the F_2 a theoretical ratio of three red-eyed flies to one white-eyed, and that the white-eyed flies should all be males. *This, of course, is just what was found in the actual cross.*

Furthermore, the hypothesis also explains the results of other crosses involving the white-eyed character. Let us ask, for example, whether it would ever be possible, on the hypothesis we have been using, to obtain white-eyed females and, if so, how we could do it. Obviously, a white-eyed female would have the genetic constitution ww. This means that one w must come from the father, one from the mother. It should be possible, then, to produce white-eyed females by mating a white-eyed male (wY) to a red-eyed female which carries the gene for white eyes (Ww). Where can we obtain such a female? We see that the F_1 females from the cross diagramed above have this formula. Crossing one of these females with a white-eyed male should therefore produce some white-eyed females, as shown below.

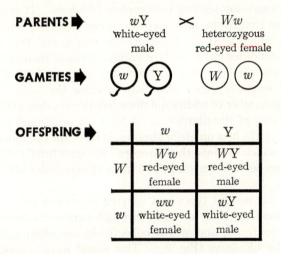

PARENTS ➡ wY   × Ww
white-eyed   heterozygous
male   red-eyed female

GAMETES ➡ w Y W w

OFFSPRING ➡

	w	Y
W	Ww red-eyed female	WY red-eyed male
w	ww white-eyed female	wY white-eyed male

Half of the females from this cross should be white-eyed if our hypothesis is correct. Morgan made this cross also, and these were in fact the results he observed. The same cross has since been made by many investigators, and the same results have regularly been obtained. Thus the hypothesis that the peculiar pattern of genetic behavior shown by the white-eye character indicates that its gene is carried on the X-chromosome is a very satisfactory one. You can use this hypothesis also to predict the F_1 and F_2 ratios from a cross between a red-eyed male (WY) and a white-eyed female (ww). Work out for yourself a diagram showing the results to be expected from this mating. Genes which are carried on the X-chromosome and are transmitted therefore like the W,w alleles in Drosophila are called **sex-linked genes.**

The working out of sex-linked inheritance in Drosophila immediately clarified some puzzling peculiarities that had long been observed in the transmission of certain human traits. A century before this work was done, medical men had noticed that at least two abnormalities in man, red-green color blindness and hemophilia, are inherited according to what became known as *Nasse's law;* that is, affected males transmit these conditions through normal daughters to about half of their grandsons. You should see at once that this is what we would expect if these are sex-linked recessive traits; it is now known with certainty that they are, and many other sex-linked abnormalities in man have been discovered. These include one form of nystagmus (an involuntary oscillation of the eyeballs), anhidrotic ectodermal dysplasia (a condition characterized by marked deficiency or total absence of hair, nails, teeth, and skin glands), progressive muscular dystrophy, and retinitis pigmentosa (a type of progressive retinal degeneration leading to complete blindness). It is important to recognize that nystagmus may also occur as a *symptom* of several conditions which need not be of genetic origin, and that the three other abnormalities mentioned, or variant types of them, are not sex-linked in all families; that is, there are autosomal dominant and autosomal recessive genes also that produce the same or similar effects. The number of additional disorders in man that exhibit a sex-linked pattern of distribution in at least an occasional pedigree is quite large; Falls lists nineteen abnormalities of the eye alone (mostly very rare) which fall into this category. We shall briefly discuss here only the two best known sex-linked traits of man, color blindness and hemophilia.

There are several types and varying degrees of color blindness. The most familiar forms are those in which various shades of red and green are confused, and which collectively are often called "red-green" color blindness (Fig. 8.3). This would include *protanopia* or "red blindness" and *deuteranopia* or "green blindness" (partial degrees of these are called protanomaly and deuteranomaly, respectively). The two types may be identified by means of any of several tests, such as the color-vision test charts designed by Ishihara.

Both protanopia and deuteranopia are hereditary and the genes responsible for them are, in each case, sex-linked and recessive to their normal alleles. To prove this it has, of course, not been possible to make breeding tests comparable to those we have described for the white-eye character in Drosophila, but the evidence for their sex-linked recessive transmission is nevertheless wholly convincing. This evidence can be summarized as follows (since the facts listed apply equally to protanopia and deuteranopia, we shall simply use the terms "color-blind" and "color blindness" as applying to both):

1. When women with normal color vision whose fathers are color-blind have children, approximately half of their sons are color-blind, half normal.

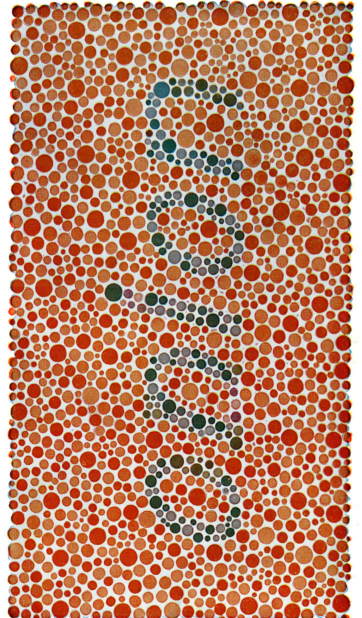

Fig. 8.3 A chart for testing color blindness. The normal-visioned person will see the word "onion." The red-green color-blind individual will see the word "color." The pastel-shade color-blind person will not be able to make out any word. (This is an original chart based on the Ishihara method of determining color blindness.)

2. The sons of color-blind women are *all* color-blind; but unless the husbands of the color-blind women are also color-blind, their daughters have normal color vision.

3. With rare exceptions, color-blind women always have color-blind fathers.

4. Color blindness is much more frequent among men than among women; in the United States, between six and eight per cent of the men are color-blind and less than one per cent of the women.

It is not difficult to see why a sex-linked recessive trait must be commoner among men than among women. About half of the sons of women who are heterozygous for a color-blindness gene are color blind; but only those heterozygous women who marry color-blind men (about one in twelve or fourteen) can have any color-blind daughters. Likewise, while all of the sons of homozygous color-blind women are color blind, only the homozygous women who have color-blind husbands will produce color-blind daughters.

Figure 8.4 shows a typical family history of color blindness. Fill in the genotypes of the individuals in this pedigree as far as you can.

It will be noted that all the color-blind individuals in this pedigree are males. Under what conditions would a color-blind girl be expected to occur? If we let C represent the gene for normal vision and c the gene for color blindness, then a color-blind man would be of the formula cY and a color-blind woman of the formula cc. Obviously a color-blind woman must have received one c from her father, one from her mother. Since a man cannot have the gene c without showing color blindness, the father of a color-blind girl must be color-blind. Likewise her mother must carry at least one c, that is, must be either a "carrier" (Cc) or color-blind herself (cc). Figure 8.5 shows a family history involving a color-blind girl. As would be expected, her father is color-blind. Her mother has several color-blind brothers, which is to be expected if she is a carrier. Fill in the genotypes of the various members of this family.

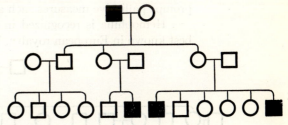

Fig. 8.4 A typical family history of red-green color blindness.

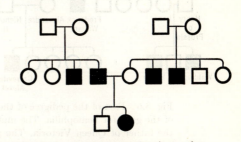

Fig. 8.5 A family history showing color blindness in a woman. Note the conditions under which this can occur.

When we find a character in human beings which is more common in men than in women, which rarely shows in both father and son, and which does not occur in a woman unless her father showed it, we are justified in inferring that it is due to a sex-linked recessive gene. "Red blindness" and "green blindness" are clearly traits which meet these requirements. All forms of color blindness are not inherited in the same way, however. *Congenital total color blindness* (monochromatism) depends on an autosomal recessive gene. The genetic basis of the very rare "blue-yellow" blindness is not known.

Sex-linked *dominants* are also known in a number of organisms. If a character in man is due to a sex-linked dominant gene, would there be more men or more women showing the character? Why?

The evidence that hemophilia in man is dependent on a sex-linked recessive gene is similar to that cited above for red-green color blindness. Hemophilia is characterized by excessive and prolonged bleeding which may occur spontaneously in various tissues, or may follow an injury or an operation. Examination of the blood of a hemophiliac usually reveals that the clotting time is greatly prolonged. A specific substance (antihemophilic globulin), which is present in the plasma of normal individuals, is absent from the plasma of hemophiliacs. As a result the blood continues to flow even from a trivial injury, and the affected individual may bleed to death unless prompt palliative measures such as transfusion are provided.

Hemophilia is recognized in many populations, but is perhaps best known in European royalty. The power which Rasputin wielded

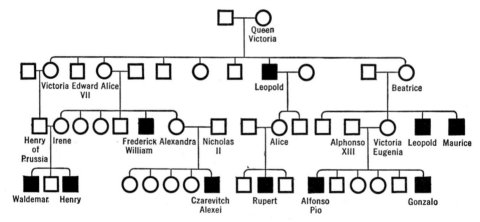

Fig. 8.6 Part of the pedigree of the royal families of Europe, showing the transmission of the gene for hemophilia. The mutation is thought to have occurred in a germ cell of the father of Queen Victoria. The present royal family of England is completely free from the gene, however, since Queen Elizabeth traces her descent through Edward VII, one of Queen Victoria's sons who did not himself have hemophilia. *Based on the researches of Haldane and Iltis*

in Russia is said to have derived from his alleged hypnotic control of this disease in the little Czarevitch. A pedigree illustrating the course of hemophilia in the royal families is shown in Figure 8.6.

As in color blindness, hemophilia would be expected to occur in a woman only if her father was a hemophiliac and her mother carried the gene. Hemophilia occurs in about one male out of 25,000. Inasmuch as many boys with hemophilia die before reaching puberty, and only one woman in about 12,500 is heterozygous for the gene, the conditions required to produce a hemophilic female are very infrequent. Under a system of random mating, only one woman in about 625 million would be expected to receive two genes for hemophilia.

Nevertheless careful search for women hemophiliacs has resulted in the recent discovery of several families in which they occur. Figure 8.7 is a pedigree in which the disease developed in five sisters, the daughters of a hemophilic man who married a heterozygous first cousin.

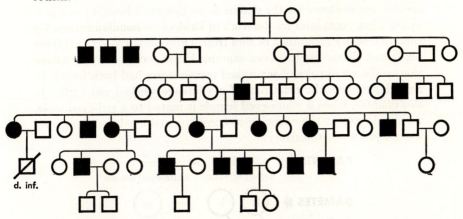

Fig. 8.7 A pedigree showing the occurrence of hemophilia in women. *Adapted and re-drawn from Merskey in the Quarterly Journal of Medicine*

Answer for yourself the following questions about hemophilia. Could it ever appear in both a father and a son? Under what conditions? Could the son in this case be said to inherit the condition from his father? What would you expect the sons of a hemophilic woman to be like? What would the children be like if both parents had hemophilia?

The presence of several clotting factors in the blood other than the antihemophilic globulin is necessary for normal coagulation. Recently several diseases have been described which are characterized by prolonged clotting time in spite of the fact that the blood contains antihemophilic globulin. In these diseases (e.g., "Christmas disease" and parahemophilia) a deficiency of one of the other clotting factors has been demonstrated. Finally, there are still other bleeding diseases or *hemorrhagic diatheses* which are sometimes confused with hemophilia, but in which the coagulation time is normal. These include hemorrhagic telangiectasia and the various purpuras. Laboratory examination of the blood is necessary to differentiate many of these conditions. Most of them have a hereditary basis, some of them being sex-linked whereas others are dependent on autosomal genes.

We have seen that the X-chromosome of a male, in organisms with XO or XY sex determination, is normally transmitted only to his daughters, and that they in turn transmit it to half of their offspring of both sexes. We have also seen that the genes for certain hereditary traits, apparent exceptions to the laws of Mendel, follow precisely the same pattern of transmission. Morgan's discovery of this new instance of parallelism between gene behavior and chromosome behavior was, of course, a substantial step toward proving the theory that the genes are carried in the chromosomes. But even more spectacular evidence for the chromosome theory of heredity was provided a few years later by the work of Bridges on **nondisjunction.** By this time many thousands of flies from Drosophila crosses involving sex-linked characters had been examined, and occasionally an exception to the usual rules of sex-linked transmission had been found. In accordance with the principles of sex-linkage worked out earlier in this chapter, when a white-eyed female is mated to a red-eyed male, we should expect the offspring to consist of red-eyed daughters and white-eyed sons exclusively:

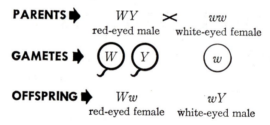

The results indicated in the above diagram are indeed the usual ones. But, as Bridges noticed, crosses of this type also produce on occasion (once among about two thousand offspring) a *white-eyed daughter* or a *red-eyed son.* The red-eyed sons from these crosses are sterile and, as we shall see shortly, breeding tests of the white-eyed daughters give results that would not be expected from ordinary *ww* females.

At this point, you should be inclined to ask the question that Bridges must have asked himself. If the W,w alleles are in fact carried on the X-chromosome, how *could* a white-eyed daughter or a red-eyed son appear from the cross diagramed above? The possibility of mutation might occur to you (as it did to Bridges). But this would not explain why the red-eyed sons are sterile, nor would it explain why the white-eyed daughters should give results in breeding tests any different from those given by ordinary *ww* females. If we rule out mutation as a satisfactory explanation, and still retain confidence in the chromosome theory, we must conclude that in some way the exceptional red-eyed sons each received its *father*'s X-chromosome (with the *W* gene), and failed to receive an X-chromosome from its mother. If it had gotten an X-chromosome from each parent, it would of course be a female. Thus, the exceptional red-eyed males would be XO in sex-chromosome composition.

Similarly, we would have to conclude that a white-eyed daughter must have received *both* of her X-chromosomes from her mother.

These were Bridges' conclusions, and he pointed out that both of these occurrences could be accounted for if, on rare occasions, the two X-chromosomes of the white-eyed mother should fail to segregate during meiosis. This would result in an egg with both of the mother's X-chromosomes or, with equal frequency, an egg with neither of her X-chromosomes. Mothers of the genotype *ww*, then, in addition to producing the usual *w* eggs, could produce some eggs which contained the genes *ww* and some which contained no *w* gene. The egg with no *w* gene is indicated by a dash (–) in the diagram on page 102, where we have shown how both the usual and the exceptional types of progeny would be produced.

If a *ww* egg is fertilized by a Y sperm, we would get an individual of the formula *ww*Y which, having only *w* genes, should be white-eyed. Bridges thought that a fly of this constitution would also be a female, because of its possession of two X-chromosomes, and *he predicted that cytological examination of the exceptional white-eyed females would show that they possess two X-chromosomes and a Y-chromosome in addition.* A *ww* egg fertilized by a *W* sperm should produce an individual of the formula *Www*. We could hardly predict what sex and eye color this would have. But Bridges found no flies which, when tested by breeding, gave any evidence of being *Www*, so he inferred that zygotes of this kind are nonviable. (It was found subsequently that they do sometimes survive; we shall have occasion to refer to them in a later chapter.)

An egg without an X-chromosome, fertilized by a Y sperm, would give a zygote of the formula –Y, that is, one with no X-chromosome at all, and with neither a *W* nor a *w* gene. It would be impossible to predict what this would look like, but there are good reasons to doubt that it could survive at all. Fertilization of a no-*w* egg by a *W* sperm, on the other hand, should produce a fly of the formula *W*–. We would expect this to be red-eyed and, since its sex-chromosome

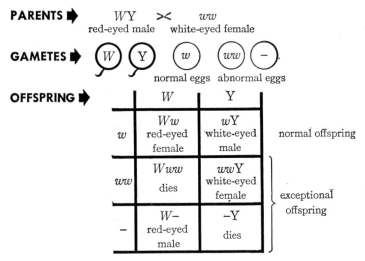

PARENTS ➡   WY   ><   ww
        red-eyed male   white-eyed female

GAMETES ➡   (W) (Y)   (w)   (ww) (−)
                  normal eggs   abnormal eggs

OFFSPRING ➡

	W	Y
w	Ww red-eyed female	wY white-eyed male
ww	Www dies	wwY white-eyed female
−	W− red-eyed male	−Y dies

normal offspring (for first row)

exceptional offspring (for second and third rows)

composition is XO, we might reasonably expect it to be male. *Bridges predicted that the exceptional red-eyed males would turn out on cytological examination to have one X-chromosome, but no Y.*

Bridges tested the exceptional white-eyed daughters from the cross shown in the preceding diagram by mating them to normal red-eyed males. If these females do have the formula wwY, we should expect that at the first meiotic division the two X-chromosomes would sometimes go into one daughter cell and the Y-chromosome into the other; segregations of this type would result in ww eggs and Y eggs. Alternatively, at the first meiotic division, the two X-chromosomes would separate, the Y-chromosome going with one or the other of them; this type of segregation would yield w and wY eggs. The breeding results indicate that the majority of primary oöcytes undergo the second type of segregation, in which the two X-chromosomes synapse and are segregated into different daughter cells. Thus about 92 per cent of the eggs produced by wwY females are of the w and wY constitutions, and only about 8 per cent are ww and Y.

The results of matings between the exceptional white-eyed females (wwY) and normal red-eyed males (WY), as worked out on Bridges' theory, are shown in the next diagram.

You will notice from the diagram that the red-eyed daughters from this cross should be of two kinds, in terms of their sex chromosomes, Ww and WwY; similarly, two kinds of white-eyed sons, wY and wYY, are expected. Although Bridges could not distinguish two phenotypically different types either among the red-eyed daughters or among the white-eyed sons, *he predicted that on cytological examination, half of the daughters would be found to have a Y-chromosome in addition to the two X-chromosomes and that half of the white-eyed sons would be XY, half XYY.*

PARENTS ➡ *WY* ✕ *ww*Y
  red-eyed male   exceptional
          white-eyed female

GAMETES ➡ (W) (Y) (ww) (Y) (w) (wY)
          only about 8%   about 92%

OFFSPRING ➡

	W	Y
ww	*Www* dies	*ww*Y white-eyed female
Y	*W*Y red-eyed male	YY dies
w	*Ww* red-eyed female	*w*Y white-eyed male
wY	*Ww*Y red-eyed female	*w*YY white-eyed male

Each of the cytological predictions italicized in the preceding discussion, made by Bridges on the basis of genetic observations alone, was subsequently verified by direct cytological examination. Figure 8.8 shows the first verification, the chromosomes found in the exceptional white-eyed females; the two X-chromosomes and the additional Y are clearly distinguishable. These studies gave almost conclusive proof that sex-linked genes are actually located on the sex chromosomes. They also provided the most convincing evidence that had yet been obtained for the validity of the chromosome theory of heredity.

The failure of the two members of a chromosome pair to separate at the first meiotic division, resulting in the formation of gametes which contain both chromosomes of the pair and of other gametes which contain neither member of the pair is called **nondisjunction.** We have been concerned in this chapter with nondisjunction of the sex chromosomes. You might guess that nondisjunction of autosomes might also occur at times. It does occur, both in animals and in plants (more frequently in the latter) and we shall consider some of its consequences in Chapter 20.

The early work on sex-linked inheritance in Drosophila, besides establishing the chromosomal

Fig. 8.8 The chromosomes of one of the exceptional white-eyed females produced by nondisjunction. *After Bridges in Genetics*

Fig. 8.9 Barred male (above) and nonbarred female (below). The barring is dependent upon a dominant sex-linked gene.

basis of sex linkage in that animal, made it possible to understand certain oddities in human heredity, as we have already seen. It also led to the recognition of types of chromosomal sex determination other than the XO and XY types. Even before the Drosophila work, sex-linked inheritance had been observed in a moth (*Abraxas*) and in poultry. But the pattern of transmission of sex-linked traits in these animals was the *converse* of that later found in Drosophila.

You will recall that a mating between a white-eyed male Drosophila and a homozygous red-eyed female gives all red-eyed flies in the F_1, and an F_2 with a ratio of three red-eyed to one white-eyed in which *all the white-eyed flies are male*. In poultry the F_1 from a cross between a male with "barred" plumage (Fig. 8.9) and a nonbarred female gives F_1 offspring which are all barred, and in the F_2 three barred to one nonbarred; *but all the nonbarred birds are females*. From matings of nonbarred males by barred females, the male progeny are all barred, the females nonbarred.

After Morgan showed that the distribution of sex-linked traits in Drosophila followed the distribution of the X-chromosome, it was immediately apparent that the distribution of sex-linked traits in the fowl and the moth could be explained in a very similar way. It was necessary only to assume that the sex chromosome which carries the sex-linked genes is *paired in the males* of these animals, *single in the females*. Thus, using Z to designate the chromosome that is present twice in the male and once in the female, males would have the sex-chromosome formula ZZ; females would be ZO or, if they are of a species in which the female has an unmatched pair of sex chromosomes, ZW. Here the W-chromosome, like the Y in Drosophila, is a sex chromosome that does not carry sex-linked genes. The sex-determining mechanisms just described may be called the **ZO–ZZ** and **ZW–ZZ types,** respectively. One or the other of these types is found in birds, in moths and butterflies, and in some fishes.

The following diagram shows how the cross of barred male with nonbarred female would give the results we have described. You should work out a similar diagram showing the results of mating a nonbarred male with a barred female.

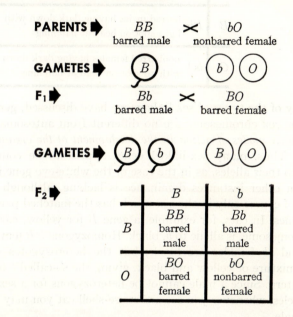

The barred pattern in poultry occurs in several breeds, including Plymouth Rocks, Dominiques, Scotch Grays, and Cuckoo Leghorns. Knowledge of its sex-linked inheritance has found practical application in providing a method for distinguishing the sex of newly-hatched chicks at a glance without recourse to "vent sexing," which requires skilled training and is therefore expensive. The identification of the sex of chicks is important to poultrymen, especially to those primarily interested in the sale of eggs, since it permits the early culling of unneeded males.

Barred females are mated to nonbarred males of any desired breed except White Leghorns (where the white is dominant) or White Rocks (which carry barring). The male chicks will later develop barred plumage but may be distinguished at hatching by the fact that they have a light patch on the head. The female chicks, which will develop nonbarred plumage, do not have this light spot on the head. The special mating must of course be made anew each generation. It may be diagramed as follows:

PARENTS ➡ bb ✕ BO
              nonbarred male   barred female

GAMETES ➡   (b)   (B) (O)

OFFSPRING ➡

	b
B Bb	barred males having dark down with light spot on head at hatching
O bO	nonbarred females having dark down with no spot on head at hatching

   In any of the types of sex linkage we have discussed, genes carried on the sex chromosome are no different from autosomal genes *as far as their modes of action in the development of the organism are concerned.* Thus, many sex-linked genes appear to be completely recessive to their alleles, as in the case of the white-eye gene in Drosophila. In other instances dominance is lacking, although this is apparent of course only in the sex which has the matched pair of sex chromosomes. In cats, for example, a gene B for yellow, carried on the X-chromosome, is allelic to b, black. Homozygous BB females are yellow, and bb females are black; but the heterozygotes show a splotchy mixture of yellow and black, giving the so-called "tortoise-shell" pattern. Since a male cannot be heterozygous for a sex-linked pair of alleles, whenever you see a tortoise-shell cat you may be sure it is a female.
   Sex-linked genes, like autosomal genes, may also have lethal effects. In animals which produce numerous progeny, a sex-linked lethal may readily be recognized even though it kills early and has no visible effect in the heterozygous state, because its presence in a parent markedly affects the sex ratio among the offspring.
   Sex-linked lethal genes affect the sex ratio because a male (in the case of XO or XY sex determination) can never be heterozygous for a sex-linked gene. Hence, if the gene is lethal, no male zygote which receives it will survive to reproduce and the gene can therefore be transmitted only by heterozygous females. The heterozygous females, although they show no visible effect of the gene if it is completely recessive, may be identified by the fact that they produce only about half as many male offspring as female offspring. Females are not

killed by a sex-linked lethal gene since, in order to have it in the homozygous state, they would have to receive it from both parents, and males carrying the gene do not survive to transmit it to them.

The way in which a sex-linked recessive gene on the X-chromosome affects the sex ratio is shown in the following diagram, where l represents the sex-linked lethal and L its normal allele.

PARENTS ▶ LY × Ll
           normal male   "carrier" female

GAMETES ▶ (L) (Y) (L) (l)

OFFSPRING ▶

	L	Y
L	LL normal female	LY normal male
l	Ll normal female	lY dies

In birds and other organisms having the ZW or ZO type of sex determination, the situation would of course be the reverse of that just presented. In carrier pigeons, for example, the Rosy Gier variety has creamy plumage with a gray head. A creamy head would be desirable from the fancier's standpoint. When a male with a creamy head was found, it seemed possible that this character could be incorporated into the breed. The cross of a creamy-headed male with a gray-headed female, however, resulted in a ratio of 1 gray-headed male : 1 creamy-headed male : 1 gray-headed female. The missing females die in the shell just before hatching time. Here we may assume a pair of sex-linked genes, G and g, such that GG results in a gray-headed male, GO in a gray-headed female, Gg in a creamy-headed male, and gO in the death of the female before hatching. Consequently we do not know what adult plumage color might be associated with the gO genotype, nor do we know what a homozygous gg male would be like, although we may suspect that this genotype, if it could be produced, would also be lethal.

In this chapter, we have shown some of the ways in which the chromosomes are involved in the determination of sex. But we have told only a small part of the story; more of it must be reserved for later consideration (Chapter 23). The analysis of *sex linkage* has provided us with a series of striking parallels between the behavior of genes and the behavior of chromosomes to add to those cited in Chapter 4.

In many animals, a particular chromosome is paired in one sex, and is either single or "mismatched" in the other sex. Similarly, *certain alleles behave as if two of them are present in one sex, but only one in the other.* In species in which the male has the unpaired or mismatched chromosome, *it is the male whose genetic behavior indicates that it carries a single member of a "sex-linked" pair of alleles;* in species in which the female has the unpaired or mismatched chromosome, *the converse genetic behavior is found.*

Genetic data sometimes indicate, as a rare exception to the rule, that a female has inherited two genes of a sex-linked allelic pair from her mother and none from her father, or that a male has received a sex-linked allele from his father. *In both instances, cytologic examination of the exceptional individuals and (in the case of the females) of their progeny reveals the precise abnormalities of sex-chromosome composition that have been predicted on the basis of the chromosome theory of heredity, from the genetic data alone.*

PROBLEMS

8.1 An albino, nonhemophilic man marries a normally-pigmented, nonhemophilic woman whose father was hemophilic and whose mother was an albino. What kinds of children can they have and in what proportions?

8.2 Two normal-visioned parents produce a color-blind son. What are the genotypes of the parents? What are the chances of their next child being a color-blind daughter?

8.3 In human beings hemolytic icterus (a type of anemia characterized by severe jaundice and other symptoms) is due to a dominant gene. A normal-visioned woman who does not have hemolytic icterus takes her daughter to a doctor for examination. In the course of the examination the doctor discovers that the girl is color-blind and has hemolytic icterus. What does the doctor automatically know about the father?

8.4 In cats yellow is due to a gene, *B*, and black to its allele, *b*. The heterozygous condition *Bb* results in tortoise-shell. The genes *B* and *b* are sex-linked. What kinds

of offspring would be expected to result from the cross of a black male with a yellow female?

8.5 What kinds of offspring would be expected to result from the cross of a black male with a tortoise-shell female?

8.6 A yellow male is mated with a tortoise-shell female. If the female has a litter consisting of four male kittens, what colors would they most probably be?

8.7 In poultry barring is the result of a dominant sex-linked gene, *B*; nonbarring is the result of its recessive allele, *b*. Black skin color is due to a dominant gene, *S*, white to its recessive allele, *s*. Rose comb is dependent upon a dominant gene, *R*, single comb upon its recessive allele, *r*. A nonbarred, white-skinned, single-combed male is crossed with a barred, white-skinned, single-combed female. What kinds of offspring will they be expected to produce?

8.8 A nonbarred, black-skinned, rose-combed male is mated to a barred, black-skinned, single-combed female. The following offspring are produced:

6 barred, black-skinned, rose-combed males

2 barred, white-skinned, rose-combed males

5 nonbarred, black-skinned, rose-combed females

2 nonbarred, white-skinned, rose-combed females

What are the probable genotypes of the parents?

8.9 A barred, white-skinned, single-combed male is mated to a nonbarred, black-skinned, rose-combed female. Eighteen offspring are produced, all barred, black-skinned, rose-combed birds. What are the probable genotypes of the parents?

8.10 In Drosophila long wings are due to a dominant gene, V, vestigial wings to its recessive allele, v. A white-eyed, vestigial-winged male is mated to a homozygous red-eyed, long-winged female. One of the F_1 females is crossed with the white-eyed, vestigial-winged parent. What kinds of offspring will they be expected to produce and in what proportions?

8.11 What kinds of offspring would be produced by the following matings: $wYVv \times WwVv$; $wYvv \times Wwvv$; $WYVv \times WWVv$; $WYvv \times WwVV$; $wYvv \times wwVv$?

8.12 A red-eyed, long-winged male Drosophila is mated to a red-eyed, vestigial-winged female. They produce the following offspring:

104 red-eyed, long-winged females

99 red-eyed, vestigial-winged females

101 red-eyed, long-winged males

102 red-eyed, vestigial-winged males

What are the genotypes of the parents?

8.13 In man pseudohypertrophic muscular dystrophy is a condition in which the muscles gradually waste away, ending in death in the early teens. In some families it is dependent upon a sex-linked recessive gene. This type occurs only in boys and has never been recorded in girls. Why is it not to be expected in girls?

8.14 Why does the sex-linked gene for pseudohypertrophic muscular dystrophy not become eliminated from the human race, since all boys showing the trait die before reaching maturity?

8.15 In a certain family there are two boys and two girls. One of the boys develops pseudohypertrophic muscular dystrophy, and dies at 14 years of age. The other boy and the two girls grow up and marry. What are the chances of their offspring showing this condition?

8.16 What proportion of human offspring receives an X-chromosome from the mother? An X-chromosome from the father? An X-chromosome from the mother and a Y-chromosome from the father?

8.17 Ichthyosis hystrix gravior (a greatly thickened horny condition of the skin) is a rare human abnormality, but in the single extensive pedigree which has been studied it occurs only in males. All the sons of each affected father have the condition. Females are not only unaffected, but never transmit the gene for this defect. Can you suggest a possible explanation for this curious and unusual type of inheritance?

8.18 In man aniridia (a type of blindness) is due to a dominant gene. Optic atrophy (another type of blindness) is due to a recessive sex-linked gene. A man blind from optic atrophy marries a woman blind from aniridia. Would any of their children be expected to be blind? Which type of blindness would they have?

8.19 A nonhemophilic man who is blind from aniridia but whose mother was not blind marries a nonhemophilic woman who is not blind, but whose father was hemophilic. If they have four sons, what combinations of these traits would they most probably show?

8.20 If the offspring in Problem 8.19 consisted of four daughters instead of four sons, what would these daughters most probably be like?

8.21 A normal-visioned man marries a normal-visioned woman whose father was color-blind. They have two daughters who grow up and marry. The first daughter has five sons, all normal-visioned. The second daughter has two normal-visioned daughters and a color-blind son. Diagram the family history, including the genotypes of all the individuals mentioned.

8.22 In canaries the green variety with black eyes is dependent upon a dominant sex-linked gene, B, the cinnamon variety with red eyes is due to its recessive allele, b. A cinnamon male is mated to a green female. What would be the appearance of the F_1? The F_2?

8.23 Another pair of genes in canaries consists of a dominant autosomal gene, C, resulting in a crest on the head, and its recessive allele, c, resulting in plain head. A homozygous green, crested male is mated to a cinnamon, plain female. What would be the appearance of the F_1? The F_2?

8.24 Two green, crested birds are mated and produce two offspring: a green, crested male and a cinnamon, plain female. What were the genotypes of the parents?

8.25 A green, plain male is mated to a cinnamon, crested female and they produce the following offspring: a cinnamon, crested male; a cinnamon, plain male; and two green, crested females. What were the genotypes of the parents?

8.26 Two Drosophila when crossed produce 420 offspring, of which only 141 are males. Suggest a possible genetic explanation for this result.

8.27 A sex-linked recessive lethal gene is known in poultry which produces no visible effect in the heterozygous state. What would be the sex ratio among the offspring of a male heterozygous for the lethal, crossed with normal females?

8.28 In poultry, a gene C produces Creeper in the heterozygous state but is lethal in the homozygous state. Barring is due to a dominant sex-linked gene B, nonbarred to its recessive allele b. A Creeper male homozygous for barring is mated with a Creeper nonbarred female. What kinds of offspring would they be expected to produce, and in what proportions?

8.29 A Creeper nonbarred male is mated to a normal barred female. What kinds of chicks could they produce and in what proportions?

8.30 A Creeper male heterozygous for the barring gene is mated to a Creeper nonbarred female. What offspring would be expected?

8.31 Two birds are mated and produce the following offspring: $\frac{1}{6}$ normal nonbarred females, $\frac{1}{6}$ normal barred males, $\frac{2}{6}$ Creeper nonbarred females, $\frac{2}{6}$ Creeper barred males. What were the genotypes and phenotypes of the parents?

8.32 In Drosophila what kinds of offspring could be produced from a mating of the following exceptional flies? wYY male $\times$ Ww female; wYY male $\times$ WwY female.

REFERENCES

BRIDGES, C. B., *Genetics* **1**:1, 107 (1916).

BRINKHOUS, K. M., *Bull. N.Y. Acad. Med.* **30**:325 (1954).

HALDANE, J. B. S., *Modern Quarterly* **2**:129 (1938).

ILTIS, H., *Jour. Hered.* **39**:113 (1948).

JULL, M. A., *Poultry Breeding, 3rd ed.* New York, John Wiley and Sons (1952).

MERSKY, C., *Quart. Jour. Med.* **20**:299 (1951).

MORGAN, T. H., *Science* **32**:120 (1910); *Amer. Nat.* **45**:65 (1911).

MORGAN, T. H., BRIDGES, C. B., and STURTEVANT, A. H., "The Genetics of Drosophila." *Bibl. Genetica* **2**:1–262 (1925).

CHAPTER NINE

Sex-influenced and sex-limited characters

Sex-influenced characters

In the genes we have discussed up to this point, we have found two possible relationships between alleles. Either there was dominance, so that one allele produced its characteristic effect even in the presence of the other, or else dominance was lacking, so that the heterozygote showed a "blending" effect. When dominance occurred, however, it was the same in one sex as in the other, that is, a single dose of the dominant allele produced the effect in males and females alike. In this section we shall discuss genes in which the dominance depends on the sex of the individual.

In Ayrshire cattle the animals are spotted, either red-and-white or mahogany-and-white (Fig. 9.1). Crosses between homozygous red-and-white and homozygous mahogany-and-white animals result in peculiar and interesting ratios. What happens is this:

Parents   mahogany-and-white male × red-and-white female

F_1 males — mahogany-and-white
             females — red-and-white

F_2 males — 3 mahogany-and-white : 1 red-and-white
             females — 3 red-and-white : 1 mahogany-and-white

The reciprocal cross between a red-and-white male and a mahogany-and-white female gives identical results. It may be seen that the character is in some way associated with sex yet it is not sex-linked, as it does not conform to sex-linked inheritance which we studied in Chapter 8. Let us further analyze this cross.

If we consider only the males we see that mahogany-and-white acts as a dominant, since the F_1 males are mahogany-and-white, and the F_2 males show a ratio of three mahogany-and-white to one red-and-white. But when we consider only the females, red-and-white appears to be dominant, as the F_1 females are all red-and-white, while the F_2 females give a ratio of three red-and-white to one mahogany-and-white. In this pair of alleles one seems to be dominant in males and the other in females.

Other such genes are known in various animals. In diagraming crosses involving such genes, we commonly let the capital letter represent the gene which is dominant in males. Letting M represent the gene for mahogany-and-white, and m the gene for red-and-white, and remembering that they are sex-influenced, we expect the genotypes to exhibit traits as follows:

GENOTYPE	MALES	FEMALES
MM	mahogany-and-white	mahogany-and-white
Mm	mahogany-and-white	red-and-white
mm	red-and-white	red-and-white

On this basis both males and females of the genotype MM would be mahogany-and-white, since the gene M can produce only this color. Likewise males and females of the constitution mm would be red-and-white, since the gene m produces this color. In the heterozygote Mm, however, the color will depend on which one is dominant. Here

Fig. 9.1   Color in Ayrshire cattle, the result of sex influence on gene action.   Top, a mahogany-and-white cow. Bottom, left, her mahogany-and-white son. Bottom, right, her red-and-white daughter. Red-and-white offspring of mahogany-and-white cows are always females, whereas mahogany-and-white may occur in both male and female offspring.

the sexes differ, *M* being dominant in males and producing the mahogany-and-white condition, while *m* is dominant in females, making them red-and-white. In reading a ratio in which sex-influenced alleles are concerned it is necessary to *read it twice*, once for males and once for females. Let us diagram a cross between a mahogany-and-white male and a red-and-white female.

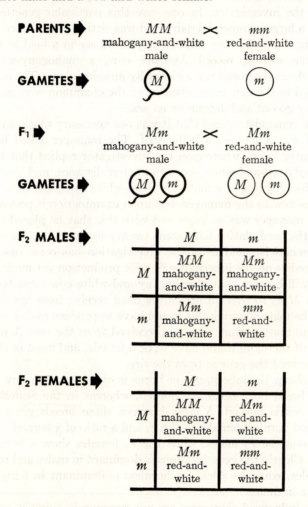

PARENTS ➡   *MM* ✕ *mm*
mahogany-and-white male   red-and-white female

GAMETES ➡   (*M*)   (*m*)

F₁ ➡   *Mm* ✕ *Mm*
mahogany-and-white male   red-and-white female

GAMETES ➡   (*M*)(*m*)   (*M*)(*m*)

F₂ MALES ➡

	M	*m*
M	*MM* mahogany-and-white	*Mm* mahogany-and-white
m	*Mm* mahogany-and-white	*mm* red-and-white

F₂ FEMALES ➡

	M	*m*
M	*MM* mahogany-and-white	*Mm* red-and-white
m	*Mm* red-and-white	*mm* red-and-white

The theoretical results on this basis agree with the results actually obtained, and leave no doubt that the genes behave in such a way that one of them is dominant in males, the other in females. Work out for yourself a diagram of the reciprocal cross.

An interesting anecdote regarding this sex-influenced character, incidentally illustrating the practical importance of a knowledge of genetics, is told by an investigator of the inheritance of milk production.* In the study of the genetics of milk production it would be extremely valuable to have access to the records of large commercial herds where a system of breeding has been followed for a long time with a large number of animals. The owners of such herds are in general quite jealous of their records and they are not always available to the investigator. In one case this particular geneticist was visiting a large commercial dairy and was sitting in the office talking to the manager. As they talked, they could see in a field in the distance the world's record Ayrshire cow, a mahogany-and-white animal. A new-born calf was awkwardly jumping about. The manager, interested in the new-born offspring of the champion cow, suggested that they go out and determine its sex.

The geneticist replied that it was not necessary to go out to see; the calf was a female, a heifer calf. The manager asked how the investigator knew, whereupon the investigator replied that the calf was clearly red-and-white, even from that distance, and that a red-and-white offspring of a mahogany-and-white cow must be a female. This was new to the manager, but upon examination it proved to be so. The manager was so impressed with this that he placed the records of the herd, dating back some twenty-five years, at the disposal of the geneticist, and from the investigation has come one of the finest studies on the inheritance of milk production yet made.

It will be seen that a mahogany-and-white cow must be of the formula MM, so that all her calves must receive from her the gene M. In the male offspring this would have to produce mahogany-and-white, no matter what gene was received from the sire. A red-and-white calf therefore would have to be a female, and must in this case have received the gene m from the sire.

In sheep the inheritance of horns is of the same nature. In the Dorset breed both sexes are horned, whereas in the Suffolk breed neither sex is horned. A cross between these breeds gives horned males and hornless females in the F_1 and a ratio of 3 horned : 1 hornless among the F_2 males, while the F_2 females show 3 hornless : 1 horned. Clearly the gene for horns is dominant in males and recessive in females, while its allele for hornless is dominant in females and recessive in males.

Sex-influenced characters are not common in animals, and none is known in plants. Several such characters have been described in man, however. They are baldness, one form of white forelock, one type of ichthyosis (a skin abnormality), absence of upper lateral incisor teeth, and Heberden's nodes (enlargement of the terminal joints of the fingers). Let us consider in detail the gene for baldness.

*Dr. E. E. Heizer.

While baldness may in some cases be due to disease such as seborrhea, syphilis, or thyroid disease, the usual types of "pattern baldness" (Fig. 9.2) seem without doubt to depend on heredity. In man, of course, we cannot make test matings, and we cannot produce F_1 and F_2 generations from known homozygous parents in order to study the type of inheritance. One of the greatest difficulties in studying human heredity is our inability to be certain in all cases whether a parent is homozygous or heterozygous for a given pair of genes. We can, however, collect family histories in man as we find them, and by a process of elimination arrive at the type of inheritance which appears to fit the facts.

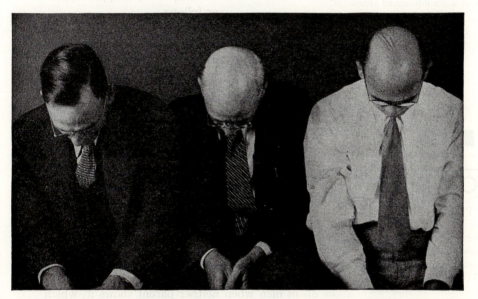

Fig. 9.2 Pattern baldness in a father and one but not the other of his two sons. The father is in the center, with one son on each side.

In the case of baldness we immediately notice several facts. First, the character is more common in men than in women. This indicates an association with sex, and we might suspect it to be due to a sex-linked recessive, like color blindness, were it not for another fact which eliminates this possibility. That fact is that when a father is bald he regularly transmits the baldness to about half of his sons. It will be remembered that in the case of a sex-linked recessive it is rarely the case that both father and son show the character. Baldness could not be due to a sex-linked dominant since no more women than men show the character.

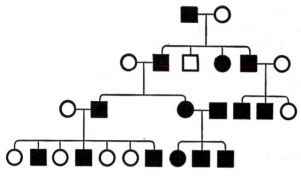

Fig 9.3 A family history of baldness, illustrating the inheritance of a sex-influenced character.

When we apply the hypothesis of sex-influenced characters to baldness, however, we find that it fits the facts admirably. Figure 9.3 shows a typical pedigree of baldness. If we let B represent a gene for baldness, and b for nonbaldness and assume that the sex influence is such that B is dominant in men and recessive in women, the genotypes appear as follows:

GENOTYPE	MEN	WOMEN
BB	bald	bald
Bb	bald	nonbald
bb	nonbald	nonbald

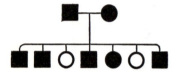

Fig. 9.4 Pedigree of baldness illustrating the sex-influenced type of inheritance, and showing that the gene for baldness could not be a sex-linked recessive. If it were, all the children would be bald. The children in this case are all over the age of forty.

Fill in the genotypes in the family in Figure 9.3 as far as possible.

Another pedigree illustrating the fact that baldness could not be sex-linked but could be sex-influenced is given in Figure 9.4. Here the parents are both bald, yet some of the daughters are not bald, although they are over forty years of age. Fill in the genotypes of this family.

When we find in human beings a character which is more common in men than in women, which can show up in men when neither parent shows it, which shows up in all the sons of a woman who has it, *and which is transmitted directly from a father to approximately half of his sons*, we are justified in assuming that the character is dependent on genes of which the expression is sex-influenced.

Sex-limited characters

We have seen that some characters are the result of sex-linked genes and some characters are sex-influenced. In this section we shall discuss still another group of traits associated with sex. These traits are due to genes which are capable of expression in one sex but not in the other, and they are known as sex-limited characters. In mammals and birds, at least, the expression of the genes involved seems to depend on the presence or absence of one of the sex hormones. The hormones, or **internal secretions,** are the products of endocrine glands, among which are the testis and ovary. These organs, in addition to producing sperms and eggs, produce secretions which get into the blood and have marked effects on various parts of the body.

There are various sex-limited characters. In the clover butterfly Gerould has shown that the males are yellow, but the females are of two sorts, yellow and white. White is dominant but can show up only in females. Letting W represent a gene for white, expressed only in females, and letting w represent its recessive allele for yellow, we find the genes acting as follows:

Genotype	Males	Females
WW	yellow	white
Ww	yellow	white
ww	yellow	yellow

The male and female types of plumage in birds present another interesting but still more complicated example of sex-limited characters. In most breeds of poultry, for instance, the plumage of the two sexes is strikingly different, the males having a showy plumage with larger comb and wattles and longer neck feathers, tail, and sickle feathers (Fig. 9.5). In some breeds, however, as the Sebright bantams,

Fig. 9.5 Brown Leghorn male (left) and female (right), showing characteristic sex differences in plumage.

both sexes are "hen-feathered" (Fig. 9.6). In still other breeds, such as the Campines and Hamburghs, both hen-feathered males and cock-feathered males occur.

Studies of this condition indicate that hen-feathering is due to a dominant gene H, and cock-feathering to its recessive allele h, which is expressed only in males. The genotypes with their corresponding phenotypes would then be as follows:

GENOTYPE	MALES	FEMALES
HH	hen-feathered	hen-feathered
Hh	hen-feathered	hen-feathered
hh	cock-feathered	hen-feathered

Ordinary breeds of poultry in which males are cock-feathered and females are hen-feathered would all be of the formula hh. Breeds in which both sexes are hen-feathered would all be of the formula HH. Breeds having both kinds of males would contain both alleles, so that some of the individuals would be HH, some Hh, and some hh. Here all the females would be hen-feathered, but only the HH and Hh males would show hen-feathering, the hh males being cock-feathered.

It is found by experimentation, however, that the above system depends upon the secretions of the sex glands. Thus removal of the testes in hen-feathered males or of the ovary (there being only one in birds) in females results in the production of cock-feathering. The gene H appears to inhibit cock-feathering in the presence of either sex hormone, that is, in normal males and females. In the absence of

Fig. 9.6 Sebright bantams. Both the male (left) and the female (right) are hen-feathered in this breed.

the sex hormone (that is, in birds whose sex glands have been removed by operation or destroyed by disease), cock-feathering can occur even though the gene *H* is present.

The allele *h* does not inhibit cock-feathering, yet cock-feathering cannot occur in the presence of the female sex hormone. Of the individuals of the formula *hh*, only males or ovariectomized females will be cock-feathered (Fig. 9.7).

Fig. 9.7 An ovariectomized female fowl, showing the development of cock-feathering. The ovary was removed when the bird was thirteen days old. The photograph was taken two years later. *Photograph courtesy of Dr. L. V. Domm*

An interesting sex-limited character has been described in the red junglefowl, the ancestor of domestic chickens. The normal down of baby junglefowl chicks is striped. A recessive mutation *s* results in yellowish white down (Fig. 9.8). The mutation expresses itself in both sexes in the down color, but as the adult plumage appears, the character behaves as sex-limited. Females of the genotype *ss* develop a creamy buff plumage, but males of this genotype develop the normal plumage, indistinguishable from that of males which are *SS* or *Ss* (Figs. 9.9 and 9.10).

Secondary sex characters in general, including not only physical traits but differential response of the nervous system, may very well depend upon genes of which the expression is sex-limited. Any gene for which both sexes are alike in constitution, but which can only express itself in one sex, would give rise to a sexual dimorphism, that is, a relatively constant difference between the sexes. Thus, in human

Fig. 9.8 Chicks of the red junglefowl. Left, wild-type down color (*SS*). Right, a chick of the genotype *ss*, showing yellowish white down. Chicks of both sexes show this down color when of the genotype *ss*. Compare with Figures 9.9 and 9.10. *From Morejohn in the Journal of Heredity*

Fig. 9.9   Adult red junglefowl of the genotype *SS*, showing wild-type adult plumage. Left, female, right, male. *Courtesy Dr. Victor Morejohn*

beings, men have beards but women normally do not. Yet Trotter, who made a study of the occurrence of hairs in the two sexes, found no significant difference in the actual number of hairs per unit area in men and women, but only a difference in the development of the hairs. Undoubtedly genes, the expression of which is controlled by the secretions of the endocrine glands, account for this character. Abnormalities in the development of the endocrine glands or in the segregation of the chromosomes might cause variations in characters such as these.

Fig. 9.10 Adult red junglefowl of the genotype *ss*. Left, female, showing the sex-limited mutant character; right, male, showing wild-type plumage in spite of the mutant genotype. *Courtesy Dr. Victor Morejohn*

Studies on the differential effects of the various hormones, the differential responses of somatic tissue, including nervous tissue, to varying thresholds of the hormones, and the differential development of sex-limited characters are among the most actively investigated problems in biology at the present time. A further discussion of some of these problems will be found in the chapter on sex determination (Chapter 23).

In this chapter we have established the fact that certain geno-types, even homozygous genotypes, may reach expression in one sex, but may normally fail to reach expression in the other sex.

PROBLEMS

9.1 A bald man whose father was not bald marries a nonbald woman whose mother was bald. What are the genotypes of these two people in regard to the genes for baldness and nonbaldness? What kinds of children can they have in regard to these characters?

9.2 A nonbald, normal-visioned man marries a nonbald, normal-visioned woman whose father was color-blind and whose mother was bald. What kinds of offspring may they have, and in what proportions?

9.3 A nonbald man marries a nonbald woman. They have a son and a daughter. At the age of thirty-five the son becomes bald. What are the chances that the daughter will also become bald because of her genetic constitution?

9.4 A red-and-white Ayrshire cow whose mother was mahogany-and-white is bred to a red-and-white Ayrshire bull. If she produces a male calf, what are the chances that it will be mahogany-and-white? If the calf is a female, what are the chances that it will be mahogany-and-white?

9.5 Outline the breeding procedure necessary to establish a homozygous mahogany-and-white Ayrshire herd.

9.6 Outline the breeding procedure necessary to establish a homozygous red-and-white Ayrshire herd.

9.7 In sheep the sex-influenced character "horns" is the result of a gene H, and "hornlessness" of a gene h. White is due to a dominant gene W, and black to its recessive allele w. A homozygous horned white ram is crossed with a homozygous hornless black ewe. What would be the phenotypes of the F_1 and the F_2 from this cross?

9.8 A hornless white ram is bred to a hornless white ewe. Their offspring is a horned black male. If they produce further offspring, what characters would these offspring be expected to exhibit and in what proportions?

9.9 What kinds of offspring in what proportions would be expected to result from the following matings in sheep? $HhWw$ male $\times$ $hhww$ female; $hhww$ male $\times$ $HhWw$ female; $Hhww$ male $\times$ $hhww$ female; $HHWW$ male $\times$ $HHWW$ female; $hhww$ male $\times$ $HhWW$ female.

9.10 A farmer obtains a hornless white ram and several horned white ewes. Both black and white lambs are born in his flock the first year. From this beginning how could he establish a homozygous hornless white flock?

In the accompanying human pedigree a certain character is represented by the solid squares and circles. Answer the following questions about this character:

9.11 Could this be a sex-influenced character due to a gene dominant in males and recessive in females?

9.12 Could the character in the foregoing pedigree be due to a simple dominant gene?

9.13 Could it be due to a simple recessive gene?

9.14 Could it be due to a recessive sex-linked gene?

9.15 Could it be due to a dominant sex-linked gene?

A second human pedigree is illustrated in the accompanying diagram. Answer the following questions about the character shown by solid symbols:

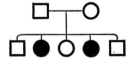

9.16 Could this be a sex-influenced character due to a gene dominant in males and recessive in females?

9.17 Could it be due to a sex-linked recessive gene?

9.18 Could it be due to a sex-linked dominant gene?

9.19 Could it be due to a simple recessive gene?

9.20 Could it be due to a simple dominant gene?

The accompanying diagram illustrates a third human pedigree. Again answer the following questions about the character shown:

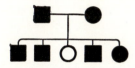

9.21 Could this be a sex-influenced character due to a gene dominant in males and recessive in females?

9.22 Could it be due to a sex-linked recessive gene?

9.23 Could it be due to a sex-linked dominant gene?

9.24 Could it be due to a simple dominant gene?

9.25 Could it be due to a simple recessive gene?

9.26 Asdell and Smith have concluded that in goats beardedness is a sex-influenced character, the gene being dominant in males and recessive in females. Likewise in goats Wassin has suggested that short ears and long ears depend upon a single pair of genes, neither being dominant, so that the heterozygote is intermediate-eared. Using the symbols B and b for bearded and nonbearded and L and l for short and long ears, respectively, answer this and the following four questions about goats: What are the possible genotypes of bearded long-eared males? Of nonbearded short-eared females?

9.27 A nonbearded long-eared male is mated to a bearded short-eared female.

What are the expected ratios in the F_1 and F_2 of this cross?

9.28 What results would be expected if the F_1 females from the above cross were mated to nonbearded long-eared males?

9.29 A nonbearded intermediate-eared male is mated each year for four years to a nonbearded long-eared female, the mother of which was bearded. If they have four female offspring, these offspring would most probably have what characters?

9.30 If the above series of matings had resulted in four male offspring, what would be the most probable distribution of characters among these offspring?

9.31 Why could the results of Gerould on clover butterflies, mentioned in this chapter, not be explained on the basis of a sex-linked pair of genes?

9.32 Using data contained in this chapter, what would be the phenotypes of the parents and what kinds of offspring would they produce, in the following crosses in clover butterflies? WW male $\times$ ww female; WW male $\times$ Ww female; Ww male $\times$ Ww female; Ww male $\times$ ww female; ww male $\times$ WW female.

9.33 A hen-feathered male bird crossed with a hen-feathered female produces seven hen-feathered males, two cock-feathered males, and eight hen-feathered females. What are the probable genotypes of the parents?

9.34 In the Hamburgh breed of poultry both cock-feathered and hen-feathered males occur. The females all show hen-feathering. Starting with a mixed flock of Hamburghs, how would you go about establishing a strain in which the males were always cock-feathered?

9.35 In the Sebright Bantams both males and females are hen-feathered. In the Rose-comb Bantams the males are cock-feathered and the females hen-feathered. If a Sebright Bantam male were crossed with a Rose-comb Bantam female, what would be the appearance of the F_1? Of the F_2?

9.36 If the sex hormones are shown to be concerned in the appearance of a character which exhibits sexual dimorphism, would this invalidate the hypothesis of a genetic basis for the character? Explain.

9.37 The male lion has a well-developed mane which the female does not have. How could you account for this fact on a genetic basis?

9.38 How does the inheritance of such a character as the mane of the male lion differ from the inheritance of a sex-linked character? Of a sex-influenced character?

9.39 Sebright Bantams have rose combs as well as hen-feathering in both sexes. Cochin Bantams have single combs, and the males are cock-feathered. If a Sebright Bantam male were crossed with a Cochin Bantam female, what would be the appearance of the F_1 and the F_2 in regard to feathering and combs?

9.40 A cock-feathered Rose-comb male Bantam is mated to a hen-feathered rose-comb female. Their offspring are as follows: 2 hen-feathered rose-comb males, 5 hen-feathered rose-comb females, 1 hen-feathered single-comb male, 2 hen-feathered single-comb females, 4 cock-feathered rose-comb males, and 1 cock-feathered single-comb male. What were the genotypes of the parents?

REFERENCES

ALLEN, E., *Sex and Internal Secretions.* Baltimore, The Williams and Wilkins Co. (1939).

DOMM, L. V., *Proc. Soc. Exper. Biol. and Med.* **22**:28 (1924), *Jour. Exper. Zoöl.* **48**:31 (1927); *Anat. Rec.* **41**:27, 43 (1928); *Proc. Soc. Exper. Biol. and Med.* **26**:338 (1929).

GEROULD, J. H., *Amer. Nat.* **45**:257 (1911); *Genetics* **8**:495 (1923).

JULL, M. A., and QUINN, J. P., *Jour. Hered.* **21**:176 (1930).

MOREJOHN, G. V., *Jour. Hered.* **44**:47 (1953).

MORGAN, T. H., *Biol. Bull.* **39**:257 (1920).

STECHER, R. M., and HERSH, H. H., *Jour. Clinical Investigation* **23**:699 (1944).

STERN, C., *Biol. Zentralbl.* **46**:344 (1926).

CHAPTER TEN

Linkage

One of the first principles of heredity that we learned — a principle discovered by Mendel himself — was that of random assortment. We have found that in an individual heterozygous for two pairs of genes, of the formula $AaBb$, the two pairs of genes assort at random; that is A may go into a germ cell with B or with b, with equal likelihood, even though the individual in question may have inherited A and B (for example) together from the same parent. The four kinds of gametes produced, AB, Ab, aB, ab are thus formed in equal numbers.

We have also learned (Chapter 4) the reason for random assortment. During meiosis, the members of different chromosome pairs are segregated into the gametes independently of one another; different pairs of allelic genes, such as A,a and B,b, carried on different pairs of chromosomes, therefore likewise show independent segregation.

But, as the student has perhaps already asked himself, what if two different pairs of alleles are carried *on the same chromosome pair?* In that case, conceivably you might expect that the law of independent assortment would not hold. In fact, exceptions to this rule were encountered quite early in the history of genetics (about 1906) although it was not until several years later that their significance in terms of the chromosome theory was understood. Let us consider what might happen when two pairs of alleles are located on the same pair of chromosomes.

You will remember that the "standard" F_2 ratio, resulting from mating together the F_1 progeny of a cross such as $AABB \times aabb$ (or $AAbb \times aaBB$) is $9\ A\text{-}B\text{-} : 3\ A\text{-}bb : 3\ aaB\text{-} : 1\ aabb$. You should remember also that this F_2 ratio results from the fact that the A,a alleles assort independently of the B,b alleles, and that independent assortment means that the $AaBb$ individuals of the F_1 generation produce gametes in the ratio $1\ AB : 1\ Ab : 1\ aB : 1\ ab$. Obviously, then, if two pairs of alleles *do not* assort at random, we should expect to find a disturbance of the $1:1:1:1$ ratio among the gametes of individuals heterozygous for both of them, and a consequent disturbance in the F_2 ratio.

We shall later be able to see just how the F_2 ratio would be affected by a failure of random assortment. Generally, however, it is much easier to see how the two pairs of alleles are distributed among the gametes by making use of a **test cross.** Since the test cross is a very useful tool in genetics, let us illustrate it with a concrete example. To start with, let us consider a case involving two pairs of genes which, like those we have dealt with earlier (Chapters 5 and 6), are in different chromosome pairs.

In Drosophila numerous genes affect the color of the body. Wild type flies have gray bodies, but there is a mutant form in which the body is black. Crosses between gray and black give all gray in the F_1 and a ratio of three gray to one black in the F_2. We know, therefore, that the genes for gray and for black are allelic, with the gene for gray dominant.

Another mutation in Drosophila changes the red eyes to sepia. Again crosses between red and sepia give all red in the F_1 and a ratio of three red to one sepia in the F_2. These genes are also allelic, red being dominant. A cross involving both black and sepia would thus be a two-pair cross. Let us cross a fly which is normal except for having a black body with one which is normal except for having sepia eyes. Letting B represent a gene for gray body, and b its allele for black, and letting S represent a gene for red eyes, and s its allele for sepia, our cross would be as illustrated in the diagram below.

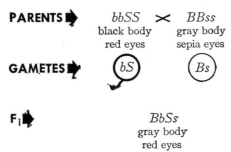

PARENTS → *bbSS* ✕ *BBss*
black body   gray body
red eyes   sepia eyes

GAMETES → (*bS*)   (*Bs*)

F₁ → *BbSs*
gray body
red eyes

If we were to mate two F_1 individuals we would, of course, obtain the familiar $9:3:3:1$ ratio. Instead, however, we shall make a test cross. This is a cross *in which an individual heterozygous for any number of genes* (here two pairs) *is mated to one which is homozygous for each recessive allele.* In this case, we shall mate an F_1 male, *BbSs*, to a female double recessive, *bbss*.

The progeny of our test cross, as seen from the next diagram, are of four types which occur in equal numbers. That is, the phenotype ratio resulting from a test cross in which there is random assortment of two pairs of alleles is 1:1:1:1, *which is exactly the same as the ratio among the different kinds of gametes produced by the BbSs parent.* Moreover, we can tell by direct examination what type of sperm produced each kind of offspring. Thus, *BS* sperms uniting with *bs* eggs were responsible for the gray-bodied, red-eyed flies, *Bs* sperms produced the gray-bodied sepia-eyed offspring, *bS* sperms produced those that are black-bodied red-eyed, and *bs* sperms those with black body, sepia eyes. Similarly, we can tell directly what kind of egg from a *BbSs* female has produced each type of offspring from a test cross in which we have mated a *BbSs* female to a *bbss* male. The test cross is unique in this respect.

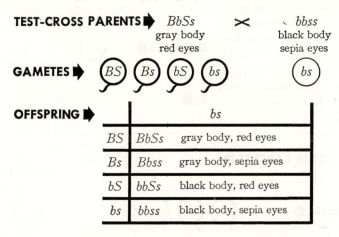

Now let us reflect a moment. If genes are carried on chromosomes, how can random assortment occur? Obviously it can happen if the different pairs of genes are carried on different pairs of chromosomes. But if two pairs of genes are on the *same* pair of chromosomes, it would seem that they should stick together; that is, wherever each chromosome of the pair went both genes in it would have to go. To show random assortment, then, the two pairs of genes would have to be on different pairs of chromosomes.

But we know more than five hundred pairs of genes in Drosophila, and there are only four pairs of chromosomes. There must therefore be many pairs of genes on each chromosome pair. If this be so, random assortment cannot always occur; we should find some exceptions to it. In fact, as we have already noted, we do find exceptions. And in these cases, the breeding results indicate that certain genes of different allelic pairs *tend to stick together in the way in which they entered the cross.* We call such genes **linked genes,** and we shall provide abundant evidence that when **linkage** is observed, the pairs of genes involved are in fact located on the same pair of chromosomes. Let us now examine a cross in which the effects of linkage can be seen.

In Drosophila there is, as we have seen, a pair of alleles, B and b, for gray and for black body, respectively. There is also a pair of alleles, V and v, affecting the length of the wings. The gene V is necessary for normal wing length while vv produces short stumpy wings known as vestigial. Thus VV and Vv flies are normal-winged, and vv flies are vestigial-winged (Fig. 8.1).

If now we make a two-pair cross involving body color and wing length, we may cross a black-bodied fly with a vestigial-winged fly. The cross would be as follows:

Now let us cross one of the heterozygous gray-bodied long-winged F_1 males to a black-bodied vestigial-winged female: in other words let us make a test cross. Such a cross would be diagramed as follows:

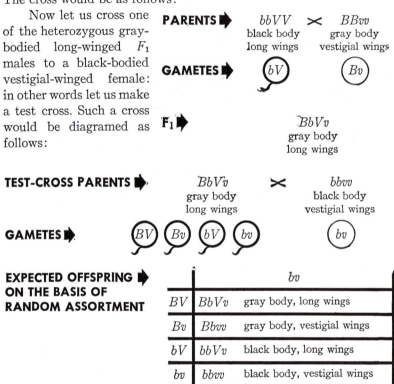

PARENTS → $bbVV$ × $BBvv$
black body   gray body
long wings   vestigial wings

GAMETES → bV Bv

F₁ → $BbVv$
gray body
long wings

TEST-CROSS PARENTS → $BbVv$ × $bbvv$
gray body   black body
long wings   vestigial wings

GAMETES → BV Bv bV bv bv

EXPECTED OFFSPRING ON THE BASIS OF RANDOM ASSORTMENT →

	bv	
BV	$BbVv$	gray body, long wings
Bv	$Bbvv$	gray body, vestigial wings
bV	$bbVv$	black body, long wings
bv	$bbvv$	black body, vestigial wings

From the above diagram we can see that, if the two pairs of genes assorted at random, we should expect the test-cross ratio of 1:1:1:1, that is, equal numbers of the four kinds of offspring. When we make the test cross in this case, however, we do not obtain the expected ratio at all. We find that no gray-bodied long-winged flies appear, nor do we obtain any black-bodied vestigial-winged flies.

Half of the offspring are black-bodied long-winged and half are gray-bodied vestigial-winged. We note that these are just like the original parents with which we started the cross in the beginning.

What does this result mean? Looking at the diagram we readily see that no gametes of the BV or bv sorts could have been produced by the F_1 male. Only gametes of the types bV and Bv were produced. *These gametes are exactly like the gametes that united and produced the F_1 male.* In other words the genes b and V came into the cross together and stayed together in forming gametes; so also did B and v. *Random assortment did not occur.* What might cause this? Obviously the possibility that the genes are on the same chromosome. If b and V were on the same chromosome we should expect that wherever gene b went, gene V would go also. Let us re-examine our cross on this basis.

Assuming that the two pairs of genes are on the same chromosome pair, let us write the genotype formula in a way which indicates this, so that whenever we see the genotype we will remember that these genes are linked. Instead of writing the formula for the black-bodied long-winged fly as $bbVV$, let us put the linked genes in parentheses thus: $(bV)(bV)$. The same genes are present as before, but now they are written in such a way that we can easily remember which two are on the same chromosome. The relationships of the genes of a Drosophila heterozygous for red and sepia eyes, gray and black body, and long and vestigial wings are shown in Figure 10.1.

Now let us rediagram our cross between a black-bodied long-winged fly and a gray-bodied vestigial-winged fly, writing the symbols on the assumption that the genes are linked.

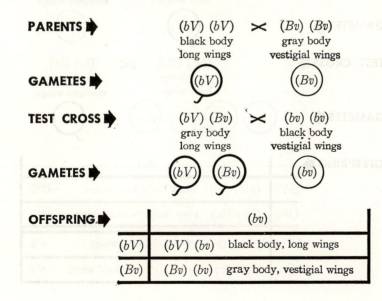

PARENTS ▶ $(bV)(bV)$ ✕ $(Bv)(Bv)$
black body / gray body
long wings / vestigial wings

GAMETES ▶ (bV) (Bv)

TEST CROSS ▶ $(bV)(Bv)$ ✕ $(bv)(bv)$
gray body / black body
long wings / vestigial wings

GAMETES ▶ (bV) (Bv) (bv)

OFFSPRING ▶

	(bv)	
(bV)	$(bV)(bv)$	black body, long wings
(Bv)	$(Bv)(bv)$	gray body, vestigial wings

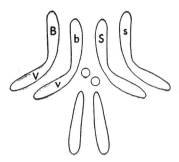

Fig. 10.1 Diagram of the chromosomes of Drosophila, showing the relationships of the genes for red and sepia eyes, gray and black body, and long and vestigial wings.

From this it is easy to see why we get only black-bodied long-winged flies and gray-bodied vestigial-winged flies from the test cross. Only two kinds of sperms are formed because the two genes on each chromosome always go together.

If linkage were always as simple as this we should have no trouble understanding it and working with it. Linkage is not always complete, however, as it is in this case. As a matter of fact, it is very rarely thus. Only in the male of Drosophila and in a few other cases do genes on the same chromosome stick completely together. In other cases they *tend* to stay together, but are able to separate under certain conditions.

Let us make the reciprocal test cross involving the same genes as the cross we have just discussed. That is, instead of mating an F_1 male to a double recessive female, let us mate an F_1 *female* to a double recessive *male*. The results of this cross are shown in the diagram below. In this cross we do get all four possible types of offspring, but not in equal numbers. We find that there are more of the original parent types than of the new types. Evidently all four types of eggs, *bV*, *Vb*, *BV*, and *bv* must have been produced, in spite of the fact that the genes are linked, although they have not been produced in equal numbers.

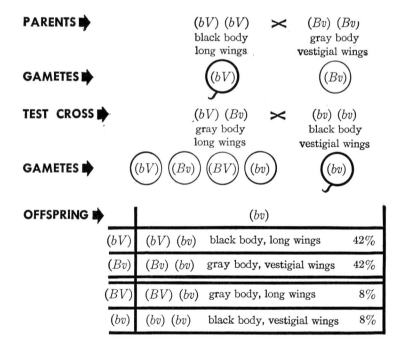

PARENTS ➡		(bV) (bV) black body long wings	✕	(Bv) (Bv) gray body vestigial wings	
GAMETES ➡		(bV)		(Bv)	
TEST CROSS ➡		(bV) (Bv) gray body long wings	✕	(bv) (bv) black body vestigial wings	
GAMETES ➡		(bV) (Bv) (BV) (bv)		(bv)	

OFFSPRING ➡		(bv)	
(bV)	(bV) (bv)	black body, long wings	42%
(Bv)	(Bv) (bv)	gray body, vestigial wings	42%
(BV)	(BV) (bv)	gray body, long wings	8%
(bv)	(bv) (bv)	black body, vestigial wings	8%

In the diagram, the double line separates the eggs and the off-spring which contain the original *parental combinations* of genes (*bV*) and (*Bv*), from those which contain *recombinations* of these same genes. We see that the parental combinations of genes are present in a majority of the eggs (84 per cent) while the new combinations occur in only 16 per cent. It would appear, then, that in the formation of most of the eggs the two linked genes stayed together, but that in the formation of a smaller proportion they somehow traded partners. The process which produces the new combinations of linked genes, such as are found in the (*BV*) and (*bv*) eggs in the present example, is called **crossing over.** The gametes containing the new combinations are known as **crossover** or **recombination gametes.** The gametes in which the linked genes remain in their original combinations, here the (*bV*) and (*Bv*) eggs, are called **noncrossover gametes.**

Now we have just seen the genetic results of crossing over, as they are observed in breeding tests involving certain pairs of allelic genes. The question immediately arises, what can be the *physical basis* of crossing over? Can it be explained in terms of chromosome behavior? If linkage between the two genes is due to the fact that they are both on one chromosome of a homologous pair, while their alleles are on the other, then crossing over would seem to require an exchange of parts between the two homologous chromosomes. Actually, we know that this does take place.

You should recall that near the beginning of the first of the two *meiotic* divisions involved in the maturation of the gametes (Chapter 4) the two members of each pair of chromosomes come into side-by-side contact. Each chromosome then becomes duplicated, so that a tetrad is formed, composed of four chromatids. In the next chapter, we shall show that, at some time during this process, there are actual exchanges of parts between homologous chromatids in the tetrad, and that these exchanges in fact are responsible for the genetic consequences of crossing over.

If the chromosomes of a pair exchange homologous parts of their lengths, the genes on the traded portions will be exchanged too. This results in new combinations such as are produced by random assortment, although the new combinations are not formed as readily nor as often by crossing over as by random assortment.

Linkage, then, is an exception to Mendel's principle of random assortment and occurs because more than one allelic pair of genes is carried on the same pair of chromosomes. Crossing over is in the same way an exception to linkage and occurs because genes may become reassorted (though not at random) even though they are linked, through exchange of material between homologous chromosomes. Mendel did not discover linkage because he happened to use genes which were on different pairs of chromosomes.

Some of this may seem a bit complicated, but another example, worked out in the light of the above explanation, should help to clear it up. Let us make a two-pair cross in rabbits and find out whether or not the two pairs of genes are linked.

In rabbits we know a pair of alleles affecting the distribution of coat color. We may let S represent a dominant gene for spotting and s represent its recessive allele for solid color. Another pair of alleles consists of a dominant gene, L, for short hair and its recessive, l, for long hair. The phenotypes produced by these genes are shown in Figures 17.4 and 17.5. Let us discover whether or not these two pairs of genes are linked.

We should do this by making a cross between, let us say, a spotted short-haired rabbit and a solid-colored long-haired rabbit and then making a test cross. If the genes are *not* linked, we should expect equal numbers of the four test-cross types of offspring. If, however, the genes *are* linked, there will be more of the parental types and fewer of the new forms. Let us diagram the cross used for the test, writing the symbols in parentheses as though the genes were linked, even before we know whether or not they are actually linked. In rabbits, as in all higher animals, we find crossing over in both sexes; hence it does not matter whether we use F_1 males or females in the test cross. The cross is diagramed below.

PARENTS ➡
(SL) (SL) ✕ (sl) (sl)
spotted / short-haired
solid-colored / long-haired

GAMETES ➡
(SL)
(sl)

TEST CROSS ➡
(SL) (sl) ✕ (sl) (sl)
spotted / short-haired
solid-colored / long-haired

GAMETES ➡
(SL) (sl) (Sl) (sL)
(sl)
noncrossover gametes / crossover gametes

OFFSPRING ➡		(sl)	Expected ratio if not linked	Expected ratio if linked
non-crossovers	(SL)	(SL) (sl) spotted, short-haired	50%	More than 50%
	(sl)	(sl) (sl) solid-colored, long-haired		
crossovers	(Sl)	(Sl) (sl) spotted, long-haired	50%	Less than 50%
	(sL)	(sL) (sl) solid-colored, short-haired		

From this diagram we can readily see that if the genes are not linked, that is, if random assortment occurs, we should expect equal numbers of the four kinds of offspring from the test cross. To put it in other words, we should expect 50 per cent of the test-cross offspring to be of the parental types, and 50 per cent to be of the new combinations. (It should be kept in mind, of course, that the laws of probability apply here as elsewhere, and that, as was shown in Chapter 7 the smaller the number of offspring, the greater the deviation may be without being significant.) However, if the genes are linked they will not assort at random, and the original arrangement of the genes will tend to hold, changing only where crossing over has occurred. There will therefore be more than 50 per cent of the test-cross offspring like the parental types and less than 50 per cent of the new combinations. In this particular cross we find 88 per cent of the offspring to be like the parental types and only 12 per cent of them to be of the new types. Obviously the genes did not assort at random; they are therefore linked, with 12 per cent crossing over.

To show how linkage affects the F_2 ratio and to illustrate by comparison the value of the test cross in linkage determinations, let us see what the F_2 would be like in this rabbit cross. We must remember that the F_1 individuals produce four kinds of germ cells, but not in equal numbers. Gametes of the types (SL) and (sl) make up 88 per cent of the germ cells produced by an F_1 rabbit in this cross, and gametes of the types (Sl) and (sL) make up but 12 per cent of the total. The cross worked out to the F_2 would be as shown on p. 134.

By adding up the percentages of the various kinds of offspring, we see that instead of the typical ratio of 9:3:3:1, it is roughly 11:1:1:3. The F_2 ratio is thus considerably modified. Instead of only one out of sixteen F_2 individuals being double recessive, as in random assortment, about one out of every five is of this type. There are more F_2 individuals showing both dominants and both recessives than would be expected, and fewer showing only one or the other dominant. The calculation of the exact amount of crossing over from F_2 ratios is more complicated than from test-cross data, as you will find out if you attempt it. Methods for doing it have been worked out, however; they will be found in the works by Immer and by Mather cited in the references at the end of this chapter.

The test cross, then, is the ideal method of studying linkage. In human beings where we cannot make test crosses to order, special statistical methods have been devised for detecting linkage and measuring crossing over. Some of these are discussed in the little book by Mather listed in the references.

You may recall from an earlier chapter (Chapter 8) that in man both hemophilia and color blindness are sex linked. We interpreted this to mean that the gene for hemophilia, h, (recessive to H, non-

| PARENTS ➡ | (SL) (SL)
spotted
short-haired | ✕ | (sl) (sl)
solid-colored
long-haired |

GAMETES ➡   (SL)   (sl)

F₁ ➡   (SL) (sl) ✕ (SL) (sl)

GAMETES ➡ (SL) (sl) (Sl) (sL)   (SL) (sl) (Sl) (sL)

| noncrossovers 88% | crossovers 12% | noncrossovers 88% | crossovers 12% |

F₂ ➡

	.44 (SL)	.44 (sl)	.06 (Sl)	.06 (sL)
.44 (SL)	.194 (SL) (SL)	.194 (SL) (sl)	.026 (SL) (Sl)	.026 (SL) (sL)
.44 (sl)	.194 (SL) (sl)	.194 (sl) (sl)	.026 (Sl) (sl)	.026 (sL) (sl)
.06 (Sl)	.026 (SL) (Sl)	.026 (Sl) (sl)	.004 (Sl) (Sl)	.004 (Sl) (sL)
.06 (sL)	.026 (SL) (sL)	.026 (sL) (sl)	.004 (Sl) (sL)	.004 (sL) (sL)

hemophilic) is carried on the X-chromosome, and that the gene for color blindness, c, (recessive to C for normal color vision) is also carried on the X-chromosome. If this interpretation is correct, we would expect the H,h alleles and C,c alleles to show linkage with each other.

Now a little consideration will show that linkage between two genes which are both *on the X-chromosome* can be detected in the *sons* of mothers who are heterozygous for both of the genes, *without the necessity of a test cross.*

Remember that a father contributes no X-chromosome to a son. Therefore, direct examination of the sons of a doubly heterozygous mother will show what kind of X-chromosome each son has received from her. If the mother's formula is (Hc)(hC), for example, noncrossover sons would be either (Hc)Y, that is, nonhemophilic but color-blind, or (hC)Y, having hemophilia, but with normal color vision; crossover sons would be (HC)Y, nonhemophilic with normal color vision, or (hc)Y, both hemophilic and color-blind. By taking advantage of this principle, it has been possible to demonstrate that there is in fact linkage between the *H,h* and *C,c* alleles. Crossing over is also found between them (see below) and Haldane and Smith calculate that about 10 per cent of the offspring of doubly heterozygous females are crossovers.

Figure 10.2 shows part of a pedigree in which we are able to identify an individual (III.2) who has certainly been produced from a crossover gamete. After a little study of the figure, you should be able to see how it was possible to work out the genotypes of all the individuals shown on the chart, but not possible to be sure whether some females were (*hC*)(*HC*) or (*hC*)(*Hc*). The mother, II.5, must have had the formula (*hC*)(*Hc*): the only X-chromosome she could receive from her father carries the (*hC*) combination; and the fact that she is neither hemophilic nor color-blind, yet transmits both the *h* and the *c* genes, tells us that her other X-chromosome was (*Hc*). Her (*hc*)Y son (III.2), therefore, could have been produced only as a result of crossing over between the (*hC*) and (*Hc*) chromosomes of his mother. No other mother in the pedigree is doubly heterozygous, so this is the only individual on the chart that gives any information on linkage or crossing over.

In the human species, the detection and measurement of autosomal linkage (that is, linkage between two pairs of alleles located on a pair of autosomes) presents exceptional difficulties. The first reports

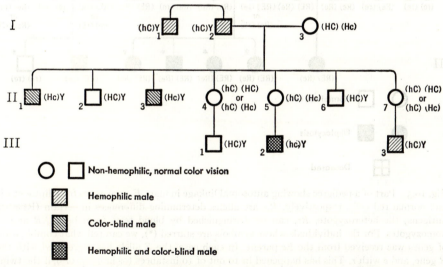

Fig. 10.2 Part of a pedigree illustrating the transmission of hemophilia and color blindness in the same family. All members of the family included here were tested for color blindness except I.1 and I.2, who were deceased at the time of the investigation. We accept I.2 as having normal color vision, however, for it can be shown that the odds are about 200 to 1 that this is correct. *Based on Riddell in the Annals of Eugenics*

of autosomal linkage in man which have succeeded both in standing up under rigorous statistical analysis and in finding confirmation in more recently accumulated data did not, in fact, appear until 1953. The linkage in question (discovered almost simultaneously in England and in the United States) involves an apparently harmless peculiarity of the red blood cells, called *elliptocytosis*, dependent on a dominant autosomal gene, *E*. In this condition, some of the red blood cells are seen under the microscope to be shaped like little footballs instead of having the normal biconcave shape. The *E,e* alleles are found to show linkage with alleles which determine certain differences in blood antigens, the so-called Rh-factors, which will be discussed in detail in Chapter 13. Crossing over occurs between the *E,e* and Rh alleles, and has been estimated as being in the neighborhood of 10 per cent (Fig. 10.3).

One interesting development of the linkage studies relating to elliptocytosis is the finding of evidence that either of two different

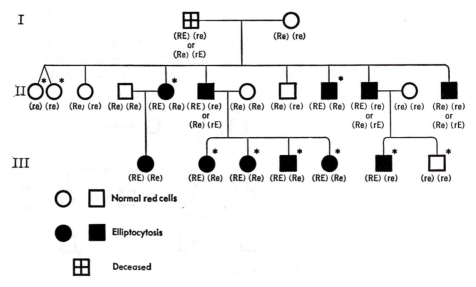

Fig. 10.3   Part of a pedigree showing autosomal linkage in man. *E,e* are genes for elliptocytosis and normal red cells, respectively. *R,r* are alleles determining differences in certain (Rhesus) antigens; the heterozygote, *Rr*, can be distinguished by blood tests from both *RR* and *rr* homozygotes. For the individuals whose symbols are starred (*), we can tell what combination of genes was received from the *Ee* parent. In each case, the *E* allele has segregated with the *R* gene, and *e* with *r*. This has happened in 10 out of 10 instances (or in 9 out of 9, if the twins in Generation II are from a single egg). The probability of this, on the basis of random assortment of the *R,r* and *E,e* alleles, would be only 1 in 1024 (or 1 in 512, if the twins are from one egg). Hence we conclude that the two pairs of alleles must be linked. On this basis, where two possible chromosomal formulas are shown on the chart for a single individual, the upper one is the more probable. *Based on Marshall et al in the Journal of Clinical Investigation*

genes, in different chromosomes, may cause what appears to be the same abnormality (cf. *duplicate dominant epistasis*, Chapter 6). In some families in which there is elliptocytosis, the gene responsible for it, which we have called E, is closely linked to one of the Rh alleles; in other families, elliptocytosis and the Rh factors show random assortment. In the latter, presumably, the red blood cell abnormality is caused not by the E gene, but by a different dominant gene in another chromosome.

Since the discovery of the elliptocytosis-Rh linkage, data which strongly suggest another case of autosomal linkage in man have been reported (Renwick and Lawler). This linkage involves the alleles which are responsible for the O, A, B, AB blood groups (discussed in Chapter 13), and a condition called the nail-patella syndrome. The syndrome is characterized by failure of the nails to develop properly, absence of the knee cap, and various bone abnormalities.

That so few cases of autosomal linkage in the human species have been discovered is not surprising. Because there are 23 pairs of autosomes in man, the probability that any two pairs of alleles picked at random should be located on the same chromosome pair is only one in twenty-three. In addition, there is the difficulty of finding persons who are heterozygous for both pairs of alleles, especially if one of them relates to a rare trait. And finally, when double heterozygotes are found, it is not always possible to tell which of their progeny are crossovers and which are not. Nevertheless, a beginning has been made, and much work on human linkage is under way, so that we may expect somewhat more rapid progress in the future.

PROBLEMS

10.1 In poultry silver plumage and gold plumage depend upon a sex-linked pair of alleles. Barring and nonbarring likewise depend upon a sex-linked pair of alleles. What is the relationship between these two pairs of genes?

10.2 In rabbits black is due to a dominant gene, B, brown to its recessive allele, b. Short hair is the result of a dominant gene, L, long hair of its recessive allele, l. A homozygous black short-haired rabbit is mated to a brown long-haired rabbit. The F_1 animals are test-crossed to brown long-

haired individuals. From many such test crosses the total results are:

black short-haired, 63
black long-haired, 59
brown short-haired, 62
brown long-haired, 60

Are these genes linked? If so, what is the per cent of crossing over?

10.3 In mice, the genes Re,re (for "rex" or short hair, and normal hair, respectively) are linked to the sh (shaker, a recessive mutant), Sh (nonshaker) alleles, with 20 per cent crossing over between them. A mouse that is (ReSh) (ReSh) is mated to one of the formula (resh) (resh), and the F_1 progeny are tested by crossing to (resh) (resh) animals. What types of mice would you expect among the offspring, and in what ratio?

10.4 A mouse that is homozygous rex and shaker is mated to a homozygous normal, and the F_1 progeny are tested by crossing to (resh) (resh) animals. What types would you expect among the offspring, and in what ratio?

10.5 In tomatoes tall growth habit is the result of a dominant gene, D; dwarf growth habit is the result of its recessive allele, d. Smooth epidermis is due to a dominant gene, P, pubescent epidermis to its recessive allele, p. A homozygous tall smooth variety was crossed with a dwarf pubescent variety. The F_1 were test-crossed to dwarf pubescent. The results of the test cross were as follows:

tall smooth,	96
tall pubescent,	4
dwarf smooth,	3
dwarf pubescent,	95

Are these genes linked? If so, what is the per cent of crossing over?

10.6 If the F_1 from Problem 10.5 were bred among themselves to produce an F_2 generation, what ratio would be obtained in the F_2?

10.7 In rabbits color is due to a dominant gene, C, albinism to its recessive allele, c. Black is the result of a dominant gene, B, brown of its recessive allele, b. Brown rabbits are crossed with albinos carrying black in the homozygous state. The F_1 are crossed to the double-recessive. From many such crosses the total results are:

black,	68
brown,	132
albino,	200

Are these genes linked? If so, what is the per cent of crossing over?

10.8 In guinea pigs short hair and long hair depend upon a pair of alleles, the gene for short hair being dominant. Rough coat and smooth coat depend upon another pair of alleles, the gene for rough coat being dominant. Suppose you had two races of guinea pigs, a rough long-haired race and a smooth short-haired race. Outline carefully the full procedure for determining whether these two pairs of genes are linked, and if so, for determining the percentage of crossing over.

10.9 In corn tallness is due to a dominant gene, D, dwarfness to its recessive allele, d. Normal leaves are due to a dominant gene, C, crinkly leaves to its recessive allele, c. Homozygous tall crinkly-leaved corn was crossed to homozygous dwarf normal-leaved corn. The F_1, which was tall normal-leaved, was crossed to double-recessive dwarf crinkly-leaved corn. The results were as follows: tall normal-leaved, 19; tall crinkly-leaved, 83; dwarf normal-leaved, 81; dwarf crinkly-leaved, 17. Are these two pairs of genes linked? If so, what is the per cent of crossing over?

10.10 In poultry white may be due to the homozygous condition of either or both of the recessive genes, c and o. Color depends upon the presence of both dominants, C and O. White males of the formula $CCoo$ were crossed to white females of the formula $ccOO$. The colored F_1 birds were crossed to double-recessives, $ccoo$. From many such crosses the total results were as follows: colored, 68; white, 204. Are these genes linked? If so, what is the per cent of crossing over?

10.11 In rabbits gray is due to a dominant gene, E, red to its recessive allele, e. Color is due to a dominant gene, C, albinism to its recessive allele, c. Homozygous gray rabbits are crossed with albinos carrying the gene for red in homozygous condition. The F_1 are crossed to the double-recessive. From many such crosses the total results are as follows: gray, 73; albino, 147; red, 74. Are these genes linked? If so, what is the per cent of crossing over?

10.12 In corn purple plant color is due to a dominant gene, P, green plant color to its recessive allele, p. Normal leaves are dependent upon a dominant gene, N, narrow leaves upon its recessive allele, n. Homozygous green plants with normal leaves were crossed with homozygous purple plants having narrow leaves. The F_1 were crossed to green plants with narrow leaves. The results of this cross were as follows: purple plants with normal leaves, 197; purple plants with narrow leaves, 201; green plants with normal leaves, 199; green plants with narrow leaves, 203. Are these genes linked? If so, what is the per cent of crossing over?

10.13 In *Drosophila melanogaster* red eyes are dependent upon a dominant gene, S, sepia eyes upon its recessive allele, s. Gray body is dependent upon a dominant gene, E, ebony body upon its recessive allele, e. A homozygous red-eyed gray-bodied male is mated to a sepia-eyed ebony-bodied female. One of the F_1 females is mated to a sepia-eyed ebony-bodied male. Their offspring consist of 65 red-eyed gray-bodied flies, 59 sepia-eyed ebony-bodied flies, 36 red-eyed ebony-bodied flies, and 40 sepia-eyed gray-bodied flies. Are these genes linked? If so, what is the per cent of crossing over?

10.14 What would have been the result if one of the F_1 *males* from the preceding cross had been mated to a sepia-eyed ebony-bodied *female?*

10.15 Splotch mice are heterozygous for a gene, Sp, which is lethal when homozygous; the gene ln (leaden) is recessive to Ln (intense). Splotch, leaden mice are mated to non-splotch, intense homozygotes. Matings of F_1 splotch with double recessive homozygotes produce: 240 splotch, leaden; 12 splotch, intense; 15 non-splotch, leaden; 233 non-splotch, intense. Are these genes linked? If so, what is the per cent of crossing over?

10.16 In poultry a gene, C, is necessary for color, its allele, c, resulting in white.

A dominant gene, I, inhibits color, resulting in white; its recessive allele, i, permits color if C is present. Homozygous colored birds are crossed with white birds of the formula $ccII$. The F_1 are crossed to double-recessives, $ccii$. From many such crosses the total results are: colored, 138; white, 415. Are these genes linked? If so, what is the per cent of crossing over?

10.17 In rabbits short velvetlike fur (rex) is produced by the homozygous state of either or both of the recessive mutations r_1 and r_2. Two varieties of rex rabbits were crossed and the F_1 were all normal. These were crossed to the double-recessive rex, and produced the following offspring: rex, 43; normal, 4. Are these two pairs of genes linked? If so, what is the per cent of crossing over?

10.18 Following the discovery of the two previously mentioned pairs of genes resulting in rex, a third pair was discovered, in which the homozygous condition of the recessive allele, r_3, results in rex coat indistinguishable from that produced by r_1 and r_2. Crosses were made between rabbits of the following formulas: $r_1r_1R_3R_3$ and $R_1R_1r_3r_3$. The F_1 were normal, and they were crossed to the double-recessive $r_1r_1r_3r_3$. The resulting offspring were as follows: rex, 45; normal, 15. Are these two pairs of genes linked? If so, what is the per cent of crossing over?

10.19 From the combined data of Problems 10.17 and 10.18, what can you infer as to the chromosome relationships of the three rex genes?

10.20 In sweet peas blue flowers are the result of a dominant gene, B, red flowers of its recessive allele, b. Long pollen is due to a dominant gene, R, round pollen to its recessive allele, r. A plant homozygous for blue flowers and round pollen was crossed with one homozygous for red flowers and long pollen. The F_1 were crossed to red-flowered round-pollened plants. The results were blue long, 23; blue round, 153; red long, 155; red round, 21. Are these two pairs of genes linked? If so, what is the per cent of crossing over?

10.21 If the reciprocal cross from Problem 10.20 should be made, that is, a plant homozygous for blue flowers and long pollen crossed with one homozygous for red flowers and round pollen, and the F_1 test-crossed to the double-recessive, what results would be obtained?

10.22 What are the advantages of the test cross over the F_2 generation in linkage studies?

REFERENCES

CASTLE, W. E., *Mammalian Genetics*, Cambridge, Harvard University Press (1940).

HALDANE, J. B. S. and SMITH, C. A. B., *Annals of Eugenics* **14**:10 (1947).

IMMER, F. R., *Genetics* **15**:81 (1930).

IMMER, F. R. and HENDERSON, M. T., *Genetics* **28**:419 (1943).

LAWLER, S. D. and SANDLER, M., *Annals of Eugenics* **18**:328 (1954).

MARSHALL, R. A., BIRD, R. M., BAILEY, H. K., and BECKNER, E., *Jour. Clinical Investigation* **33**:790 (1954).

MATHER, K., *The Measurement of Linkage in Heredity*, Second edition. New York, John Wiley and Sons (1951).

RENWICK, J. H. and LAWLER, S. D., *Annals of Human Genetics* **19**:312 (1955).

RIDDELL, W. J. B., *Annals of Eugenics* **13**:30 (1946).

CHAPTER ELEVEN

The cytological basis of crossing over

We have learned (Chapter 10) that some pairs of alleles do not assort at random: that, instead, in these cases most of the gametes formed by an individual contain one or the other of the same combinations of alleles that it received from its parents. We have seen that this phenomenon, linkage, can be explained by assuming that the alleles which tend to remain together are carried on the same chromosome; and that when recombination between these alleles and those on the homologous chromosome is found, an exchange of parts has taken place between the two homologous chromosomes.

The theory of linkage and crossing over which we have just outlined was proposed by Morgan as early as 1911. By this time several pairs of alleles had been found which all showed linkage with one another, that is, they all appeared to be located on the same chromosome pair. But there were different amounts of crossing over between any one of these allelic pairs and each of the others. Morgan suggested that the genes of the different allelic pairs were arranged in a linear series along the length of the chromosome, and that the amount of crossing over between two pairs of alleles might be related to the distance between them on the chromosome — that is, the farther apart

Fig. 11.1 A pair of chromosomes carrying three pairs of genes. It may be seen that an exchange of homologous parts of the chromosomes would cause a crossover between pair Aa and pair Bb only if the exchange took place in the relatively short region between A, a and B, b. On the other hand, an exchange anywhere along the chromosomes would cause a crossover between pair Aa and pair Cc.

two pairs of alleles are, the greater would be the amount of crossing over between them (Fig. 11.1).

Sturtevant undertook to test Morgan's idea. He made linkage tests involving several pairs of alleles each of which exhibited sex linkage and all of which, therefore, were presumably carried on the X-chromosome. He found that the amount of crossing over between any two pairs of these alleles was related in a very definite way to the respective amounts of crossing over between each of these pairs and a third pair. We can best understand the nature of the relations he found by considering a concrete illustration. The data we shall use relate to autosomal genes, but the principles they illustrate are identical with those discovered by Sturtevant.

In Drosophila there is a gene sp (spineless, so called because it causes marked reduction of bristles) recessive to Sp (normal bristles). Another gene sr (stripe), producing a dark stripe on the thorax, is recessive to Sr (nonstripe). The gene delta (D) causes a triangular thickening at the junction of certain wing veins; it is dominant to d, nondelta. (You will notice that in two cases we have used two letters instead of one as a gene symbol. This is necessary because there are more genes than letters. In this instance, the first letters alone would not distinguish "spineless" from "stripe.")

When test crosses were made involving the genes stripe and spineless, it was found that these genes are linked, with about 3.5 per cent crossing over between them. When stripe and delta were tested, they were also found to be linked, with about 5.5 per cent crossing over. The three pairs of alleles must, then, be located on the same pair of chromosomes. Now if the genes are in a line on the chromosome, it is possible for them to be arranged in one of two ways, as follows:

$$\text{either} \quad \left.\begin{array}{l} \text{—}sr \\ \text{—}sp \\ \text{—}D \end{array}\right\} \begin{array}{l} 3.5 \\ 5.5 \end{array} \quad \text{or} \quad \left.\begin{array}{l} \text{—|—}sp \\ \text{—|—}sr \\ \text{—|—}D \end{array}\right\} \begin{array}{l} 3.5 \\ 5.5 \end{array}$$

How would we determine which of these relationships is correct, since either one of them fits the crossover percentages found between stripe and spineless and between stripe and delta? Obviously by determining the crossover percentage between spineless and delta. If the genes are arranged sr, sp, D, the crossover per cent between spineless and delta should be 5.5 minus 3.5, or 2.0, whereas if they are arranged sp, sr, D, the crossover per cent between spineless and delta should be 5.5 plus 3.5, or 9.0, as may be seen above. As a matter of fact, the crossover per cent between spineless and delta was found to be 8.5: certainly near enough to 9.0 to indicate that the gene spineless is on one side of the stripe gene and delta on the other.

The crossover percentages given above were found, as we have indicated, in separate experiments, each of which involved just two of the pairs of alleles at a time ("two-point" crosses). Crossover values, even between the same two pairs of alleles, may fluctuate somewhat from one experiment to another, the fluctuations being partly due to chance and partly to varying conditions of temperature and other factors which in some degree affect the frequency with which crossing over occurs. The lack of perfect agreement between the observed value of 8.5 per cent crossing over between spineless and delta and the calculated value of 9.0 was shown to be due to fluctuations of this kind by the use of "three-point" crosses. A *three-point* linkage test is one in which individuals heterozygous for each of three linked pairs of alleles are mated to the triple recessive homozygotes. In this instance, the matings were between females that were (*Sp Sr D*)(*sp sr d*) and (*sp sr d*)(*sp sr d*) males. The results are given in Table 11.1.

Table 11.1. Results of "Three-Point" Linkage Tests in Drosophila. Progeny from Matings of (*Sp Sr D*)(*sp sr d*) Females to (*sp sr d*)(*sp sr d*) Males. (*Data from Bridges and Morgan, 1923*)

	Phenotype	Chromosome Received from Mother	Number	Per Cent of Total	Gene Combinations
(a)	Normal bristles, nonstripe, delta	(*Sp Sr D*)	658	91.1	Noncrossovers (parental combinations)
	Spineless, stripe, nondelta	(*sp sr d*)	606		
(b)	Normal bristles, stripe, nondelta	(*Sp sr d*)	25	3.4	Crossovers between *Sp* and *Sr*
	Spineless, nonstripe, delta	(*sp Sr D*)	22		
(c)	Normal bristles, nonstripe, nondelta	(*Sp Sr d*)	41	5.5	Crossovers between *Sr* and *D*
	Spineless, stripe, delta	(*sp sr D*)	35		
	Totals		1387	100.0	

If we look in Table 11.1 for the progeny with chromosomes containing recombinations between the *Sp,sp,* and the *D,d* alleles, we see, of course, that they include both those in rows marked (b) and those in the (c) rows. The table shows, therefore, 8.9 per cent crossing over between the *Sp* and *D* loci, and this is the *exact sum* of the crossover per cents between *Sp* and *Sr* (3.4) and between *Sr* and *D* (5.5) as found in the same experiments.

Similar relationships have held for all pairs of genes studied. If crosses involving two pairs of genes show that they are not linked, we know that they are located in different pairs of chromosomes. If, however, they are linked, we know that they are in the same pair of

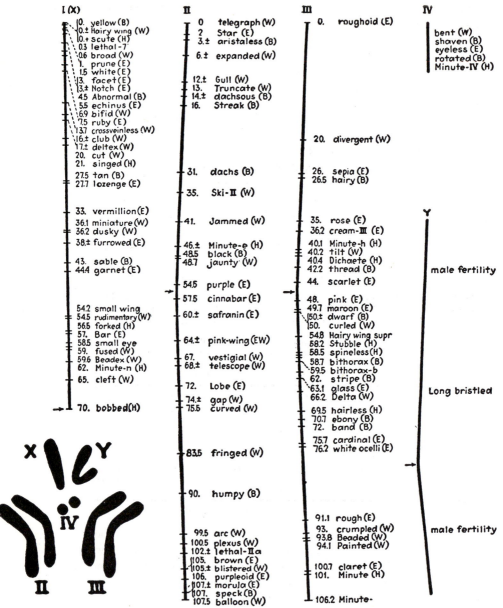

Fig. 11.2 Linkage map for *Drosophila melanogaster*, showing relative positions of many of the known genes in the chromosomes as determined genetically. The letters in parentheses indicate the portion of the fly in which the characters appear. B, body. E, eye. H, hairs. W, wings. The arrows indicate positions of spindle-attachment regions. In the Y-chromosome, "long-bristled," which is the normal allele of "bobbed," and the two genes for male sterility have not been precisely located. In chromosome IV the genes are all very closely linked. *Adapted from Morgan, Sturtevant and Bridges, and Stern; from Sharp, Introduction to Cytology, McGraw-Hill Co., New York*

chromosomes, and furthermore, we may locate them in the chromosome in relation to any other gene. To put it in general terms, if, in regard to three linked genes, A, B, and C, A crosses over from B with a certain percentage, and B crosses over from C with a certain percentage, then the crossover percentage between A and C will be either the sum or the difference of these two percentages. Since these relationships are also those of points on a line, we have a strong indication that the genes are located in a definite linear order along the chromosomes, the crossover percentages being more or less proportional to the distances between their locations.

Findings like those we have just discussed soon firmly established the theory of the **linear order of the genes.** In accord with Morgan's suggestion mentioned above, this theory states that the various alleles carried on any given chromosome *are arranged in a definite linear sequence* and that *the different amounts of crossing over between different pairs of alleles is a measure of the relative distances between their positions on the chromosome.* The position occupied by one or the other member of a pair of alleles is called the **locus** of that pair (plural, **loci**).

In 1913, from the results of his linkage experiments Sturtevant was able to construct a **chromosome map** showing the relative positions of five different loci on the X-chromosome of Drosophila, together with the approximate distances of each from the other as measured by percentages of crossing over. This seemed a daring idea to many geneticists at the time, and they did not all immediately accept the Morgan-Sturtevant theory or the reality of Sturtevant's "map." But in the years following more and more mutants were discovered in Drosophila; their linkage relations were exhaustively studied; and by 1925 it was possible to construct the rather detailed maps of all four chromosomes shown in Figure 11.2.

These maps were based on many thousands of linkage tests in numerous laboratories. Checked and double-checked against one another the results were always mutually consistent. Meanwhile linkage experiments with maize and other organisms were being made; the data from these were far less extensive than those from the Drosophila studies, but they were likewise always consistent with the linear-order theory. Even those who had most vigorously criticized the theory of the linear order of the genes as rash or speculative were by now convinced that there was no other way to explain the vast accumulation of interlocking data which supported it.

An essential part of the linear-order theory, of course, is the idea that genetic crossovers *are the result of physical exchanges of parts between homologous chromosomes.* The genetic data from the linkage studies left no doubt that these exchanges actually occur, even though it had been entirely impossible to observe them cytologically. It was not until 1931 that the cytological demonstration of genetic crossing over was accomplished, simultaneously by Stern and by McClintock.

The reason it had not been possible to demonstrate by cytological examination that homologous chromosomes exchange parts when crossing over occurs has been hinted at in an earlier chapter (Chapter 4). Ordinarily there is no visible difference between the two chromosomes of a homologous pair. Therefore, even though we can see that the two chromosomes are in intimate contact (synapsis) throughout their lengths with their chromatids closely twisted about each other prior to the first meiotic division, we cannot be sure whether they have or have not traded parts before separating.

In order to be able to see whether or not an exchange takes place, it is necessary that the two synapsing chromosomes differ visibly in two different regions. Then, if between these two points an exchange does occur, the crossover chromosomes (or chromatids) will be distinguishably different from the original chromosomes.

Stern was able to study crossing over between two chromosomes that met the requirements we have just noted. He discovered a strain of Drosophila in which a portion of the Y-chromosome had broken off and become attached to the end of one of the X-chromosomes. This X-chromosome with the piece of the Y attached could be readily recognized under the microscope. Stern also discovered another strain of Drosophila in which one of the X-chromosomes was broken in two. By suitable crossing Stern was able to produce female flies in which one of the X-chromosomes had the fragment of the Y attached, and the other X-chromosome was broken in two. The broken X-chromosome carried the dominant gene, B, for bar eye, in which the eye becomes much narrowed, and the recessive gene, c, for carnation eye, a color change. The X-chromosome with the piece of the Y attached carried the recessive gene, b, for nonbar eye, and the dominant gene, C, for red eye.

When such a female was bred to a nonbar carnation-eyed male (having in its X-chromosome the genes b and c), the offspring would be of four types, two of which would be noncrossovers and two crossovers. Figure 11.3 will make this clear.

The chromosomes of the female offspring were then studied. If crossing over of genes is accompanied by exchange of parts of chromosomes, it should be possible to see the results of the chromosomal exchange in the crossover offspring. The cytological results showed definitely that crossing over of genes *was* accompanied by chromosomal exchange. In these female offspring one X-chromosome always came from the father, and should therefore be normal. The other came from the mother, and should either be broken in two or should have a piece of the Y attached.

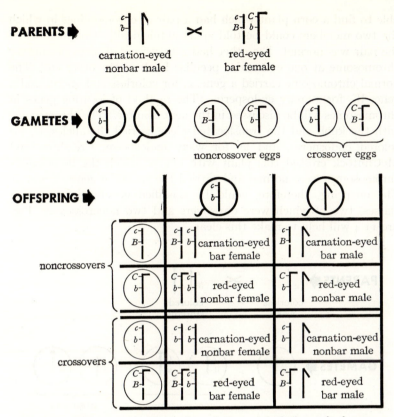

PARENTS ➡ carnation-eyed nonbar male × red-eyed bar female

GAMETES ➡ noncrossover eggs crossover eggs

OFFSPRING ➡

noncrossovers {
carnation-eyed bar female / carnation-eyed bar male
red-eyed nonbar female / red-eyed nonbar male
}

crossovers {
carnation-eyed nonbar female / carnation-eyed nonbar male
red-eyed bar female / red-eyed bar male
}

Fig. 11.3 Diagrammatic illustration of the cytological proof of cross-ing over between chromosomes of a pair and the concurrent crossing over of genes. For explanation see text. *Based on the work of Stern with Drosophila*

In the noncrossover females this was true. In the crossover fe-males, however, it was clear that the X-chromosome from the mother was the result of a chromosomal crossover. In the carnation-eyed nonbar offspring the maternal X-chromosome was apparently normal, neither broken nor carrying a piece of the Y. In the red-eyed bar offspring the maternal X-chromosome was not only broken, but one of the broken pieces carried the piece of the Y-chromosome. The figure indicates how the crossing over must have occurred. This, then, is clear proof that genetic crossing over is accompanied by and de-pendent upon cytological crossing over, that is, an actual exchange of material between a pair of homologous chromosomes.

A similar demonstration in the same year (1931) by Creighton and McClintock, indicated that cytological crossing over occurs in plants just as it does in animals. Creighton and McClintock were able to find a corn plant which had a pair of chromosomes in which the two members could be told apart cytologically. One member of the pair was normal. The other had a translocated piece of another chromosome at one end and a peculiar knob at the other end. The normal chromosome carried a gene, c, for colorless endosperm and a gene, W, for starchy endosperm. (The method of locating genes in chromosomes will be discussed in the next chapter.) The chromosome with the knob and the translocated piece carried the alleles, C, for colored endosperm, and w, for waxy endosperm. Creighton and McClintock crossed this plant with one in which the homologous chromosomes were normal and carried the recessive genes, c and w. The offspring, therefore, could be classified genetically into four classes, two of which were crossovers and two noncrossovers. Figure 11.4 will help to make this clear.

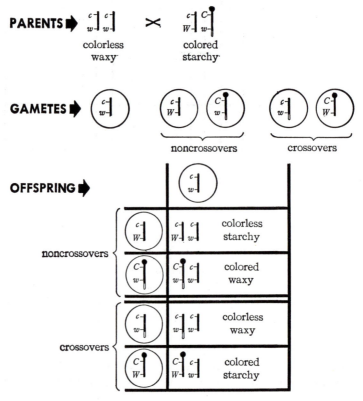

Fig. 11.4 Diagrammatic illustration of the cytological proof of crossing over in the chromosomes and the parallel crossing over of genes. For explanation see text. *Based on the work of Creighton and McClintock with corn*

The crossover plants clearly had one chromosome of this particular pair which was the result of an exchange of parts. As may be seen from Figure 11.4 the noncrossovers (colorless starchy and colored waxy) had received from the plant with the peculiar chromosome either a normal chromosome or one with the knob and the translocated piece. The crossovers, however, when examined under the microscope, showed cytological evidence of the crossing over. The colorless waxy plants showed a chromosome with the translocated piece but no knob, while the colored starchy plants showed a chromosome with the knob but no translocated piece. Thus, whenever genetic crossing over occurred, a corresponding exchange of homologous parts took place between the members of the pair of chromosomes.

There is no doubt, then, that linkage and crossing over have a definite cytological basis. This provides more parallels between the behavior of chromosomes and the behavior of genes to add to our list. Let us state these parallels precisely. We learned in an early chapter that genes assort at random. We know now that only certain genes assort at random. Others do not, but are linked instead. The parallels are thus as follows. Certain genes do not assort at random, but occur in paired groups (linkage groups) which tend to be transmitted as units. *The chromatin material is also gathered into paired groups (chromosomes) which tend to be transmitted as units.* The genes of a linkage group do not stay completely together as a rule, but during maturation homologous parts of the paired groups of genes are exchanged with a definite frequency (genetic crossing over). *The paired chromosomes also exchange homologous parts of their lengths during the maturation of the germ cells (cytological crossing over).*

Considerable experimental work has been done on the time, place, and mode of the exchange of parts by chromosomes. Some mention of this was made in Chapter 4, and a preliminary diagram was shown in Figure 4.7. We may now consider cytological crossing over in more detail.

We should remember (Chapter 4) that during the prophase of the first meiotic division in the formation of the germ cells, the two members of each pair of chromosomes undergo *synapsis*, a close side-by-side union. Each chromosome then becomes duplicated, so that for a time there are four threadlike chromatids in close association. This association of four chromatids is called a tetrad. Later in the prophase of the first meiotic division the two centromeres (spindle-fiber attachment regions) to each of which two chromatids are attached, are seen to move apart. But the attached chromatids do not, as might be expected, separate uniformly along their entire lengths. Instead, at one or more points along the tetrad two of the four chromatids appear to lie across each other (Fig. 11.5, G), forming what is known

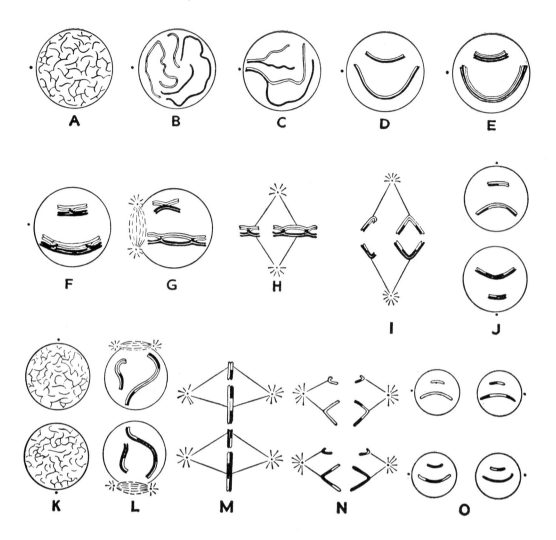

Fig. 11.5 Diagrammatic illustration of the maturation of the germ cells in the male. To save space only the nuclei are shown. Two pairs of chromosomes are indicated, those from the father (the paternal chromosomes) being solid, while those from the mother (the maternal chromosomes) are shown in outline. A, primary spermatocyte interphase. B, the appearance of the threads, each representing a chromosome. C, the beginning of synapsis. D, synapsis completed. E, the splitting of each thread to form four chromatids in each pair of chromosomes (the tetrad). F, the exchange of parts by two of the four chromatids in each tetrad. G, the partial opening out of the tetrads, showing one chiasma in the smaller pair and two in the larger. H, the aligning of the chromosome pairs across the spindle. I, separation of the chromatid pairs. J, K, the secondary spermatocytes. L, M, N, the division of the secondary spermatocytes, showing the random distribution of crossover and noncrossover chromosomes. O, the spermatids, with the haploid number of chromosomes, some of which are qualitatively changed due to crossing over. The tetrad (E) is drawn as though the four chromatids were all in one plane, so that an end view would look like this . . . . Actually the four chromatids are so associated that an end view of the tetrad would look like this : :

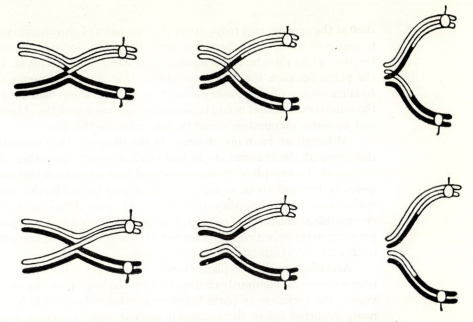

Fig. 11.6 Diagram of a tetrad with one chiasma. Top row shows how crossing over and segregation are conceived to occur on the one-plane theory, the chiasma being the result of a previous crossing over. Bottom row illustrates the same thing interpreted on the two-plane theory, the crossing over being the result of the chiasma. The final result is the same on either interpretation.

as a **chiasma** (plural, **chiasmata**) from its resemblance to the Greek letter χ. There is one or more of these chiasmata in each dividing tetrad, but their number and positions vary from cell to cell.

As early as 1909 Janssens suggested that a chiasma represented an exchange of parts between homologous chromosomes. But he then thought that the exchange at each chiasma was frequently between *whole chromosomes*, that is, that both chromatids of each homologous chromosome traded parts with both chromatids of the other, at the same point; this view we now know was erroneous. There can be little doubt that chiasmata do represent exchanges, but the exchange at any one point is between single chromatids, one of paternal and one of maternal origin, as shown in Figure 11.6. Nevertheless, there has been extended controversy regarding the time relation between the appearance of the chiasmata and the exchange of parts by homologous chromatids.

The difference between the two most persistent viewpoints regarding the significance of chiasmata can be seen by examining the two diagrams on the left in Figure 11.6. One interpretation, sometimes called the "two plane" theory, is presented in the lower of the two diagrams. According to this view, a chiasma results from the fact that as the centromeres move apart the two pairs of chromatids start to separate along one plane, the synaptic plane, for part of their lengths, while elsewhere the separation is along another plane, i.e., the plane between the two sister chromatids of each chromosome. In consequence of this, sister chromatids (that is, those belonging to the same chromosome) would be associated on one side of the chiasma, and nonsister chromatids would be associated on the other.

Although we have not shown it in the diagram, the chromatids that cross at the chiasma are in fact twisted about each other. Advocates of the two-plane theory contended that a strain at this point would be brought about as the two centromeres moved farther apart during anaphase; this, they thought, could cause breakage of the chromatids at the point of contact, followed with an exchange of parts (crossing over) by which the strain would be relieved. Thus, according to this theory, *chiasmata cause crossing over*.

According to the one-plane theory (suggested by Janssens in his later writing and vigorously championed by Darlington in subsequent years), the exchange of parts between nonsister chromatids has already occurred *before* the chiasmata appear, and chiasmata result from the tendency of all segments of sister chromatids to remain together during the first meiotic division. Thus, as we see from the upper diagram of Figure 11.6, the chromatids would separate in a single plane (corresponding to the plane of synapsis) along their entire lengths. According to this view, then, *chiasmata are the consequence, not the cause, of crossing over*.

The bulk of evidence accumulated since these two theories of chiasma formation were proposed has supported the one-plane theory. Much of the evidence is too complex for us to discuss here, but one kind of observation on which the argument rests is both simple and convincing. We have already mentioned the occasional occurrence of chromosome pairs in which the two members are distinguishably different. Sometimes the difference is one of length, such as may result from a part of one chromosome having been broken off and lost during a prior cell division. When there is a difference in length between two synapsing chromosomes, the two theories would lead us to predict quite different appearances for chiasmata formed between them. Figure 11.7 shows what the one-plane (A) and the two-plane (B) theories would each lead us to

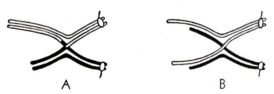

A   B

Fig. 11.7 Diagram showing the expected appearance of a chiasma formed between a pair of chromosomes of unequal lengths: (A) if exchange of chromatid segments has previously occurred (one-plane theory) and (B) if exchange has not yet taken place (two-plane theory). Configurations like that in (A) are the only ones that have actually been observed.

expect. Actually, the chiasmata that are seen to result from the synapsis of chromosomes of unequal length are always like A; that is, they never present the appearance which we should find if the two-plane theory were correct.

Our interpretation of chiasmata formation, then, would lead us to locate the *time of crossing over* as being prior to the opening out of the chromatids of the tetrad. That is, crossing over takes place some time during the close synapsis of the chromosomes, and perhaps, as Belling suggested years ago, at the very time the two original chromosomes are becoming duplicated. Thus, crossing over may be more intimately related to the chemical (and, especially, the self-duplicating) properties of chromosomes than to mechanical stresses involved in their movements (see Haldane). We shall, in fact, see evidence in the next chapter that mechanical models of crossing over, though often helpful in giving a general idea of the process, are inadequate to explain some aspects of it.

The student has perhaps noticed that the immediate genetic consequences of the first meiotic division are the same, on either theory of chiasma formation. In each case (see diagrams on the right of Figure 11.6) two of the four chromatids have exchanged parts at the site of the chiasma and two have not. Following the second meiotic division, each of the gametes, in the case of the male (in the female, the egg and each of the three polar bodies) will receive *one* of the four chromatids. Thus, half of the sperms derived from a primary spermatocyte in which a single chiasma has occurred in a given tetrad will receive a crossover chromatid, and half will receive a noncrossover chromatid. Similarly, on the average, for the eggs derived from primary oöcytes in each of which a given tetrad exhibits one chiasma: half will receive a crossover, and half a noncrossover, chromatid. We shall see in the next chapter what the consequences of more than one chiasma in a tetrad are.

The student should take careful note that, *as a consequence of crossing over both of the two meiotic divisions are required* to effect segregation in all allelic pairs. A division which separates paternal parts of chromosomes from maternal parts (separating black from unshaded, in the diagram) is commonly called **reductional.** A division separating parts of sister chromatids from each other (black from black and unshaded from unshaded) is called **equational.**

It is extremely important to recognize that, as a result of crossing over, *neither of the meiotic divisions is wholly reductional nor wholly equational.* Each is reductional for some parts of the tetrad (therefore for some pairs of alleles), equational for others. Thus, our diagram shows a first meiotic division which is reductional for the right end of the chromosomes, to which the spindle fibers are attached, and equational for the other end. The second division will of necessity be equational for the end with the centromere, reductional for the other end. In most organisms in which genetic study has made it possible to analyze the two divisions from this point of view, the first meiotic division *is regularly reductional at and immediately adjacent to the centromere;* this, of course, is consistent with cytological findings in those cases in which the centromere can be seen to remain undivided through the first division of meiosis.

PROBLEMS

11.1 Why is it essential to be able to differentiate one end of a chromosome from the other as well as to be able to differentiate the two members of the pair, in order to prove that genetic crossing over is accompanied by an exchange of chromosome material?

11.2 Would you expect to find chiasmata in the spermatogenesis of Drosophila? Give reasons for your answer.

11.3 In Problem 4.6 it was found that human beings could produce 16,777,216 different kinds of gametes on the basis of the random assortment of chromosomes. Would this number be increased or decreased by the fact that homologous chromosomes may exchange homologous parts?

11.4 What effect do you think crossing over has had upon the rate of evolutionary progress?

11.5 In what ways has the proof of cytological crossing over helped to strengthen the hypothesis that genes are carried on the chromosomes?

11.6 Why was the proof of cytological crossing over delayed for such a long time after it was suspected? Does the fact that it finally turned out to be just as predicted add strength to the chromosome hypothesis of heredity?

REFERENCES

BELLING, J., *Proc. Nat. Acad. Sci.* **13**:717 (1927); *Biol. Bull.* **52**:480 (1927); *ibid.* **54**:465 (1928); *Univ. Calif. Pub. Bot.* **14**:283, 307, 335 (1928); *ibid.* **16**:311 (1931); *Genetics* **18**:388 (1933).

CREIGHTON, H., and McCLINTOCK, B., *Proc. Nat. Acad. Sci.* **17**:492 (1931); *Proc. 6th Internat. Cong. Genetics* **2**:392 (1932).

DARLINGTON, C. D., *Proc. Roy. Soc. London B* **107**:50 (1930); *Biol. Rev.* **6**:221 (1931); *Recent Advances in Cytology.* Philadelphia, P. Blakiston's Son and Co. (1932).

HALDANE, J. B. S., *The Biochemistry of Genetics.* London, George Allen and Unwin, Ltd. (1954).

JANSSENS, F. A., *La Cellule* **25**:389 (1909); *ibid.* **34**:135 (1924).

MORGAN, T. H., *Science* **34**:384 (1911).

SAX, K., *Jour. Arnold Arboretum* **11**:193 (1930); *ibid.* **13**:180 (1932).

STERN, C., *Biol. Zentralbl.* **51**:547 (1921).

STURTEVANT, A. H., *Jour Exper. Zool.* **14**:43 (1913).

WHITE, M. J. D., *The Chromosomes*, Fourth Edition. New York, John Wiley and Sons, Inc. (1950).

CHAPTER TWELVE

The mapping of chromosomes

The subject of chromosome mapping was introduced in the last chapter, with a brief account of linkage experiments involving the loci of the genes spineless, stripe, and delta in Drosophila. The experiments provided evidence that these three genes are located on the same chromosome and established the order of the loci as Sp, Sr, D. The data also showed that the per cent of crossing over between the two loci which are farthest apart, Sp and D, is the sum of the crossing-over percentages between Sp and Sr and between Sr and D.

The simple additive relation of crossover values just illustrated is a special case of a more general relation, and it is exactly true only for loci which have relatively little crossing over between them. Suppose, however, there are three loci, R, S, and T, linked in the order shown and that there is a moderate or large amount (say 10 per cent or more) of crossing over between R and S, and between S and T. The crossover percentage between R and T in such a case is usually not equal to the sum of these percentages, but is less than the sum. Let us look at a specific illustration of this kind of situation and then seek an explanation for it.

In Drosophila the Sp, sp (spineless) locus to which we have just referred is also linked to the locus of the gene se (sepia eyes), recessive to Se (red eyes). Linkage tests show about 22 per cent crossing over between Se and Sp. Another pair of genes, Ro, ro, affect the texture of the eyes, ro (rough) being recessive to Ro (normal texture). Ro and Sp are linked, with about 31 per cent crossing over.

Ro and Se are, of course, also linked. Crossing over between these loci is about 40 per cent. It seems evident that the order of the loci is, as shown below, Se, Sp, Ro; but 40 per cent falls far short of being the sum of 22 per cent and 31 per cent.

$$40 \left\{ \begin{array}{l} \left. \begin{array}{l} -Se \\ \\ -Sp \end{array} \right\} 22 \\ \\ \left. \begin{array}{l} \\ -Ro \end{array} \right\} 31 \end{array} \right.$$

We shall be able to see the reason for this discrepancy from the additive rule of crossover values if again we examine the results from a three-point cross involving the same genes. A three-point linkage test, you will recall, is one in which individuals heterozygous for each of three linked pairs of alleles are mated to the triple-recessive homozygotes. One kind of mating made in this instance was between females that were (*Se Sp Ro*)(*se sp ro*) and (*se sp ro*)(*se sp ro*) males. The results are given in Table 12.1.

Table 12.1. RESULTS OF "THREE-POINT" LINKAGE TESTS IN DROSOPHILA. PROGENY FROM MATINGS OF (*Se Sp Ro*)(*se sp ro*) FEMALES TO (*se sp ro*)(*se sp ro*) MALES. (*Data from Bridges and Morgan, 1923*)

	PHENOTYPE	CHROMOSOME RECEIVED FROM MOTHER	NUMBER	PER CENT OF TOTAL	GENE COMBINATIONS
(a)	Red eyes, normal bristles, not rough	(*Se Sp Ro*)	338	53.0	Noncrossovers (parental combinations)
	Sepia, spineless, rough	(*se sp ro*)	370		
(b)	Red eyes, spineless, rough	(*Se sp ro*)	114	15.7	Single crossovers, between *Se* and *Sp* loci only
	Sepia, normal bristles, not rough	(*se Sp Ro*)	96		
(c)	Red eyes, normal bristles, rough	(*Se Sp ro*)	156	24.6	Single crossovers, between *Sp* and *Ro* loci only
	Sepia, spineless, not rough	(*se sp Ro*)	173		
(d)	Red eyes, spineless, not rough	(*Se sp Ro*)	46	6.7	Double crossovers (recombinations between both *Se*, *Sp* and *Sp*, *Ro* loci)
	Sepia, normal bristles, rough	(*se Sp ro*)	43		
	Totals		1336	100.0	

Now let us carefully examine Table 12.1 and ask ourselves what crossover values we would have gotten from these matings *if we had been following only two of the three loci* involved in the cross: the *Se* and *Sp* loci, for example. To do this, we simply look at the column showing the composition of the chromosome received from the mother and pretend the *Ro,ro* genes are not there. Which chromosomes would we interpret as crossovers between *Se,se* and *Sp,sp?* Obviously, those in rows (b) and (d). Adding the frequencies of these together, we obtain 15.7 + 6.7 = 22.4 as the percentage of recombination between *Se* and *Sp;* that is, of course, just about the value we would get in a two-point cross that involved only these two loci. Similarly (ignoring this time the *Se,se* genes) the recombinations between *Sp,sp* and *Ro,ro* are those in row (c) and, again, in row (d); adding these, we get 24.6 + 6.7 = 31.3 as the percentage of crossovers between the *Sp* and *Ro* loci. Finally, the sum of rows (b) and (c) gives us the number of recombinations between Sp and Ro, the two loci that are farthest apart; this is $15.7 + 24.6 = 40.3$ per cent, once more practically the same value as we obtain in a two-point test.

How and why does this value of 40.3 per cent crossing over between Se and Ro differ from the sum (53.7) of the crossover percentages between Se and Sp and between Sp and Ro? If we compare Table 12.1 with Table 11.1 of the preceding chapter, where the additive rule *does* hold, we see at once the crucial difference between the two sets of results. When, as in Table 11.1, the data are from a test involving three closely linked loci, *there are no double crossovers;* when more distant loci are involved, double crossovers occur. Evidently these are responsible for the discrepancy from the additive rule. The nature of the discrepancy can perhaps best be seen if we summarize the paragraph just preceding this one in tabular form. We then have the following:

Per cent crossovers between Se and Sp:
$$15.7 \text{ (row b)} + 6.7 \text{ (row d)} = 22.4$$
Per cent crossovers between Sp and Ro:
$$24.6 \text{ (row c)} + 6.7 \text{ (row d)} = 31.3$$
Sum of "crossover distances," $Se — Sp$ and $Sp — Ro$: 53.7
Per cent crossovers between Se and Ro:
$$15.7 \text{ (row b)} + 24.6 \text{ (row c)} = 40.3$$

From the above we see that the double crossovers of row (d) have not contributed at all to the 40.3 per cent crossovers between the Se and Ro loci. But they have counted as crossovers between Se and Sp and *again* as crossovers between Sp and Ro. Consequently the total of 53.7 per cent obtained by adding the $Se — Sp$ and $Sp — Ro$ crossovers exceeds the observed crossing-over percentage (40.3) by twice the percentage of double crossing over. This leads immediately to the rule which relates crossover percentages of *any* three linked genes, E, F, G, arranged in that order: The percentage of crossovers between E and G is equal to the sum of the $E — F$ and $F — G$ crossover percentages *minus twice the percentage of double crossovers.*

It is of some interest to notice the frequency of double crossovers (6.7%) in Table 12.1 and to compare it with what we would expect if crossing over between Se and Sp on the one hand, and between Se and Ro on the other, *are mutually independent events* (see page 81). A crossover between Se and Sp is found in 0.224 (22.4%) of the gametes, and a crossover between Sp and Ro in 0.313 of the gametes. We would therefore expect that about (0.224) × (0.313) or 7.0% of the gametes would contain double crossovers, if the occurrence of a crossover in one region is independent of the occurrence of one in the other region. The actual figure, 6.7%, which was observed in this case is close enough to be possibly only a chance deviation.

But it is by no means true that we always get about the percentage of double crossovers expected on the basis of chance. Usually, in fact, when we make linkage tests involving three linked loci, A, B, C, the amount of double crossing over is less, and often much less, than we expect on the assumption that crossing over between A and C and between B and C are independent events.

Consider, for example, the linkage relations between the Ro,ro (rough) alleles in Drosophila and two other pairs of alleles on the same chromosome pair, e (ebony body), recessive to E (gray body), and ca (claret eyes), recessive to Ca (red eyes). Table 12.2 shows the results of test crosses of $(E\ Ro\ ca)(e\ ro\ Ca)$ females mated to $(e\ ro\ ca)(e\ ro\ ca)$ males. (Notice that in these crosses the three dominant alleles are not all in one of the female's chromosomes and the three recessives in the other. What difference does this make in the results?)

Table 12.2. RESULTS OF "THREE-POINT" LINKAGE TESTS IN DRO-SOPHILA. PROGENY FROM MATINGS OF $(E\ Ro\ ca)(e\ ro\ Ca)$ FEMALES TO $(e\ ro\ ca)(e\ ro\ ca)$ MALES. *(Data from Bridges and Morgan, 1923)*

	PHENOTYPE	CHROMOSOME RECEIVED FROM MOTHER	NUMBER	PER CENT OF TOTAL	GENE COMBINATIONS
(a)	Gray, not rough, claret Ebony, rough, red eyes	$(E\ Ro\ ca)$ $(e\ ro\ Ca)$	395 370	70.2	Noncrossovers
(b)	Gray, rough, red eyes Ebony, not rough, claret	$(E\ ro\ Ca)$ $(e\ Ro\ ca)$	119 89	19.1	Single crossovers, between E and Ro only
(c)	Gray, not rough, red eyes Ebony, rough, claret	$(E\ Ro\ Ca)$ $(e\ ro\ ca)$	49 66	10.6	Single crossovers, between Ro and Ca only
(d)	Gray, rough, claret Ebony, not rough, red eyes	$(E\ ro\ ca)$ $(e\ Ro\ Ca)$	1 1	0.2	Double crossovers
	Totals		1090	100.1	

The percentage of crossovers between E and Ro shown in Table 12.2 is 19.1 + 0.2 or 19.3; between Ro and Ca, it is 10.6 + 0.2 or 10.8. If the occurrence of crossovers in regions $E - Ro$ and $Ro - Ca$, respectively, are independent of each other, we should expect about (0.193) × (0.108) or 2.1% double crossovers. Actually, only 0.2% of the gametes contain double crossovers, a little less than one tenth of those expected on a chance basis.

Evidently, then, crossovers in these two regions do not occur independently. Since the frequency of double crossovers is *less* than that predicted on the assumption of independence, it is clear that in any one tetrad the occurrence of a crossover in one of these regions in some way reduces the probability of a crossover in the other.

The phenomenon which we have just illustrated is called **interference.** We customarily express its effects, however, in terms of **coincidence.** That is, we compare the number (or percentage) of double crossovers actually observed in linkage tests with the number that would be expected if crossovers in the two regions we are studying occurred independently of each other. *Coincidence* is simply the ratio of the observed number of double crossovers to the expected number.

In the data we have just examined (Table 12.2) there are two double crossovers; the expected number, on the assumption of independence, is $(0.193) \times (0.108) \times 1090$, or 0.0208×1090, which is 22.7. Coincidence of double crossing over is therefore $2/22.7 = 0.088$, or about 9 per cent. That is, only 9 per cent of the expected double crossovers actually occurred. In the data of Table 12.1, on the other hand, we find 89 double crossovers; the expected number is 0.07×1336 or 93.5, so that coincidence here is $89/93.5 = 0.95$. This figure means that there is very little interference between crossovers in the two regions to which these data relate; perhaps, in fact, there is none, since the 89 doubles observed may represent merely a chance deviation from the expected 93.5. When interference is complete, coincidence is zero; when there is no interference, coincidence is unity; it may, of course, have any intermediate value under other conditions.

Let us now examine the cytological basis of double crossing over, and see what light it may shed on the problem of interference. If a single crossover, as discussed in the last chapter, is caused by an exchange of parts between homologous chromatids in a tetrad, one would reasonably suppose that double crossovers would result from two exchanges in a tetrad, and this is in part true, but not completely so. How double exchanges are related to crossing over may be explained with the aid of Figure 12.1.

It was suggested in the last chapter on the basis of cytological observations that a chiasma involves only two of the four chromatids of a tetrad; and it has been securely established by genetic studies in a variety of organisms that only two of the four chromatids exchange parts at any one point, or level, of the tetrad.

A double exchange, however, (that is, two exchanges at different levels in the same tetrad) may be of several kinds (Figure 12.1). A *reciprocal* (two-strand) double exchange is one in which the same two chromatids are involved at both levels where exchange occurs. A *diagonal* (three strand) double exchange is one in which each of two sister chromatids exchanges with the same chromatid of the homolo-

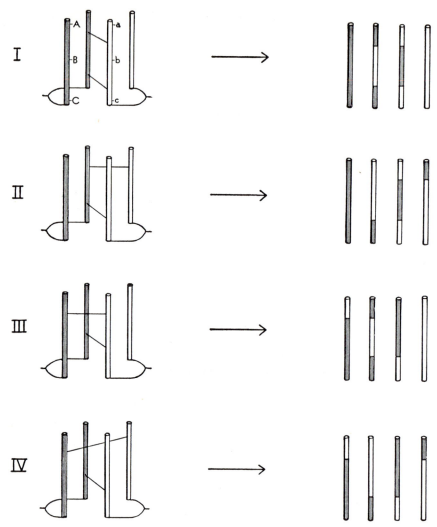

Fig. 12.1 Diagrammatic illustration of the consequences of various types of double exchanges in a tetrad.

TYPE OF EXCHANGE		NUMBER OF RESULTING CHROMATIDS WITH		
		NO CROSSOVER	SINGLE CROSSOVER	DOUBLE CROSSOVER
I	Reciprocal	2	0	2
II	Diagonal	1	2	1
III	Diagonal	1	2	1
IV	Complementary	0	4	0
	Sum	4	8	4
	Average per tetrad	1	2	1

gous chromosome; this can happen in twice as many ways as the reciprocal type. A *complementary* (four-strand) double exchange involves two different chromatids at each level. The diagrams in Figure 12.1 show clearly the genetic consequences of each of the four types, and in the legend below the figure the tabulated results are given.

Let us assume that the four types of double exchange occur with equal frequency. This would mean that the chromatids involved in an exchange at one level have no effect on what chromatids are involved at another. Then, on the average, two out of four, or one half, of all chromatids from tetrads with double exchanges between A and C would be single-crossover chromatids, showing recombination between alleles at A and C. One quarter would be noncrossovers, and another one quarter would be double-crossovers with the original parental combinations restored. On this assumption of equal likelihood of the four types, then, double exchanges could result in 50 per cent recombination at most, that is, if there were one between the A and C loci in every tetrad.

On the same assumption of the independence of exchanges at different levels with respect to the chromatids involved, it is easy to show that there could never be more than 50 per cent recombination between remote loci, no matter how many exchanges take place between them in each tetrad. We have just seen, for two exchanges per tetrad, that the frequencies of chromatids with 0, 1, and 2 crossovers are, respectively, $\frac{1}{4}, \frac{1}{2}, \frac{1}{4}$. You may recognize these as the successive terms of the expansion of $(\frac{1}{2} + \frac{1}{2})^2$. Similar reasoning shows that for any number, n, of exchanges per tetrad, the frequencies of chromatids with 0, 1, 2, 3, . . . n crossovers are given by the terms of the binomial expansion $(\frac{1}{2} + \frac{1}{2})^n$. But only chromatids with odd numbers of crossovers will exhibit recombination between the terminal loci. The frequencies of chromatids with odd-numbered crossovers are, of course, the alternate (second, fourth, etc.) terms of $(\frac{1}{2} + \frac{1}{2})^n$, and the student can easily verify that the sum of these is always one half. Thus, we reach a quite general conclusion, if our assumption of the independence of exchanges is correct, that recombination between genes at different loci in the same chromosome can never exceed fifty per cent, no matter how far apart the loci may be.

Suppose, however, the assumption of independence is not correct. Conceivably, the occurrence of an exchange between a given pair of chromatids in the region B — C of our diagram might render it less likely for this pair again to exchange in region A — B than for the other pair to do so. Under these circumstances, *reciprocal* double exchanges would be less frequent than *complementary* doubles. This would be one way in which we might account for the phenomenon of interference. But the assumption involved is an unsatisfactory one, as we shall see.

We must recall that on our earlier assumption, the chromatids involved in an exchange in region B–C in no way influence which pair will exchange in region A–B; that is, all types of double exchanges are equally likely. Now consider two pairs of genes, such as *A,a* and *C,c* in the diagram, far enough apart so that there is a double exchange between them in every tetrad. On the assumption of independence of exchanges, we should expect the different types to occur with equal frequency as shown below, with the result (as we have already learned) that 50 per cent of the chromatids would exhibit recombination between *A* and *C*.

TYPE OF EXCHANGE	NONCROSSOVER CHROMATIDS	SINGLE CROSSOVER CHROMATIDS	DOUBLE CROSSOVER CHROMATIDS
I Reciprocal	50	0	50
II Diagonal	25	50	25
III Diagonal	25	50	25
IV Complementary	0	100	0
Total	100	200	100

Recombinations A — C: 200/400 = 50%

If, however, we assume that reciprocal double exchanges are less likely to occur than complementary doubles, we might expect something like this:

TYPE OF EXCHANGE	NONCROSSOVER CHROMATIDS	SINGLE CROSSOVER CHROMATIDS	DOUBLE CROSSOVER CHROMATIDS
I Reciprocal	40	0	40
II Diagonal	25	50	25
III Diagonal	25	50	25
IV Complementary	0	120	0
Total	90	220	90

Recombinations A — C: 220/400 = 55%

Thus, the hypothesis that reciprocal exchanges are less frequent than the complementary type would lead us to expect that crossing over between remote loci might well exceed 50 per cent. In fact, however, crossing over significantly in excess of 50 per cent, if it occurs at all, is extremely rare.

For Drosophila and corn at least, in both of which there are chromosomes with an average of more than two exchanges per tetrad (see below) we can be fairly certain that reciprocal and complementary double exchanges occur with about equal frequency. We must conclude, therefore, that the genetic phenomenon of interference results, not from a differential reduction in frequency of a particular kind of double exchange (the reciprocal type), but more probably from a lessened likelihood of second exchanges of all types taking place in tetrads in which one exchange has already occurred.

Now it is not difficult to imagine in purely mechanical terms (supposing a certain amount of chromatid rigidity) how the occurrence of an exchange between two chromatids tightly twisted together could in some way relieve a strain which otherwise might result in an exchange between the *same two* chromatids at another point. An imaginary model such as this might thus explain a reduction, below chance expectancy, in the frequency of reciprocal double exchanges. It is a little harder to see on this basis, however, how an exchange between two given chromatids could also lessen the likelihood of an exchange between the *other two* chromatids. The purely mechanical model meets further difficulty when we attempt to explain *inter-chromosomal* effects on crossing over (see Schultz and Redfield).

It has been found, for example, that when a certain type of structural abnormality (*inversion*, see Chapter 21) is present in one chromosome of a pair, while the other member of the pair is of normal structure, crossing over between the two chromosomes of this pair is suppressed, probably because normal synapsis cannot occur. But, as Steinberg and Fraser, among others, have shown, the suppression of crossing over in one pair of chromosomes in this manner results, in many cases, in abnormally high frequencies of crossing over between various loci *in other chromosome pairs*. It is such facts as these (for which there is at present no clear explanation) that led us to suggest in the last chapter that the causes of crossing over and related phenomena are likely to lie rather in the chemical than in the mechanical properties of the chromosomes.

Although the frequency of genetic crossing over between alleles at any two loci, however far apart, does not exceed 50 per cent, a chromosome map may have a total length of 100 or even 200 units of crossover percentage. This is because map length is determined by measuring small distances at a time, where recombination percentage is a direct measure of exchange frequency. But it should be understood that the total map distance is a measure of the average number of crossovers found along the whole chromosome. If we can determine cytologically the average number of chiasmata for any chromosome, we should be able to predict the maximum total map length for that chromosome. For any one chiasma one half, or 50 per cent, of the four chromatids have crossovers. For two chiasmata there would be four

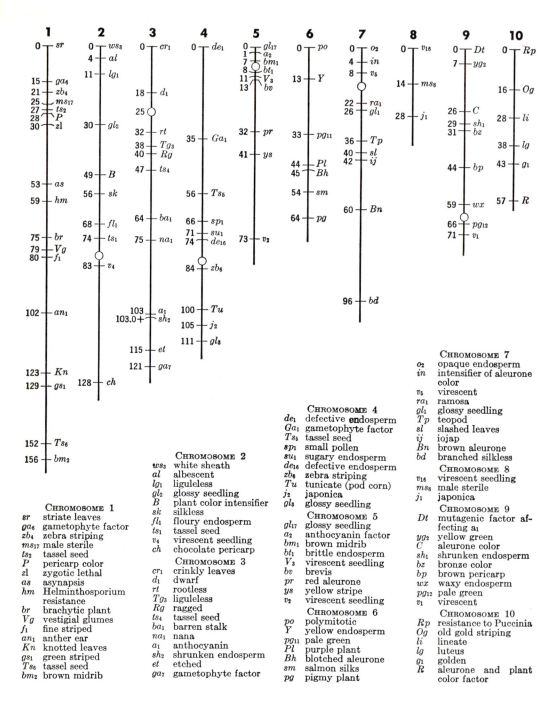

Chromosome 1
sr   striate leaves
ga₆   gametophyte factor
zb₄   zebra striping
ms₁₇   male sterile
ts₂   tassel seed
P   pericarp color
zl   zygotic lethal
as   asynapsis
hm   Helminthosporium
       resistance
br   brachytic plant
Vg   vestigial glumes
f₁   fine striped
an₁   anther ear
Kn   knotted leaves
gs₁   green striped
Ts₆   tassel seed
bm₂   brown midrib

Chromosome 2
ws₃   white sheath
al   albescent
lg₁   liguleless
gl₂   glossy seedling
B   plant color intensifier
sk   silkless
fl₁   floury endosperm
ts₁   tassel seed
v₄   virescent seedling
ch   chocolate pericarp

Chromosome 3
cr₁   crinkly leaves
d₁   dwarf
rt   rootless
Tg₃   liguleless
Rg   ragged
ts₄   tassel seed
ba₁   barren stalk
na₁   nana
a₁   anthocyanin
sh₂   shrunken endosperm
et   etched
ga₇   gametophyte factor

Chromosome 4
de₁   defective endosperm
Ga₁   gametophyte factor
Ts₅   tassel seed
sp₁   small pollen
su₁   sugary endosperm
de₁₆   defective endosperm
zb₆   zebra striping
Tu   tunicate (pod corn)
j₂   japonica
gl₃   glossy seedling

Chromosome 5
gl₁₇   glossy seedling
a₂   anthocyanin factor
bm₁   brown midrib
bt₁   brittle endosperm
V₃   virescent seedling
bv   brevis
pr   red aleurone
ys   yellow stripe
v₂   virescent seedling

Chromosome 6
po   polymitotic
Y   yellow endosperm
pg₁₁   pale green
Pl   purple plant
Bh   blotched aleurone
sm   salmon silks
pg   pigmy plant

Chromosome 7
o₂   opaque endosperm
in   intensifier of aleurone
       color
v₅   virescent
ra₁   ramosa
gl₁   glossy seedling
Tp   teopod
sl   slashed leaves
ij   iojap
Bn   brown aleurone
bd   branched silkless

Chromosome 8
v₁₆   virescent seedling
ms₈   male sterile
j₁   japonica

Chromosome 9
Dt   mutagenic factor af-
       fecting a₁
yg₂   yellow green
C   aleurone color
sh₁   shrunken endosperm
bz   bronze color
bp   brown pericarp
wx   waxy endosperm
pg₁₂   pale green
v₁   virescent

Chromosome 10
Rp   resistance to Puccinia
Og   old gold striping
li   lineate
lg   luteus
g₁   golden
R   aleurone and plant
       color factor

Fig. 12.2   A chromosome map for corn (*Zea*). *Courtesy Dr. Rhoades*

crossovers in the four chromatids (Fig. 12.1). In a tetrad with three chiasmata there would be a total of six crossovers in the four chromatids. Rated on the basis of 100 chromatids this would give 150 crossovers in 100 chromatids. The total map length, then, for a chromosome with a chiasma frequency of three would be 150 crossover units. Each chiasma, then, corresponds to 50 crossover units, and the total map length will be 50 times the average number of chiasmata. Nevertheless, as we have seen, there will not be more than 50 per cent recombination even for genes at opposite ends of a chromosome. For example, in the map in Figure 11.2 the distance between roughoid and minute on the third chromosome is 101. The observed recombination percentage between them, however, is only 45.8.

By studying the crossover percentages, then, genes may be located in their relative positions along chromosomes. By considering each per cent of crossing over as a unit of distance, we may make maps of chromosomes of any species in which we know a sufficient number of genes. A series of gene pairs which are linked with each other is of course considered to be on the same pair of chromosomes, and such a series of gene pairs is known as a **linkage group.** The members of a linkage group not only show linkage with each other, but show random assortment with regard to the genes of any other linkage group. Moreover, the number of linkage groups should be equal to the number of pairs of chromosomes.

This has been found to be the case in those species in which we know sufficient characters to make adequate maps. In *Drosophila melanogaster*, the species which we have been discussing, for example, four pairs of chromosomes occur and four linkage groups are known. One of these linkage groups contains sex-linked genes, and belongs to the sex chromosomes. Another is very small, containing only five genes, and is associated with the small pair of chromosomes. The other two linkage groups are large and are carried on the two pairs of long chromosomes. Figure 11.2 shows a map of the chromosomes of *Drosophila melanogaster*.

In other species of Drosophila the number of linkage groups also corresponds to the number of pairs of chromosomes. Thus, in *Drosophila obscura* Lancefield has shown that there are five linkage groups, and cytological studies show five pairs of chromosomes. In *Drosophila willistoni* Metz has found only three linkage groups, and correspondingly only three pairs of chromosomes. In corn Emerson and his students found ten pairs of chromosomes and ten linkage groups. In garden peas there are seven pairs of chromosomes and seven linkage groups. Chromosome maps of corn, tomatoes, and mice are shown in Figures 12.2, 12.3 and 12.4.

In some instances there are not enough genes known or studied

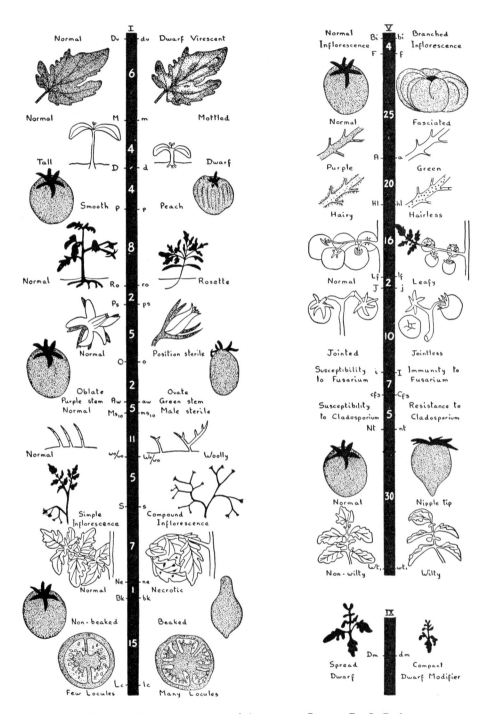

Fig. 12.3 Chromosome maps of the tomato. *Courtesy Dr. L. Butler*

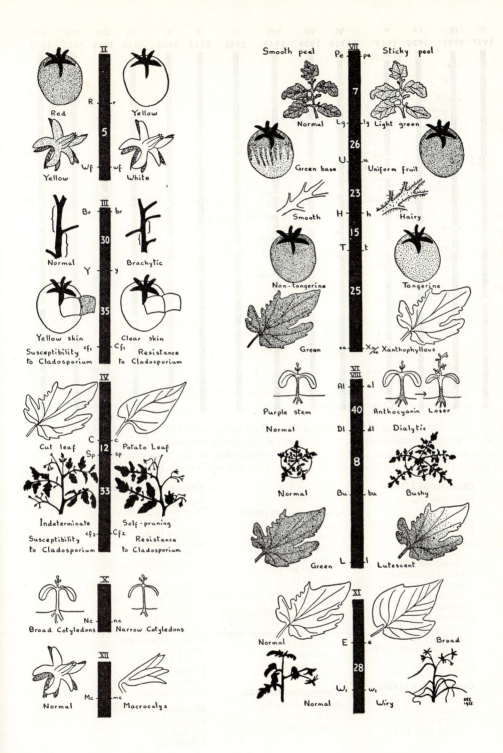

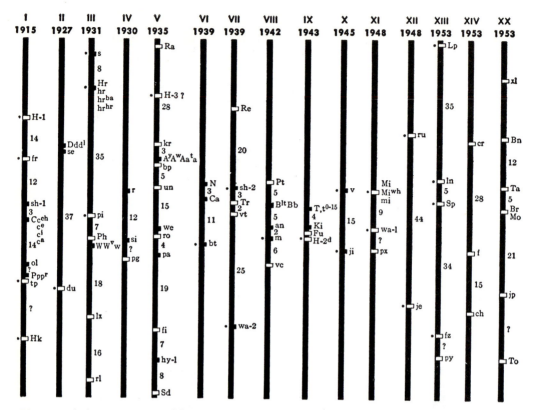

Fig. 12.4 A chromosome map of the mouse as of 1954. Linkage groups have been determined for 15 of the 20 pairs of chromosomes. The numbers along the chromosomes represent cross-over percentages between genes. The characters corresponding to the gene symbols are shown below. *From Margaret Dickie in the Journal of the National Cancer Institute*

Chromosome I (1915)
histocompatibility-1
  (H-1)
frizzy (fr)
shaker-1 (sh-1)
albino series
  full color (C)
  chinchilla (c^{ch})
  extreme dilution (c^e)
  intense chinchilla (c^i)
  albino (c)
oligodactyly (ol)
pink-eye series
  normal-eye (P)
  pink-eye (p)
  Japanese ruby (p^r)
taupe (tp)
hook (Hk)

Chromosome II (1927)
dilution series
  intense color (D)
  dilution (d)
  dilute lethal (d^l)

short ear (se)
ducky (du)

Chromosome III (1931)
piebald (s)
hairless series
  full coat (Hr)
  hairless (hr)
  bare (hr^{ba})
  rhino (hr^{rh})
pirouette (pi)
patch (Ph)
dominant spotting series
  dominant spotting (W)
  viable dominant spot-
    ting (W^v)
  normal (w)
luxate (lx)
reeler (rl)

Chromosome IV (1930)
rodless retina (r)
silver (si)
pygmy (pg)

Chromosome V (1935)
ragged (Ra)
histocompatibility-3
  (H-3)
kreisler (kr)
agouti series
  yellow (A^y)
  light-bellied agouti
    (A^w)
  dark-bellied agouti (A)
  black and tan (a^t)
  nonagouti (a)
brachypody (bp)
undulated (un)
wellhaarigkeit (we)
rough (ro)
pallid (pa)
fidget (fi)
hydrocephalus-1 (hy-1)
short Danforth (Sd)

Chromosome VI (1939)
naked (N)
caracul (Ca)
belted (bt)

to make complete chromosome maps, so that the number of known linkage groups may be less than the number of pairs of chromosomes. In rice, for example, there are 12 pairs of chromosomes, but as of 1956 only eight linkage groups have been determined. Future research will undoubtedly fill in these gaps. It is important to note that in no case has the number of linkage groups been found to be greater than the number of pairs of chromosomes.

Recent work on chromosome aberrations makes it possible to state just which pair of chromosomes carries each linkage group. This has been done by utilizing the occasional discovery of an individual in which there appears an extra chromosome of one pair. Such individuals are "trisomic," and of course some of their gametes will contain one chromosome of this set, others two. Hence the genes carried on this particular set of chromosomes should produce abnormal ratios in future generations. By comparison of the genes which give abnormal ratios with the chromosomes which show corresponding variation in numbers, the linkage group may be assigned to the proper pair of chromosomes. The whole question of chromosomal aberrations will be discussed in more detail in Chapters 20 and 21.

Although the proportion of crossing over between any two pairs of genes is in general constant, various conditions may influence it. In Drosophila, Bridges has shown that crossing over tends to become less frequent as the individual grows older. Plough has shown that heat or cold (27° C., 10° C.) will increase crossing over. Radiation may also affect the proportion. Certain genes are known which have an effect upon crossing over, either in part of a chromosome or in the whole chromosome. The abnormal arrangement of part of a chromosome may prevent crossing over in that part. Under given conditions, however, the proportion of crossing over between any two pairs of genes is remarkably constant.

Chromosome VII (1939)
rex (*Re*)
shaker-2 (*sh-2*)
trembler (*Tr*)
vestigial tail (*vt*)
waved-2 (*wa-2*)

Chromosome VIII (1932)
pintail (*Pt*)
brown series
  light (B^{lt})
  black (*B*)
  brown (*b*)
anaemia (*an*)
misty (*m*)
vacillans (*vc*)

Chromosome IX (1943)
brachyury *T*
anury series (t^e-t^{15}, t^{w1-w6})
kinky (*Ki*)

fused (*Fu*)
histocompatibility-2
  (H-2^d, etc.)

Chromosome X (1945)
waltzing (*v*)
jittery (*ji*)

Chromosome XI (1948)
microphthalmia series
  normal (*Mi*)
  dominant white (Mi^{wh})
  microphthalmia (*mi*)
waved-1 (*wa-1*)
postaxial hememelia (*px*)

Chromosome XII (1948)
ruby (*ru*)
jerker (*je*)

Chromosome XIII (1953)
loop tail (*Lp*)
leaden (*ln*)
splotch (*Sp*)
fuzzy (*fz*)
polydactyly (*py*)

Chromosome XIV (1953)
crinkled (*cr*)
flexed tail (*f*)
congenital hydrocephalus
  (*ch*)

Chromosome XX (1953)
sex-linked lethal (*xl*)
bent tail (*Bn*)
tabby (*Ta*)
brindled (*Br*)
mottled (*Mo*)
jimpy (*jp*)
tortoise shell (*To*)

One final point should be emphasized. When two pairs of genes are linked, we know them to be located in the same pair of chromosomes. Either allele of one pair may be located in the same chromosome with either allele of the other pair, however. For example, in peach trees Bailey and French state that soft melting flesh is dominant to tough nonmelting flesh, and freestone type of fruit is dominant to clingstone; these two pairs of genes are linked, with 8 per cent crossing over. Designating the two pairs of genes as T and t, C and c, respectively, a chromosome of the pair carrying these genes could carry either T and C, T and c, t and C, or t and c.

If T and C were in one chromosome they would be separated in only 8 per cent of the gametes. However, when crossing over did occur in such a way that T and c were placed in the same chromosome, these two genes would remain just as closely linked as T and C formerly were: that is, they would be separated in only 8 per cent of the gametes.

Crossing over changes the relationships of two pairs of genes only when both pairs are heterozygous. A tree homozygous for the genes for melting flesh and freestone would be of the genotype $(TC)(TC)$. Crossing over occurs in the maturation of the germ cells of such a tree, but it has no effect, since even after crossing over T and C would still be on the same chromosome in each member of the pair.

Likewise a tree homozygous for melting flesh but heterozygous for freestone, of the formula $(TC)(Tc)$, will have crossing over taking place in the maturation of its germ cells, but again the relationships of these genes will not be altered. T and C will still be together, as will T and c, even after crossing over.

A double heterozygote, however, will have its gene relations affected by crossing over. A tree of the formula $(TC)(tc)$ will produce noncrossover gametes of two kinds (TC) and (tc), but will also produce crossover gametes of two new combinations (Tc) and (tC). Thus it is seen that only in double heterozygotes is crossing over followed by a change in the relationships of the genes concerned.

A double heterozygote may be one of two sorts, however. Both dominant genes may be on one chromosome of the pair, both recessives on the other. We speak of this as the **coupling phase.** Again, one dominant gene and one recessive gene may be on one chromosome of the pair, the other dominant and the other recessive on the other chromosome. This condition we speak of as the **repulsion phase.** Thus a tree of the formula $(TC)(tc)$ would be in the coupling phase, one of the formula $(Tc)(tC)$ would be in the repulsion phase. Yet the same genes are present in both. The distinction is very important, however, in linkage studies, and becomes of particular importance in studies of human linkage.

We have learned in this chapter that corresponding to each chromosome there is a group of linked genes which occur in a definite linear order in the chromosome, and that maps of the chromosomes showing the location of the genes may be constructed. From this there emerge new parallels between the behavior of genes and the behavior of chromosomes, which we may add to those we have already drawn. The parallels are as follows:

At the time when genetic crossing over takes place, the genes are arranged in linear order. *At the time when cytological crossing over takes place, the chromatin material is in an attenuated linear arrangement.*

The number of pairs of chromosomes is, in general, definite and constant for any given species. *The number of linkage groups in those species which have thus far been studied is equal to, or at least never exceeds, the number of pairs of chromosomes in the species.*

PROBLEMS

In the next five problems, use the following facts: In a small wasp, *Habrobracon*, Whiting and his collaborators have shown that the following three pairs of genes are linked: *Vl,vl* (normal wings, veinless wings); *Ho,ho* (dark body, honey body color); *L,l* (normal antennae, long antennae). The crossover value between *Vl* and *Ho* is 8 per cent; between *Vl* and *L*, 17 per cent; and between *Ho* and *L*, 10 per cent.

12.1 In what order do these genes occur on the chromosome?

12.2 The genes *C,c* (black eyes, cantaloup eyes) are linked with *L,l* showing 15 per cent crossing over. Where would you place *C* on the map? What further data would you need in order to place it accurately?

12.3 The crossover per cent between *C* and *Vl* is found to be 28. With this information, where would you place *C* on the map?

12.4 The sum of the crossover per cents between *Vl* and *L* and between *L* and *C* is 32. Yet the crossover per cent actually found between *Vl* and *C* is only 28. How do you account for this?

12.5 Approximately what crossover per cent would you expect to find between *C* and *Ho?*

12.6 In poultry the following four pairs of genes are linked: *F,f* (frizzled feathers, plain feathers); *H,h* (crested, noncrested); *I,i* (white, colored); *G,g* (nonfrayed feathers, frayed feathers). The crossover value between *H* and *I* is 18 percent; between *G* and *H* is 30 per cent; between *I* and *F* is 18 per cent; and between *G* and *I* is 36 per cent; and between *H* and *F* is 27 per cent. In what order do these genes occur on the chromosome?

12.7 Another pair of genes in poultry consists of *R* (rose comb) and its recessive allele *r* (single comb). A homozygous nonfrayed hen (see Problem 12.6) with single comb was mated to a frayed, homozygous rose-comb rooster. The F_1 were crossed to frayed, single-comb fowls. The results were as follows:

nonfrayed, rose comb	58
nonfrayed, single comb	56
frayed, rose comb	51
frayed, single comb	55

Are the genes *G,g* and *R,r* linked?

12.8 Referring to Problems 12.6 and 12.7, would you expect to find the alleles *R,r*, linked with *F,f,* if you made the appropriate linkage tests? With *H,h?* With *I,i?* Add *R,r* to the chromosome map of the fowl.

12.9 Mendel worked with 7 pairs of contrasting genes in peas. The pea has 7 pairs of chromosomes. Why did Mendel not discover the principle of linkage?

12.10 If Mendel had studied one more pair of genes in relation to the 7 pairs he did investigate, what would necessarily have happened?

12.11 More than 200 pairs of genes are known in the garden snapdragon, but their linkage relationships are not yet thoroughly worked out. The snapdragon has 8 pairs of chromosomes. Into how many linkage groups will these 200 pairs of genes be expected to fall?

12.12 The rabbit has 22 pairs of chromosomes. Seventeen pairs of genes are known from the standpoint of their linkage relations. Thirteen of these pairs fall into five small groups. The remaining four pairs do not belong to these linkage groups and are not linked with each other. How many more pairs of genes can be discovered in the rabbit which will be independent of those already mentioned and independent of each other?

12.13 In the vetches (leguminous plants) the various genes which have been studied fall into seven linkage groups. How many chromosomes would you expect to find in vetches?

12.14 Why have we made so little progress in mapping the chromosomes of man and other mammals compared to the extensive results in Drosophila and many plants?

12.15 In what ways have the mapping of chromosomes and the discovery of linkage groups helped to strengthen the hypothesis that genes are carried on the chromosomes?

12.16 Below are given some data from Metz on the crossovers between the linked genes yellow, vesiculated, magenta, forked, rugose, glazed, and hairy in *Drosophila virilis*. On the basis of these data, map these genes as accurately as possible.

GENES	TOTAL FLIES	CROSSOVERS
yellow-vesiculated	766	124
yellow-magenta	586	218
yellow-forked	699	295
yellow-hairy	162	65
vesiculated-magenta	263	85
vesiculated-forked	814	313
vesiculated-glazed	579	229
magenta-forked	262	13
magenta-rugose	361	106
hairy-forked	162	5
forked-rugose	286	81
forked-glazed	451	113

12.17 The chromosome map of *Drosophila melanogaster* (Figure 11.2) shows that these genes are all on the third chromosome: *p* (pink eyes, recessive to *P*, red eyes), *cu* (curled wing, recessive to *Cu*, normal wing), and *sr* (stripe, recessive to *Sr*, nonstripe). It shows also that the map distance between *p* and *cu* is 2 units and the distance between *cu* and *sr* is 12 units. Diagram the crosses necessary to verify this mapping, and indicate the expected percentage of each phenotypic class in the progeny of your test matings.

12.18 Sturtevant (1921) reported the following data from crosses made with *Drosophila simulans*. The genes involved were *Yl,yl* (gray body, yellow body), *Cm, cm* (red eyes, carmine eyes) and *F,f* (normal bristles, forked bristles). Like the corresponding recessive mutants in *D. melanogaster*, these genes are sex-linked. Yellow, carmine, nonforked females were crossed with gray, red-eyed, forked males. The F_1 females were mated to yellow, carmine, forked males. The test-cross progeny showed the following gene combinations in the numbers indicated:

yl cm F	725	
Yl Cm f	719	
yl Cm f	419	
Yl cm F	383	
yl cm f	134	
Yl Cm F	109	
yl Cm F	34	
Yl cm f	32	
TOTAL	2555	

Map the loci of the genes involved in this test.

12.19 In corn, a test cross of (ABC) $(abc) \times (abc)(abc)$ produced the following:

$$\left.\begin{array}{l} ABC \\ abc \end{array}\right\} 422$$

$$\left.\begin{array}{l} Abc \\ aBC \end{array}\right\} 145$$

$$\left.\begin{array}{l} ABc \\ abC \end{array}\right\} 356$$

$$\left.\begin{array}{l} AbC \\ aBc \end{array}\right\} 77$$

Indicate the relative positions of A, B, and C on the chromosome.

12.20 A corn plant which in the seedling stage was *glossy* leafed, *virescent* (poor in chlorophyll), and *liguleless* (lacking certain appendages at the bases of the leaves) was crossed to a plant which as a seedling had dull leaves, normal chlorophyll content, and ligules. The F_1 seedlings all had dull leaves, normal chlorophyll content, and ligules. F_1 plants were test-crossed to plants from glossy, virescent, liguleless seedlings. The leaf characters of the resulting seedlings are tabulated below, where "green" means having normal chlorophyll.

dull, green, with ligules	313
dull, green, liguleless	86
dull, virescent, with ligules	224
dull, virescent, liguleless	29
glossy, green, with ligules	36
glossy, green, liguleless	232
glossy, virescent, with ligules	86
glossy, virescent, liguleless	247
TOTAL	1253

From these data, determine the order of the *glossy*, *virescent*, and *liguleless* loci, and the percentage of crossing over between *glossy* and *virescent*, *glossy* and *liguleless*, and *virescent* and *liguleless*.

REFERENCES

BABCOCK, E. B. and CLAUSEN, R. E., *Genetics in Relation to Agriculture*, 2nd edition. New York, McGraw-Hill Book Co. (1927).

BRIDGES, C. B., *Carneg. Inst. Wash. Publ.* 391 (1929).

BRIDGES, C. B., and MORGAN, T. H., *Carneg. Inst. Wash. Publ.* 327 (1923).

DICKIE, M. M., *Jour. Nat. Cancer Inst.* **15**:679 (1954).

HUTT, H. B., *Genetics of the Fowl.* New York, McGraw-Hill Book Co. (1949).

LANCEFIELD, D. E., *Genetics* **7**:335 (1922).

MATHER, K., *Biol. Reviews* **13**:252 (1938).

METZ, C. W., *Amer. Naturalist* **57**:381 (1923); Section XLIII in *Special Cytology*, edited by Cowdry (1932).

PERKINS, D. D., *Jour. Cell. and Comp. Physiol.* **45** Suppl. 2:119 (1955).

PLOUGH, H. H., *Jour. Exper. Zoöl.* **24**:147 (1917); *ibid.* **32**:197 (1921).

RILEY, H. P., *An Introduction to Genetics and Cytogenetics.* New York, John Wiley and Sons (1948).

SCHULTZ, J., and REDFIELD, H., *Cold Spring Harbor Symposium on Quantitative Biology* **16**:175 (1951).

SCHWARTZ, D., *Jour. Cell. and Comp. Physiol.* **45** Suppl. 2:171 (1955).

STEINBERG, A. and FRASER, F. C., *Genetics* **29**:83 (1944).

STURTEVANT, A. H., *Genetics* **6**:43 (1921).

WEINSTEIN, A., *Jour. Cell. and Comp. Physiol.* **45** Suppl. 2:249 (1955).

CHAPTER THIRTEEN

Multiple alleles

We have been using the term "alleles" to apply to the members of a pair of contrasting genes. We have become familiar with this usage of the term, and we have learned that the two alleles of a pair segregate at the reduction division, with the result that each gamete contains only one allele of each pair. On the basis of the chromosome hypothesis, we assume that a gene always occupies a particular spot or **locus** in a chromosome, so that the chromosome could contain one or the other of a pair of alleles, but normally not both.

In speaking of alleles we have up to this point considered them as occurring in pairs. We now come to a discussion of the fact that a set of alleles may contain more than two members. Cases are known where sets of alleles contain three, four, and even twenty or more members. We call such sets **multiple alleles.** No matter how many members a set of alleles may contain, only two of them may normally occur in a somatic cell, and only one in a gamete.

One of the most interesting characters known in human beings is inherited on the basis of multiple alleles. We shall discuss it later in this chapter.

We have learned in preceding chapters how to recognize the fact that two genes are alleles. Let us now see how we would recognize the presence of a third allele.

If we cross a homozygous colored rabbit with an albino, we obtain an F_1 generation in which all the individuals are colored. The F_2 generation from this cross consists of both colored and albino rabbits in the ratio of three to one. We know from this that color is dependent upon a dominant gene, albinism upon a recessive gene, and the two genes are alleles.

In addition to complete (or full) color, however, we know a condition in rabbits in which only the extremities are colored, the rest of the fur being white. This condition is known as the Himalayan. Himalayan rabbits have pigmented ears, nose, tips of feet, and tip of tail. The Himalayan condition is a partial color, obviously different from the full color of a completely gray or black rabbit, for example.

Now if we cross a full-colored rabbit with a Himalayan, we obtain an F_1, all of which are full-colored. The F_2 generation consists of full-colored rabbits and Himalayan rabbits in the ratio of three to one. Obviously full color is dependent upon a dominant gene and Himalayan upon its recessive allele.

What, then, would be expected to happen if we should cross a Himalayan rabbit with an albino? If the Himalayan and the albino mutations represent changes in *different* genes, we should expect two pairs of genes to be involved in the cross. In this case we should obtain a two-pair ratio in the F_2, just as we found to be the case in Chapter 5 when an albino rat was crossed with a black one. When the cross is made between a Himalayan rabbit and an albino, however, a surprising result is obtained.

In such a cross the F_1 are all Himalayan, not full-colored as would be expected if two pairs of genes were concerned. The F_2 does not give a two-pair ratio, but consists only of Himalayans and albinos in the ratio of $3:1$. We must conclude, therefore, that the genes for Himalayan and for albinism are alleles. *But if the full color and the albino genes are allelic, and the full color and the Himalayan factors are allelic, and finally the genes for Himalayan and for albinism are allelic, it is evident that all three genes must belong to the same set of alleles.*

If this is the case and a gene always occupies a particular locus on a chromosome, it is evident that any individual rabbit could carry only two of these three genes at a time, and any gamete could carry only one. This is found to be the case by breeding experiments. If we designate C as the gene for full color and c as the gene for albinism, we may designate the third allele in the series as c^h. The superscript h stands for Himalayan. It is customary in designating multiple alleles to give the one which is dominant to all others a capital letter, the one which is recessive to all others the corresponding small letter, and the alleles which are in between the small letter with an appropriate superscript. Thus, in this case, color is dominant to both Himalayan and albinism. We therefore designate it C. Himalayan is recessive to color, but dominant to albinism. We designate it then as c^h. Albinism, being recessive to both the others, receives the designation c. Of course, in some instances dominance may be lacking between two members of a set of multiple alleles, just as we have found to be the case between the two members of a pair.

Rabbits could then be of the following formulas in regard to this particular set of genes.

Fig. 13.1 Coat colors in rabbits
due to multiple alleles. From top
to bottom: full color, chinchilla,
Himalayan, and albino.

$$\left.\begin{array}{l} CC \\ Cc^h \\ Cc \end{array}\right\} \text{result in full color}$$

$$\left.\begin{array}{l} c^h c^h \\ c^h c \end{array}\right\} \text{result in Himalayan}$$

$$cc \quad \text{results in albinism}$$

Still another allele has been found in this series. There are rabbits known as chinchillas, in which all traces of yellow are lacking in the fur, giving it a characteristic silvery gray appearance (Fig. 13.1). When homozygous chinchillas are crossed with full-colored rabbits or with Himalayans or with albinos, the F_2 always show a one-pair ratio, indicating that the gene for chinchilla is allelic to the other three. It is recessive to full color, but dominant to the other two, so that we designate it as c^{ch}. Taking all of these alleles into consideration, a rabbit could carry any two of them, and a gamete could contain but one of them, so that rabbits could be of the following formulas in regard to these genes:

$$\left.\begin{array}{l} CC \\ Cc^{ch} \\ Cc^h \\ Cc \end{array}\right\} \text{result in full color}$$

$$\left.\begin{array}{l} c^{ch} c^{ch} \\ c^{ch} c^h \\ c^{ch} c \end{array}\right\} \text{result in chinchilla}$$

$$\left.\begin{array}{l} c^h c^h \\ c^h c \end{array}\right\} \text{result in Himalayan}$$

$$cc \quad \text{results in albinism}$$

We may consider for a moment how this state of affairs came about. The original wild rabbits from which the tame rabbits have been domesticated were gray and must have carried the genes CC. Somewhere, at some time, by mutation, a process of which we know very little, the chemical composition of one of the C genes in a developing germ cell became changed in such a way as to be unable to function in the production of color. Let us call the changed gene c.

The gamete containing c in place of C would probably unite with one containing the usual C, since mutations are relatively rare. The resulting individual would be of the formula Cc and would show no sign that its genotype was any different from other rabbits. It would, however, produce germ cells of two kinds, half of them containing C and half c. Eventually in a later generation two gametes each containing c might unite, thus producing an individual of the formula cc,

Fig. 13.2 Plumage color in ducks, dependent upon multiple alleles. Males at left, females at right. Top, restricted mallard; center, mallard; bottom, dusky mallard. Dominance is from top to bottom. *From Jaap in Genetics*

which would be albino. The phenotypic
appearance of a mutation thus occurs
much later than the mutation itself if the
mutation is a recessive autosomal one,
as in this case. A dominant mutation
would show up in the first generation. Even
a recessive mutation, if it were sex-linked,
could show up in the first generation in
one sex.

In addition to the mutation from C to
c, it has happened at some time or times in
the past that in a rabbit of the formula CC
the chemical composition of one of the C
genes in a developing germ cell became
changed by mutation, this time resulting
in a gene which partially restricts the
development of color, forming it only in
the extremities, where the temperature is
lower than in the rest of the body. Let us
designate this changed gene as c^h. Eventually, as we have just seen in the case of the
gene for albinism, a rabbit could receive the
gene c^h from each parent, and a Himalayan
individual, $c^h c^h$, would result. Obviously,
when Himalayans and albinos were finally
crossed, the genes c^h and c would have to
behave as alleles.

In this way numerous series of multiple alleles have been formed in various
animals and plants and in man. Not
always do the various alleles exhibit dominance. Sometimes blending occurs between
them.

In our discussion of sex-linked inheritance we considered the genes for red eyes
and white eyes in Drosophila. This set of
alleles has many members, including not
only red and white, but wine, coral, blood,
eosin, cherry, apricot, buff, tinged, and

Fig. 13.3 Ducklings of the three plumage
types shown in Figure 13.2. Top, restricted
mallard; center, mallard; bottom, dusky
mallard. *From Jaap in Genetics*

ivory. In snapdragons one set of nine alleles for flower color ranges
from red through paler shades to ivory with red stripes. In ducks
Jaap has worked out an interesting set of three alleles affecting
plumage color (Figs. 13.2 and 13.3), each of which produces a variation of the mallard pattern.

In man the **blood groups** are inherited on the basis of multiple alleles. Since they are among the most interesting of human characters, we shall discuss them in some detail.

Whenever a foreign protein is injected into the blood stream of an animal, the cells of the animal produce a characteristic substance which will react with the foreign protein. This substance produced by the cells is known as an **antibody,** and becomes particularly abundant in the blood stream. The foreign protein which causes the production of the antibody is called an **antigen.** Whenever an antigen and its antibody are brought together in solution, a typical reaction occurs. This **antigen-antibody reaction** may be of various sorts.

If the antigen is a poison, or **toxin,** the antibody which is formed may neutralize the toxin and is called an **antitoxin,** the reaction being the **toxin-antitoxin** reaction. If the antigen is in solution the antibody may be a **precipitin,** which will cause the antigen to settle out of the solution by **precipitation.** If the antigen is in the form of cells the antibody may be a **lysin,** which will disintegrate the cells. Such a reaction is **lysis,** well-known examples being **hemolysis,** the disintegration of blood cells, and **bacteriolysis,** the breaking down of bacteria. Finally, if the antigen is in the form of cells, the antibody formed may react with it in such a way as to cause the clumping, or **agglutination,** of the cells. The antibody in this case is an **agglutinin,** the antigen being called an **agglutinogen.**

Antibodies produced by a foreign protein getting into the system are **immune antibodies.** In addition to this, certain antibodies occur naturally in the body and do not have to be produced by injection or otherwise. Such antibodies are **normal antibodies.**

The characters we are about to discuss involve the agglutination reaction.

In 1900 Dr. Karl Landsteiner, working in a medical laboratory in Vienna, discovered that when the red blood cells of one person were mixed with the blood serum of another person agglutination sometimes occurred. The reaction did not happen in every combination of serum and cells, but only when the red cells of certain people were mixed with the serum of certain other people. Obviously, normal antibodies must occur in some bloods, and normal antigens must occur in the red cells of some people.

Further investigation of this phenomenon disclosed the fact that there were two such antigens in human red cells and two corresponding antibodies in the serums. The two antigens were, for convenience, named A and B. Landsteiner and others who took up the investigations found that a person might have one of these antigens in his cells or he might have the other or both or neither. There are thus four kinds of persons in the world in regard to the two antigens, and these four possibilities are known as the **blood groups.** A person having antigen A in his cells is said to belong to **group A;** a person having antigen B belongs to **group B;** a person having both antigens is in **group AB;** and a person having neither belongs to **group O.**

The groups were originally designated by numbers (I, II, III, and IV) instead of letters, but unfortunately Moss in America and Jansky in Europe independently numbered them, and groups I and IV were reversed in the two systems. The resulting confusion led to the adoption of the letter system, which is now universally used.

Whatever antigen a person has in his cells, the corresponding antibody is lacking in the serum. This obviously must be so, since if a person of group A had the antibody against A in his serum, he would agglutinate his own cells, and die. When an antigen is not present in the cells, the corresponding antibody *is* present. Thus a person of group A has antigen A but no antibody against A; he has no antigen B but does have the antibody against B. The antigens in the cells and the antibodies in the serums of all four groups are shown in Table 13.1.

Table 13.1. THE ANTIGENS AND ANTIBODIES OF THE A–B BLOOD GROUPS

BLOOD GROUP	ANTIGENS IN CELLS	ANTIBODIES IN SERUM
O	—	anti-A, anti-B
A	A	anti-B
B	B	anti-A
AB	A, B	—

The first practical importance of the blood groups was in connection with blood transfusions. It may readily be seen that if a person loses blood in an accident and needs to have blood given him, it would not do to have the introduced blood cells clump up into bunches as fast as they were given. For one thing, they could not go through the fine capillaries which connect the arteries and veins. A test is made before every transfusion, therefore, to make sure that the blood given will not have its cells agglutinated by the serum of the patient.

The application of the blood groups to transfusion has, of course, nothing to do with genetics, but genetic applications do exist. The fact that people differ in regard to their blood groups makes it possible to study the inheritance of these antigens in the cells. Thousands of families in all parts of the world have been examined, with the result that the inheritance of the blood groups is now well understood.

The various combinations of blood groups which can occur in parents and the various kinds of children which these parents can produce are shown in Table 13.2. These results are explainable on the basis of multiple alleles. The standard notation for the genes concerned is as follows: I^A represents the gene for antigen A, I^B represents the gene for the production of antigen B, and i represents the gene which results in neither antigen. I^A and I^B are each dominant to i, but neither is dominant to the other. When they are both present in an individual, both antigens are produced. (The letter "I" was chosen because it is the first letter of the word isoagglutinogen). The genotypes of various persons and the consequent blood groups of these persons are shown in Table 13.3.

Table 13.2. The Inheritance of the Blood Groups, Based on the Study of Thousands of Families

Blood Groups of Parents	Blood Groups Which May Occur in Children	Blood Groups Which Do Not Occur in Children
O × O	O	A, B, AB
O × A	O, A	B, AB
A × A	O, A	B, AB
O × B	O, B	A, AB
B × B	O, B	A, AB
A × B	O, A, B, AB	—
O × AB	A, B	O, AB
A × AB	A, B, AB	O
B × AB	A, B, AB	O
AB × AB	A, B, AB	O

Table 13.3. The A-B Blood Groups

A-B Group	Genotype	Reactions with Antiserum	
		Anti-A	Anti-B
O	ii	—	—
A	I^AI^A, I^Ai	+	—
B	I^BI^B, I^Bi	—	+
AB	I^AI^B	+	+

From the above facts and from Tables 13.2 and 13.3 it will be seen that antigen A never appears in a child's blood unless it was present in the blood of at least one of the parents. Likewise antigen B never appears in a child's blood unless it was present in the blood of the father or mother or both. From these facts are derived practical applications in the field of legal medicine.

It is possible, for example, to determine parenthood of babies who may have been inadvertently exchanged in a hospital. In one case two mothers went home from the hospital at the same time, each with a new baby. When mother number one bathed her baby, she found the name of mother number two on a tag on the baby's body. Mother number two refused to exchange babies and a court case resulted.

After various attempts to settle the case had failed, the blood groups were studied and the problem was solved at once. The parents of family number one were both of group O, and the baby they took home with them was group A. In family number two, the father was group O, the mother was group AB, and the baby they took home with them was group O. Comparison with Table 13.2 will show that neither family could have produced the child they took home, while each could have produced the other. It was clear that the babies had inadvertently been given to the wrong mothers; and the court ordered the babies exchanged.

It may of course happen in such cases that both babies are of the same group or that both families are of the correct blood group combination to produce either child. In such instances the blood tests would prove nothing. They are potentially valuable, however, and always worth trying in circumstances of this nature.

The blood groups are also valuable in helping to settle cases of disputed parentage. The fact that these antigens never appear in a child's blood unless they were present in the blood of at least one parent may be used in legal proceedings, as shown in Table 13.4. A man of the wrong group may be unhesitatingly stated not to be the father of the child concerned.

Table 13.4. MEDICO-LEGAL APPLICATIONS OF THE BLOOD GROUPS

BLOOD GROUP OF CHILD	BLOOD GROUP OF MOTHER	BLOOD GROUPS TO WHICH FATHER CANNOT BELONG
O	O	AB
O	A	AB
O	B	AB
A	O	O, B
A	B	O, B
B	O	O, A
B	A	O, A
AB	A	O, A
AB	B	O, B
AB	AB	O

The test for the blood groups is made by mixing suspensions of the red cells under the microscope with various serums, each of which is known to have a particular antibody. If any serum produces agglutination, the cells must contain the antigen which that particular antibody agglutinates. The diagrammatic appearance of the groups under the microscope is shown in Figure 13.4 and their appearance to the unaided eye in Figure 13.5.

Further work on the blood groups indicates that two additional alleles exist, resulting in subgroups of group A. Furthermore, antigens

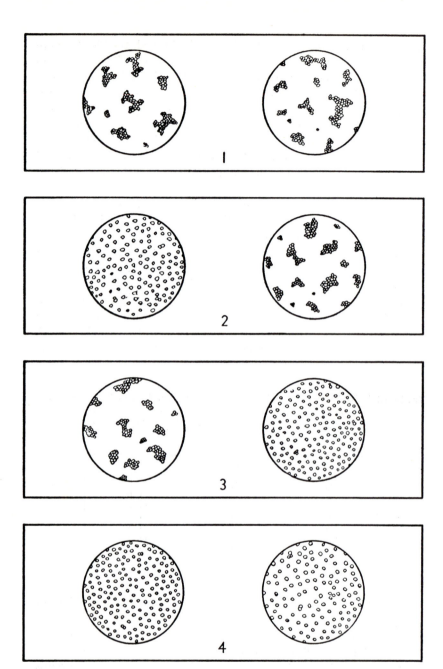

Fig. 13.4 Diagrammatic appearance of the four blood groups under the microscope. Serum of group A on left, serum of group B on right. Slide 1, group AB; slide 2, group A; slide 3, group B; slide 4, group O. *From Snyder, Blood Grouping in Relation to Clinical and Legal Medicine, by permission of The Williams and Wilkins Co.*

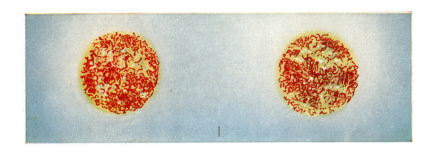

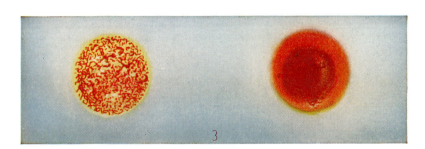

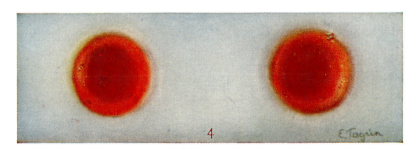

Fig 13.5 The four blood groups as seen with the naked eye. Compare with the microscopic appearance shown in the diagram in Figure 13.4. (*Drawing by Edith S. Tagrin, Medical Art Department, Massachusetts General Hospital, Boston, Massachusetts.*)

A and B are found in two chemical forms. In some persons they are soluble only in alcohol, but in other persons they are also soluble in water. Individuals having water-soluble antigens are known as "secretors," those not having them as "nonsecretors." The "secreting" ability is inherited on the basis of an autosomal dominant gene.

Two new and independent red-cell antigens were discovered in 1927. These were named M and N. Unlike antigens A and B, no natural antibodies against them are found in human serums. Moreover, they practically never provoke the formation of antibodies against themselves when one or the other of them gets into the blood of a person lacking it. They are therefore of no practical consequence in transfusions. Antiserums (serums containing antibodies) with which these antigens will react must be artificially produced by injecting the antigens into rabbits. By the use of anti-M and anti-N serums produced in this way, it has been found that every individual possesses either antigen M, antigen N, or both M and N, so that every member of the human species can be classified as belonging to one of three types, M, N, or MN. Genetic studies of large numbers of families have shown that matings between two M-type persons produce only M children, and that two N-type parents have only N children; when one parent is type M and the other N, the children are invariably MN, and when both parents are MN, all three types of children occur, in close approximation to a 1:2:1 ratio. These and other observations lead us to conclude that a single pair of alleles, commonly designated as *M* and *N* (sometimes as *M* and *m*) are responsible for the production of M and N antigens respectively, and that neither allele is dominant to the other. Table 13.5 shows the serologic reactions and genotypes, and Tables 13.6 and 13.7 show the inheritance and medico-legal applications of the M,N types.

Table 13.5. The M–N Blood Types

M–N Type	Genotype	Reaction with Antiserum	
		Anti-M	Anti-N
M	*MM*	+	−
N	*NN*	−	+
MN	*MN*	+	+

In 1947 and 1951, respectively, new antiserums were discovered (anti-S and anti-s) which have permitted subdivision of M, N, and MN type bloods according to whether their cells agglutinate in anti-S serum only, in anti-s only, or in both anti-S and anti-s serums. No human blood has been found which both serums fail to agglutinate. It now appears that there are at least four alleles at the *M,N*

Table 13.6. The Inheritance of the Antigens M and N

Antigen Type of Parents	Antigen Types Which May Occur in Children	Antigen Types Which Do Not Occur in Children
M × M	M	N, MN
M × N	MN	M, N
N × N	N	M, MN
M × MN	M, MN	N
N × MN	N, MN	M
MN × MN	M, N, MN	—

Table 13.7. Medico-Legal Applications of the Antigens M and N

Antigen Type of Child	Antigen Type of Mother	Antigen Type to Which Father Cannot Belong
M	M	N
M	MN	N
N	N	M
N	MN	M
MN	M	M
MN	N	N

Table 13.8. The MNSs Blood Types

MN Type	MNSs Type	Genotype	Reactions with Antiserum			
			Anti-M	Anti-N	Anti-S	Anti-s
M	MS	M^SM^S	+	−	+	−
	MSs	M^SM^s	+	−	+	+
	Ms	M^sM^s	+	−	−	+
N	NS	N^SN^S	−	+	+	−
	NSs	N^SN^s	−	+	+	+
	Ns	N^sN^s	−	+	−	+
MN	MNS	M^SN^S	+	+	+	−
	MNSs	M^SN^s, M^sN^S	+	+	+	+
	MNs	M^sN^s	+	+	−	+

locus, rather than two. There is not yet an established notation for these alleles, but we shall call them here M^S, M^s, N^S, and N^s. The nine serologically distinguishable phenotypes which they yield in various combinations are shown in Table 13.8, together with the antiserum reactions by which we can identify them.

It is perhaps worth noting that because the S antiserum was found some years before the discovery of antiserum s, M^S was originally described as "dominant" to M^s (and N^S to N^s), for there was no way of distinguishing serologically between M^SM^S and M^SM^s

genotypes, or between N^sN^s and N^sN^s. Since the s antiserum has been discovered, however, there is no reason for ascribing dominance to any of the alleles.

In addition to the antigens of the A–B and M–N–S systems, numerous other antigens, inherited independently of these, are now known. The ones which have aroused greatest interest, largely because of their medical importance, are those belonging to the Rh–Hr series.

The Rh antigens, like those of the M–N–S series, differ from the A and B antigens in that normal antibodies against them are not found in human serums. They also differ from the M–N–S antigens, however, because the introduction of an Rh antigen into blood which does not already possess it does induce antibody production. They thus become of importance in transfusion practice. A first transfusion of blood containing an Rh antigen ("Rh-positive" blood) into a person whose blood lacks the antigen (Rh-negative) is harmless, if the bloods of donor and recipient match on the A–B–O system. But it is likely to provoke antibody formation in the recipient, so that in a subsequent transfusion of blood containing the same antigen the transfused cells may become agglutinated, with serious and sometimes fatal results. Even more important, from a standpoint of frequency of occurrence, is the phenomenon of **maternal-fetal incompatibility.** If a pregnant woman is Rh-negative and her fetus is Rh-positive (we shall see presently how this situation can arise) the escape of relatively small numbers of fetal red blood cells (no more than are present in one or two tenths of a cubic centimeter of blood) through the placental barrier into the mother's circulation can cause antibodies to develop. The antibodies readily return through the placental membranes into the fetal blood stream, causing agglutination and hemolysis of the red cells of the fetus. The result is a severe hemolytic anemia called **erythroblastosis,** which is frequently fatal to the fetus or the newborn infant. Physicians have long been familiar with erythroblastosis, but its cause was a complete mystery until 1941, when Levine and his collaborators presented convincing evidence that almost every case is a consequence of maternal-fetal Rh incompatibility.

The original Rh antigen was discovered by Landsteiner and Wiener, who injected the blood cells of Rhesus monkeys into rabbits. The rabbits produced an antibody against an antigen of monkey cells. When the antiserum thus prepared was tested against human blood, it agglutinated the red cells of about 85 per cent of persons tested, but failed to react with the cells of the remaining 15 per cent. The human antigen identified in this way was called Rh, from the first two letters of Rhesus. Subsequently, human serums with essentially the same antibody content as the artificially prepared antiserums have been recovered from the blood of persons who have had repeated transfusions, and from the mothers of erythroblastotic infants.

Those persons whose red cells were agglutinated by the original anti-Rh serum (now called antiserum Rh_o) were referred to as Rh-positive, and the nonreactors (lacking the Rh antigen) as Rh-negative. Genetic investigation revealed a situation that seemed to be very simple: the difference between Rh-positive and Rh-negative depended on a single pair of genes, with the gene responsible for the Rh-positive condition dominant. Serologic reactions and genotypes could be indicated, therefore, as follows:

Rh Type	Reaction with Rh_o antiserum	Genotype
Positive	+	*RR, Rr*
Negative	−	*rr*

The Rh picture quickly became more complicated, however. Two new antiserums were discovered, each of which agglutinated the blood cells of some, but not all, of the persons who were positive to the original (Rh_o) antiserum. With the use of these serums, which have been designated as anti-rh′ and anti-rh″, together with the Rh_o antiserum, it was possible to distinguish eight different Rh phenotypes, as shown in Table 13.9.

Table 13.9. Rh Blood Types Distinguishable Using Only Three Antiserums

Rh Type		Genotype	Reaction with Antiserum		
			Anti-Rh_o	Anti-rh′	Anti-rh″
"Rh positive"	Rh_o	R^oR^o, R^or	+	−	−
	Rh_1	R^1R^1, R^1R^o, R^1r', R^1r, R^or'	+	+	−
	Rh_2	R^2R^2, R^2R^o, R^2r'', R^2r, R^or''	+	−	+
	Rh_z	R^zR^z, R^zR^o, R^1R^2, R^zR^1, R^zR^2, R^zr', R^1r^y, R^zr'', R^2r^y, R^zr^y, R^zr, R^or^y, R^1r'', R^2r'	+	+	+
"Rh negative"	rh′	$r'r'$, $r'r$	−	+	−
	rh″	$r''r''$, $r''r$	−	−	+
	rh_y	r^yr^y, r^yr', r^yr'', r^yr, $r'r''$	−	+	+
	rh	*rr*	−	−	−

To explain the hereditary transmission of the Rh types, Wiener proposed a series of multiple alleles, and the genotypes shown in Table 13.9 are based upon his theory. Eight alleles (R^o, R^1, R^2, R^z, r', r'', r^y, and r) are involved. If we study this table we can see what the postulated effect of each of the eight alleles is. R^o is responsible for the development of antigenic properties which cause the blood to react with antiserum Rh_o but not with rh' or rh'' antiserums. The presence of the gene R^1 results in positive reactions to both Rh_o and rh' antiserums (but not to antiserum rh''); R^z results in reaction with all three antiserums, and so on, as shown below:

Gene	Presence results in development of antigen agglutinable by antiserum		
R^o	Rh_o		
R^1	Rh_o,	rh'	
R^2	Rh_o,		rh''
R^z	Rh_o,	rh',	rh''
r'		rh'	
r''			rh''
r^y		rh',	rh''
r	—	—	—

It is easy to see from the above what phenotypes would be produced by various combinations of the genes, and why the phenotype Rh_2 for example (cells agglutinated by rh'' as well as by Rh_o antiserum) can result from either genotype R^2r, R^or'' or any of the others listed along with them in Table 13.9.

At this point, many students may feel that the genetics of the Rh types is already sufficiently complicated. Further developments which have increased its complexity, however, have in another sense perhaps also simplified it. A number of additional antiserums have been found, and tests with these have shown that each of the phenotypes listed in Table 13.9 can be subdivided into two or more serologically distinguishable types. The discovery of additional antigenic reactions in the Rh system has of course required the recognition of more alleles; currently more than 14 alleles are known. At the same time, the newer serums have made it possible to identify many of the genotypes which in Table 13.9 are lumped together as serologically indistinguishable. Among the first of the additional antiserums to be discovered was one which, rather surprisingly, agglutinated the cells of all bloods which were not agglutinated by rh' antiserum; because of its reciprocal relation to the rh' antiserum, it has been designated as anti-hr'. Later an antiserum (anti-hr'') was found which exhibited a similar relationship to anti-rh''. An anti-Hr$_o$ serum has also been reported, but it has not yet become available for general use.

Table 13.10. Rh-Hr Blood Types Distinguishable Using Six Antiserums

Rh-Hr Type	Genotype	Reaction with Antiserum					
		Anti-Rh_o	Anti-rh′	Anti-rh″	Anti-Hr_o	Anti-hr′	Anti-hr″
Rh_o	R^oR^o	+	−	−	−	+	+
	R^or	+	−	−	+	+	+
Rh_1	R^1R^1	+	+	−	−	−	+
	R^1R^o	+	+	−	−	+	+
	R^1r'	+	+	−	+	−	+
	$R^1r,\ R^or'$	+	+	−	+	+	+
Rh_2	R^2R^2	+	−	+	−	+	−
	R^2R^o	+	−	+	−	+	+
	R^2r''	+	−	+	+	+	−
	$R^2r,\ R^or''$	+	−	+	+	+	+
Rh_z	R^zR^z	+	+	+	−	−	−
	$R^zR^o,\ R^1R^2$	+	+	+	−	+	+
	R^zR^1	+	+	+	−	−	+
	R^zR^2	+	+	+	−	+	−
	$R^zr',\ R^1r^y$	+	+	+	+	−	+
	$R^zr'',\ R^2r^y$	+	+	+	+	+	−
	R^zr^y	+	+	+	+	−	−
	$R^zr,\ R^or^y,$ $R^1r'',\ R^2r'$ }	+	+	+	+	+	+
rh′	$r'r'$	−	+	−	+	−	+
	$r'r$	−	+	−	+	+	+
rh″	$r''r''$	−	−	+	+	+	−
	$r''r$	−	−	+	+	+	+
rh_y	r^yr^y	−	+	+	+	−	−
	r^yr'	−	+	+	+	−	+
	r^yr''	−	+	+	+	+	−
	$r^yr,\ r'r''$	−	+	+	+	+	+
rh	rr	−	−	−	+	+	+

The interactions of the eight alleles listed in Table 13.9 are presented in Table 13.10 as they would now be distinguishable by the use of antiserums Hr_o, hr′, and hr″ in addition to the three formerly used, namely Rh_o, rh′, and rh″.

The symbols we have used in Table 13.10 and elsewhere are those proposed by Wiener, and they have been widely adopted. Another notation, however, that of Fisher and Race, is also frequently used. Because a laboratory report of an individual's blood may be made in either the Wiener or the Fisher-Race notation, it is desirable that we be acquainted with both of them; moreover, an understanding of the relation between the two systems of notation is instructive from the standpoint of genetic interpretation.

The Fisher-Race notation derives from a theory regarding the genetic and serological mechanisms concerned in the Rh antigen system which differs from that of Wiener. When the discovery of the hr′ antiserum was reported, Fisher was impressed by the antithetical nature of the reactions of different bloods with the rh′ and hr′ antiserums, respectively. Some bloods give a positive reaction with anti-rh′, some with anti-hr′, and others with both, but no blood has been found in which the cells are not agglutinated by either serum. This is obviously what we would expect if reactions to the rh′ and hr′ antiserums were determined by a pair of alleles (say C and c), one of which is responsible for the formation of an antigen agglutinated by anti-rh′ and the other for the formation of an antigen agglutinated by anti-hr′. The heterozygote Cc would show agglutination by both antiserums.

This, in fact, is what Fisher suggested was the case, assigning the symbol C to the gene responsible for the antigen agglutinated by anti-rh′ serum (which in the Fisher-Race notation is called anti-C), and c to its allele responsible for the antigen agglutinated by anti-hr′ (anti-c). Genes D and E are considered responsible for corresponding reactions with anti-Rh_o (anti-D) and anti-rh″ (anti-E) respectively. Fisher considers that genes C, D, and E are situated at three adjacent loci, and he predicted that alleles of D and E, namely d and e, would be found, just as c had already been reported as an allele of C.

The subsequently discovered hr″ antiserum is the predicted anti-e, and the reported discovery of anti-Hr_o will be, if confirmed, Fisher's postulated anti-d.

The Fisher-Race theory in its original form, therefore, is that the interactions of three pairs of alleles, C,c, D,d, and E,e at immediately adjacent loci (and hence very closely linked) account for the Rh-Hr types shown in Table 13.10. Presence of the gene C results in the development of an antigen, C, which is agglutinated by anti-C serum; gene c produces antigen c, agglutinable by anti-c serum, and so on. Discoveries of new antigens in the Rh family have necessitated the postulation of additional alleles at the C,c locus (C^u, c^v, C^w), and at the D,d locus (D^u). Another locus F,f, in the linked series has also been added. Tables 13.11 and 13.12 show the relation between the Wiener and the Fisher-Race systems of notation, and make it possible readily to convert from either system to the other.

A basic difference between the two interpretations lies in their differing concepts of serological mechanisms. According to both views, a single gene is responsible for the production of a single agglutinogen; but in the Fisher-Race scheme each agglutinogen reacts with but a single antibody, whereas according to Wiener an agglutinogen may possess several "blood factors," each reacting to a different antibody.

The Fisher-Race theory implies, of course, that the alleles present in any given chromosome are at least potentially separable by crossing over, but at the time of this writing no instance of crossing over has been confirmed. If crossing over does not occur at all, it should be evident that as far as genetic predictions are concerned, the two

Table 13.11. COMPARISON OF ANTISERUMS IN THE TWO SYSTEMS OF NOTATION AS OF 1956

ANTISERUMS	
WIENER	FISHER-RACE
anti-Rh_0	anti-D
anti-rh′	anti-C
anti-rh^W	anti-C^W
anti-rh″	anti-E
anti-rh (hypothetical)	anti-F
anti-Hr_0	anti-d
anti-hr′	anti-c
anti-hr″	anti-e
anti-hr	anti-f

Table 13.12. COMPARISON OF GENE SYMBOLS IN THE TWO SYSTEMS OF NOTATION AS OF 1956

GENE SYMBOLS	
WIENER	FISHER-RACE
R^0	$cDef$
R^1	$CDeF$
R^{1W}	$C^W DeF$
R^{1v}	$c^v DeF$
R^2	$cDEF$
R^z	$CDEF$
$\mathfrak{R}^0$	$CD^u ef$
$\mathfrak{R}^1$	$CD^u eF$
$\mathfrak{R}^2$	$cD^u EF$
$\mathfrak{R}^z$	$CD^u EF$
r'	$CdeF$
r'^W	$C^W deF$
r''	$cdEF$
r^y	$CdEF$
r	$cdef$

theories lead to identical results; indeed, each set of linked genes in the Fisher-Race scheme (*cedf, cDef, CDeF,* etc.) behaves precisely as an allele in the Wiener scheme.

Since predictions of the progeny which are possible from matings between various Rh-Hr types can be made with assurance, data on Rh-Hr types can contribute valuable information in medico-legal cases. In a number of instances, it has been possible to decide cases of disputed paternity or of exchanged children by the use of Rh-Hr data when the results of A–B–O and M–N–S typing were inconclusive. An illustrative example, based on a report of Cotterman, is given below.

Mrs. W. suspected that a child, X, which was given to her when she left the maternity hospital was not the one she had given birth to. Determinations of A–B–O and M–N groups provided no evidence to confirm her suspicion. Both Mrs. W. and the child were group O;

Mrs. W. was N, her husband M, the child MN. Tests for Rh-Hr type were then made, using anti-Rh$_0$, anti-rh', anti-rh'' and anti-hr' serums, the only ones available. Mrs. W's blood gave a positive reaction with all of the test sera, while the child's was positive only to anti-hr'. Thus the child's genotype was clearly rr. But as we may see by referring to Table 13.10, the mother might have any of nine genotypes (those in the Rh$_z$ block of the Table which have a + in the anti-hr' column). One of the possibilities is R^zr, and if this was her genotype, the rr child could of course be hers. In an effort to decide on this possibility, an earlier child of Mrs. W's, known certainly to be her own, was tested. This child's blood proved positive to anti-Rh$_0$ and anti-rh', but negative to anti-rh'' and anti-hr'. The tests thus established that this child was either R^1R^1 or R^1r', and this determination reduced the number of genotypes possible for Mrs. W. to three (R^1R^2, R^1r'', R^2r'), ruling out the possibility that she was R^zr. The disputed child, X, whose genotype had been found to be rr could not, therefore, be hers.

We have already mentioned briefly the relation of Rh type to erythroblastosis, pointing out that this can occur when an "Rh-positive" fetus is borne by an "Rh-negative" woman. This means that the fetus must have inherited from its father an Rh-antigen which is lacking in its mother; hence, the father must be "Rh-positive." Fortunately, although any of the Rh-Hr antigens can provoke antibody formation (and often will, if introduced *by transfusion* into a person who does not possess it), only the antigens of cells which are agglutinated by antiserum Rh$_0$ are likely to cause antibody formation in a pregnant woman through maternal-fetal incompatibility. The designation, "Rh-positive" in this context, therefore, is restricted to those persons whose blood cells give a positive reaction with anti-Rh$_0$ serum; all others are "Rh-negative." We must note that this classification does not afford a completely safe basis for screening donors for blood transfusion. For this purpose it is desirable that the donor's blood cells should contain *no* antigen which is absent from the recipient's cells.

The possibility of erythroblastosis occurring in a child of an Rh-negative mother and an Rh-positive father has been widely publicized in magazines and newspapers and has caused some unnecessary alarm to prospective parents who have this combination of Rh types (found in ten or twelve per cent of all marriages in this country). It is important therefore, to recognize that only a small minority of children from matings of this kind actually have the disease. This is in part due to the fact that more than half of the Rh-positive fathers are heterozygous, so that about half of their children will be Rh-negative and incur no risk.

But even in those cases in which the fetus is Rh-positive and mother Rh-negative, erythroblastosis almost never occurs if the pregnancy is a first one. The reason for this appears to be simply that there has not been time for the mother's body to build up antibodies in sufficient strength to damage the red cells of the fetus. Furthermore, erythroblastosis develops in only a fraction of second (and subsequent) pregnancies in which there is maternal-fetal incompatibility. The net result is that erythroblastosis occurs only about once in twenty-five or thirty full-term pregnancies of Rh-negative women with Rh-positive husbands. The risk is nearly zero, as we have already noted, in a first pregnancy, but it is very great (almost a certainty, if the father is homozygous positive) in the case of a mother who has already borne one or more erythroblastotic children.

Summing up this chapter we find that allelic genes are not restricted to occurring in pairs, but may exist in sets of three, four, or more. An individual may carry any two of such a set of multiple alleles, and a gamete may carry only one at a time. Crosses involving any two characters dependent upon a set of alleles will always give a one-pair, or monohybrid, ratio.

PROBLEMS

13.1 Would it be possible for a cross between two chinchilla rabbits to result in both Himalayan and albino offspring?

13.2 A litter of rabbits contains four full-colored animals, two chinchillas, and one albino. What must have been the genotypes of the parents?

13.3 What would be the phenotype of each parent, and what kinds of offspring would be produced, in each of the following rabbit crosses? $Cc \times Cc^{ch}$; $c^{ch}c \times c^{ch}c$; $Cc^h \times Cc^h$; $c^hc \times cc$; $c^hc \times c^hc$.

13.4 In screech owls, the color may be gray, red, or intermediate. Two gray owls produce only gray offspring. When gray is crossed with red, the results are sometimes all red, sometimes 1 gray : 1 red, and sometimes 1 intermediate : 1 red. Gray crossed with intermediate produces either all intermediate or else 1 intermediate : 1 gray. When both parents are intermediate, the offspring may be all intermediate, or 3 intermediate : 1 gray. Red crossed with intermediate sometimes results in all red, sometimes in 1 red : 1 intermediate, and sometimes in 1 intermediate : 2 red : 1 gray. When both parents are red, the offspring may be all red, or 3 red : 1 intermediate, or 3 red : 1 gray. Construct a hypothesis to explain these results.

13.5 In mice the following series of multiple alleles is known: A^y is a gene resulting in yellow coat color, A results in agouti (gray), a results in nonagouti (black). A^y is lethal. What kinds of offspring in what proportions will result from the following crosses? $A^ya \times Aa$; $A^ya \times A^ya$; $AA \times Aa$; $A^yA \times A^ya$; $A^yA \times A^yA$.

13.6 Suppose a child is of blood group A and the mother is of group O. What group or groups may the father belong to?

13.7 Suppose a father of group A and a

mother of group B have a child of group O. What groups are possible in their subsequent children?

13.8 Suppose a father of group B and a mother of group O have a child of group O. What are the chances that their next child will be group O? Group B? Group A? Group AB?

13.9 Suppose a father and mother claim that they have been given the wrong baby at the hospital. Both parents are group A. The baby they have been given is group O. What evidence bearing on the case does this fact offer?

13.10 If the baby in the preceding problem had been group B, what evidence as to the relationship would this fact offer?

13.11 Brown mink may transmit steel-blu color and silverblu color as well as brown. Steelblu mink may transmit steel-blu or silverblu but never brown. Silverblu mink transmit only silverblu. What kind of hereditary behavior appears to be operating here?

13.12 A brown mink crossed with a silver-blu produces a litter of two brown kits and two silverblu kits. If the same two parents were mated again, could they produce some steelblu offspring?

13.13 A litter of mink kits contains a brown animal, a steelblu animal, and a silverblu animal. What were the colors of the parents?

13.14 In *Drosophila melanogaster* the following series of multiple alleles affecting eye color occurs: W, red; w^w, wine; w^{ce}, coral; w^{bb}, blood; w^c, cherry; w^a, apricot; w^e, eosin; w^i, ivory; w^b, buff; w^t, tinged; w^{ec}, ecru; and w, white. These genes are sex-linked. How many of these genes can any Drosophila female carry? How many can any Drosophila male carry?

13.15 What is the largest number of different kinds of gametes which any individual Drosophila male could produce in regard to these genes? Any individual female?

13.16 A red-eyed female crossed with a white-eyed male produced the following offspring: 23 red-eyed males, 26 eosin-eyed males, 25 red-eyed females, 24 eosin-eyed females. What are the genotypes of the parents?

13.17 When one parent is blood group AB and the other is group O, how many times in families of three would you expect one child of group A and two children of group B?

13.18 A normal-visioned man of group A marries a normal-visioned woman of group A. They have two children, a color-blind boy of group A and a normal-visioned girl of group O. What were the genotypes of the parents?

13.19 A color-blind man of group O marries a normal-visioned woman of group AB whose father was color-blind. If they have four sons, what will these sons most probably be in regard to vision and blood group?

13.20 If the parents in the preceding problem had four daughters, what would they most probably be?

13.21 In the Chinese primrose the flower normally has a yellow eye. A recessive mutation has occurred, resulting in a very large yellow eye (Primrose Queen type). Later another mutation of this same gene arose, this time dominant to the normal type, resulting in a white eye (Alexandra type). The resulting three genes, A (Alexandra), a^n (normal), and a (Primrose Queen), form a series of multiple alleles. What various genotypes may be concerned in the Alexandra type? In the normal type? In the Primrose Queen type?

13.22 An Alexandra plant was crossed with a normal plant and produced 36 Alexandra, 17 normal, and 19 Primrose Queen offspring. What were the genotypes of the parents? Of the offspring?

13.23 Two Alexandra plants were crossed and produced 45 Alexandra and 16 Primrose Queen offspring. If these plants could be crossed again, would they be expected to produce any normal offspring?

13.24 In ducks Jaap has demonstrated a series of alleles affecting the mallard plumage pattern. M^R is a gene for restricted pattern, M for mallard pattern, and m for dusky pattern. Dominance is in the order named. Another pair of genes includes C, a dominant gene for color, and c, its recessive allele for white. How many different genotypes in regard to these various genes could be concerned in the White Pekin breed?

13.25 A homozygous mallard was crossed with a White Pekin and all the offspring were restricted pattern. What were the genotypes of the parents? What would be obtained in the F_2 from the cross?

13.26 A male with restricted pattern was mated to a white female. She laid 14 eggs, which hatched out as follows: 7 white, 4 restricted, 2 mallard, and 1 dusky. What were the genotypes of the parents?

REFERENCES

CASTLE, W. E., *The Genetics of the Domestic Rabbit.* Cambridge, Harvard University Press (1930).

HRUBANT, H. E., *Amer. Nat.* **89**:223 (1955).

JAAP, R. G., *Genetics* **19**:310 (1934).

RACE, R. R., and SANGER, R., *Blood Groups in Man* (2nd ed.). Oxford, Blackwell Sci. Publ. (1954).

The Rh Factor and Immunohematological Procedures. Raritan, N. J., Ortho Pharm. Corp. (1953).

WIENER, A. S., *Blood Groups and Transfusion.* 3rd ed. Springfield, Ill., Charles C. Thomas (1943); *Rh-Hr Blood Types.* New York, Grune and Stratton (1954).

CHAPTER FOURTEEN

Quantitative inheritance I. Multiple genes

A little reflection on the kinds of characters we have studied up to this point will convince us that they have been to a large extent superficial traits. Color of eyes, hair, feathers, or flowers, presence or absence of horns, structure of eye or ear, texture of hair: none of these is a deep-seated fundamental character of the species. A little further reflection, however, will show us that the traits thus far studied are *discontinuous*, that is, each character may be sharply divided into two or more clearly differentiated classes.

Thus a cow either has horns or has not: we are seldom in any doubt as to which is the case. A group of rabbits may be separated into black, brown, red, and white ones with little difficulty. But, if we were asked to separate these same rabbits into large and small ones, a difficulty would arise, for we would find that there was no sharp dividing line between large and small. Instead the animals would form a *continuous* series from the largest to the smallest.

In the poultry yard it would be a simple matter to classify the hens as barred or nonbarred, rose-combed birds or single-combed birds, black ones or white ones; it would be much more difficult if not impossible to divide them satisfactorily into high egg-producers and low egg-producers.

A group of people could be readily separated into those with five fingers on each hand and those with six fingers, but it would not be so simple to classify the group into tall people and short people. The heights of people range continuously from very tall to very short, with no fixed point at which tallness ends and shortness begins.

The fact that some characters are sharply differentiated into relatively few clear-cut *qualities* is the very reason why we have been able to analyze their heredity so easily. Variations in characters of this nature are usually dependent upon one, or at least only a few, sets of alleles, acting in the simple manners with which we have become familiar. The more deep-seated characters of a race, however, such as form, yield, intelligence, speed, fertility, strength, development of various parts, and so on, are in general characters which grade in *quantity*. Such quantitative gradations are usually *continuous* from one extreme to the other, not discontinuous and clearly defined, as qualitative variations are. For this reason they are harder to study from a hereditary standpoint, and we have postponed their discussion until we should be thoroughly acquainted with the more simple types of hereditary behavior.

We are now ready, however, to discuss characters which vary quantitatively, and we shall find them to be, in general, the most fundamental and important characters of the organism. We shall also find that many sets of alleles may be concerned in the variation of a single one of these characters. Moreover, there is usually no dominance between the alleles, so that they are cumulative in their effects. When several sets of alleles produce more or less equal and cumulative effects on the same character, we speak of them as **multiple genes.**

As long ago as 1760 Kölreuter, a botanist, studied the inheritance of characters in tobacco. Mendel's laws were, of course, unknown at that time, and Kölreuter did not discover them for himself because the characters were quantitative, continuous, not sharply defined. Mendel's genius lay in the choosing of sharply distinguished contrasting characters.

Kölreuter found what we nearly always find in the inheritance of quantitative characters, that, when two parents which differ in such a character are crossed, *the F_1 are all more or less intermediate between the parents, and the F_2 show many gradations from one extreme to the other*. There is no apparent segregation, no sharply defined classes in the F_2, and hence no clear "ratio." Kölreuter, then, was completely unable to discover any laws for the inheritance of these characters, although by means of reciprocal crosses he did discover the important fact, until then unrecognized, that the male and the female gametes contribute equally to the hereditary make-up of the offspring.

No clear understanding of the genetic nature of quantitative characters could be had until after simple Mendelian inheritance was understood. One hundred and fifty years after Kölreuter's pioneer experiment the same experiment was repeated by East, this time with knowledge of Mendel's laws on which to base conclusions (Fig. 14.1). From the results of this cross and others of a similar nature, the hypothesis of multiple genes has grown.

Let us view the problem clearly. Here is a type of heredity in which no clear-cut classes of offspring are produced. No obvious ratios

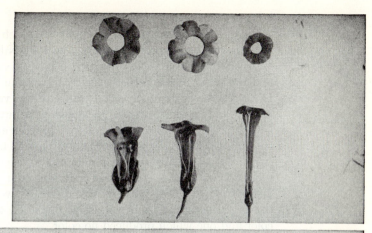

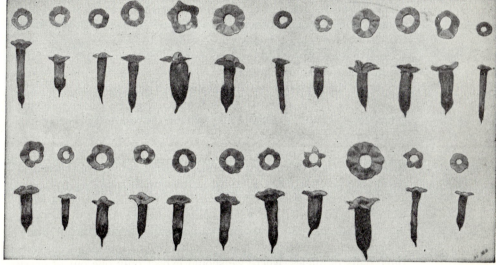

Fig. 14.1 East's repetition of Kölreuter's work. Top, left, a flower of *Nicotiana paniculata;* right, a flower of *N. rustica;* between them, a flower from the F_1 hybrid. Bottom, flowers from some F_2 plants. There is partial sterility in this cross, so that all the possible combinations are not realized. Multiple genes are involved. *From East in Genetics*

may be found. The F_1 are not like either parent, but are as a rule intermediate between them and fairly uniform. The F_2 are of all grades, and if enough of them are produced they range continuously from the extreme represented by one of the original parents to the extreme represented by the other. In the F_2 the extremes are less abundant than the intermediate types. The inheritance does not appear at first glance to be Mendelian at all, and indeed was thought for many years not to be. However, let us analyze such crosses a little further.

Among the first crosses of this type which gave a clue to their true nature were those made with wheat by Nilsson-Ehle. In a cross between two varieties of wheat, one having very dark red kernels and the other white kernels, the F_1 were of an intermediate shade. In the F_2 the color of the grains ranged from very dark red through various intermediate shades to white. One out of every sixteen F_2 kernels was as dark as the dark red parent, and one out of every sixteen was white. This immediately reminds us of a modified two-pair ratio, where the double dominant and the double recessive each occurs once out of every sixteen individuals on the average. Nilsson-Ehle proposed the hypothesis that perhaps two pairs of genes were concerned here, each pair containing one allele which produced some color and one which produced no color.

East, on the basis of crosses in corn and tobacco, independently suggested a similar hypothesis. On this hypothesis of multiple genes, the alleles producing the effect are assumed to be *cumulative* in their action, that is, two would produce more effect than one, three would produce more than two, and so on.

If for the color in wheat we assume two pairs of genes, A and a, B and b, with the capital letters representing the color-producing genes, acting cumulatively, we may explain the results by the diagram on the opposite page.

The F_2 results on this hypothesis show one out of every sixteen to be white, the rest varying through shades of red. These theoretical results are just what was obtained in the actual cross.

In a cross between a different red-kerneled strain with the same white-kerneled variety of wheat, Nilsson-Ehle found the F_1 to be intermediate and the F_2 to give variations between red and white, *with one out of every sixty-four F_2 individuals white*. This suggests three pairs of alleles, where we should expect only one out of every sixty-four to have all the recessive genes. The parents could be represented as $AABBCC$ (red) and $aabbcc$ (white), with an F_1 of the formula $AaBbCc$ (intermediate shade of red). Work out a diagram of the F_2 and convince yourself that it would give on the multiple-gene hypothesis a series of shades of red varying from very dark red to white, with one out of every sixty-four kernels as dark as the dark parent and one as light as the light parent.

The multiple-gene hypothesis in its original form assumes that when two parents produce an intermediate and uniform F_1 and a variable F_2, the genes concerned are equal and cumulative in their effects. The number of pairs of genes concerned is arrived at by an examination of the F_2. If one out of every sixteen is like each original parent, two pairs of genes are concerned. When only one out of sixty-four is as extreme as each of the original parents, three pairs of genes

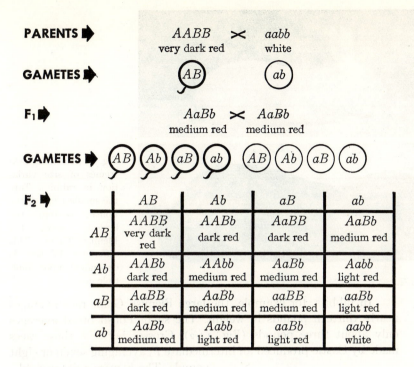

PARENTS ➡ $AABB$ ✕ $aabb$
           very dark red   white

GAMETES ➡ (AB) (ab)

F₁ ➡ $AaBb$ ✕ $AaBb$
             medium red   medium red

GAMETES ➡ $(AB)(Ab)(aB)(ab)$ $(AB)(Ab)(aB)(ab)$

F₂ ➡

	AB	Ab	aB	ab
AB	$AABB$ very dark red	$AABb$ dark red	$AaBB$ dark red	$AaBb$ medium red
Ab	$AABb$ dark red	$AAbb$ medium red	$AaBb$ medium red	$Aabb$ light red
aB	$AaBB$ dark red	$AaBb$ medium red	$aaBB$ medium red	$aaBb$ light red
ab	$AaBb$ medium red	$Aabb$ light red	$aaBb$ light red	$aabb$ white

Table 14.1. PROPORTION OF F_2 AS EXTREME AS EACH PARENT ON THE HYPOTHESIS OF MULTIPLE GENES

NUMBER OF PAIRS OF GENES CONCERNED	PROPORTION OF F_2 AS EXTREME AS EITHER PARENT
1	1 out of 4
2	1 out of 16
3	1 out of 64
4	1 out of 256
5	1 out of 1,024
6	1 out of 4,096
7	1 out of 16,384
8	1 out of 65,536
9	1 out of 262,144
10	1 out of 1,048,576
20	1 out of 1,099,511,627,776

must be postulated. The more pairs of genes concerned, the smaller will be the proportion of the F_2 like the parents. Table 14.1 shows the proportion for various numbers of pairs of genes.

It is readily seen that as the number of pairs increases, the proportion of the F_2 which is as extreme as either parent becomes smaller, so that with as many as eight or ten pairs it is so small that in the ordinary cross it would be impossible of realization. This explains why in so many crosses of this nature the parental extremes have never been recovered in the F_2.

Fig. 14.2 The extremes of size variation in rabbits. Top, the smallest breed, the Polish; bottom, the largest breed, the Flemish Giant. This difference in size is dependent upon multiple genes.

In rabbits, for example, the large Flemish Giant race averages nearly thirteen pounds in weight. The small Polish breed averages only about three pounds (Fig. 14.2). Crosses between these races made by Castle produced an intermediate F_1 averaging seven or eight pounds. The F_2 were quite variable, ranging from individuals nearly as small as the Polish to those approaching the Flemish Giant in size, but no individuals reaching the extremes of the parental races were obtained in a series of several hundred F_2 individuals. Evidently several pairs of genes are concerned here. It may be assumed that if enough F_2 individuals were raised the parental extremes would eventually be obtained. The growth rates of the parents and the F_1 in this cross are shown in Figure 14.3.

Sometimes it is found that not only do the parental extremes appear in the F_2, but individuals more extreme than either parent occur. In this case it is necessary to assume that each parent contributed some of the effective alleles. For example, in a cross between Sebright

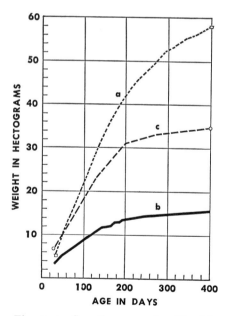

Fig. 14.3 Growth curves for Flemish Giant rabbits (a), Polish rabbits (b), and their intermediate F_1 (c). *From Castle in the Journal of Experimental Zoology*

Bantams and Golden Hamburgh fowls, which differ considerably in size, Punnett found that the F_1 were intermediate, but the F_2 were so variable as to exhibit extremes beyond the parental weights. While most of the F_2 were more or less intermediate as would be expected, a few F_2 birds were lighter than the Bantams or heavier than the Hamburghs. Such an effect is known as **transgressive variation.**

This is explained by Punnett on the basis of a four-pair difference between the two parents, the Hamburghs being of the formula *AABBCCdd*, while the Bantams may be considered as *aabbccDD*. The F_1 would then be *AaBbCcDd*, giving an intermediate weight. In the F_2, however, some individuals of the formula *AABBCCDD* could occur, and these would be heavier than the original Hamburgh parent. Also some F_2 birds could be of the formula *aabbccdd*, and these would be even smaller than the Bantam parent. Thus in some cases the F_2 may show extremes beyond the parental range.

Jull and Quinn in studies of body-weight in fowls found evidence that more than four pairs of genes are concerned in crosses between Rosecomb Bantams and Barred Plymouth Rocks. The F_1 birds were intermediate and fairly uniform, and the F_2 were much more variable, but none of the F_2 individuals was as extreme as either parent. In this case the Plymouth Rock parent was five times as heavy as the Bantam parent.

A clear case of multiple genes has been worked out by Wexelsen regarding the length of the internode of the spike in barley (Fig. 14.4). A cross between a variety having an internode length of 2.1 mm. and one of 3.2 mm. was made.

The F_1 had an intermediate length of 2.7 mm. In the F_2 a symmetrical curve of variation occurred, ranging from one parental extreme to the other, with one plant out of sixteen as extreme as either original parent. Two pairs of multiple genes are indicated, and the symmetrical curve of distribution in the F_2 denotes equal and cumulative effects of the genes. If we designate the long internode parent as *AABB* and the short internode parent as *aabb*, we may readily see that they differ in two pairs of genes, that is, in four different genes each of which in the *AABB* parent adds a certain amount of length to the internode. The difference in internode length between the two parents

NODE
INTERNODE
NODE

Fig. 14.4 Barley spike, partially dissected. It shows nodes and internodes.

is one millimeter; hence we may assign to each capital letter (that is, each length-producing gene) an effect of about a quarter of a millimeter.

It is not always as easy as this to determine the number of pairs of genes concerned in a multiple-gene cross or to assign the proper value to each gene. Sometimes, as we have seen in the case of weight in rabbits, the number of pairs of genes involved is so great that it is a practical impossibility to raise enough F_2 individuals to obtain the parental extremes. Other genes may hinder the determination. The genes may not be strictly cumulative in their effects; they may show partial or even complete dominance; there may be partial sterility concerned. Due to these and other causes the proportion of parental extremes in the F_2 may not fit any of the ratios shown in Table 14.1.

In a cross between Golden Glow corn, having sixteen rows to the ear, and Black Mexican, having only eight rows to the ear, Lindstrom found the F_1 to be intermediate, averaging twelve rows. The F_2 was quite variable, ranging from eight to eighteen rows, but one out of every thirty-two individuals was as extreme as either parent (Fig. 14.5). This is in between the proportions of one out of sixteen and one out of sixty-four. It may be due to partial dominance, to partial sterility, to interactions of the genes other than cumulative, to linkage, or to chromosomal aberrations, but it illustrates the fact that the analysis of the number of genes concerned is not always a simple cut-and-dried affair. We can be fairly sure in this case, however, that the number of genes involved is small.

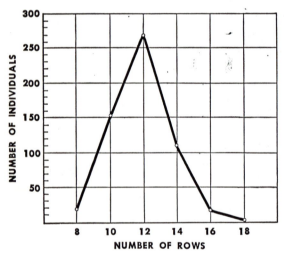

Fig. 14.5 The distribution in regard to number of rows on the ear in the F_2 of a cross in corn. The parental generation consisted of Golden Glow with sixteen rows to the ear and Black Mexican with eight rows to the ear The F_1 were mostly intermediate, with twelve rows. The F_2, as may be seen, form a normal curve ranging from eight to eighteen rows to the ear. *Based on data from Lindstrom*

An illustration of partial dominance is seen in crosses made by Lindstrom involving fruit size in tomatoes (Fig. 14.6). Here the F_1 is much nearer to the small-sized parent than to the large, indicating partial dominance of the genes for small size.

If the effects of the genes concerned in a multiple-gene cross were always equal and cumulative, we should expect symmetrical distri-

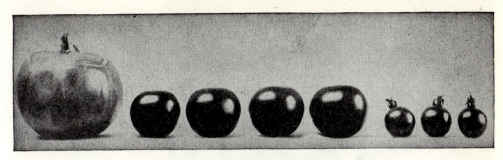

Fig. 14.6 A multiple gene cross in tomatoes. At left a New Globe; at right three fruits of Yellow Cherry; between them four F_1 hybrids, showing partial dominance of small size genes. *From Lindstrom in Research Bulletin 93 of the Iowa Agricultural Experiment Station*

butions in the F_2 about the mean of the parents. Frequently, however, we find skew distributions too great to be due entirely to partial dominance. Such distributions must be accounted for in other ways.

Rasmussen, on the basis of results of many crosses among plants in Sweden, considers that multiple genes probably act in a way that is not usually cumulative. He considers that many more pairs of genes are involved in multiple-gene crosses than is usually believed; that the number is usually 100 to 200 pairs. These, he postulates, interact in such a manner that the greater the number of effective genes concerned in producing a given phenotype the smaller will be the added effect of an additional effective gene. On this hypothesis the combined effects of added alleles are calculated by means of a logarithmic function or a function of a convergent geometric series. Sinnott, on the other hand, believes, as a result of numerous crosses among cucurbits, that each additional effective gene has a progressively *greater* effect, the additional gene adding a definite percentage to what the rest of the genotype produces.

Future critical research may indicate whether or not the assumption of equal and cumulative effects of multiple genes is justified in every case. Be that as it may, we are justified at present in accepting the hypothesis that multiple genes are concerned in cases where the F_1 is more or less intermediate, and the F_2 shows a continuous range of variation grouped largely about the mean of the parents, the extremes being rare as compared with the intermediate forms.

An interesting special case of multiple genes occurs when such genes produce their effect in a character which is itself dependent for its initial occurrence upon another gene. For example, the spotted coat such as is found in certain breeds of cattle is due to a recessive gene. Letting S represent the gene for solid color and s the gene for spotting, SS and Ss animals are solid-colored and ss animals are

Fig. 14.7 Variations in the degree of spotting in cattle, due to multiple modifying genes.

spotted. However, the spotted individuals vary considerably, ranging from those which are nearly solid-colored with a few white patches to those which have only a trace of color on a white background. Selection for more or less color brings positive results, showing that the variation is hereditary (Fig. 14.7). Apparently there are multiple genes influencing the degree of spotting. Since spotting itself is dependent upon a single gene, we speak of the multiple genes which affect it as modifying genes. Such genes are known in many organisms.

In man multiple genes and modifying genes are suspected in numerous characters. As we have seen before, we cannot analyze hereditary characters in man by means of F_1 and F_2 generations because of the impossibility of experimenting with human material. We find, however, that many characters in man show a continuous gradation from one extreme to the other. In these cases we may suspect that any hereditary characters would be determined by multiple genes. Great care must be taken in these cases to exclude the possible effects of variations in the environment before assigning a genetic basis to the character.

Where, under a relatively constant environment, we find continuous variation in a human character, we may legitimately investigate the possibility of multiple genes. The investigation in such cases must proceed along statistical lines. If, for example, we find a positive correlation between parents and offspring in the degree of expression of the character, we are justified in assigning at least part of the variation to genes. One of the earliest studies of this nature was that of Galton, who showed that a definite correlation existed between heights of parents and offspring. That is, in the long run, tall parents tend to have tall offspring and short parents tend to have short offspring. Fisher later analyzed stature from a statistical viewpoint and showed that multiple genes were most probably involved.

Intelligence in man is another character apparently dependent on multiple genes. The correlation in intelligence is very high between identical twins and becomes lower and lower as we pass through fraternal twins, brothers and sisters, parents and children, cousins, and unrelated children, finally becoming zero in the unrelated children. This correlation might indicate an effect of the environment as well as a hereditary effect, since related individuals tend to live in similar environments. We shall see later, in fact, that there is evidence for the significance of both genetic and environmental factors in the determination of intelligence, and that it is very difficult to disentangle them. This matter will be dealt with in Chapter 29, where we shall discuss at some length the "nature-nurture" problem in relation to intelligence.

The differences in skin color between whites and Negroes appear to be dependent upon multiple genes. Davenport considers that two pairs of genes are responsible for the various grades of color between black skin and white. The offspring of a Negro-white cross is medium brown, "mulatto," and the offspring of mulattoes are very variable in skin color. If we let S and s, T and t represent genes for pigment control, the capital letters standing for the pigment-producing alleles, Davenport's hypothesis would work out as follows:

$SSTT$ produces black skin

$\left. \begin{array}{l} SSTt \\ SsTT \end{array} \right\}$ produce dark brown skin

$\left. \begin{array}{l} SsTt \\ SStt \\ ssTT \end{array} \right\}$ produce medium brown skin

$\left. \begin{array}{l} Sstt \\ ssTt \end{array} \right\}$ produce light brown skin

$sstt$ produces white skin

This appears to be a reasonable explanation of the inheritance of skin color, based on many carefully collected family histories. In spite of popular belief to the contrary, it does not appear to be possible for a white woman and a light-skinned Negro to produce a black child. Still other genes are concerned in crosses between the white and yellow races, and probably many minor genes as yet unrecognized affect skin color.

Other characters in man thought to be dependent upon multiple genes are shape of head, general bodily conformation, special abilities, longevity, and a host of quantitatively varying traits. In general the more fundamental and deep-seated qualities of a race seem to be the results of genes of this nature.

PROBLEMS

14.1 In a cross between a large breed of poultry and a small breed the F_1 are intermediate and uniform. Among 550 F_2 individuals two are as large as the large breed and three are as small as the small breed. How many pairs of genes are involved in the cross, and how are they acting?

14.2 What facts would cause you to suspect that a certain character in human beings was the result of multiple genes?

14.3 Upon which would you expect ordinary changes in the environment to exert the greater effect, a character due to multiple genes or a character due to a single gene or pair of genes? Why?

14.4 In a cross between a large breed of rabbits and a small breed the F_1 are intermediate and uniform. Among a thousand F_2 rabbits raised from many crosses among the F_1, however, no individual as small as the small breed is found, nor is any individual found to be as large as the large breed. What can you say as to the possible number of genes concerned?

14.5 In human beings the difference in skin color between Negroes and whites is thought to be determined by two pairs of genes with cumulative effects. On this basis five grades of pigment are recognized, white, light, mulatto, dark, and black. Using the symbols S, s, and T, t, write out the possible genotypes for these five skin colors.

14.6 Which of the skin colors may be represented by the largest number of genotypes? Which by the smallest?

14.7 Why is it that the offspring of some mulattoes are very variable as to skin color, while the offspring of other mulattoes are very uniform?

14.8 If the hypothesis presented in Problem **14.5** is correct, could two light-skinned Negroes produce a black child?

14.9 A variety of squash bearing six-pound fruits is crossed with one bearing three-pound fruits. The F_1 plants bear four-and-a-half-pound fruits. Among the F_2 fruits there is considerable variation, but out of 200 such fruits there are three which weigh as little as three pounds and three which weigh six pounds. How many pairs of genes are responsible for the difference in weight between the two parent lines, and how much does each effective allele contribute to this difference?

14.10 How many different homozygous strains bearing four-pound fruits could be developed?

14.11 A race of oats yielding 10 grams per plant was crossed with a race yielding 4 grams per plant. The F_1 plants yielded 7 grams per plant. Out of 253 F_2 plants four yielded as much as 10 grams per plant and four yielded as little as 4 grams per plant. How is yield inherited in these oats?

14.12 In the preceding problem how much does each effective allele contribute to yield?

14.13 A breed of rabbits having an ear-length of two inches was crossed with one having an ear-length of four inches. The F_1 had ears three inches long. Out of 504 F_2 rabbits two had ear-lengths of four inches and two had ear-lengths as little as two inches. How many pairs of genes are concerned, and how are they acting?

14.14 How much does each effective allele contribute to ear-length in the foregoing cross?

14.15 Two different races of corn each averaging 68 inches in height were crossed. The F_1 also averaged 68 inches in height. In the F_2, however, there was considerable variation, ranging from 36 inches to 100 inches. Out of 1942 F_2 plants eight reached a height of 100 inches and seven were as short as 36 inches. Explain these results in terms of genes, assuming that the environment was held similar for these plants.

14.16 What is the type of variation which appeared in the F_2 of the preceding problem called?

14.17 On the basis of the factorial explanation worked out for Problem 14.15, explain by means of genotypes the following facts. Two 52-inch plants are crossed and produce offspring in the following ratios: one 68-inch plant, four 60-inch plants, six 52-inch plants, four 44-inch plants, and one 36-inch plant. Two other 52-inch plants are crossed and produce all 52-inch offspring. Two more 52-inch plants are crossed and produce offspring in the proportion of one 60-inch plant, two 52-inch plants, one 44-inch plant.

14.18 A certain plant breeder has two homozygous varieties of corn, a green variety which grows to 36 inches in height and a purple variety which reaches 100 inches in height. The gene for purple is dominant to that for green. He wants to develop from these a green variety 100 inches tall. If he crossed these two varieties and then crossed the F_1 plants among themselves to obtain an F_2 generation, what proportion of the F_2 plants would be the type desired?

14.19 If the breeder did not have enough

space available to raise a sufficient number of F_2 plants to obtain the desired individuals, what could he do to eventually obtain them?

14.20 How many different genotypes could result in 68-inch corn? How many of these would be homozygous genotypes?

REFERENCES

CASTLE, W. E., *Mammalian Genetics*. Cambridge, Harvard Univ. Press (1940).

DAVENPORT, C. B., *Carnegie Inst. Wash. Publ.* **188** (1913).

DAVENPORT, C. B., and STEGGERDA, M., *Carnegie Inst. Wash. Publ.* **395** (1929).

EAST, E. M., *Amer. Naturalist* **44**:65 (1910).

JULL, M. A., and QUINN, J. P., *Jour. Heredity* **22**:283 (1931).

LINDSTROM, E. W., *Iowa Agr. Exper. Sta. Research Bull.* **93** (1926); *Amer. Naturalist* **63**:317 (1929).

MATHER, K., *Biometrical Genetics*. New York, Dover Publications (1949).

NILSSON-EHLE, H., *Lunds Univ. Arsskrift N. F. Avd.* **2,** Bd. 5 (1909).

PUNNETT, R. C., *Heredity in Poultry*. London, The Macmillan Co. (1923).

RASMUSSEN, J. A., *Hereditas* **18**:245 (1933).

SCHWESINGER, G. C., *Heredity and Environment*. New York, The Macmillan Co. (1933).

SINNOTT, E. W., *Proc. Nat. Acad. Sci.* **23**:224 (1937).

WEXELSEN, H., *Hereditas* **17**:323; *ibid.* **18**:307 (1933).

CHAPTER FIFTEEN

Quantitative inheritance II. Statistical considerations

In the preceding chapter on multiple genes we dealt with continuously variable traits. The variability was particularly noted in the F_2 generation, whereas we spoke of the parental lines and the F_1 as though they were not variable. For instance, the case was cited of a variety of barley having an internode length of 2.1 mm. and another variety having an internode length of 3.2 mm. The F_1 had an intermediate length of 2.7 mm. The F_2 ranged in a normal curve of distribution from one parental extreme to the other.

However, in stating that one parental variety had an internode length of 2.1 mm., we do not mean that each internode in this variety was exactly 2.1 mm. long. Some variation always occurs even among individuals which are all alike in genotype. This is environmental, or nongenetic, variation. The variation in the F_2 was far greater than the variation in the parent lines or in the F_1 because in the F_2 a large amount of *genetic* variation due to segregation and recombination of genes was added to the environmental variation.

The environmental variation may partially obscure the genetic variation, making it difficult for us to determine the number of pairs of genes involved in a multiple-gene cross. If, for example, the internodes in the parental variety of barley under discussion range from 2.06 mm. to 2.16 mm., with the average, or mean, at 2.1 mm., when shall we say an F_2 plant is as extreme as this parent? Must it have 2.06 mm. internodes, or shall we use the mean, 2.1 mm., or is it like the parental variety if the internodes are as small as the largest of the parental internodes, 2.16 mm.? Obviously only a rough estimate of the number of pairs of genes in a cross may be made by this method.

In some instances the number of pairs of multiple genes involved in a cross is so large that even in a good-sized F_2 generation no individual even approaches the parental extremes.

In cases like the two just mentioned, we may arrive at an estimate of the number of pairs of multiple genes concerned by making use of statistical measures of the variability of the parents, the F_1 and the F_2.

How may we describe a variable distribution? Obviously we shall need to know the number of individuals measured and the average, or **mean,** of the group. But these two figures are not enough.

Consider a class of three graduate students whose grades are respectively 70, 70, and 70. Obviously the mean is 70. Consider another class of three whose grades are respectively 50, 70, and 90. Again the mean is 70. Consider yet a third class of three, with grades of 40, 70, and 100. Again the mean is 70. In each instance we have a class of three students with a mean grade of 70. But are the distributions alike? Obviously not. They differ in spread. It is not enough to have the number of individuals and the mean; we must also have a measure of spread, or variability about the mean. For this measure we use a statistic known as the **standard deviation,** designated as σ (small sigma). The standard deviation, together with the mean and the number of individuals concerned, makes up the basic statistics for the description of a variable distribution.

The most interesting and important fact about the measurements of any quantitative variation in living things is that when they are plotted out in a graph they usually form a normal curve or some modification of a normal curve. This applies to quantitative differences which are environmental in nature as well as to those which are genetic. Purchase a pound of navy beans from the grocery, and measure the lengths of the individual beans. There will be a few very large ones, more and more in the smaller classes until a class is reached which contains the most individuals; then each smaller class will contain fewer and fewer individuals until finally there will be only a few of the very small beans. When the results are placed on a graph, a "bell-shaped" or "normal" curve results, high in the center and sloping off on the two sides toward the extremes.

Pick a hundred leaves from a tree, and measure their lengths. Again these measurements will follow the same sort of curve. There will be a few of each of the extremes, more and more of the less extreme lengths, and most of the intermediate lengths. Go into the apiary and count the number of bristles on the left hind leg of each bee. The numbers are again distributed in a normal curve. The statistics we shall use are based on normal curve distributions.

Let us take an actual example of a cross involving multiple genes, and describe the variability in terms of the mean and the standard

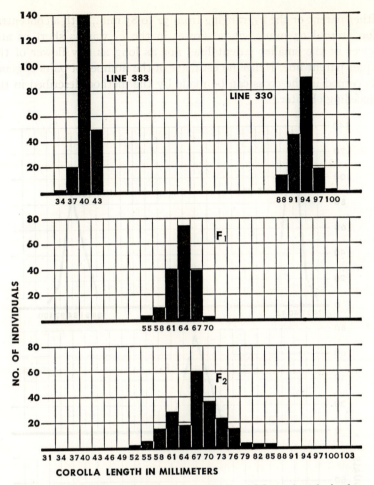

Fig. 15.1 Histograms showing the distribution of flower lengths in the parent lines, the F_1 and the F_2 in a cross in tobacco. Compare with Figure 15.2. *Drawn from the data of East*

deviation. When we have learned to do this, we shall be in a position to use such statistics in determining the number of pairs of genes involved in the cross.

East made a cross between two varieties of tobacco having flowers of different lengths. In one (line 383) the flowers ranged in length from 34 to 43 mm., most of them being about 40 mm. long (Fig. 15.1). In the other (line 330) the flower length ranged from 88 to 100 mm., most of them being about 94 mm. long.

The F_1 were intermediate in length, varying from 55 to 70 mm., grouped about a length of 64 mm. The F_2 were more variable than either parent or the F_1, ranging from 52 to 85 mm., with a concentration around 67 mm., but no flower in the F_2 was as short as any flower of the smaller parent line, nor as long as any flower of the larger parent line. Hence no estimate of the number of pairs of genes concerned in the cross can be made by the method described in the preceding chapter.

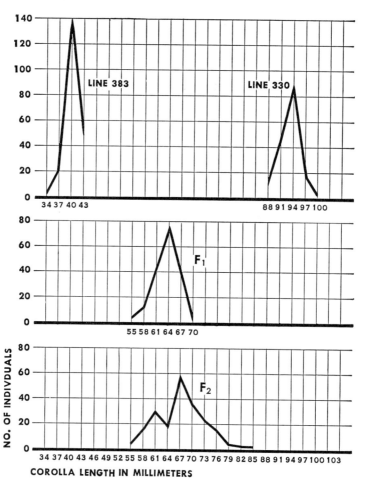

Fig. 15.2 Frequency polygons illustrating the distributions which were shown in the form of histograms in Figure 15.1.

Note that there was some variability even in the relatively homozygous parent lines and in the F_1. Figure 15.1 shows this variability in the form of *histograms*. A histogram is made by plotting the measurement values along the horizontal axis (abscissa) and the frequencies along the vertical axis (ordinate) and constructing a series of rectangles in which the widths correspond to the class ranges and the heights correspond to the frequencies of the respective classes.

Another common method of recording data of this sort is to draw a curve which would run through the top of each rectangle in the histogram. Such curves are called frequency polygons, and the data of Figure 15.1 are presented in this form in Figure 15.2. Comparison of the two figures will show that they are essentially the same, and it is only a matter of choice which method of reproduction is used.

Let us choose the F_1 from this cross as a variable distribution to be described in terms of the mean and the standard deviation. The mean is computed by adding the individual measurements and dividing by the number of individuals which were measured. To facilitate this we may group the data. That is, instead of using each individual measurement, we may collect those ranging from, let us say, 56.5 mm. to 59.5 mm., and assume that they average 58 mm. This class range is therefore assigned a class value of 58. The data are grouped this way in column 2 of Table 15.1.

The number of individuals in any class value is called the frequency (f). For example, there were 10 individuals having the class value 58. We may, therefore, simply multiply 58 by 10, instead of adding 58 ten times. This is done in column 3 of Table 15.1, the column headed fV.

Adding up this column we get the sum of the measurements. Dividing this by the number of individuals measured (n), we have the average, or mean. We designate the mean by a bar over the letter used to stand for the individual measurements. Here we used V for the value of a measurement, so that the average or mean of the V's would be $\overline{V}$. (We read this as V-bar.)

Table 15.1. MEAN AND STANDARD DEVIATION OF COROLLA LENGTH IN THE F_1 OF A CROSS IN TOBACCO

CLASS RANGE	CLASS VALUE (V)	FREQUENCY (f)	fV	DEVIATION OF EACH CLASS FROM THE MEAN ($V - \overline{V}$)	$f(V - \overline{V})^2$
53.5–56.5	55	4	220	−8.53	291.0436
56.5–59.5	58	10	580	−5.53	305.8090
59.5–62.5	61	41	2501	−2.53	262.4369
62.5–65.5	64	75	4800	+0.47	16.5675
65.5–68.5	67	40	2680	+3.47	481.6360
68.5–71.5	70	3	210	+6.47	125.5827
Totals		173	10991		1483.0757

We use the symbol Σ to mean "the sum of"; hence the formula for the mean is written $\overline{V} = \dfrac{\Sigma fV}{n}$. The mean for this distribution is 63.53 mm.

$$\overline{V} = \frac{\Sigma fV}{n} = \frac{10991}{173} = 63.53$$

$$\sigma = \sqrt{\frac{\Sigma f(V - \overline{V})^2}{n - 1}} = \sqrt{8.6225} = \pm 2.94$$

Now let us obtain the standard deviation of this distribution. It is computed by squaring the deviation of each individual from the mean $(V - \overline{V})$, adding all the squared deviations, dividing by $n - 1$, and extracting the square root. This may be done efficiently by again making use of the class frequencies. Reference to Table 15.1 will show that the operation is expressed by the formula

$$\sigma = \sqrt{\frac{\Sigma f(V - \overline{V})^2}{n - 1}}.$$

The standard deviation for this F_1 distribution turns out to be 2.94 mm. This figure can be used in various ways. One way is in comparing the variability of two distributions. The distribution with the larger standard deviation is the more variable. The value of σ for the F_2 in the cross under discussion was 5.93, indicating more variability in the F_2 than in the F_1. We shall use these values of σ more specifically a little farther on.

In comparing the variability of two distributions by means of standard deviations, it should be kept in mind that the values of the two sigmas must be expressed in the same units, that is, both must be in terms of millimeters, pounds, or some other unit of measurement. When we wish to compare the variability of two groups measured in *different* units, such as when we ask the question "Are the flowers more variable in length than in color?", we must express the standard deviation as a per cent of the mean. We call this expression the **coefficient of variation** (C.V.), and it is obtained by the formula C.V. $= \dfrac{\sigma}{\overline{V}} \times 100$. The coefficients of variation may be directly compared for two sets of data, even though one be expressed in millimeters, the other in shades of color.

A further importance of the standard deviation lies in the possibility of determining from it the chances that the mean of the sample which was measured lies within a given range of the true mean of the population. This is usually done through the medium of the **standard error,** which we shall now discuss.

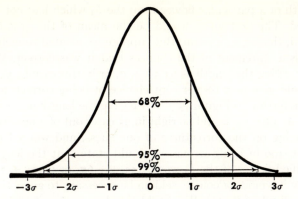

Fig. 15.3 A normal curve. The proportional areas included between successive standard deviations from the mean are shown.

Let us consider a perfect normal curve, such as is shown in Figure 15.3. The center vertical line is erected at the mean. It divides the area under the curve into two equal parts. A vertical line which does this is called a median. In a perfect normal curve the median meets the abscissa at the mean. In a curve made up of a finite series of measurements the median may not be exactly at the mean, but it will usually be close to it.

Now let us erect lines on either side of the mean at the distance represented by the standard deviation, again at the distance represented by twice the standard deviation, and yet again at the distance represented by three times the standard deviation.

In normal or near-normal curves we may predict quite accurately what percentages of the individuals concerned may be expected to fall between plus and minus one standard deviation, two standard deviations, and so on. It can be seen from Figure 15.3 that about 68 per cent of all the individuals are included between plus one standard deviation and minus one standard deviation from the mean. In other words, about 68 per cent of a normal distribution will deviate from the mean by less than the standard deviation. The chance of an individual deviating from the mean by more than $\pm \sigma$ would then be 32 per cent. About 95 per cent of the individuals will deviate from the mean by less than twice the standard deviation. In other words, the chance that any individual lies outside the interval marked by $\pm 2\sigma$ is only 5 per cent. Since in statistics we often want to know the limits beyond which an individual has only a 1 per cent chance of occurring, this interval has been marked off on Figure 15.3. It occurs between $\pm 2.6\sigma$.

Now let us see how we might use these facts. Returning to the frequency distribution of flower lengths, suppose we wanted to guess the length of a particular flower from the F_1 which had not yet been measured. The best guess would be the mean of the group already measured, that is, 63.53 mm. But suppose we wanted to include with our guess a statement of the chances that it was correct. We could do so by giving the length as 63.53 ± σ, or in this case 63.53 ± 2.94. This would give us a 68 per cent chance of being correct, as can be seen by referring to Figure 15.3. If we gave the length as 63.53 ± 2σ, or 63.53 ± 5.88, we would be right in 95 cases out of a hundred. If we were betting on the correctness of our guess, and wanted only one chance in 100 of being wrong, we could state that the length of an unidentified flower of the F_1 was 63.53 ± 2.6σ, or 63.53 ± 7.64.

Now it would, of course, seldom be necessary to guess the length of any individual flower. We would simply measure it and not have to guess. But there is something at which we *do* have to guess. We have to guess at the results we would obtain if we should measure an infinite number of F_1 flowers from the cross of line 383 with line 330. It never happens that we are able to measure the total theoretical population in regard to any character. We are seldom even able to measure the total population existing at any one time. We must usually be content with measuring a small sample of the population. It is important to know how near our figures come to representing the true figures for the total population.

Here is where the guessing comes in. When we make a guess in science, however, we want it to be based on a firm foundation of fact, and we want to be able to designate how much chance there is of our guess being correct. How near is the mean of 63.53, which we calculated from our sample of 173 F_1 flowers, to the true mean of an infinite number of such F_1 flowers? If we state that the mean length of F_1 flowers from the cross of line 383 with line 330 is 63.53 mm., we are guessing at the true mean on the basis of the sample of 173 flowers which were measured. How may we estimate the true mean of such F_1 flowers in such a way as to indicate our chances of being correct?

If we should measure successive samples of such flowers, we would probably obtain a slightly different mean each time. The means of the various samples, however, would fluctuate about a mean of their own, in a typical normal curve distribution. Hence we may obtain a standard deviation for the normal distribution of means of F_1 flower lengths. From the standard deviation of a distribution we may estimate the standard deviation of the normal curve of means by dividing σ of the distribution by the square root of the number of items in the distribution. We call this estimate the standard error (S.E.) of the mean. In other words, S.E. of a mean = $\dfrac{\sigma}{\sqrt{n}}$.

We may say, then, that the mean length for F_1 flowers from the cross under discussion is $63.53 \pm \dfrac{\sigma}{\sqrt{n}}$, which is $63.53 \pm .223$. That is to say, if we measured an infinite number of such flowers, there would be only 32 chances in 100 that the true mean would be found beyond $63.53 \pm .223$. There would be only 5 chances in 100 that it would be found beyond $63.53 \pm 2\dfrac{\sigma}{\sqrt{n}}$, or $63.53 \pm .446$. There would be only one chance in 100 that it would be found beyond $63.53 \pm 2.6\dfrac{\sigma}{\sqrt{n}}$, or $63.53 \pm .5798$. Thus our "guess" at the true mean of an infinite number of F_1 flowers from the cross is made quite accurate after all.

An important standard error is that of a difference between the means of two samples. If the means have been independently derived or are otherwise uncorrelated, the standard error of a difference is computed by the formula, S.E. of a difference $= \sqrt{(\text{S.E.}_1)^2 + (\text{S.E.}_2)^2}$, where S.E.$_1$ is the S.E. of the mean of the first sample and S.E.$_2$ is the S.E. of the mean of the second sample. In practice a difference must be at least as great as twice its standard error before we accept it as a true difference, that is, a difference not due to chance sampling.

Sometimes the limits within which certain proportions of the distribution occur are given in terms of **probable error** (P.E.) instead of standard error. Where the standard error gives limits within which 68 per cent of the distribution occurs, the probable error gives limits within which 50 per cent of the distribution occurs. Probable errors are directly derived from standard errors by multiplying the standard error by the constant .6745. It is important to state in using limiting values whether P.E. or S.E. is being used.

We have digressed considerably from the problem with which we started this chapter, namely the determination of the number of pairs of genes concerned in a multiple-gene cross. However, we were faced with the problem of describing variable distributions, and our digression has given us an insight into descriptive methods for such distributions. Let us return to the problem of analyzing multiple-gene crosses. It will be recalled that such analyses are often complicated by the fact that the parental extremes did not occur in the F_2 and that environmental variations in the character somewhat obscure the genetic differences. In such cases we may make an estimate of the number of genes concerned by using means and standard deviations.

In the tobacco cross which we have been discussing there was some variation within each of the two parent lines, and within the F_1, and considerable variation within the F_2. These variations are precisely expressed by the statistics of the distributions. The mean of line 383 was 40.37 ± .120, that of line 330 was 93.11 ± .183. The F_1 mean was 63.53 ± .223, while the F_2 mean was 67.51 ± .408. The greater variability in the F_2 is indicated even more strikingly by the standard deviations of the distributions themselves. The standard deviations of the P_1, P_2, and F_1 are all about the same (1.74, 2.37, and 2.94), while that of the F_2 is definitely larger (5.93).

Since the individuals within each parent line were alike or nearly alike genetically, the variation that did occur within these lines must have been largely environmental. The F_1 generation would be composed of individuals which were genetically similar, so that the variation that occurred within this generation would also be largely nongenetic. In the F_2, however, the variability was much larger because it was made up of nongenetic variability plus genetic variability which resulted from the segregation and recombination of the genes concerned in the cross.

It is fair to assume that the nongenetic variation of the F_2 is approximately the same as the nongenetic variation in the F_1. The genetic variation in the F_2, then, will be the excess variation over that of the F_1, that is, genetic $\sigma^2 F_2$ = total $\sigma^2 F_2 - \sigma^2 F_1$. Mathematically the genetic variation in the F_2 can be shown to be $\sigma = \sqrt{\dfrac{Ne^2}{2}}$, where N represents the number of pairs of genes concerned and e represents the contribution of each effective allele. An estimate of e is made by the formula $e = \dfrac{D}{2N}$, where D is the difference between the mean of one parent line and the mean of the other parent line. Substituting these in the formula genetic $\sigma^2 F_2$ = total $\sigma^2 F_2 - \sigma^2 F_1$, we have the final formula $N = \dfrac{D^2}{8(\sigma^2 F_2 - \sigma^2 F_1)}$.

To estimate the number of pairs of multiple genes concerned in corolla length in the cross between the two strains of tobacco, we substitute the means and standard deviations in the formula as follows:

$$N = \frac{(93.11 - 40.37)^2}{8[(5.93)^2 - (2.94)^2]}$$

$$= \frac{2781.7984}{212.1139}$$

$$= 13.115 \text{ or approximately 13 pairs.}$$

In these estimations we assume equal and additive effects, no dominance, no epistasis, and no linkage. The occurrence of any of these phenomena would, of course, make added corrections necessary.

PROBLEMS

15.1 In Black Mexican corn the ears average 16.8 ± 0.12 cm. in length. In a variety of popcorn the ears average 6.6 ± 0.07 cm. in length. East found the F_1 from a cross between these two varieties to be distributed as follows:

EAR LENGTH IN CENTIMETERS	FREQUENCY
9	1
10	12
11	12
12	14
13	17
14	9
15	4

Compute the mean and the standard deviation of the distribution and the standard error of the mean.

15.2 In rabbits the Flemish race has a mean weight of 3600 grams, while the Himalayan race averages 1875 grams. In a cross between these two races, Castle found the standard deviation of the F_1 distribution to be ± 162 grams and the standard deviation of the F_2 distribution to be ± 230 grams. Compute the number of pairs of genes probably involved in the cross.

REFERENCES

EAST, E. M., *Genetics* **1**:164 (1916).

FISHER, R. A., *Statistical Methods for Research Workers*, 7th Ed. Edinburgh, Oliver and Boyd (1938).

SMITH, H. H., *Genetics* **22**:227 (1943); *Botanical Review* **10**:349 (1944).

SNEDECOR, G. W., *Statistical Methods*. Ames, Iowa, Collegiate Press (1938).

WRIGHT, S., *Genetics* **19**:537 (1934).

CHAPTER SIXTEEN

Selection and methods of breeding

One of the most powerful tools in the hands of the breeder of animals and plants is **selection.** The use of selection extends as far back as records go in the history of breeding. Long before the genetic basis for selection was known, breeders picked out the animals or plants most nearly approaching the ideal they had in mind, and from them raised the next generation. From such selections have come the many improved breeds of livestock, poultry, pets, and cultivated plants. Nearly every attempt at selection has resulted in some success.

From such successful attempts there grew a belief that selection could improve a race indefinitely. The method by which selection operated was not understood until after Mendelian inheritance was understood, but was thought of as a more or less mysterious process which could be effectively continued as long as desired. With the advent of the scientific knowledge of genetics, however, came the understanding that selection is actually a sorting out and preserving of certain combinations of genes to the exclusion of others. A selected group of animals or plants thus represents a restricted portion of the total possible range of variation in the species.

Selection is of two general kinds, which in principle are really the same. The two kinds referred to are *natural selection* and *artificial selection.* In natural selection certain genetic combinations are preserved because the individuals possessing them are better able to survive through the reproductive period, better able to secure food, more adept at escaping enemies, or better able to procure mates; or perhaps merely because they are biologically or geographically isolated. In artificial selection certain combinations of inheritable characteristics are preserved because they please man's fancy or contribute to his well-being.

It is useless to select individuals on the basis of variation resulting from differences in environment. Such variations, which are spoken of as fluctuations, are not transmitted to the offspring. Selection, then, must be based on hereditary variations. Furthermore, the race must be heterogeneous as to the character or characters to be selected. When a race becomes homogeneous as to certain characters, selection cannot change the genetic composition in regard to these characters.

These two fundamental points were first proved by the classic experiments of Johannsen, a Danish botanist. Johannsen chose garden beans as the material for his study, since they were self-fertilized, thus making groups of related individuals genetically similar, and since each seed could produce relatively large numbers of offspring.

When a mixed population of seeds from the Princess bean was planted, the plants which grew from the larger seeds produced seeds of large size, and the plants that grew from the smaller seeds produced seeds of small average size. The seeds on any one plant varied considerably in size, but the seeds on plants from large seeds were larger on the average than the seeds on plants from small seeds. Thus the first effect of selection was positive, that is, effective. Since the seeds on any plant varied somewhat in size, due to their number and position in the pod and the time of flowering, Johannsen investigated this variation.

Here for instance is plant A, raised from a *large* seed from the original mixed population. Its seeds vary somewhat in size, but their average size is large. Choosing the largest and smallest seeds of those on the plant and planting them, the results are surprising. The average size of the beans from both seeds is the same. This happens generation after generation following the first selection which alone was effective.

As another example plant B, raised from a *small* seed from the original mixed population, produces beans which are in general small as compared with those of plant A. Selection here is effective. However, when the largest and smallest of these seeds are selected and planted, the average of the offspring produced by each is the same. Selection is no longer effective.

In all these experiments the beans were self-fertilized and care was taken to prevent contamination. It is apparent that the original population which Johannsen used was a mixture of various true-breeding (homozygous) lines. The first generation selection sorted out these various lines, which thereafter produced similar progeny within the line because of homozygosity, which was the result of the fact that beans do not normally cross-fertilize.

From the original population Johannsen isolated, by one generation of selection, nineteen such homozygous true-breeding lines, which he called pure lines. The variation within a pure line is environmental in nature, and selection in regard to variation within a pure line cannot affect the genetic make-up of the next generation.

The actual results of selection in two of these pure lines are shown in Table 16.1 where size is expressed in terms of weight. It will be seen that in a line of beans averaging 55.8 centigrams the offspring of beans of 40, 50, 60, and 70 centigrams, respectively, all averaged approximately the same, this average being essentially that of the pure line itself. The same thing is true in the line averaging 40.8 centigrams in weight; and similar results were found in the other seventeen lines not listed in the table.

Table 16.1. AVERAGE WEIGHT OF OFFSPRING FROM SISTER SEEDS OF VARIOUS SIZES IN A PURE LINE WITH LARGE SEEDS (A) AND ONE WITH SMALL SEEDS (B). (*From data of Johannsen*)

PURE LINE	AVERAGE WEIGHT OF PURE LINE IN CENTIGRAMS	WEIGHT OF MOTHER BEAN					
		20	30	40	50	60	70
A	55.8			57.2	54.9	56.5	55.5
B	40.8	41.0	40.7	40.8			

All this means that in order to have selection effective, we must deal with hereditary characters, not environmental fluctuations, and the group of individuals must be heterogeneous as to the characters to be selected. Given a group of individuals which are heterozygous for a number of characters, it is possible by selection to obtain one or more pure lines, homozygous for certain combinations of these characters. After pure lines are obtained selection can make no further progress.

The number of pure lines which can be developed in regard to any character depends upon the number of pairs of genes concerned. If one pair of genes, A and a, is involved, obviously two pure lines can occur, AA and aa. With two pairs of genes, A and a, B and b, four pure lines are possible, $AABB$, $AAbb$, $aaBB$, and $aabb$. A general formula for the number of pure lines possible when dealing with n pairs of genes is 2^n. Thus, with twelve pairs of genes concerned, 4096 different pure lines are possible, and with twenty pairs, more than a million pure lines may be formed.

Frequently it is desirable in selection to produce a certain very definite combination of characters. Hence perhaps only one of the many possible pure lines is the one desired, all others being eliminated by purposeful selection. Thus, in the case of dairy cattle, breeders are constantly striving to obtain animals which are homozygous for all the genes for high milk production. Since it is by no means improbable that there are twenty or more pairs of genes concerned in milk production, it may be seen that the pure line desired is only one out of more than a million possible pure lines for these genes, to say nothing of the innumerable heterozygous combinations that may occur.

It is evident that the amount of continued progress which may be made by selection is dependent upon the number of gene pairs concerned. In the case of a single pair of genes, the effects of selection are very quickly exhausted. Thus in poultry rose comb is dominant to single comb. In Leghorns single combs are desired. Letting R represent the gene for rose comb and r the gene for single comb, it is seen that the mere choosing of single-combed birds will produce a line of fowls breeding true for this trait, since *all* single-combed birds are of the formula rr.

In White Wyandottes rose combs are desired. Here the selective process is somewhat more difficult. A pure line of rose-combed birds must be of the formula RR. The mere selection of rose-combed birds from a mixed group of rose-combed and single-combed individuals will not insure such a pure line, however, as some of them will be RR while others are Rr. These two kinds can be distinguished only on the basis of their progeny.

Even in the case of a single pair of genes such as this, however, there may be concerned a set of multiple modifying genes. Variations occur in the type and form of rose combs. These variations are due to multiple modifying genes, and the development of a particular form of rose comb requires selection for particular combinations of these modifiers.

The greatest room for improvement, however, occurs in those characters which are themselves directly dependent upon multiple genes. As we have seen in Chapter 14, such characters as egg production, milk production, size, weight, conformation, speed, yield in plants, and other variable traits are apparently dependent upon multiple genes. Moreover, a great deal of heterozygosity still exists in nearly all domestic animals and cross-fertilized plants in regard to these characters, in spite of the selection already practiced. The reason for the great degree of heterozygosity still existing is the fact that the methods of selection commonly used in the past have not been genetically the best.

The earliest method of selection used was **phenotypic selection.** That is, selection was based on the appearance of the trait in the individual. Those individuals which most nearly approached the ideal were selected. Although gradual progress was made in this way, there were many individual failures. Many fine-looking animals have failed to improve the race at all. Particularly is this true in the "production" characters, such as egg production and milk production. The reason for this is of course that the phenotype is not always an indication of the genotype.

The practice of "judging" dairy cows, dairy bulls, poultry, and other animals has grown around the belief that the appearance of the individual is a guide to its transmitting ability. This is not necessarily true. Even the animal's own production record is not always a valid criterion. Milk production, for example, is inherited on a multiple-gene basis, and many different genotypes may result in the same phenotype, especially among individuals with average records. Particularly in dairy bulls has phenotypic selection proved valueless. Here the actual milk production does not occur in the male, and selection has been based on the appearance and "show points" of the animals. An example shows the lack of value of this type of selection.

A certain large dairy company purchased a young dairy bull calf for the herd. The calf was a show-ring prize winner and had a good pedigree. The price paid was in excess of $100,000. Yet, when it grew up and produced offspring, it consistently lowered the milk production of its daughters below that of their dams.

Another type of selection that became popular was the method of choosing individuals on the strength of the pedigree. This was based on ancestry and was perhaps an improvement over phenotypic selection, especially when the two were used together. Even here, however, practically all the offspring of good ancestors were raised because of their fine ancestry. They were not always an improvement, however, nor even always as good as the line from which they came. This, of course, is due to segregation and recombination of genes. One of the oldest fallacies of heredity and one of the hardest to eradicate is the belief that "like produces like." Our previous study of genetics has shown us that heterozygous animals produce *varied* offspring. The statement may be made correct by changing it to read "like *genes* produce like *genes*." It is the genes, then, not their phenotypic expressions, which must be the basis of selection.

The modern genetic type of selection does not place the emphasis on the appearance of the individual or on the ancestry, although both may be taken into consideration. Instead, the emphasis is placed on the *progeny*. In this way the genotype becomes the basis of selection. Individuals are selected for breeders only if they produce offspring of the desired type. This type of selection is known as **progeny selection** or the **progeny test**.

An example will show the value of this method. At the Maine Experiment Station eight years of phenotypic selection had failed to increase egg production. At the end of this time progeny selection was begun. Both males and females were selected for breeding based on the egg production of their daughters. Striking results were obtained. In two years egg production in this flock was nearly double and remained at this high level.

Hays and Sanborn have reported the results of an experiment at the Massachusetts Experiment Station in which the average annual egg production was raised from 145 eggs to 235 eggs by a system of progeny selection. In this experiment attention was paid to the various genes for early sexual maturity, high intensity, lack of winter pause, nonbroodiness, persistency, egg size, and hatchability.

In dairy cattle similar striking results have been obtained. Various methods have been worked out for determining the transmitting ability or "index" of sires and dams, particularly sires. The work of Heizer is outstanding in this respect. Working with a large herd of Ayrshires, where the same methods of handling and rearing have been used for a quarter of a century, and where careful individual lifetime records have been kept, Heizer was able to develop a mathematical formula for determining the transmitting ability of individual bulls in regard to milk production. The method is based on progeny selection, in this case on the records of the first six daughters. Thus an index is available while the prospective sire is still young. In the course of this work numerous instances appeared which proved the inability of even an expert judge to select, on the basis of appearance and show points, sires which transmit genes for high milk production. Figures 16.1 and 16.2 illustrate this very well. The progeny

Fig. 16.1   This bull is a very superior sire by accepted show-ring standards. Yet he consistently lowered the average milk production of his daughters below that of their dams. Only by the progeny test could the true transmitting value of this bull have been determined.

Fig. 16.2   A very inferior sire by accepted show-ring standards. Yet he consistently raised the milk production of his daughters far above that of their dams. Only a progeny test could show the true transmitting value of this bull.

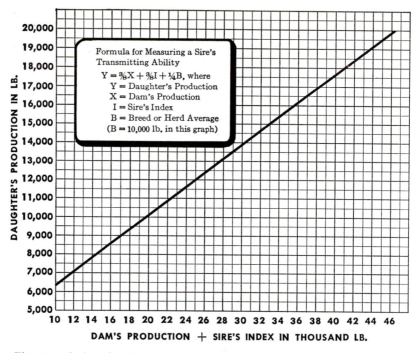

Formula for Measuring a Sire's
Transmitting Ability

$Y = \frac{3}{8}X + \frac{3}{8}I + \frac{1}{4}B$, where
Y = Daughter's Production
X = Dam's Production
I = Sire's Index
B = Breed or Herd Average
(B = 10,000 lb. in this graph)

Fig 16.3   A chart for determining the transmitting value of a bull in regard to milk production. The formula is based on progeny tests. To use the chart, locate the daughter's average production at the left, follow horizontally to the right until the diagonal is intersected, then follow vertically down and read the figure on the horizontal axis. Subtract from this figure the dam's average production. The result is the sire's transmitting ability (index).

test formula for determining the index of sires is shown in Figure 16.3.

Certain characters are more susceptible to phenotypic selection than others. Characters which are readily visible in both sexes, such as size, conformation, and the like, may be selected phenotypically, by "judging" or otherwise, with some success. Even here, however, progeny selection will increase the effectiveness of selection greatly.

An interesting example of the practical value of genetic selection is furnished by the work of East and Jones in producing a new kind of tobacco to order. In the Connecticut Valley a great deal of tobacco is grown, producing the finest cigar wrappers in the United States. Two of the popular varieties of tobacco formerly grown there in abundance were Broadleaf and Sumatra. Both of these, unfortunately, had certain defects which were a source of dissatisfaction to the farmer, the manufacturer, or the consumer.

The farmer desires a many-leaved plant with no lateral branches, resistant to disease, standing up well in the face of wind and rain, and maturing quickly. The manufacturer desires a thin leaf, covering as many cigars as possible per pound of material; a broadly rounded leaf, since the finest portion is near the tip; a strong leaf which will not tear, at least until after the consumer has obtained the cigar. The consumer himself demands tobacco which burns freely — but not too freely — and leaves a gray-white ash which does not flake off at each puff. The flavor must be of the character which is acceptable to the connoisseur, and the aroma must be agreeable. The texture must be velvety and the color must be uniform and intermediate in shade, showing no coarse veins or white markings.

With these facts in mind a new variety of tobacco was made to order, embodying all the desired qualities. Broadleaf and Sumatra tobaccos, which possessed between them most of the requirements, were crossed. The F_1 was intermediate, as would be expected, and the F_2 was quite variable. From subsequent generations, by the use of progeny selection, there was eventually obtained a true-breeding variety which was named Round Tip. Reference to Table 16.2 will show its characters as compared with those of the parental forms. In some of its characters Round Tip exceeded either parent, particularly in its leaf number, its excellent root system, and its resistance to disease. The yield is very high, having reached under favorable conditions 2800 pounds per acre. Leaves of the three varieties are shown in Figure 16.4.

Table 16.2. CHARACTERS OF THE NEW VARIETY OF BROADLEAF TOBACCO MADE TO ORDER BY THE GENETICIST, COMPARED WITH THOSE OF THE PARENT VARIETIES FROM WHICH IT WAS DEVELOPED. (*From East and Jones*)

BROADLEAF	SUMATRA	NEW VARIETY ROUND TIP
large leaf	small leaf	large leaf
narrow tip	round tip	round tip
drooping leaf	upright leaf	upright leaf
leaves close	leaves apart	leaves close
texture coarse	texture fine	texture intermediate
leaves thick	leaves thin	leaves intermediate
flavor good but strong	flavor none	flavor intermediate
yield high	yield low	yield high
18 leaves per plant	20 leaves per plant	26 leaves per plant
fair root system	fair root system	wonderful root system

Hand in hand with the problem of selection goes the problem of **inbreeding.** By inbreeding is meant the mating of closely related individuals. It is plain that there may be various grades of inbreeding depending on the closeness of the relationship, varying from self-fertilization in many plants and a few animals, through brother-sister matings, to the mating of distant cousins.

Fig. 16.4 Representative leaves of Sumatra tobacco (top); Broadleaf (center); and the new variety Round Tip (bottom). *From East and Jones in the Journal of Heredity*

Popular belief has it that inbreeding is dangerous. Breeders frequently hesitate to inbreed their stock, fearing that it will degenerate. Human laws nearly everywhere forbid brother-sister marriages and even cousin marriages. These beliefs have some basis in fact, as popular beliefs usually do, but they do not represent the whole truth. Again, as in selection, the truth has had to await the development of the scientific knowledge of the facts and principles of heredity.

The facts are that inbreeding does not *create* any weaknesses or defects. In itself it is not harmful. What inbreeding does is to increase rapidly the homozygosity of the population, to isolate pure lines, to bring to light in the homozygous condition any recessive genes which may have been carried in the heterozygous state in the stock. We now know that most mutations are recessives and that most are harmful. It follows that, because of natural selection, the individuals having the harmful genes in the homozygous state will be eliminated. This leaves, however, many individuals in the population carrying one or more of these recessive deleterious genes in the heterozygous state. Under a system of random mating, these are to a large extent carried along, in the heterozygous condition, from generation to generation. Under any system of inbreeding, however, the heterozygotes in the population rapidly become less frequent and the homozygotes more frequent. Since many of the recessive genes affect vigor, fertility, and viability, the race as a whole tends to degenerate under inbreeding.

Not only are deleterious characters brought to light, however, but other genetic characters of the race become apparent through increasing homozygosity. Some of these characters may be beneficial, or at least not harmful. Thus, if rigid selection accompanies inbreeding, it is usually possible to preserve certain of the desirable combinations in more or less homozygous form. Large numbers of individuals must usually be discarded in the process, however. Moderate inbreeding, with careful selection, has been the basis of the building up and improving of most of the modern breeds and varieties of livestock and cultivated plants.

In any group of individuals with which man is concerned, it is desirable to know what hereditary traits are carried. Inbreeding quickly tells this by bringing to light all hidden recessives. Pure lines are rapidly formed and from these the desired ones may be selected and the rest discarded (Fig. 16.5). Pure lines are of considerable value in many ways. They may be, because of selection, free from defects, particularly hidden defects. They will breed true for all their characters. Certain of the best varieties of wheat, cotton, and other crop plants are pure lines, in some cases tracing back to a single individual. Thus the billions of Kanred wheat plants which for many years were

Fig 16.5 A number of pure lines of wheat planted in adjoining plots, showing differences between the lines in resistance to winter killing.

grown annually on millions of acres were direct descendants of a single seed selected at the Kansas Experiment Station in 1915.

A better and more recent variety is Concho, developed by the Oklahoma Agricultural Experiment Station, seed of which was first released in 1953. It will probably soon be the most widely grown variety of hard red winter wheat. The pedigrees of Concho and other varieties are shown in Figure 16.6.

These wheats, however, are quite susceptible to such diseases as leaf rust. To overcome this susceptibility, more than selection and inbreeding is required. At this point we may see the advantage of the other cornerstone of genetic improvement, hybridization. Certain grasses, such as *Agropyron*, are resistant to leaf rust and have better straw than wheat, although their seeds do not have the valuable qualities of wheat. By careful hand pollination, it is possible to achieve an occasional cross between *Agropyron* and *Triticum* (wheat), and then, by repeated crossing of the hybrids back to wheat, to combine the desirable qualities of the grass with the commercial characteristics already developed in Concho and other varieties of wheat.

The results of one set of experiments in hybridization, back-crossing, and selection are shown in Figure 16.7. The selected plants resulting from several generations of back-crossing are practically indistinguishable from wheat, but have better straw and are highly

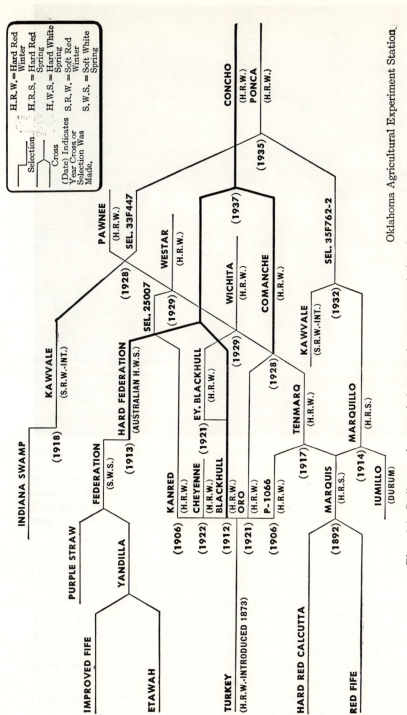

Fig. 16.6 Pedigrees of some of the more important varieties of winter wheat. Following the crosses which led to Concho, selection was practiced until 1953 when the first Concho seed was released to the public. *Courtesy of the Oklahoma Agricultural Experiment Station*

Fig. 16.7 Wheatgrass, wheat, and a commercially valuable hybrid. Left, wheatgrass (Agropyron), which is highly resistant to leaf rust but lacks the economic characteristics of wheat. Right, wheat (Triticum), which is highly selected for commercial value but is very susceptible to leaf rust. Center, a plant developed by crossing wheatgrass with wheat, then back-crossing the hybrid to wheat until the result is a variety having the fine characteristics of wheat plus a high degree of leaf rust resistance. *Courtesy of Dr. A. M. Schlehuber*

resistant to leaf rust. Continued selection, together with the self-pollination which is characteristic of wheat, will preserve this combination of genes in the new variety.

It must always be remembered, however, that a breed or variety selected for yield or performance in one locality at a certain time may not be as well adapted to another locality or at another period. Environmental circumstances are variable from place to place and from time to time. Among the changing environmental agencies are the climate, the soil, the art of husbandry, and the infectious organisms and parasites which may attack the breed or variety.

Leaf rusts, for example, occur in several genetically different races. A variety of wheat may be resistant to the more common races of rust found in its growing area; but over the years, due to the resistance, these more common races will tend to diminish, and others, to which the wheat variety is susceptible, will tend to increase until they become a real threat. A continuing battle must be waged between the development of resistance to parasites and the expansion of virulent races of the parasite. Moreover, as will be seen in Chapter 27, the invaders may develop increased virulence by mutation as well as by expansion in numbers.

Hawaiian pineapples have been bred to a high degree of perfection by careful selection. Size, shape, taste, and canning qualities are all important to the industry. The commercial variety has one characteristic, however, which lowers its efficiency: it is susceptible to heart rot and root rot. In an effort to overcome this defect, the Pineapple Research Institute has crossed the cultivated variety with wild relatives which, although lacking marketable fruits, are immune to these diseases. In the segregating generations following the original crosses, many bizarre phenotypes occur as a result of recombination of genes (Fig. 16.8). There is little reason to doubt, however, that the desired combinations of quality and immunity will eventually be obtained from the crosses.

Fig. 16 8   Segregating pineapple fruits following crosses between the cultivated variety and wild relatives. The fruit in the upper right-hand corner has the desired outward characteristics. On being cut it was found to possess good qualities of taste and texture, but to be full of seeds.

Fig. 16.9 The Santa Gertrudis breed and its antecedents. Top, a Brahman bull; center, a Shorthorn cow; bottom, a Santa Gertrudis bull. *Courtesy of The Cattleman*

Hybridization, followed by selection and inbreeding, is of practical value in animal breeding as well as in plant breeding. Along the Gulf Coast of southern United States the standard breeds of beef cattle (*Bos taurus*) do not fare as well as they do in the north because of the heat. The Zebu (*Bos indicus*), which is native to India, is much more heat-tolerant. The United States Department of Agriculture has for some years experimented with Zebu-Angus crosses, and has selected superior strains combining the best traits of both species. Zebu-Hereford crosses have also been made by breeders, and some excellent strains have been selected and developed. An entirely new breed, the Santa Gertrudis, has been developed by the King Ranch of Texas, combining Zebu and Shorthorn characteristics. This is the first distinctively North American breed of beef cattle.

When the various breeds of imported Zebu were first used in America, about 1910, exploratory crosses with our beef breeds were initiated. From these there was developed the American Brahman, about seven-eighths *Bos indicus* and one-eighth *Bos taurus*. The Santa Gertrudis breed resulted from a Brahman-Shorthorn cross, followed by more than thirty years of back-crossing, careful genetic selection, and inbreeding. The result is a valuable new breed for the south, comparing favorably in homozygosity to the older breeds, and superior to them in many ways (Figure 16.9).

In addition to the practical value of pure lines in agriculture because of their possession of highly selected, true-breeding qualities, pure lines may also be of scientific value. Since the individuals of a pure line are genetically alike, the modifying effects of the environment may be studied. Variations within a pure line are seldom genetic. Of course an occasional mutation may occur which will be genetic, but this very fact is of value, since the frequency of mutation may profitably be studied in a pure line. Such occasional hereditary variations are true mutations and not the result of recombinations which often cannot be distinguished phenotypically from mutations in heterozygous populations. Pure lines are valuable in controlled experimental work because they have a low standard deviation, a fact the importance of which will be appreciated from the discussion of biometry in the preceding chapter.

The rapidity with which homozygosity is reached will depend upon the degree of inbreeding and the number of pairs of genes concerned. Self-fertilization will bring about a condition of homozygosity most rapidly, eight or ten generations of self-fertilization resulting in an almost complete homozygous condition of even a large number of allelic pairs. Brother-sister mating is next most effective, followed by double first cousins, half brothers and sisters, and single first cousins. When the inbreeding is as far removed as second cousins the per-

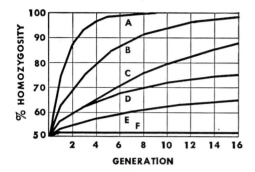

Fig. 16.10 Graph showing the percentage of homozygosity in successive generations under various systems of inbreeding. A, self-fertilization. B, brother-sister matings. C, double first cousins. D, half brothers and sisters. E, single first cousins. F, second cousins. *Adapted from Wright in Genetics*

centage of homozygotes, as Wright has shown, does not materially increase as a result (Fig. 16.10).

Two particularly extensive investigations are available as experimental evidence that vigorous fertile uniform races of animals may be developed under a system of close inbreeding. At the Wistar Institute rats were inbred by King for more than twenty-five generations, using brother-sister matings. Although many weak, sterile, or abnormal individuals appeared, especially in the earlier generations, it was possible by careful selection to continue the line in such a way that a uniform race was obtained in which growth, fertility, and constitutional vigor were not lessened, but if anything, increased.

At the United States Department of Agriculture guinea pigs were inbred by brother-sister matings for more than twenty generations. Again, particularly in the earlier generations, marked loss of vigor and fertility appeared. More than 30,000 animals have been recorded by Wright in this experiment. At the end of twenty-three generations of close inbreeding about half of the original thirty-two separate lines were still alive. They showed marked differences between the lines, but notable uniformity within the line (Fig. 16.11). Certain families were characterized by definite color combinations or by polydactylism or by low vitality or various other traits. Some of the lines were below average vigor, others above.

Fig. 16.11 Four generations of inbred guinea pigs in family 35. Note the uniformity of color. This family is characterized by high vigor and disease resistance. The pair at the left represents the 16th inbred generation, the others representing the 17th, 18th, and 19th generations, respectively. The right-hand pair are young animals, which accounts for their smaller size. *From Wright, in U.S. Dept. of Agriculture Bulletin 1090*

In both the experiments cited above, inbreeding with careful selection has resulted in living, vigorous, fertile races even after many generations of brother-sister matings. In plants such results are more readily obtained. Peas, beans, wheat, oats, barley, tobacco, rice, and some other cultivated plants are normally self-fertilized, which is the very strictest type of inbreeding. Yet none of these species is lacking in vigor or fertility.

It is obvious that pure lines may be most efficiently established by raising the offspring of a single individual, which can be done successfully only in self-fertilizing species such as wheat. In animals, where self-fertilization is not usually possible, some form of inbreeding is required. At what point may the mating of related individuals be considered inbreeding? In practice, inbreeding is usually defined as the mating of individuals that are more closely related than the average relationship in the population concerned. Thus the precise meaning of inbreeding may vary from species to species, from breed to breed, and even from herd to herd.

One form of inbreeding commonly used by animal breeders is "linebreeding." By linebreeding is meant the mating of animals in such a way that the descendants will be kept continually related to some individual whose characteristics are admired. Thus in any mating the parents will be chosen because of their descent from the admired ancestor, although they need not be themselves closely related to each other. With judicious selection, linebreeding may often result in improvement.

Another way in which inbreeding is commonly used is in "grading." Numerous experiments, particularly with dairy cattle, beef cattle, and hogs, have demonstrated the value of grading a herd. By grading is usually meant the crossing of mediocre or "grade" females to a selected pure-bred sire, then continuing the process by breeding the hybrid female offspring to the same sire or one from the same pure-bred strain. Rapid improvement has been brought about by this method in such characteristics as milk production, meat production, fecundity, and efficient use of feed. In genetic terms the method is one of continued back-crossing (often called by the animal breeder "top-crossing"). From the genetic viewpoint it is readily perceived that the progress is likely to be rapid in the first few back-crosses, where the percentage of introduced genes from the pure-bred strain is high, and to slow down in later generations as fewer and fewer genes from the pure-bred strain are lacking in the herd.

Through the use of genetic principles and of the advances in husbandry, geneticists and plant and animal breeders have cooperated to increase the commercial value of many kinds of crops and livestock. The yields of wheat, oats, barley, rye, and clover have been increased by 15 to 25 per cent. The average annual production of eggs per hen has increased in the last 25 years from about 110 to about 165, and of pounds of butterfat per cow from about 270 to about 350. Better methods of feeding and rearing, together with an understanding and application of the genetic principles of hybridization, selection, and inbreeding, have accounted for the advances.

Closely correlated with the problem of inbreeding is the phenomenon of **heterosis.** By this is meant the excess vigor which so often occurs in hybrids. It is frequently spoken of as **hybrid vigor.** The word heterosis was coined by Shull in 1914 as a result of a long series of experiments on the effects of inbreeding and subsequent crossing. Many manifestations of heterosis are available in plants and livestock. Whenever crosses between individuals of two races which differ one from the other in a number of genes are made, the hybrid is apt to differ from both parents by greater vitality, sturdiness, and resistance to unfavorable environmental conditions. Thus the cross between Poland China and Duroc Jersey pigs produces an animal larger and more vigorous than either parent. The same is true of the Duroc Jersey-Berkshire cross. Many such cases are known in both animals and plants.

Fig. 16.12 Heterosis in corn. At the top are shown two inbred lines, free from all abnormalities but lacking in vigor. In the center is the type of ear which results when pollen from the right-hand inbred line is placed on the silks of the left-hand line. At the bottom are the ears from plants which grow from the seed of the center ear.

Advantage of this fact may be taken in connection with the loss in vigor which frequently occurs in inbred lines. Thus Shull and, independently, East and Jones have shown that inbreeding in corn results in various pure lines which by selection may be free from all recessive harmful genes, but which nevertheless, in spite of the best selection, lack vigor. When, however, two different inbred lines are crossed, the hybrid offspring are more vigorous than either of the original stocks from which the inbred lines were derived, in addition to being free from genetic defects. Such "hybrid corn" is of considerable value because of the great increase in yield and uniformity and the freedom from abnormalities (Fig. 16.12).

The large and uniform ears produced as a result of heterosis must not be used for seed, however, as the hybrid vigor declines rapidly in later generations. Instead, the inbred defect-free lines must be continued and re-crossed every year in order to produce the hybrid seed from which the plants showing heterosis are derived.

One good explanation of hybrid vigor seems to be that there exist numerous genes for growth and vigor, each one dominant to its allele for lack of vigorous growth. These dominant vigor genes are scattered on various chromosomes and thus exist in linkage groups. Any inbred line is apt to have some of these dominant genes in homozygous condition, but also to have some of the recessive genes in homozygous form. Crosses between inbred lines may bring all the dominant genes together in the hybrid, if each inbred line carries the vigor genes which the other one lacks. Thus all crosses between inbred strains do not result in the same degree of heterosis.

On the basis of this explanation it should be theoretically possible to obtain varieties homozygous for all the dominant vigor genes, so that the heterosis would "breed true." Since, however, there are many such genes, some in one linkage group and some in another, it would not be easy to obtain them all in homozygous form in one variety because of the difficulty of recombining, through crossing over, so many linked genes, none of which is individually recognizable. The best indication that varieties of cross-pollinated species like corn may some day be made homozygous for vigor lies in the fact that varieties of self-pollinated species like wheat and oats are found in nature in a vigorous condition even though they are undoubtedly highly inbred. If natural selection can accomplish this result in self-pollinated species, man should be able to duplicate it by careful genetic technique in cross-pollinated species.

Another suggested explanation of heterosis which has received much support is that certain genes in the heterozygous state result in the production of greater vigor than either allele produces when homozygous. Crow has demonstrated on statistical grounds that the dominance hypothesis cannot account for all the observable increase in vigor. Perhaps both hypotheses are correct, and heterosis is the result of a combination of dominant vigor genes and vigor resulting from heterozygosis.

The mule is a good example of heterosis. Although the two parents, the mare and the jack, are not particularly homozygous in regard to the genes of their own breeds, nevertheless the various individuals of each breed are relatively similar as compared to the differences between breeds. The mule apparently receives different genes for vigor from the two parents, and is more sturdy than either and better able to withstand hardships. Mules are usually sterile, due to the fact that the chromosome numbers and kinds are different in the two parent species. When maturation starts there are no homologous chromosomes to undergo synapsis, and almost no viable gametes are produced. There are on record occasional cases of fertile mare mules, in which apparently the entire chromosome complement characteristic of the mare is segregated into the germ cells. Curiously enough there is no evidence that viable eggs produced by mules ever contain any of the chromosomes which the mule received from the jack.

Thus, if a fertile mare mule is bred to a stallion, the colt is a typical horse colt, with no evidence of its donkey ancestry. Conversely, when a fertile mare mule is bred to a jack, the colt is a perfectly typical mule. Obviously the eggs contain only horse chromosomes in these instances. This is not too surprising when it is considered that the cytoplasm of a mule, as originally received through the egg from which it developed, is horse cytoplasm. Horse chromosomes, then, might be expected to be functionally "at home," so to speak, in horse cytoplasm during maturation. Anderson has collected and discussed in an informative article the known cases of fertile mare mules.

The advantages of heterosis are now being used in practical animal breeding. By obtaining homozygous or nearly homozygous lines through inbreeding, and then crossing the inbred lines, hybrid vigor is being exploited in a number of domestic animals. Millions of hybrid chicks are now produced each year, and thousands of hybrid pigs. A start has been made in sheep and dairy cattle, but the slowness of reproduction in these animals makes the production of the requisite pure lines somewhat less practicable.

General conclusions

We may briefly delineate the principles and practices of selection and inbreeding as follows. Selection, to be effective, must deal with *heterogeneous or heterozygous* populations. If the environment is kept fairly constant, the bulk of the observed variation may reasonably be considered to be genetic in nature. Selection must be applied to the *individual*, not the mass. It must be based on the *genotype* of the individual, not the phenotype. A definite genotype must be the end in view, usually a homozygous genotype, that is, a pure line. This is most efficiently reached by some system of inbreeding in connection with vigorous progeny selection. After the race is homozygous, selection can bring about no further advance. Even in homozygous lines, however, selection may serve a purpose, since mutations, chromosomal aberrations, and accidental crossing occasionally occur, producing individuals which are subject to selective elimination.

Selection does not create anything new. It merely sorts out, isolates, recombines, and differentially preserves the genes responsible for the characters selected. Even after a race is homozygous so that further selection is ineffective, however, there may still be room for improvement. New mutations may occur, especially now that the artificial production of mutations is possible, and some of these may be desirable variations. Improvements in the environment, particularly in feeding and rearing, may be feasible. Outcrossing with another race so as to introduce new desirable genes for further selection may be advisable. Finally, heterosis may be utilized in certain cases for increased vigor.

The inbreeding which must so often accompany selection does not *create* weakness or defects: it merely brings them to light. Crossbreeding, on the other hand, does not eliminate them; it merely covers them up, while still carrying them along. Inbreeding in connection with rigid selection, however, may result in the complete elimination of undesirable genes.

These same principles apply to man as well as to domestic animals and plants. Thus when two first cousins marry and produce, let us say, a feeble-minded child, it is not because they were first cousins, but because they both carried the gene or genes necessary for the production of feeble-mindedness. Two unrelated parents who carried similar genes could also produce such a child. If, however, a certain man does carry the recessive gene or genes responsible for this condition, it is more probable that a close relative will also carry these particular recessives than that an unrelated woman chosen at random would happen to carry them. Therefore, it frequently happens that inbreeding in man results in undesirable traits. If no undesirable recessive genes are present, however, first cousins could and frequently do produce normal and even superior children.

Selective agents are constantly at work in the human race just as in any other species. Such agents will be considered in detail in a later chapter, but some of them may be indicated at this time as a basis for thought and study. Immigration, emigration, disease, war, assortative mating, medical attention, charity, higher education, and many other sociological conditions of the environment are continually tending to preserve or eliminate certain genetic components of the population. The problems evolved from these facts are of sufficient importance to warrant their separate treatment, and they will therefore be reserved for the chapter on eugenics (Chapter 29).

PROBLEMS

16.1 A certain large herd of cattle is very uniform in regard to milk production, but very variable in regard to the degree of spotting. How would you explain this?

16.2 A breeder has a variety of wheat in which he has tried for several seasons to increase the yield, but without success. He then crosses it with another variety having the same yield, and finds that the hybrids resemble the two parent varieties. However, in later generations he is able by selection to increase the yield considerably. Explain these facts.

16.3 After an inbred line becomes relatively homozygous, is it advisable to discontinue selection? Explain.

16.4 Would it be possible to take advantage of the effects of heterosis within a breed of cattle? How?

16.5 In which would you expect selection to have the greater effect, cross-fertilized plants or self-fertilized plants? Why?

16.6 In a large dairy herd the average annual milk production of which is 10,000 lb., the records of the first six daughters of each of two bulls compared with the dams of the daughters are as follows:

	DAUGHTER	DAM
Bull A	11,154 lb.	12,255 lb.
	13,768 lb.	15,350 lb.
	10,756 lb.	9,160 lb.
	10,135 lb.	8,742 lb.
	11,750 lb.	12,104 lb.
	9,894 lb.	7,211 lb.
Bull B	8,716 lb.	10,112 lb.
	6,947 lb.	9,283 lb.
	10,154 lb.	15,350 lb.
	7,012 lb.	8,742 lb.
	9,219 lb.	12,019 lb.
	6,153 lb.	7,103 lb.

Compute the index for each bull, using the graph in Figure 16.3. Which is the better bull?

16.7 There are many varieties of wheat, each of which is noted for one or more desirable characteristics. Red Fife, for example, has a fine bread-baking quality which is due to the presence of certain proteins in the kernels. American Club is resistant to yellow rust. Certain English varieties are noted for their high yields. Black Persian is resistant to mildew. Resistance to drought and early ripening characterize certain Chinese varieties. These various traits have genetic bases. Should it be possible to combine all of these desirable characters in one variety of wheat? In general, how would you proceed to do this?

16.8 What are some of the environmental factors which are acting as selective agencies on human beings? In general, how is each of these working?

16.9 Barley ordinarily has barbed beards, or awns, on the heads which make it difficult to handle before threshing. A barbless variety was discovered and was crossed with commercial barley in the hope of producing by selection good barley with no barbs on the beards. It was found, however, that the barbless mutation was linked with susceptibility to blotch and to colored grains — two undesirable characters. Would this aid or hinder the development of a resistant variety with white grains and barbless awns? Would it make the production of such a variety impossible? Explain.

16.10 What would be the relative values of heterosis in plants propagated only from seeds and in plants which could be vegetatively propagated (cuttings, grafting, etc.)?

16.11 Suppose that the difference between a variety of grain bearing one stalk per plant and a variety bearing nine stalks per plant is due to four pairs of multiple genes with no dominance. Suppose further that the difference between high yield and low yield per stalk in this grain is due to three other pairs of multiple genes with no dominance. If you had a nine-stalked variety with low yield and a one-stalked variety with high yield, how could you obtain a nine-stalked variety with high yield per stalk? How many F_2 plants would have to be raised in order to obtain a plant of the desired kind?

16.12 If the new variety of nine stalks with high yield did not have to be produced as quickly as the second generation, how could it be obtained without raising so many plants each year?

16.13 Is progeny selection as important with multiple genes as with single gene pairs in which there is dominance? Explain.

REFERENCES

ANDERSON, W. S., *Jour. Heredity* **30**:549 (1939).

BYERLY, T. C., *Sci. Month.* 79:323 (1954).

CROW, J. F., *Genetics* **33**:477 (1948).

DOBZHANSKY, TH., *Revista de Agr.* **18**:397 (1943).

EAST, E. M., and JONES, D. F., *Jour. Heredity* **12**:51 (1921).

GUSTAFSSON, A., *Hereditas* **32**:263 (1946).

HAYS, F. A., and SANBORN, R., *Mass. Agr. Exp. Station Bull.* **307** (1934).

JOHANNSEN, W., *Über Erblichkeit in Populationen und in reinen Linien.* Jena (1903); *Zeitschr. f. ind. Abstamm.-u. Vererbungsl.* **1**:1 (1908).

JONES, D. F., *Genetics in Plant and Animal Improvement.* New York, John Wiley and Sons (1925).

JULL, M. A., *Poultry Breeding.* 3rd. Ed. New York, John Wiley and Sons (1952).

KING, H. D., *Jour. Exp. Zoölogy* **26**:1, 55; **27**:1 (1918); *ibid.* **29**:135 (1919).

LUSH, J. L., *Animal Breeding Plans.* Ames, Iowa, Iowa State College Press (1945).

MARTIN, J. H. and LEONARD, W. H., *Principles of Field Crop Production.* New York, the Macmillan Co. (1949).

PEARL, R., *Amer. Naturalist* **49**:595 (1915).

SHULL, G. H., *Amer. Breeders' Assn. Rept.* **4** (1908); *ibid.* **5** (1909).

WHALEY, W. G., *Bot. Review* **10**:461 (1944).

WINTERS, L. M., *Animal Breeding.* New York, John Wiley and Sons (1948).

WRIGHT, S., *Genetics* **6**:111 (1921); *U.S. Dept. Agr. Bull.* **1121** (1922).

WRIGHT, S., and EATON, O. N., *U.S. Dept. Agr. Tech. Bull.* **103** (1929).

CHAPTER SEVENTEEN

The genetics of domestic animals I. Genic interaction as illustrated in the coat of the rabbit

Among man's requirements are food, shelter, clothing, transportation, recreation, and aid in doing heavy work. Throughout the ages these requirements have been met largely by the animals and plants which man has domesticated. The development of breeds and varieties for various uses has depended largely upon selection from generation to generation, a fact which implies a faith in heredity that existed long before the specific principles of genetics were known. The results of selection in the past have been remarkably successful in spite of the fact that the selection was not always carried out according to the best genetic methods known today.

Our present-day knowledge of heredity allows us to explain the results of the past on a scientific basis and to predict more accurately what may be expected in particular crosses in the future, but it does not give us any great mysterious power to improve suddenly every living thing. We may learn from genetics how to make more efficient use of new variations as they appear, by better methods of selection, by an understanding of the more complicated interactions of genes, and by the proper evaluation of the hereditary and environmental influences in the development of characters. And we may learn how efficiently to rid a strain of its undesirable traits.

The recent demonstration that mutations and chromosomal aberrations may be greatly increased by irradiation adds another possibility. Instead of waiting for new mutations to appear of themselves, man can now produce them artificially; and among great numbers of such induced mutations some advantageous new ones may be expected to appear. These may then be incorporated into the race in desired combinations by proper genetic methods.

Mutations have appeared from time to time in all domestic animals. Certain of these have been chosen by man as adding to the desirable qualities of the animals concerned and have been made the basis of breeds and varieties. Mutations in domestic animals, as in other organisms, have been of three main kinds: mutations with visible effects, mutations with such slight effects that only the cumulative effects of many similar ones are recognizable, and lethal mutations. All these have played parts in the development of the various breeds of livestock and pets.

The mutations with gross visible effects are usually of importance only in developing "trade-marks" for breeds. Such are the numerous color genes, spotting and pattern genes, hair-form and hair-length genes, and so on. The mutations with slight effects, on the other hand, are usually at the basis of the "economic" characters. Multiple genes for size, conformation, speed, milk production, egg production, wool production, meat production, and so forth are examples. Lethal genes are of course always undesirable from the economic standpoint except in the rare cases of balanced lethals which may preserve a desired heterozygous character while killing the unwanted homozygotes.

A "breed" of animals, therefore, consists of a group of individuals which have certain striking characters in common, such as color or structure of hair or feathers; and which have in addition certain well-developed characters dependent upon multiple genes. The study of breeds within a species may help in understanding something of the interactions of genes, particularly the modern idea of genic balance. Let us investigate some of the known genes in domestic animals. We may start with a species which has been very extensively studied: the domestic rabbit.

Rabbits are raised for food, for fur, and for pleasure as pets. They are also extensively used in laboratories, for the study of immunity and susceptibility to disease, the production of serums and antibodies, and the experimental analysis of genetic problems. The genetics of rabbits has been extensively studied by Castle and Sawin in America and by Punnett, Pease, Nachtsheim, and others in Europe. More than thirty sets of alleles with visible effects are known, some of these sets having several members (multiple alleles). In addition there are many multiple genes which have been investigated.

Wild rabbits have a gray coat. As long as all the rabbits we examine have gray coats, we can know nothing of the genes responsible for coat color. It is only when we discover mutations and study their behavior in crosses that we learn anything of the genetic basis for any character. If we examine the gray coat of a rabbit, we find that each hair is dark at the base, then has a band of light color, and finally a dark tip. This banded pattern of the hairs is known as the "agouti"-pattern. Wild animals of many kinds have agouti coats. The under surface of agouti animals is lighter, the hairs having no dark tips, but whitish tips instead.

A mutation is known in rabbits in which the hairs are dark all over, the light bands being entirely obliterated by the dark pigment. Such animals are "nonagouti." The nonagouti coat is dependent upon a single recessive gene. We call the genes concerned A and a. There is a third allele in the series, a^t, which produces the so-called black-and-tan coat, nonagouti above and light below.

The dark color of the hairs of wild rabbits is black, and the light color is yellow. Thus wild rabbits have each hair banded *black-yellow-black*, while the nonagouti mutation produces animals which are black all over. A homozygous wild rabbit is thus of the formula AA, while a black rabbit is aa.

Another mutation is known which changes the dark color from black to brown. It is a recessive mutation, and the genes concerned are known as B and b. A rabbit may have the agouti pattern with the dark color black, so that each hair is banded *black-yellow-black*, or it may have the agouti pattern with the dark color brown, so that each hair is banded *brown-yellow-brown*. Nonagouti animals may of course be either solid black or solid brown. The genes interact as follows:

$A-B-$ results in agouti black or "wild-type gray"
$A-bb$ results in agouti brown or "cinnamon"
$aaB-$ results in nonagouti, or plain "black"
$aabb$ results in nonagouti brown, or "chocolate"

Although when we started we knew nothing of the genetic formula of wild rabbits, it may now be seen that they contain the genes $AABB$. The mutation of B to b is a recent one, having occurred in Holland about 1900.

Still another mutation in rabbits involves the very production of color. Pure white rabbits with pink eyes (albinos) are known. Albinism is recessive to full color, the genes being known as C and c. This mutation has been known for a very long time. It will be recalled from Chapter 13 that two other alleles of the gene C occur. One of these is a gene for chinchilla, c^{ch}. In this mutation all the yellow is removed from the fur. Wild rabbits having this mutation would then have each hair banded *black-white-black*. The other allele is c^h, a gene producing white rabbits with dark extremities, the so-called Himalayan. The order of dominance of these alleles is C, c^{ch},

c^h, c. Any rabbit having the genes cc is an albino, regardless of the other color genes it may carry. On the other hand we must now extend the formula of wild rabbits to read $AABBCC$.

Another mutation is one which causes the normal intense pigment to become dilute. The recessive gene responsible for the dilution has been designated d. The pigment granules become clumped in the hair cells, and the color is thus diluted. Fur which would otherwise be black becomes blue under the influence of this mutation; other colors are correspondingly paler. Another pair of genes is thus found to occur in rabbits, and a wild rabbit may now be seen to have the formula $AABBCCDD$.

We have said that in wild rabbits the hairs are banded *black-yellow-black*. This is because in wild rabbits, as in most wild animals, there is an underlying layer of yellowish or reddish pigment, overlaid by a darker pigment (black or brown) which may completely hide the yellow, as in nonagouti animals, or expose it in bands, as in agouti animals. A mutation is known, however, which removes the dark overlying pigment from the fur, restricting it to the eyes. The coat is then yellowish because the underlying yellowish pigment layer is thus exposed. The genes concerned were first named E, a gene for extension of dark pigment, and e, a gene for its restriction.

Two other alleles have been found in this set. One produces a "steel-gray" color; the other produces a mosaic of black and yellow, called "Japanese." While the Japanese coat is recessive to the wild-type extension, the steel-gray is *dominant*. Steel-gray thus receives the capital letter E as a designation, while the wild-type gene must be given a small letter with a superscript, e^g. The gene for Japanese is called e^J. The order of dominance is E, e^g, e^J, e. Here one of the mutant alleles is dominant to the original wild-type gene, while the other two are recessive.

Wild-type rabbits thus become $AABBCCDDe^ge^g$. As we discover more and more mutations and study their inheritance, we learn more and more about the genes necessary to produce the wild-type coat.

It will be recalled that the chinchilla mutation (c^{ch}) removes the yellow from the fur. We now see that the restriction mutation removes the black or brown, leaving it only in the eyes. A rabbit with both these mutations, of the formula $c^{ch}c^{ch}ee$, should then have all pigment removed from the fur. We find this to be so, such rabbits being white, with pigmented eyes.

In addition to the solid-color types of rabbits, there are some which have spotted coats. One such mutation produces irregularly arranged colored spots on a white background. It is the so-called "English" spotting, and behaves as a dominant to solid color. We may call the genes En and en. Wild rabbits, having solid-colored coats, have the homozygous recessive condition of this pair of genes. We must therefore include them in the formula of wild rabbits, which must now read $AABBCCDDe^ge^genen$.

Another type of spotting is the white-belted or "Dutch" type. This is due to a recessive mutation, du. It produces a white belt on a colored background, the color of the background depending on the other color genes of the animal. It seems probable that there are other alleles in this series forming various grades of the Dutch pattern. Wild rabbits do not have this white belt; hence have the dominant allele of this pair. Again we must extend the formula of wild rabbits, which now must be made to read $AABBCCDDe^ge^genenDuDu$.

One last color mutation is known. In Vienna about 1909 there was observed a white rabbit with blue eyes. The gene responsible for this "Vienna White" is a recessive gene, which we name v. We have thus found three kinds of white rabbits: first, albinos; second, restriction chinchillas; and third, Vienna Whites. Crosses between any two of these produce colored offspring, since each parent contributes the dominant which the other one lacks. Because of the discovery of Vienna White rabbits, we have knowledge of another pair of genes in rabbits. Wild rabbits then carry the dominant of this pair, so that their complete formula thus far must be $AABBCCDDe^ge^genenDuDuVV$. It is thus obviously impossible to consider any one gene or pair of genes as producing the wild-type coat color.

In addition to the color mutations, genes affecting the form of the hair are known. Wild rabbits have typical short hair. A recessive mutation is known in which the hair is several times as long as that of wild rabbits. Rabbits with this type of long woolly hair are known as angoras. The genes concerned are known as L and l.

Another recessive mutation affects the hair in an opposite manner, producing a very short plush-like coat, "rex." Either rex or angora may occur in any color, depending on the particular color genes the rabbit carries. Actually three different recessive mutations for rex have been found, any one of which in the homozygous state will produce the short coat. The genes are named r_1, r_2, and r_3.

A recessive gene sa is known which in homozygous condition results in smooth, glossy hair, referred to as "satin." The trait may occur in any of the known colors. Another recessive gene br causes the production of an abnormality of the toes, brachydactyly. A recessive lethal gene dw results in dwarf rabbits which die soon after birth. Another recessive gene f prevents any development of fur except at the extremities. The gene is semilethal, the viability of furless animals being very low. Since wild rabbits normally do not contain any of the eight recessive genes just described, we may extend the known genetic formula of a wild rabbit to read $AABBCCDDe^ge^venenDuDu\text{-}VVLLR_1R_1R_2R_2R_3R_3SaSaDwDwBrBrFF$.

The fat under the skin of wild rabbits is white. This is because the xanthophyl from green food is broken down in the liver by an enzyme, and thus does not reach the fat deposits. A recessive mutation has been described, however, in which the liver enzyme is lacking, so that the yellow coloring matter is deposited in the fat. Yellow fat is thus dependent upon a recessive gene, y.

Another set of alleles with recognizable effects has been described in rabbits. This set includes genes for agglutinogens, similar to those producing the four blood groups in man (Chapter 13). In rabbits we likewise find four blood groups, dependent upon three allelic genes H, h^B, and h. Genes H and h^B each produce an antigen, while h produces none. It is not known which of these alleles is found in wild rabbits.

Thus we now know a series of definite genes in rabbits due to mutation. The complete genotype for a wild rabbit as far as we know it is $AABBCCDDe^ge^venenDuDuVVLLR_1R_1R_2R_2R_3R_3SaSaDwDwBr\text{-}BrFFYY$. Undoubtedly many thousands of other genes also occur in the wild rabbit, but since they have not produced observed visible mutations, we cannot list them. It must be realized that no gene or pair of genes exists by itself in any organism, but always occurs in company with all the other genes of the species. Hence we cannot say that any single gene produces any particular character. A gene always exerts its effect in the presence of other genes; hence has arisen the idea of genic balance, by which is meant that any character is the result of the entire gene complex acting in a given environment. Variations in a character may be produced by variations in a single gene, but always in the presence of the rest of the genes.

Returning to rabbits, in addition to the specific genes which may be isolated because of visible effects, many genes are known in the aggregate because of their cumulative effects. Thus size, ear length, amount of silvering in the hair, and other variable characters have been shown to be dependent upon multiple genes. Some of these were discussed in detail in Chapter 14.

A beginning has been made in the mapping of the chromosomes of the rabbit. The genes en and Du are very closely linked indeed, with only about one per cent crossing over between them. The gene L is also on this chromosome, giving about 14 per cent crossing over with English and Dutch. Another linkage group consists of the genes C, Y, and B. C and Y are linked with 14 per cent crossing over, and C and B with about 43 per cent. The order is CYB. The genes A, Dw, and W are arranged in that order in still another linkage group, with about 15 per cent crossing over between A and Dw and about

Fig. 17.1 Four breeds of rabbits. From top to bottom: Belgian Hare, Black Flemish Giant, Silver Marten, Himalayan.

30 per cent between A and W. A fourth linkage group contains two of the rex genes R_1 and R_2, with 17 per cent crossing over between them, while a fifth group consists of the genes F and Br, with a crossover value of 28 per cent.

Domestic rabbits are descended from the wild European rabbit (*Lepus cuniculus*), which existed throughout southern Europe, and still occurs there in certain parts. They were domesticated as early as A.D. 1000. The culture and development of rabbits spread northward, reaching a high degree of perfection in England, and in recent times has encompassed nearly all civilized countries. As mutations have arisen they have been preserved, new combinations of the various genes have been produced by crossing, and the various breeds developed. It is possible to produce any combination of the different genes, and the number of such combinations is very large. Nevertheless only certain combinations have proved pleasing to fanciers and have become recognized as standard "breeds." The present-day breeds, each having a certain combination of the multiple genes for size, proportions, and so on, are as follows:

Breeds having none of the visible mutations

The Belgian Hare and the Flemish Giant are the only breeds which are built around the original wild type. They differ from each other and from the wild type, however, in certain multiple genes.

The Flemish Giant has been selected for large size, while the Belgian Hare (Fig. 17.1) has been selected for a reddish tinge of the yellow bands. Both of these breeds, however, have the more-or-less typical wild-type coat.

Breeds built around the nonagouti mutation

There are several breeds which differ from the wild type in having the recessive *aa* instead of *AA*. Among these breeds are the Black Flemish (Fig. 17.1), the Black Siberian, the Alaska, the Nubian, the Sitka, the Black Bevern, and the Black Vienna. While these breeds are alike in having all the wild-type genes except *AA*, they differ in multiple genes for size and relative proportions of various parts.

Breeds built around the brown mutation

Curiously enough there is no recognized breed which differs from the wild type only in having *bb* instead of *BB*. There is, however, one breed which has two recessive mutations, being of the formula *aabb*. (To save space only those genes of a breed which *differ* from the wild-type genes are listed in the formula. The genes not listed will be understood to be the same as in the wild type.) The breed having the formula *aabb* is the Havana (Fig. 17.2), one of the best known breeds of rabbits. Another breed, having the dilute mutation in addition to the nonagouti brown, is the Gouda, of the formula *aabbdd*.

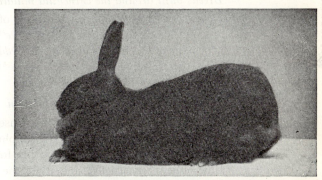

Fig. 17.2 Two color mutations in rabbits. Upper figure, a brown, or Havana rabbit. Lower figure, a dilute black, or American Blue rabbit.

Breeds built around the albino mutation

White rabbits with pink eyes have always been favorites, and several breeds have been based on this character. All of them have the formula cc, but may carry any other combination of color genes, which of course will not show up in the presence of the albino genes. The White Flemish, the Polish, the American White, and the New Zealand White are examples of the albino breeds. Nowhere is selection for multiple genes shown better than among these breeds, the Polish being very small, the White Flemish very large, and the others more or less intermediate.

Breeds built around the Himalayan mutation

One popular breed is based on the c^h gene, the Himalayan or Russian rabbit (Fig. 17.1). The nose, ears, feet, and tail are colored, the rest of the animal being white. The eyes are pink like those of an albino. The colored extremities are black in the standard Himalayans, so that these animals are really nonagouti blacks in addition to being Himalayan. The genetic formula of the breed is thus aac^hc^h. It is possible, however, to produce Himalayans in which the extremities are gray, brown, blue, or other colors.

Breeds built around the chinchilla mutation

The c^{ch} gene has been the basis of many fancy varieties. Chief among them is the chinchilla itself, $c^{ch}c^{ch}$, a very popular breed. Other types include "blue squirrel," $c^{ch}c^{ch}dd;$ "silver marten," $a^ta^tc^{ch}c^{ch}$ (Fig. 17.1); "silver beaver," $a^ta^tbbc^{ch}c^{ch};$ and "sable" $aac^{ch}c^{ch}$.

Breeds built around the dilute mutation

The dilution gene, d, has been used principally in the development of the "blue" breeds. To form blue fur the rabbit must be nonagouti dilute, $aadd$. Breeds of this formula include the American Blue (Fig. 17.2), the Vienna Blue, the Imperial Blue, and the Blue Bevern, differing one from the other only in multiple genes for conformation. One other dilute breed, the Gouda, or Lilac, $aabbdd$, has already been mentioned.

Breeds built around the restriction mutation

One of the most popular of all breeds of rabbits, the New Zealand Red (Fig. 17.3), has the formula ee, differing from the wild type in this one pair of genes. In addition the yellow has been selected for dark shades, reaching almost a "red." The Tortoise-shell is another restriction form in the nonagouti pattern, having the formula $aaee$.

Breeds built around the blue-eyed white mutation

The Vienna White (Fig. 17.3), the Saxony White, and the Blue-eyed White Bevern are white breeds with blue eyes, all having the formula *vv*.

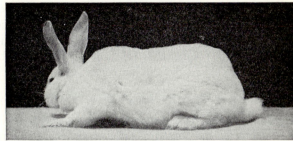

Fig 17.3 Two mutations restricting color in the rabbit. Upper figure, Vienna White, in which color is restricted to the posterior layer of the iris, making the fur white and the eyes blue. Lower figure, New Zealand Red, in which the black (or brown) is restricted to the eye, leaving the fur yellowish-red.

Breeds built around the dominant spotting mutation

The dominant gene *En* produces a striking effect of spotting, particularly in the heterozygous condition, and has been incorporated into various breeds, among which are the Checkered Giants and the Butterflies (Fig. 17.4). Both of these breeds have been selected for large size. The usual color of the spots is black, so that the animals are nonagouti; but blue, gray, red, and other colors are found.

Fig. 17.4 Two types of spotting in rabbits. Upper figure, Dutch pattern, dependent on a recessive gene. Lower figure, English pattern, dependent on the dominant gene of another pair. The two pairs of genes concerned are closely linked.

Breeds built around the recessive spotting mutation

One chief breed, the Dutch Belted, or simply "Dutch," has been developed on the basis of the gene *du*. Dutch rabbits vary considerably, in both the extent of the white and the color of the background, the former probably being due to alleles of the *du* gene, and the latter dependent upon the other color genes of the animal. Dutch rabbits are typically white-belted black, but may be in blue, red, or other colors (Fig. 17.4). The "Dutch" rabbits are small and trim, in contrast to the large "English" breeds.

Breeds built around the hair-length mutations

The recessive gene, *l*, responsible for long hair has been used in forming the well-known Angora breed, sometimes known as "Woolers." Angoras are usually albinos, *ccll* (Fig. 17.5), but may be found in almost any color. The more recent mutation *r*, producing short plush-like fur, is rapidly being made the basis of definite varieties, which may eventually obtain the status of recognized breeds. Among those which appear to be most popular are the castorrex, differing from the wild rabbit only in having *rr* instead of *RR* (Fig. 17.5), the chinchillarex, $c^{ch}c^{ch}rr$, and the blue rex, *aaddrr*.

In addition to the breeds listed above, based largely on single-pair variations plus multiple gene selections, one breed is based strictly on a group of multiple genes. This group consists of the genes affecting the proportion of white hairs in the coat. When the proportion reaches a certain amount, the rabbits are known as Silver. The French Argente de Champagne is a breed in which selection for silvering has been carried to a very high degree. Silver animals are usually nonagouti black, so their single-pair formula is *aa*.

In the light of the foregoing

Fig. 17.5 Two recessive mutations for length of hair. Upper figure, a Rex rabbit, with very short velvetlike fur. Lower figure, an Angora rabbit, with long woolly fur.

discussion of breeds of rabbits, we may repeat what was stated at the beginning of the chapter. A breed of animals is a group of individuals having in common a small number of distinguishing qualitative characters, and in addition a definite degree of development of some quantitative character or characters. This applies equally well to all domestic animals, and we may now turn our attention to some of the other species which man has domesticated.

PROBLEMS

17.1 Which breed of rabbits could be the more heterozygous for color genes, the Gouda or the Polish?

17.2 What kind of offspring would be expected in a cross between the American White and the Vienna White? What would be expected in the F_2?

17.3 Suppose you had a male blue Dutch rabbit and a homozygous female Himalayan with agouti extremities. Starting with these two animals, could you obtain a homozygous race of Himalayan rabbits with blue extremities? What proportion, if any, of the F_2 would be of the desired phenotype? What proportion of the F_2 would be of the desired homozygous genotype?

17.4 In a cross between a homozygous red-spotted English rabbit and a homozygous blue Dutch rabbit, what proportion of the F_2 would resemble the wild-type rabbits?

17.5 In a cross between a chinchilla and a New Zealand Red, what proportion of F_2 would be expected to be dark-eyed white?

17.6 Two wild-type agouti rabbits are crossed and produce the following offspring: 3 wild-type agouti, 1 black, 1 chocolate, 1 lilac, and 2 albinos. What were the genotypes of the parents?

17.7 A wild-type agouti male is bred to an albino female. In a total of several litters they produce the following offspring: 12 albino, 3 wild-type agouti, 2 brown agouti (cinnamon), 4 black, and 3 chocolate. What were the genotypes of the parents?

17.8 Suppose you had a strain of lilac rabbits and a strain of black Dutch and wanted to produce a homozygous strain of blue Dutch rabbits from them. Outline the breeding procedure.

17.9 Suppose you had a homozygous English male rabbit with black spots and an albino female whose mother was New Zealand Red. How would you go about developing a homozygous red-spotted English variety?

17.10 Name some combinations of characters due to single gene pairs in rabbits which could be produced, but which are not recognized as breeds. Why do you suppose these have not been recognized as breeds?

REFERENCES

CASTLE, W, E., *Jour. Heredity* **15**:211 (1924); *Bibliographia Genetica* **1**:420 (1925); *Jour. Heredity* **20**:193 (1929); *Genetics of Domestic Rabbits*. Cambridge, Harvard University Press (1930).

CASTLE, W. E., and LAW, L. W., *Jour. Heredity* **27**:235 (1936).

MEEK, W. M., *The Standard of Perfection for American Domestic Rabbits*. Los Angeles (1928).

PEASE, M. S., *Zeitschr. f. ind. Abstamm.- u. Vererbungsl. Suppl.* **2** (1928).

SAWIN, P. B., *Advances in Genetics* **7**:183 (1955).

CHAPTER EIGHTEEN

The genetics of domestic animals II. Other farm and ranch animals

Let us consider briefly the interactions of Mendelian genes in some of the more important domestic animals. In recent years the commercial breeding of ranch mink has become popular. Many pigment mutations have occurred under domestication, and some of them, singly and in combination, have resulted in colors which are highly prized. About eighteen sets of alleles are recognized, some sets having two known alleles, others three.

The standard wild-type mink is dark black-brown. Some of the more significant mutations are as follows. A recessive gene a results in blueish underfur with dark guard hairs. An allele, a^i, makes the entire fur blueish. Another recessive gene, b, results in light brown fur (pastel). A gene g produces pastel with green eyes. The mutant gene p results in blue-gray color (silverblu, or platinum), and its allele p^s produces a duller darker blue-gray (steelblu). A recessive mutation pl gives rise to the beautiful golden palomino. A lethal gene S results in a lightening of the color plus some small white markings, or "ticking," (blufrost).

Combinations of some of the mutations result in colors which are much sought after. Commercial varieties have been built around the mutations and their combinations, and some of the more valuable ones are shown in Table 18.1 and Figure 18.1.

Turning now to horses it is found that color variations depend upon several recognized gene pairs. A dominant gene, A, is responsible for a color pattern on the hair, similar to the agouti pattern in rabbits discussed in the preceding chapter. This gene tends to restrict the dark pigment to the mane and tail. The recessive allele, a, does not produce this color pattern. A dominant gene, B, is responsible for the production of black pigment in the hair, skin, and eyes, while

Fig. 18.1 Coat colors in mink. Upper left, standard brown; upper right, gunmetal; center left, platinum; center right, palomino; lower left, sapphire; lower right, pearl.

Courtesy of Dr Richard M Shackelford

Table 18.1. VARIETIES OF RANCH MINK

VARIETY	GENES					
	A, a^i, a	B, b	G, g	P, p^s, p	Pl, pl	S, s
Wild Type:						
Standard (brown)	AA	BB	GG	PP	$PlPl$	ss
One Mutation:						
Blue Iris	a^ia^i	BB	GG	PP	$PlPl$	ss
Aleutian (Gunmetal)	aa	BB	GG	PP	$PlPl$	ss
Pastel	AA	bb	GG	PP	$PlPl$	ss
Green-eyed Pastel	AA	BB	gg	PP	$PlPl$	ss
Steelblu	AA	BB	GG	p^sp^s	$PlPl$	ss
Silverblu (Platinum)	AA	BB	GG	pp	$PlPl$	ss
Palomino	AA	BB	GG	PP	$plpl$	ss
Blufrost	AA	BB	GG	PP	$PlPl$	Ss
Two Mutations:						
Sapphire	aa	BB	GG	pp	$PlPl$	ss
Steelblu Sapphire	aa	BB	GG	p^sp^s	$PlPl$	ss
Topaz	AA	bb	gg	PP	$PlPl$	ss
Platinum Blond	AA	bb	GG	pp	$PlPl$	ss
Pastel Palomino	AA	bb	GG	PP	$plpl$	ss
Breath of Spring	AA	bb	GG	PP	$PlPl$	Ss
Pearl	AA	BB	GG	pp	$plpl$	ss
Three Mutations						
Winterblu	aa	bb	GG	pp	$PlPl$	ss
Paradise	aa	BB	GG	pp	$plpl$	ss

its recessive allele, *b*, results in brown pigment, variously called by horsemen brown, chestnut, sorrel, or liver. The basic colors of horses depend upon the interactions of these genes, as follows:

> $A-B-$ results in bay
> $aaB-$ results in black
> $A-bb$ results in chestnut, sorrel or "brown"
> $aabb$ results in liver

A recessive gene, *f*, reduces the intensity of the dark pigments without affecting that of the lighter yellow-red pigments. In the presence of $A-bb$, *ff* results in sorrels with light manes and tails.

A dominant gene, *G*, epistatic to all the color genes listed above, results in the production of a black coat at birth, followed by the interspersion of more and more white hairs after each successive molt, until in old age such horses may become practically white. The white horses commonly seen in pastures are of this type.

A dominant gene, *R*, results in the presence of white hairs even in the juvenile coat. Such horses are roan. The gene *R* with black results in blue roan; with bay, in red roan; and with chestnut, sorrel, or liver in strawberry roan.

White coat color in horses may be produced by various genes.

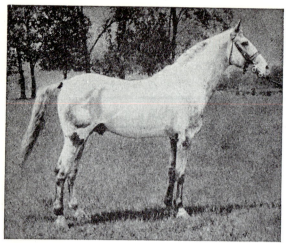

Fig 18.2 A colt, which appeared to be born white, and its parents. Top, a roan skewbald stallion, showing a relatively extreme condition of the extent of white. Center, a chestnut mare. Bottom, their offspring, a strawberry roan skewbald colt, inheriting the dominant gene for roan and for skewbald from the father and a recessive for chestnut from each parent, resulting in an almost white coat with a few spots on the ears, rump, and legs. The spots, being chestnut plus roan (or "strawberry roan," as this combination is called), are almost indistinguishable from the white.

One of these is the dominant white spotting gene. A pair of alleles S and s is known, in which S is responsible for calico spotting (irregular white spots on a colored background). When the white spots occur on black the condition is spoken of as "piebald"; when they occur on any other color the condition is termed "skewbald." This type of spotting is affected by multiple modifying genes, the extreme being almost completely white. This extreme condition is rather rare.

Fig. 18.3 White blaze and stockings, a recessive spotting in horses.

The attention of one of the writers was once called to a colt which was said to have been born pure white. Upon investigation it was found that the colt was a strawberry roan skewbald, representing nearly the extreme of white spotting (Fig. 18.2). The parents were a gray skewbald stallion which was heterozygous for the chestnut gene, and a chestnut mare. Both are shown in the figure. The colt received the genes for roan and for extreme calico spotting from its sire and the gene for chestnut from both parents. The resulting small spots were strawberry roan in color and were nearly indistinguishable from the white.

Another spotting gene, a recessive, produces the familiar white blaze and stockings (Fig. 18.3).

Horses are white or near-white also when they are homozygous for the dilution gene, D. When D occurs with its recessive allele, d, along with the genes that produce bay, black, chestnut, or liver, unusual dilute colors are produced, of which Palomino is the best publicized at present. The genes interact as follows:

DD + bay results in creamy white color and blue eyes, with mane darker than body (Fig. 18.4).

DD + black results in sooty cream color and blue eyes, with mane and body the same in color.

DD + chestnut results in ivory white color and blue eyes, with mane lighter than body (Fig. 18.4).

DD + liver results in very pale cream color and blue eyes, with mane and body similar in color.

Dd + bay results in dun color (sometimes called buckskin) and dark eyes, with mane and tail black.

Dd + black results in yellowish black color, called "mouse," and dark eyes, with mane and tail the same as the body.

Dd + chestnut results in Palomino, a golden yellow color, with dark eyes, and very light mane and tail.

Dd + liver results in cream color and dark eyes, with mane and tail similar in color to the body.

Finally the color of some white horses is the result of a white gene W, epistatic to all other color genes (Fig. 18.4). These horses are a pure clear white with pink skin, but almost always with brown eyes. Once in a while the eyes may be blue. Only Ww horses are known, which indicates that the WW condition may be lethal.

Both the white horses due to the genes DD and those resulting from Ww are commonly referred to as albinos. In fact, there exists The American Albino Horse Club which registers such animals. Genetically, of course, they are not albinos at all, since all have pigmented eyes. No mutation of gene C to c has been recorded in horses.

Through the interactions of the various genes just described, a great variety of colors is brought about. In addition to color genes, a pair of genes is said to occur of which the dominant results in the trotting gait, the recessive in the pacing gait. Natural pacers are homozygous recessives and breed true. Of course a trotter may be taught to pace by careful training, which is an illustration of the fact well known to geneticists that a trait which in some individuals is the result of genes may in other individuals be produced by the appropriate environment in the absence of these genes.

Bleeding at the nose sometimes occurs in horses during a race. This is due to

Fig. 18.4 White horses resulting from three different interactions of genes. Top, A–bbDD; center, A–B–DD; bottom, Ww. *From Castle in Genetics*

breaking of the blood vessels, and is an exceedingly undesirable character in race horses. It appears to be dependent upon a recessive gene. Roaring, a breathing defect of horses, when not due to injury or poisoning, is the result of a dominant gene.

Size, weight, conformation, speed, and other variable characters are apparently due to multiple genes (Fig. 18.5).

Turning now to cattle it will be recalled that we have already taken up in previous chapters many of the known characters. Lethals in cattle were discussed and illustrated in Chapter 3; the heterozygous roan coat produced by the cross between red and white in Shorthorns was outlined and illustrated in Chapters 3 and 6, as was the genetics of the polled and horned conditions; and the sex-influenced characters of Ayrshires were examined and illustrated in Chapter 9. The effects of selection on the multiple modifying genes for the extent of spotting were illustrated in Figure 14.7.

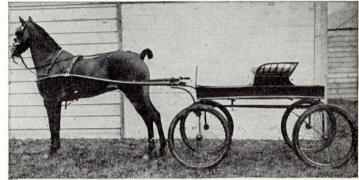

Fig. 18.5 The extremes of size and conformation in horses. Top, a Hackney mare; bottom, a Shire mare, photographed to same scale.

In addition to the genes already discussed we may list the following. A gene for red apparently occurs in all cattle, no allele being known for it. The red may be covered up, however, by the effect of a gene, *B*, which produces black, its allele, *b*, not producing any black. A recessive gene, *d*, for dilution is known. Cattle of the formula *B–D–* are black (Galloway, Aberdeen Angus, etc.); *B–dd* are dun (Scotch Highland, etc.); *bbD–* are red (Herefords, Shorthorns, etc.); and *bbdd* are yellow (Guernseys, Jerseys, etc.).

White spotting is a characteristic of many breeds. The various types of white spotting appear to depend upon a series of multiple alleles. The Dutch belted pattern is due to a dominant *S*, the white-faced or Hereford pattern to its allele s^h, the solid color (absence of spotting) to another allele s^c, and the recessive white spotting found in Holsteins, Guernseys, and others to the ultimate recessive *s* (Fig. 18.6). The order of dominance is S, s^h, s^c, s.

A dominant white mutation is found in England among the semi-wild park cattle (Fig. 18.7). An interesting dominant mutation occurs in some breeds, which produces notched ear (Fig. 18.8). This character has no effect on the animal's production of milk or meat, but disqualifies animals having the trait for show purposes.

Fig. 18.6 Types of spotting in cattle, dependent upon four multiple alleles. From top to bottom: belted, Hereford spotting, solid color, and recessive spotting.

Fig. 18.8 Notched ear, a dominant mutation in Ayrshire cattle.

Fig 18.7 Three of the oldest known breeds of cattle. Top, a Welsh Longhorn; center, Scottish Highland cattle; bottom, an English Park animal, carrying a gene for dominant white. None of these breeds is used in America.

Milk production and bodily conformation, the two important economic characters in cattle, depend upon a large series of multiple genes. The inheritance of milk production was considered in some detail in the chapter on selection (Chapter 16).

Recent researches of Irwin and his collaborators have shown that the red blood cells of cattle contain many antigens which can be demonstrated by means of appropriate immune antiserums. Forty such antigens have been detected. Since each separate antigen may be present or absent in any individual animal, the number of possible combinations in cattle is 2^{40}, which is more than a trillion. Thus it appears that each individual cow or bull is specifically identifiable by immunochemical tests.

The presence of each antigen is dominant to its absence, so that it is often possible to determine the paternity of a calf, a problem of some importance in pure-bred registry. Since the number of known antigens is greater than the haploid number of chromosomes in cattle, either some of the antigen genes must be linked or else there are sets of multiple alleles involved. Some cases of multiple alleles are known, but most probably linkage also occurs.

As has been found in the study of human genetics, different races (breeds, in the case of cattle) differ one from the other almost entirely in the *proportions* of the various genes and not in the *kinds* of genes they possess. For example, Holsteins and Guernseys show quantitative differences in regard to the various antigens, but all are present in both breeds to a greater or lesser extent.

An interesting corollary of the work with bovine antigens is that fraternal twins in cattle are frequently identical in their antigens, in spite of being genetically different. Owen, who has demonstrated this, believes that anastomoses of the blood vessels *in utero* results in the exchange of embryonal cells which develop into red blood cells. The blood of a twin calf therefore contains a mixture of its own blood cells and those of its twin.

In recent years dwarfism has presented a very practical problem to cattle breeders, particularly in the beef breeds. Although dwarfs have been recorded occasionally for many years, their occurrence has increased markedly of late, and breeders are understandably concerned. The typical dwarf, commonly referred to as "snorter dwarf," has practically normal bodily proportions except that all dimensions are greatly reduced (Fig. 18.9). Dwarfs frequently die within a year of being born, and seldom if ever live beyond the second year.

Dwarfism is inherited on the basis of an autosomal recessive gene. The heterozygotes tend to be a little thicker and blockier than those not carrying the gene, and therefore it is likely that some inadvertent

Fig 18.9 Hereford calves. Left, normal; right, dwarf Each of these calves was 15 months old when the picture was taken.

Courtesy Dr. Doyle Chambers

selection in favor of carriers has been practiced. Several popular bulls have been heterozygotes, and have spread the gene widely.

It would be of advantage to the breeder to be able to recognize heterozygotes easily, and thus to eliminate them as breeding stock. Several attempts have been made to provide criteria for distinguishing carriers, but none has proved highly successful. The general blockiness, the "dished in" profile of the face, the growth pattern of the spinal column as revealed by X-ray pictures, the biochemical analysis of various body fluids and tissues, and other characteristics have been suggested and tried, without marked success as yet.

Meanwhile several large ranches are using standard genetic technique for recognizing carriers. Such ranches may sell many breeding bulls each year. To insure that the bulls are not heterozygous for dwarfism, a special herd of perhaps one hundred cows is kept, each of which is known to be a carrier by virtue of having produced a dwarf calf. Promising young bulls to be tested are mated to at least fifteen of these cows. If no dwarf calf is produced, the bull is considered as not heterozygous.

This procedure may seem expensive and troublesome, but its value is evident when it is realized that a bull certified not to be a carrier will bring up to $500 more than an untested animal.

Rife and his collaborators have made an interesting observation in regard to the genetics of the gestation period in cattle. The average length of the gestation period in Herefords is 289 days; in Angus, 273 days. In crosses between the two breeds, the cross-bred calves took 281 days to develop, no matter which way the cross was made. This gestation period is midway between those of the two pure breeds. It would therefore seem that the gestation period is determined by the genotype of the embryo and not by that of the mother, a fact which has important implications for the genetics of development.

We may close our study of genes in domestic animals with a brief résumé of poultry. Many of the characters of poultry have already been discussed in previous chapters and have been illustrated in various figures. The numerous breeds of poultry have become so familiar through the keeping of back-yard flocks and the exhibits of state and county fairs, however, that a short discussion of the genes producing them may be of interest. Frequent reference will be made to figures in earlier chapters.

Three separate kinds of white are known in poultry. White Leghorns (Fig. 6.2) have a dominant inhibitor, *I*. Therefore, unless they are homozygous, White Leghorns may produce colored offspring. The other two genes for white are recessives. White Silkies (Fig. 6.2) and Rose-comb Bantams are white because of a recessive gene, *c*, which determines the lack of a chromogen necessary for color. White Wyandottes, Cochin Bantams, Dorkings, Langshans, Minorcas, and Rocks are white because of a different recessive, o, which determines the lack of an oxidase also necessary for color. The colored breeds must therefore have all three color genes, that is, their formula must be $iiC–O–$.

A dominant gene, E, extends black pigment throughout the plumage, its recessive allele, e, revealing the underlying yellowish (known to poultry breeders as buff) pigment. Buff Brahmas, Cochins, Leghorns, Orpingtons, Wyandottes, and other buff breeds therefore have the formula ee, while the black breeds (Black Java, Black Langshans, etc.) are EE (Fig. 18.10).

It will be recalled (Fig. 3.1) that the splashed-white gene, w, produces Blue Andalusians (Ww) when it occurs with its allele W. This is one of the few cases where a heterozygous character has been chosen as the basis of a breed.

A spangled pattern of feathering occurs in Spangled Hamburghs. This is dependent upon a dominant gene.

Several sex-linked genes occur in poultry. Among them are "silver" and "gold" plumages, the silver being dominant. The silver gene interacting with the recessive ee results in the "Columbian" pattern characteristic of Columbian Wyandottes, Light Brahmas, Light Sussex, and similar breeds.

In addition to color mutations, a number of genes affect the form of the feathers, the comb, and other parts of the bird. A dominant mutation produces a crest, characteristic of the Houdan and Polish breeds (Fig. 18.10). Another gene produces "frizzled" feathers, which curl upward and forward. A recessive mutation in which the hooks are eliminated from the feather barbules produces silky feathers, characteristic of the Silkies (Fig. 6.2). A peculiar dominant mutation results in the absence of feathers on the neck: not a very attractive condition. Yet it has been made the basis of a breed, the Transylvanian Naked-neck. Close feathering such as found in the Cornish and Game breeds is due to a dominant gene.

A curious recessive mutation results in unique long feathers at the hock joint. This "vulture hock" has been made characteristic of the Sultan breed and of the Mille Fleur Booted Bantams. A recessive gene for "ropy" feathers results in the failure of the down to fluff out in the newly-hatched chick and causes the formation of a groove in the feather shafts of the adult. Another recessive gene results in frayed feathers, having a poorly formed web, though not as extreme as in Silkies. A mutation resulting in "flightlessness" produces feathers so defective that they break off as soon as they emerge, so that the homozygote is virtually featherless at maturity. In the heterozygote only the large wing and tail feathers break off, but the birds are unable to fly.

Fig. 18.10 Top, photo
of Buff Rock rooster;
bottom, a white-crested
Black Polish hen.

A dominant gene is found in some of the continental breeds of poultry, resulting in the lengthening of the feathers on the cheeks, known as a "muff." A recessive gene for retarded feathering, which expresses itself only in the presence of a sex-linked gene for early feathering, inhibits the development of tail feathers and secondary flight feathers. A dominant mutation is known which prevents the development of the caudal vertebrae, resulting in "rumplessness." Many mutations result, of course, in undesirable traits.

Several genes affect the legs of birds. The two pairs of genes affecting feathered shanks were discussed in Chapter 6. Another mutation produces triple instead of single spurs on each leg and is found in the Sumatra breed. A dominant mutation results in polydactylism (five toes instead of four), while another similar dominant gene results in "duplicate," having six toes. A recessive gene produces a webbing between the third and fourth toes, known as syndactylism. This trait has not been made a breed characteristic, although it is found commonly in some breeds such as White Plymouth Rocks.

The form of the comb has been studied, and it is found that the four principal types of combs depend upon the interaction of two pairs of genes, R and r, P and p. Single combs are characteristic of Leghorns and other breeds; rose combs are found in Hamburghs, White Dorkings, Wyandottes, and others; pea combs occur in Brahmas and Cornish; and walnut combs characterize the Malays. The genes concerned interact as follows:

$R-P-$ results in walnut comb
$rrP-$ results in pea comb
$R-pp$ results in rose comb
$rrpp$ results in single comb

Many series of multiple genes have been investigated in poultry. Egg production has been studied by many investigators. All agree that, while egg production is undoubtedly influenced to a certain extent by environmental factors such as feeding and rearing, it is clearly a hereditary character. The latest hypothesis of the number of pairs of genes concerned postulates eight pairs, one sex-linked; affecting total egg production through time of sexual maturity, intensity and persistence of production, broodiness, and winter pause.

Disease resistance, constitutional vigor, hatchability, body weight, rate of growth, and numerous other characters have been shown to depend upon an undetermined number of multiple genes.

Thus in horses, cattle, and poultry we find the same principles of breed formation that we have already discussed: the combination of a relatively few distinguishing qualitative characters with a definite degree of development of one or more quantitative characters. The same principles apply to all species, and we could list single gene pairs and multiple genes for dogs, cats, sheep, pigs, ducks, canaries, and others. Enough has been said, however, to outline the principles involved in the production of breeds. Selection and other breeding methods have been discussed in a previous chapter. For the specific characters known in animal species other than those treated here, the attention of the reader is called to the problems at the end of this and other chapters, where many of them are described. Much valuable information is also available in the Yearbooks of the U.S. Department of Agriculture for the years 1936, 1937, and 1943–47.

The chromosomes of domestic animals have not been studied as intensively as those of plants; hence it cannot be stated whether or not chromosomal aberrations account for any of the variations in live stock and pets. Probably they do, however, and future research will undoubtedly add much to our knowledge of this potential source of differentiation of animal breeds.

PROBLEMS

18.1 A bay mare is the result of a mating between a chestnut stallion and a black mare. If the bay mare is bred to a cream stallion ($aabbDd$), what kinds of offspring would it be possible for her to produce?

18.2 Two strawberry roan horses produce a colt which develops into a liver stallion. What were the genoytpes of the parents?

18.3 In cattle the following genes are known to affect coat color: B results in all the pigmented hairs being black, b does not result in black pigment; D results in intense pigment, d in dilute pigment; K in the presence of bb results in black-and-red, in which only some of the pigmented hairs are black, the others being red, k does not result in this black-and-red condition; M is a gene modifying the effect of K in such a way that most but not all of the pigmented hairs are black, resulting in "mahogany," m, its allele, results in most but not all of the pigmented hairs being red. This character is sex-influenced. M and m thus produce noticeable effects only in the presence of $bbK-$; R in the homozygous state in the presence of $bbkk$ results in all the pigmented hairs being red, r in the homozygous state results in white, the heterozygote Rr (in presence of $bbkk$) being roan; S, s^h, s^c, and s are multiple alleles, resulting respectively in belted, Hereford spotting, solid color, and recessive white spotting. The genotypes of seven breeds of cattle in regard to color are as follows:

BREED	B,b	D,d	K,k	M,m	R,r	S,s^h,s^c,s
Holstein	BB	DD	?	?	RR	ss
Jersey	bb	dd	KK	$\begin{cases} MM \\ Mm \\ mm \end{cases}$	RR	$\begin{cases} s^c s^c \\ s^c s \\ ss \end{cases}$
Guernsey	bb	dd	kk	?	RR	ss
Ayrshire	bb	DD	KK	$\begin{cases} MM \\ Mm \\ mm \end{cases}$	RR	ss
Shorthorn	bb	DD	kk	?	$\begin{cases} RR \\ Rr \\ rr \end{cases}$	ss
Hereford	bb	DD	kk	?	RR	$s^h s^h$
Aberdeen Angus	BB	DD	?	?	RR	$s^c s^c$

From the above data answer this and the following nine questions about cattle: Why are the question marks placed after the Holstein breed in the columns headed K,k and M,m? Explain fully.

18.4 The masking of the effect of one gene by a gene of a different pair is spoken of as *epistasis*. Thus B is epistatic to K and k. To what genes is k epistatic? To what genes besides K and k is B epistatic?

18.5 What crosses would have to be made to determine the genotype of Holsteins in regard to K and k?

18.6 Why are Herefords never roan?

18.7 How could roan Herefords be produced? Would the first cross have to be followed by subsequent selection?

18.8 What crosses would have to be made to determine the genotype of Guernseys in regard to genes M and m?

18.9 How could solid black Holsteins be produced? Would the selection following the first cross have to take into account the multiple genes by which all breeds differ? Would it be better to breed the F_1 animals together or constantly to breed back to Holsteins?

18.10 What would be the color and markings of the F_1 from a cross between Herefords and Aberdeen Angus?

18.11 Why are Jerseys somewhat darker than Guernseys?

18.12 What would be the color and markings of the F_1 from a cross between a Holstein and a solid-colored Jersey? What are some of the various combinations which would be expected to result in the F_2?

18.13 In turkeys the following genes are known to affect plumage color: B results in black pigment throughout the feathers, b results in many of the feathers having light edges, the heterozygote being black with a few scattered light-edged feathers; R is an extension gene which permits the presence of overlying dark pigment, thus obscuring the underlying red, r restricts the overlying pigment, thus showing up the underlying red, the heterozygote tending to be "rusty";

D is a dominant dilution gene, d is its recessive allele for intensity; P is a dominant color gene, p is its recessive allele for white plumage (not albinism, since the eyes of pp birds are pigmented); N is a dominant gene for bronze pigment in the light-edged feathers, n resulting in black pigment in the light-edged feathers (Narragansett), the genes N and n being sex-linked. (N and n therefore show their effects only in the presence of $bbRR$.) The genotypes of eight varieties of turkeys are as follows (the W in the last column stands for the W chromosome which does not carry sex-linked genes):

VARIETY	B,b	R,r	D,d	P,p	N,n Males	Females
Bronze	bb	RR	dd	PP	NN	NW
Bourbon Red	bb	rr	dd	PP	NN	NW
Narragansett	bb	RR	dd	PP	nn	nW
Black	BB	RR	dd	PP	NN	NW
Slate	bb	RR	DD	PP	NN	NW
Blue	BB	RR	DD	PP	NN	NW
Buff	BB	rr	dd	PP	NN	NW
White Holland	—	—	—	pp	—	–W

From the above data answer this and the following four questions about turkeys· Why are the dashes placed in all columns but the "pp" for the White Holland variety?

18.14 If you wanted to discover which color genes a white bird carried, to what variety or varieties should it be mated in order to discover this most quickly?

18.15 Of the many possible homozygous genotypes which may be produced, using the above genes, only a few have been developed as recognized varieties. What are some other homozygous genotypes which might be developed? From your knowledge of the color genes involved, what is your best guess as to the colors which would be developed from these additional homozygous genotypes?

18.16 What would be the results in the

F_1 and F_2 of crossing a Bronze male to a Narragansett female? A Narragansett male to a Bronze female?

18.17 What would be the result in the F_1 and the F_2 of crossing a Black male to a Bourbon Red female?

REFERENCES

CASTLE, W. E., *Genetics* **33**:22 (1948).

HUTT, F. B., *Genetics of the Fowl.* New York, McGraw-Hill Book Co. (1949).

IRWIN, M. R., *Advances in Genetics* **1**:133 (1947).

RIFE, D. C., P. GERLAUGH, L. KUNKLE, G. W. BRANDT and L. H. SNYDER, *Jour. Animal Science* **2**:50 (1943).

SHACKELFORD, R. M., *The Genetics of the Ranch Mink.* New York, Pilsbury Publishers (1950).

SHRODE, R. R., and J. L. LUSH, *Advances in Genetics* **1**:209 (1947).

WARREN, D. C., *Genetics* **34**:333 (1949).

Yearbook of Agriculture, U.S. Dept. of Agriculture (1936, 1937, 1943–47).

CHAPTER NINETEEN

Plant life cycles
and their genetic implications

No less important to man than the domestic animals are the cultivated plants. Food, lumber, oils, rubber, fibers, drugs, paper pulp, and other plant products are essential to man's daily existence. Plant breeding and the development of new or better varieties of plants are essential parts of modern agronomy, horticulture, and forestry. The basis for such improvement is a knowledge of the facts and principles of genetics. While the fundamental genetic principles are the same in plants as in animals, there are enough practical differences to warrant a special examination of the formation of gametes and the process of fertilization in plants.

The first important fact to be noted is the difference in the life cycles of the higher plants and the higher animals. Since it is the higher plants which are of the most economic importance, we shall center our attention on them, although it will be necessary to review the life cycles of some lower plants in order to understand fully the life cycle of the higher forms.

Briefly, the life cycle of an animal consists of the *body*, or mature animal in which the *maturation process* goes on, forming *gametes* which unite in *fertilization*, as a result of which a new body is formed and the cycle continues.

In contrast to that of an animal, the life cycle of a plant consists of *two* generations, the *sporophyte*, corresponding to the body of the animal, and the *gametophyte*, which has no parallel in animals. In the sporophyte generation, which is the familiar plant body in the higher plants, the maturation process takes place. In plants, however, fertilization is not the next step. Instead the cells produced by the maturation undergo further division, producing a distinct generation, the gametophyte. Finally from the gametophyte, with no further reduction division, are produced gametes which unite in fertilization.

After fertilization the zygote develops into the embryo and finally into the adult, in plants as well as in animals. In the higher plants, however, the embryo may undergo a dormant stage before developing into the adult. This we know as the *seed* stage. Since the seed is of considerable economic importance, especially in such food plants as corn, wheat, and others, and since the genetic characters of the seed are closely correlated with the events of the gametophyte generation, it is important in our study of genetics to examine the whole life cycle of a plant with care.

The body of an animal and the corresponding sporophyte of a plant have chromosomes in *pairs* in the cells. In other words these cells contain the $2n$ number of chromosomes. Because of the reduction division the cells resulting from the maturation process contain the n number. In animals such cells are gametes. In plants, however, they are not gametes, since they do not unite in fertilization. They are termed *spores*. These spores, containing the n or haploid number of chromosomes, divide by mitosis, forming a more or less extensive generation, the gametophyte, which has the n number of chromosomes in all its cells. The gametes produced by the gametophyte also have the n number of chromosomes and upon uniting form a zygote with the diploid number.

In the higher plants the dormant stage of the embryo forms part of the *seed*. There is another part of some seeds, however, the endosperm, which is genetically distinct from the embryo and contains the $3n$ number of chromosomes instead of the $2n$, due to a fusion of three nuclei (*triple fusion*). This condition we shall discuss later in the chapter.

We may contrast the life cycles of plants and animals thus:

ANIMAL	PLANT	
	Seed (in higher plants) $\begin{cases} \text{Embryo } (2n) \\ \text{Endosperm } (3n) \end{cases}$	
Body ($2n$)	Body, or sporophyte ($2n$)	
Maturation (to n)	Maturation (to n)	
	Spores (n)	
	Gametophyte (n)	
Gametes (n)	Gametes (n)	
Fertilization (to $2n$)	$\begin{cases} \text{Fertilization (to } 2n) \\ \text{Triple fusion (in higher plants) (to } 3n) \end{cases}$	

In order to understand the genetics of the gametophyte generation and thus of the seed, let us start with a simple type of plant, the moss, and work towards the higher economic forms.

Mosses are familiar plants in moist shady habitats. The soft velvety or fluffy mass which we commonly call the moss plant does not correspond to the animal body or the corn plant. Its cells under the microscope are seen to contain the n number of chromosomes. It is the *gametophyte*, having developed from a spore, following the reduction division.

At certain seasons of the year there may be seen growing up from the mass of the moss plant little slender stalks each surmounted with a capsule (sporangium). Each stalk contains the $2n$ number of chromosomes and is the *body*, or *sporophyte generation*, of a moss. In the sporangium at the top of the stalk the maturation process takes place, resulting in cells which contain the n number of chromosomes. In an animal such cells would be *gametes*, and the next stage in their history would be fertilization, but in a plant they are *spores* and do not undergo fertilization.

Instead, the sporangium bursts, the spores are scattered, and upon reaching the ground each spore develops into a branching, filamentous structure which spreads, forms buds, and eventually becomes a thick cluster which is the familiar moss. Since it develops from a spore with the haploid number of chromosomes, all its cells will contain this n number. This is the gametophyte generation. Cell proliferations (rhizoids) penetrate the soil and afford an anchorage for the plant.

On the branches of this gametophyte are eventually formed structures of two sorts. One kind, the *antheridia*, produces many sperms. The other kind consists of *archegonia*, each of which produces an egg. When the moss is wet the sperms swim through the film of water on the plant and reach the eggs. Fertilization follows. From the zygote grows the slender sporophyte stalk, having the diploid number of chromosomes. It never becomes separated from the gametophyte and

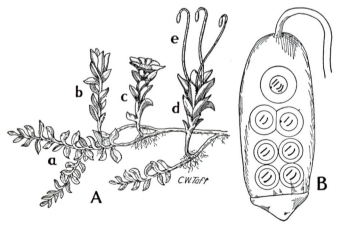

Fig. 19.1 The life history of a moss. A, drawing of the moss plant *Mnium;* a, the gametophyte; b, a branch bearing archegonia; c, a branch bearing antheridia; d, an archegonial branch from which three sporophytes are growing. B, diagrammatic enlargement of the sporangium, illustrating the reduction division taking place within it, resulting in spores which can grow into gametophytes.

is dependent upon it for minerals, water, and possibly a portion of its food. The life cycle thus consists of alternate sporophyte and gametophyte generations (Fig. 19.1).

It will be noted that the gametophyte generation in mosses is more conspicuous than the sporophyte, which is partially dependent upon the gametophyte.

Going a step higher we find in the ferns that the familiar fern plant has the diploid, or *2n*, number of chromosomes. It represents the *body*, or sporophyte, having been produced from the union of two gametes. In the *sori*, or fruiting bodies, on the under sides of the leaves, the maturation process takes place. Again, instead of the resulting cells undergoing fertilization, they are scattered from the sori and each develops into a many-celled structure, the gametophyte. The gametophyte of a fern, however, is a very small affair, smaller than a finger-nail, and is not at all conspicuous.

On the under side of this gametophyte (which in ferns is termed a *prothallus*), antheridia and archegonia appear, and in these, sperms and eggs are formed. In wet weather the antheridia swell and burst, and the archegonia open. The sperms swim to the archegonium (presumably attracted by chemical products of the archegonium) and fertilize the egg. When one sperm has fertilized an egg, further development of arche-gonia ceases. From the zygote resulting from fertilization a new fern plant grows, thus completing the life cycle (Fig. 19.2). At first the young sporophyte is dependent upon the

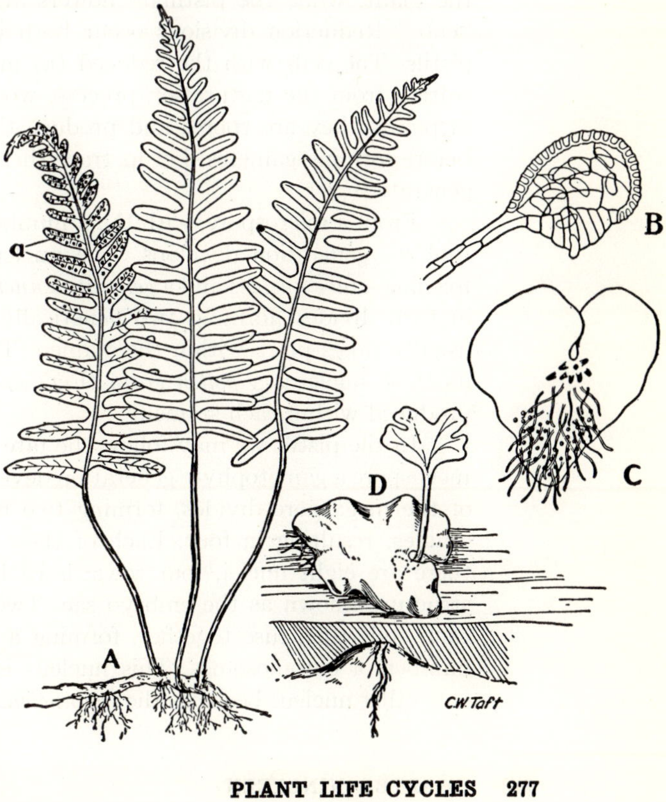

Fig. 19.2 The life history of a fern. A, the fern plant (sporophyte); a, the sori on the undersides of the leaves. B, enlarged view of a sporangium within a sorus. C, the underside of the prothallus (gametophyte), showing antheridia and archegonia. D, the prothallus growing close to the ground, with the new sporophyte, resulting from fertilization, beginning to grow from it.

archegonium and the old gametophyte for its food supply, but it soon grows into an independent plant with roots, a stem, and leaves.

It will be noted that as we go up the scale the sporophyte is becoming the more conspicuous part of the life cycle, and the gametophyte is becoming inconspicuous.

Continuing up the scale let us examine a seed plant. We may choose corn as an example, inasmuch as it is of considerable economic importance and its life history is typical. The cells of the corn plant contain the $2n$ number of chromosomes, and the familiar corn plant itself is the body, or sporophyte, having arisen from the union of two gametes. In it the maturation process takes place. In seed plants such as this, however, two kinds of spores result from maturation: one kind (microspores) which will eventually produce male gametes, the other (megaspores) which will eventually produce female gametes.

Higher plants have specialized structures known as *flowers* in which the maturation process occurs, producing spores. The microspores are produced in the *stamens* of the flowers; the megaspores in the *pistils* of the flowers. In most plants the same flower contains both stamens and pistils. In corn and some others, however, some of the flowers contain only stamens, while others contain only pistils. The staminate flowers in corn are clustered in the "tassel" at the top of the plant, while the pistillate flowers are arranged in rows on the "cob." Reduction divisions occur both in the stamens and in the pistils. The cells with the reduced (n) number of chromosomes, resulting from the maturation process, would in animals be gametes; in plants they are spores and produce the gametophyte generation before forming gametes. Let us trace them through the gametophyte generation.

From a microspore, with the n number of chromosomes, a gametophyte generation develops. The nucleus divides within the cell, forming a *tube nucleus* and a *generative nucleus*. The generative nucleus in turn divides, forming two genetically identical sperms. All this usually takes place within the stamen. The resulting structure with its three nuclei is a *pollen grain* (Fig. 19.3). Many pollen grains are produced within each stamen.

In the pistils we may follow the fate of the megaspores. From a megaspore a gametophyte generation develops as follows: The nucleus of the megaspore divides, forming two nuclei, each of which again divides, resulting in four. Each of these four then divides, so that there are eight nuclei, four towards each end, within an elongated structure known as the embryo sac. Two of these nuclei (one from each end) then fuse together, forming a single nucleus with the $2n$ number of chromosomes. This nucleus is called the *fusion nucleus*. One other nucleus becomes the *egg nucleus*. The five remaining nuclei

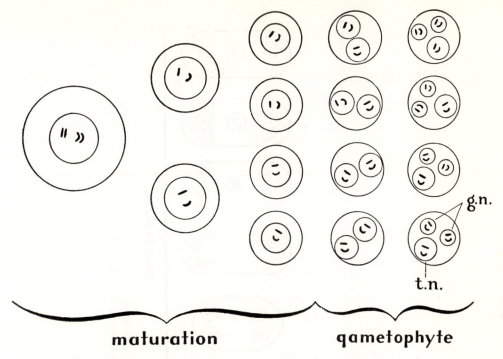

g.n.

t.n.

maturation   gametophyte

Fig. 19.3 Diagrammatic illustration of maturation and the gametophyte in the stamens. The resulting pollen grains, each containing three nuclei, are shown at the extreme right—g.n., sperms; t.n., tube nucleus.

become separated from one another by cell walls and take no further part in the life history. These few divisions (and the corresponding ones in the development of pollen grains) are all that remain in the higher plants of the gametophyte generation. All this takes place within the pistil. Each pistil in corn produces one gametophyte, which consists of an embryo sac containing seven nuclei, one of which is the *egg nucleus* (n), another the *fusion nucleus* ($2n$); the remaining five, as stated above, playing no further part (Fig. 19.4).

We have previous to fertilization, then, a pollen grain containing three nuclei, each with n chromosomes, and an embryo sac containing two essential nuclei, one of which has n chromosomes and the other $2n$. It is to be noted that the two haploid chromosome complements of the fusion nucleus are identical, and that they are identical with the haploid complement of the egg nucleus. The haploid chromosome complements of the pollen grain nuclei are also identical. The embryo sac is within the pistil. The outer end of each pistil in corn extends as a long slender "silk."

When pollen is shed from the tassels, it may fall on the silks. When a pollen grain alights on a silk it germinates, and from it a

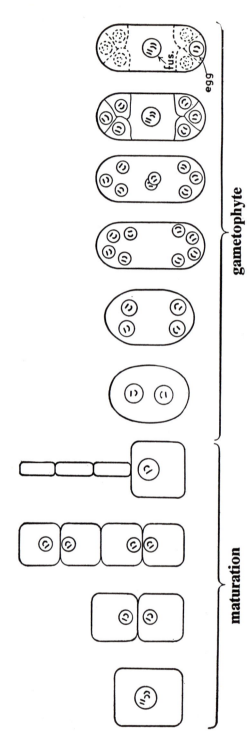

maturation

gametophyte

Fig. 19.4 Diagrammatic illustration of maturation and the gametophyte in the pistils. The resulting embryo sac with the fusion nucleus (fus.) and the egg nucleus (egg) is shown at the extreme right.

microscopic hollow tube, the pollen tube, grows down the silk to the ovulary of the pistil. Eventually the tube reaches the embryo sac and grows into it. Down the tube come the two sperms (the male gametes) and enter the embryo sac. One of the sperms unites with the egg nucleus, forming the zygote, with $2n$ chromosomes, which will develop into the new plant. This union of sperm and egg nuclei is true fertilization. The other sperm unites with the fusion nucleus, forming a nucleus with $3n$ chromosomes, the *endosperm nucleus*. This union of sperm and fusion nucleus is called *triple fusion*.

The zygote immediately begins to develop into an embryo plant. It grows for a while and then becomes dormant for a time: the seed stage.

The endosperm nucleus also develops, forming a mass of tissue around the embryo. This surrounding tissue is *endosperm*. Its outermost cells form a specialized layer, a single cell in thickness, known as the *aleurone layer*. This is important to us because certain genes in corn affect only this aleurone layer. The endosperm, each cell of which has $3n$ chromosomes, almost encloses the embryo, the cells of which have $2n$ chromosomes. Around endosperm and embryo, enclosing them both, is the *pericarp*, or grain coat, part of the mother's own tissue. (In corn and other grasses the tissues surrounding the embryo and endosperm consist of the seed coat fused to the ovary wall. In most other plants the seed coat is separate. However, both seed coat and ovary are $2n$.)

Thus the following tissues make up a grain of corn (Fig. 19.5). Outside of all is the grain coat, with $2n$ chromosomes derived wholly from the mother. Inside of the grain coat is the thin aleurone layer of the endosperm, the cells of which have $3n$ chromosomes ($2n$ from the female parent and n from the male parent). Within the aleurone layer the remainder of the endosperm forms the bulk of the grain. All the cells of the endosperm have $3n$ chromosomes.

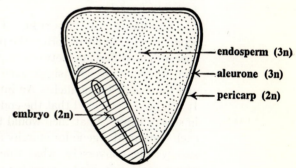

Fig. 19.5 Diagrammatic cross section of a grain of corn, showing the various parts which may be independently affected by genes.

Finally within and almost entirely surrounded by endosperm is the embryo, with $2n$ chromosomes (n from each parent). To produce each grain of corn on an ear there must be one fertilization and one triple fusion.

All this is of considerable importance to us because the hereditary characters of the embryo, the endosperm, and the pericarp are determined independently, and each of these parts is of economic value. The endosperm particularly is of economic value, since it contains a large part of the food accumulated in the grain.

When a grain of corn is planted, the embryo, which has been dormant in the seed stage, begins to grow, using the food which has accumulated in it and in the endosperm. The endosperm thus disappears, and the mature corn plant has the usual $2n$ chromosomes. In some species of plants, such as peas and beans, the endosperm makes very little growth, and the bulk of the seed is composed of the two enlarged cotyledons (leaves) of the embryo.

With the above facts in mind we may examine some of the hereditary characters of cultivated plants and the genetic basis for these characters. The genetics of corn has been extensively investigated by Emerson, East, Jones, Lindstrom, Stadler, and others, and we may profitably use corn as an example. The genetic characters of corn may be classified as seed characters, including endosperm structure, endosperm colors, aleurone colors, pericarp colors, and embryo characters; plant structures, plant colors, leaf structures, inflorescence characters, root characters, and physiological characters. More than 200 pairs of genes have been studied in corn, in addition to several series of multiple genes. Only a few of the more important of these will be mentioned.

1. *Seed Characters*

A. ENDOSPERM STRUCTURE. One of the most important of the economic characters of corn is the presence or absence of sugary endosperm. The difference between starchy corn (field corn) and sugary corn (sweet corn) is a single-gene difference, the genes for starchy and for sugary being alleles. An interesting point intrudes itself here. It will be remembered that the endosperm cells contain chromosomes in sets of three. What then would happen if two of the chromosomes each contained a gene for starchy and the third contained a gene for sugary? Or, conversely, what would happen if two of the chromosomes each contained a gene for sugary and the third chromosome contained a gene for starchy?

By experiment and observation we find that a single dose of the gene for starchy is sufficient to produce starchy endosperm even in the presence of two doses of the gene for sugary (Fig. 19.6). Thus it might be said that starchy shows dominance over sugary. We have reserved the term *dominance*, however, for cases where one member of a pair of alleles masks the effect of the other member of the pair. Here we have one masking the effect of a double dose of its allele. We call such

Fig. 19.6 Genetic variations in corn. Upper row, purple and colorless aleurone from different causes: left, a few purple grains due to xenia; right, many purple grains due to segregation. Middle row, the plant colors: left, purple; right, green. Lower row, left, segregating starchy and sugary grains; right, pod corn, in which each grain is covered with a peculiar pod.

a phenomenon **xenia**. Designating the genes as S for starchy, s for sugary, we say that S shows xenia over s. The various genotypes of the endosperm of corn in regard to these genes may thus be as follows: SSS, SSs, Sss, sss. The first three will result in starchy endosperm, the last in sugary endosperm.

If a field of sweet corn were adjacent to a field of starchy corn, it might happen that some of the pollen from the starchy corn would blow over and pollinate some of the silks of the sweet corn. The embryos within the resulting seeds would be Ss, heterozygous for the starchy and sugary genes, but the visible endosperm around the embryo would be Sss, and would be starchy. Thus on an ear of sweet corn we may find a few starchy kernels, the result of pollination by alien starchy pollen. The interesting thing about this case is that the starchy endosperm appears while the seed is still on the mother plant, since the endosperm grows to maturity the first season. This is the manifestation of xenia.

Similar manifestations may occur in most of the other endosperm and aleurone characters, where the chromosomes (and therefore the genes) are in threes instead of in pairs (Fig. 19.6). Continuing with endosperm structures, genes are known for waxy endosperm, shrunken endosperm, and scarred endosperm. The normal allele of each of these genes manifests xenia. Sixteen different genes are known for *defective* endosperm, any one of which in the absence of its normal allele prevents normal development of endosperm tissue.

A condition of particular interest occurs in the pair of genes F and f, where F represents a gene for flinty endosperm and f represents its allele for floury endosperm. Here the normal manifestations of xenia are not present, so that a curious situation develops in crosses involving these genes. Crosses involving these characters in the homozygous condition always produce an F_1 with seeds like that from which the mother developed, regardless of which way the cross is made. This is due to the fact that one dose of the gene F is not enough to produce its effect in the presence of ff. In other words an endosperm of the formula Fff is floury, not flinty. We may diagram crosses of this nature, remembering that each pollen grain contains two sperms and each embryo sac also contains two nuclei, one having $2n$ chromosomes. Using pollen from the flinty parent, we may work out a cross as shown on this page.

It will be seen that the endosperm of the F_1 is like that of the seed from which the mother developed, and the endosperm ratio of the F_2

PARENTS → plant FF × ff
 endosperm FFF fff

GAMETES → $\binom{F}{F}$ $\binom{f}{ff}$
 pollen   embryo sac

F₁ → plant Ff × Ff
 endosperm Fff Fff

GAMETES → $\binom{F}{F}$ $\binom{f}{f}$ $\binom{F}{FF}$ $\binom{f}{ff}$
 pollen   embryo sac

F₂ →

	F F	f f
F FF	FF FFF flinty	Ff FFf flinty
f ff	Ff Fff floury	ff fff floury

is one to one instead of three to one. The F_2 from the reciprocal cross would be identical. This case was a very puzzling one until the knowledge of the genetics of endosperm cells made it explainable.

B. ENDOSPERM COLOR. Several pairs of genes affect endosperm color. There is a gene for white which shows xenia over its allele for yellow. Conversely, there are three genes for yellow which show xenia over their alleles for white. In the absence of the first-mentioned white gene any one of the three separate yellow genes is sufficient to produce yellow endosperm.

C. ALEURONE COLOR. A large series of genes affects aleurone color. Several pairs of alleles exist in which color shows xenia over white. There is also a white showing xenia over color. Another gene produces purple aleurone and shows xenia over its allele for red (Fig. 19.6). There is a gene for brown aleurone. In order for purple, red, or brown to show up it is of course necessary that none of the white genes be present in such genotypic arrangements as to prevent the development of pigment. Another pair of genes affecting aleurone color consists of a gene for dilution and its allele for intensity of pigment, dilution manifesting xenia over intensity.

D. PERICARP COLORS. Three sets of genes affect pericarp colors, the various interactions producing red, brown, cherry, or colorless.

The color of the kernels on an ear of corn, then, depends on a large and varied series of genes. Since the pericarp is the outer layer, its color will show if it has any color. If the pericarp is colorless the aleurone color will show through. If the aleurone layer is in turn colorless (white), the endosperm color may show through. The color of corn grains illustrates very nicely the complications which may exist in the genetic determination of a character. Because of these complications, especially where we are dealing with pericarp genes and endosperm genes in the same cross, it may be helpful at this point to diagram a cross involving such genes. Let us use S, a gene for starchy endosperm showing xenia over its allele s, a gene for sugary endosperm. Let us also use B, the dominant gene for brown pericarp and its recessive allele b for colorless pericarp.

If we cross a homozygous variety having starchy endosperm and brown pericarp with a homozygous variety having sugary endosperm and colorless pericarp, we may obtain an F_1 and an F_2 generation. We must remember that the endosperm genes affect the endosperm but not the plant itself, while the pericarp genes affect the pericarp of the seed but not the endosperm. We must also remember that the endosperm genes in the cells of the endosperm came from the triple fusion, and thus of the three genes in each cell of the endosperm, one came from the pollen grain and two from the fusion nucleus. On the other hand the pericarp genes in the cells of the pericarp are derived

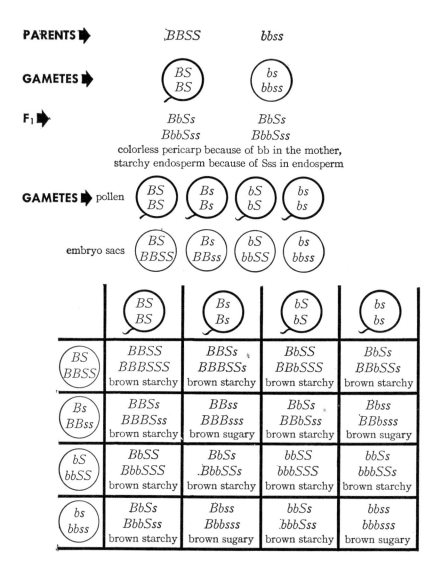

PARENTS ➡   *BBSS*   *bbss*

GAMETES ➡

$$\binom{BS}{BS}$$ $$\binom{bs}{bbss}$$

F₁ ➡   *BbSs*   *BbSs*
         BbbSss   *BbbSss*

colorless pericarp because of bb in the mother,
starchy endosperm because of Sss in endosperm

GAMETES ➡ pollen

	$\binom{BS}{BS}$	$\binom{Bs}{Bs}$	$\binom{bS}{bS}$	$\binom{bs}{bs}$
$\binom{BS}{BBSS}$	BBSS BBBSSS brown starchy	BBSs BBBSSs brown starchy	BbSS BBbSSS brown starchy	BbSs BBbSSs brown starchy
$\binom{Bs}{BBss}$	BBSs BBBSss brown starchy	BBss BBBsss brown sugary	BbSs BBbSss brown starchy	Bbss BBbsss brown sugary
$\binom{bS}{bbSS}$	BbSS BbbSSS brown starchy	BbSs BbbSSs brown starchy	bbSS bbbSSS brown starchy	bbSs bbbSSs brown starchy
$\binom{bs}{bbss}$	BbSs BbbSSs brown starchy	Bbss Bbbsss brown sugary	bbSs bbbSss brown starchy	bbss bbbsss brown sugary

embryo sacs $\binom{BS}{BBSS}$ $\binom{Bs}{BBss}$ $\binom{bS}{bbSS}$ $\binom{bs}{bbss}$

wholly from the mother and are not affected by the fertilization or the triple fusion.

Thus the cross is as shown above, using pollen from the variety having brown pericarp and starchy endosperm.

The result in the F_2 generation is three brown starchy to one brown sugary. The F_2 seeds all have brown pericarp regardless of the genes contained in the endosperms or in the embryos because the F_1 mother plants are of the formula *Bb* and thus will produce seeds all with brown pericarp. The endosperms of the F_2 seeds, however, are affected by the triple fusion and thus are starchy if they are of the formulas *SSS*, *SSs*, or *Sss* and sugary if they contain the genes *sss*.

E. EMBRYO CHARACTERS. Four different recessive genes affect the embryo of corn, producing, when in the homozygous state, abortive embryos, germless seeds, seeds with miniature embryos, and premature germination, respectively.

2. Plant Structures

Many different recessive genes are known, any one of which in the homozygous condition produces dwarf plants (Fig. 19.7). The number and distribution of the stomata depend on at least three pairs of recessive genes. A dominant gene produces "teopod" corn, in which the whole plant is affected to such an extent that it would in nature unquestionably be called another species.

Fig. 19.7 Dwarf corn (left) and narrow-leaved corn (right) compared with a normal plant (center). *From Jones in the Journal of Heredity*

3. Plant Colors

A series of gene pairs has been isolated controlling the general anthocyanin and flavone pigments of the plant. These may in the dominant state produce purple plants, brown plants, salmon-colored silks, and intense or dilute shades of these, respectively. In addition to such pigments the chlorophyl content is subject to much modification, nearly seventy recessive genes being known which affect it. Ten different recessive genes are known for albinism (Fig. 19.8), and thirty or more which produce striping, blotching, and yellowing. Albino seedlings, of course, cannot live past the stage when they have used up the food contained in the seed. Striped, yellow, and blotched plants live, but are not vigorous, and wilt in hot weather.

4. Leaf Characters

Many pairs of genes are known which affect the leaves of corn, producing, respectively, narrow, twisted, slashed, frayed, striate, knotted, crinkly, adherent, glossy, or liguleless leaves (Fig. 19.7).

5. Inflorescence Characters

Nearly two dozen recessive mutations are known which affect the staminate or pistillate inflorescence. These include tassel ear, tassel seed, silkless (sterile), barren, anther ear, coherent tassel, pod (Fig. 19.6), ramose, sorghum tassel, weak tassel, fasciated ear, and others.

Fig. 19.8   Albino corn seedlings. *From Jones and Mangelsdorf in Bull. 266 of Conn. Agr. Exp. Station*

6. Root Characters

Only one gene is known to affect root characters, a recessive which prevents the emergence or development of the secondary roots.

7. Physiological Characters

A number of genes are known which variously affect the resistance to disease, such as smut or rust. Another recessive gene produces a lack of lignin, and still another produces "diabetic" corn.

8. Multiple-gene Characters

Many series of multiple genes in corn have been investigated, although much work remains to be done. The protein content of seeds, the oil content, the number of rows on the ear, the vigor and size of the plant all appear to depend upon multiple genes.

The above list of the various kinds of characters in corn and their known hereditary basis has been given in order to demonstrate the fact that the same principles of genetics and breeding apply to plants as to animals. The linkage relations of many of the genes are known, and a linkage map of corn was presented in Figure 12.2. It will be noted that the genes affecting one character are not all on the same chromosome. Those affecting chlorophyl, for example, occur on at least nine of the ten pairs of chromosomes, those affecting anthocyanin and flavone pigments on eight, and those affecting the leaves on at least five.

As we have seen to be the case in other organisms, most of the mutations in corn are recessives, and most of them are deleterious. Hence the breeder is faced with two problems: first, getting rid of the undesirable characters, and second, combining the desirable characters in the most efficient manner. The various combinations of desirable genes have resulted in the different breeds, or as they are usually called in plants, *varieties*.

In a similar way the mutations of other plants have been investigated, and many genes are known in most species of cultivated grains, fruits, vegetables, and flowers, and in wild species as well. The methods of preserving and combining good characters while eliminating the undesirable ones were discussed in the chapter on selection (Chapter 16).

Chromosomal aberrations have contributed relatively little to variation in corn. The striking differences that are commonly seen come from the various combinations of genes. Many other cultivated plants, however, do have some of their interesting and useful differences determined by chromosomal aberrations. This source of new characters will be discussed in Chapters 20 and 21.

In addition to variations dependent upon chromosomal genes, a type of variation has long been recognized in plants which depends on gene-like bodies in the cytoplasm, transmitted only by means of the cytoplasm. The studies of this type of transmission have recently taken on new impetus, and examples of cytoplasmic inheritance have been found in protozoa, insects, and mammals, as well as in plants. The genetic implications of these new researches are of such importance that a chapter will be devoted to them (Chapter 25).

PROBLEMS

19.1 A homozygous variety of corn with purple aleurone and flinty endosperm is crossed with a homozygous variety having red aleurone and floury endosperm. Pollen from the purple flinty variety is used. What would be the appearance of the endosperm and the genotypes of the embryos in the F_1 and the F_2?

19.2 What differences would occur in the F_1 and the F_2 if pollen from the red floury variety were used in making the cross?

19.3 Along one edge of a field of sweet corn the ears contain occasional starchy grains, while along the other edge the ears contain all sugary grains. What is the probable explanation of this?

19.4 On a certain ear of corn all the grains have colorless pericarp except one, which is red. Could this be an effect of xenia? If not what could be the explanation?

19.5 A certain strain of corn when inbred produces colored and albino seedlings in the ratio of 27 colored : 37 albino. What is the explanation of this ratio?

19.6 In which one of the following plants would you expect xenia to produce the most noticeable effect: cabbages, onions, potatoes, wheat, tomatoes?

19.7 In snapdragons a gene W permits the development of flower color, its recessive allele, w, prevents the development

of color so that the flowers are white. In the presence of $W-$, the effects of several other genes are as follows: Y results in ivory base pigment, its recessive allele, y, results in yellow base pigment; I converts ivory base pigment to purple anthocyanin and yellow base pigment to red anthocyanin, its recessive allele, i, does not carry out these conversions; D results in intense anthocyanin pigment, its recessive allele, d, results in dilute anthocyanin pigment, diluting purple to pink and red to bronze. These four pairs of genes segregate independently. The genotypes of eleven commercial greenhouse varieties as recorded by Haney are as follows:

VARIETY	W,w	Y,y	I,i	D,d
Windemer's Lilac (purple)	WW	YY	II	DD
Scarlett O'Hara (red)	WW	yy	II	DD
Cheviot Maid (pink)	WW	YY	II	dd
Lady Dorothy (bronze)	WW	yy	II	dd
Margaret (ivory)	WW	YY	ii	dd
Ball Gold (yellow)	WW	yy	ii	DD
Ethel (yellow)	WW	yy	ii	dd
Rockwood's Crystal White	ww	YY	II	DD
Armstrong's White	ww	YY	II	dd
Peace (white)	ww	YY	ii	dd
Yuletide (white)	ww	yy	ii	dd

From the above data answer these and

the following three numbered questions about snapdragons: What would be the flower color of the F_1, and the colors and ratio of the F_2, from a cross between Windemer's Lilac and Yuletide? What other crosses would give identical results?

19.8 Inasmuch as the genes Y, y, I, i, D, and d cannot express themselves in the presence of ww, what is probably responsible for the fact that the last four varieties in the list are distinct one from the other?

19.9 If you had an unknown white snapdragon, and wished to learn as quickly as possible what color genes it carried, to what variety should you cross it?

19.10 If you had available only Lady Dorothy and Peace, could you develop from them a pink-flowered plant? Ivory? Red? Purple? Yellow?

19.11 In tomatoes the following genes occur: A,a (purple stem, green stem); D,d (tall, dwarf); F,f (fasciated fruit, nonfasciated fruit); O,o (oblate fruit shape, ovate fruit shape); P,p (smooth-skinned fruit, pubescent fruit); R,r (red flesh, yellow flesh); S,s (simple inflorescence, compound inflorescence); Y,y (opaque skin resulting in bright fruit, transparent skin resulting in dull fruit). The genes D, P, O, and S belong to one linkage group, A and F to another, while R and Y are independent of these linkage groups and of each other. From the above facts answer this and the following seven questions. How many homozygous varieties, each having a different combination of these characters, could be produced?

19.12 Write the genotype, showing linkage relations, of a homozygous tall green-stemmed plant with simple inflorescence, having bright red, smooth-skinned, ovate, nonfasciated fruit.

19.13 Write the genotype of a homozygous dwarf purple-stemmed plant with compound inflorescence, having dull yellow, pubescent, oblate, fasciated fruit.

19.14 What would be the genotype and phenotype of the F_1 from a cross between the preceding two varieties?

19.15 How many kinds of germ cells would the F_1 in the preceding problem produce if there were no crossing over?

19.16 How many kinds of gametes could the F_1 in Problem 19.14 produce, taking into consideration single crossovers?

19.17 If double crossing over occurred, would the number of kinds of gametes be increased or decreased?

19.18 What effect would the fact that certain characters in tomatoes are linked have on the ease of producing new varieties? What would be the relation between the strength of the linkage and the ease of production of new varieties?

19.19 In corn W is a gene for starchy endosperm, showing xenia over w, its allele for waxy endosperm. Red pericarp is due to a dominant gene R, colorless pericarp to its recessive allele r. A plant from a homozygous colorless waxy variety is used to pollinate a plant from a homozygous red starchy variety. The seeds from this cross are planted the following year in an isolated plot, free from contamination by foreign pollen. What kinds of grains would be found on the resulting ears of corn and in what proportions?

19.20 In corn, Wellhausen has shown that an accurate test of resistance or susceptibility to bacterial wilt may be made by inoculating seedlings with a suspension of the bacteria by means of a hypodermic syringe. In this way varieties of corn are found to belong to one of four classifications. The various degrees of susceptibility depend upon the interaction of two pairs of genes with complete dominance. The classifications with their genotypes are as follows:

S_1–S_2– Very resistant. Recovers fully from infection.

S_1–s_2s_2 Moderately resistant. Dies only when attacked by highly virulent strain of bacteria, and then only about five weeks after infection.

$s_1s_1S_2-$ Susceptible. Dies about five weeks after infection when attacked by either highly virulent or slightly virulent strain.

$s_1s_1s_2s_2$ Very susceptible. Dies in two weeks when attacked by either strain.

From the above data answer this and the following eight questions. Starting with a very resistant homozygous variety and a very susceptible homozygous variety, what results would be obtained in the F_1 of the cross between them? In the F_2?

19.21 If you tested the F_2 from Problem 19.20 only with a highly virulent strain and classified them only as living or dead, what ratio would be found after two weeks? After six weeks?

19.22 If you tested the F_2 of Problem 19.20 only with a slightly virulent strain, classifying them as living or dead, what results would be found after two weeks? After six weeks?

19.23 If the F_1 from Problem 19.20 were back-crossed to the very susceptible variety, what would be the genotypic and phenotypic results?

19.24 What ratio would be observed in the offspring of the back-cross of Problem 19.23 after two weeks if they were tested only with a highly virulent strain and classified as living or dead? After six weeks?

19.25 What ratio would be observed in the offspring of the back-cross of Problem 19.23 after two weeks if they were tested only with a slightly virulent strain and classified as living or dead? After six weeks?

19.26 The genes for susceptibility to bacterial wilt are not linked with each other and are not linked with the genes for starchy and sweet endosperm (Su and su), nor with the genes for yellow and white endosperm (Y and y). Starting with a very resistant yellow starchy corn and a very susceptible white sweet corn, how could you obtain a very resistant yellow sweet corn? A very resistant white sweet corn?

19.27 One of the pairs of genes for resistance and susceptibility to bacterial wilt (S_1,s_1) is linked with the genes for red and white cob color (P and p). Starting with a very resistant red-cob variety and a very susceptible white-cob variety, would the fact of linkage make it impossible to establish a very resistant strain of white-cob corn? Explain.

19.28 If the crossover percentage between the genes for red cob and white cob and the genes for resistance and susceptibility (s_1 and S_1) is 40, what ratio would be obtained in the F_2 from a cross between a very susceptible red-cob variety and a very resistant white-cob variety?

19.29 In nasturtiums the flowers may be single (5 petals), double (about 15 petals), or super-double (about 40 petals). D is a gene for single, d is its recessive allele for double. Single and double flowers, however, can show up only in the presence of the genes ss. The gene S results in super-double, no matter what the combination of the D and d genes may be. Super-double flowers produce stamens but have no pistil and are known only in the heterozygous Ss condition. From the above facts answer this and the following five questions. Why can we not readily obtain homozygous SS plants?

19.30 If a mutation should change an Ss nasturtium zygote to the SS condition, would it necessarily result in a super-double plant? Might it be lethal?

19.31 A super-double nasturtium was crossed to a double. They produced many offspring, half of which were super-double and half of which were double. What were the genotypes of the parents?

19.32 A super-double nasturtium was crossed to a double. They produced many offspring, half of which were super-double and half of which were single. What were the genotypes of the parents?

19.33 A super-double nasturtium was

crossed to a single. Of their many offspring one half were super-double, three eighths were single, and one eighth were double. What were the genotypes of the parents?

19.34 A super-double nasturtium was crossed to a single. A large number of offspring was produced, half of which were super-double, one quarter of which were single, and one quarter of which were double. What were the genotypes of the parents?

REFERENCES

CASPARI, E., *Advances in Genetics* **2**:1 (1948).

CRANE, M. B., and LAWRENCE, W. J. C., *The Genetics of Garden Plants*. London, Macmillan Ltd. (1934).

HANEY, W. J., *Jour. Heredity* **45**:146 (1954).

JONES, D. F., *Jour. Heredity* **15**:291 (1924); *Genetics in Plant and Animal Improvement*. New York, John Wiley and Sons (1925).

JONES, D. F., and MANGELSDORF, P. C., *Conn. Agr. Exp. Station Bull.* **266** (1925).

KARPER, R. E., *Jour. Heredity* **25**:49 (1934).

LINDSTROM, E. W., *Bull. Torrey Bot. Club* **57**:221 (1931).

MANGELSDORF, P. C., *Advances in Genetics* **1**:161 (1947).

WELLHAUSEN, E. J., *Iowa Agr. Exp. Sta. Bull.* 224 (1937).

CHAPTER TWENTY

Chromosomal aberrations I.
Variation in numbers of chromosomes

In our discussion of sex-linked genes in Chapter 8, attention was called to the fact that cytological evidence for the X-chromosome location of genes of this nature is provided by nondisjunction. It should now be pointed out that nondisjunction is not confined to the X-chromosome of Drosophila, but takes place in various chromosomes of other species, particularly of plants. In the Jimson weed, for example, Blakeslee and others have found many instances of the addition or subtraction of one or more chromosomes of the set through nondisjunction.

The Jimson weed has twelve pairs of chromosomes. In addition to the normal type of plant, twelve types, each having characteristic variations in form and structure, are recognized, each one having an extra chromosome of one pair. The chromosome complement of such plants would thus be $2n + 1$. Some types which conversely lack a chromosome of one pair ($2n - 1$) have been recognized. In some cases through nondisjunction two extra chromosomes are added, one of each of two pairs. Many such types have been recognized. Various other types with added or subtracted chromosomes are known in this plant, and the variation in chromosome number is always correlated with a corresponding variation in the structure of the plant. The chromosomes of the Jimson weed are diagramed in Figure 20.1, and the capsules of plants of the normal type and each of the primary $2n + 1$ types are shown in Figure 20.2.

Darlington has shown that the varieties of cultivated cherries differ one from the other in having an extra chromosome of one or another pair. Thus this condition may give rise to important economic variations, which in the case of cherries may be perpetuated by grafting.

Individuals with $2n + 1$ chromosomes are spoken of as **trisomics;** those with $2n$ plus more than one (for example $2n + 1 + 1$) are known as **polysomics.** In generations following a nondisjunction, a *pair* of chromosomes rather than a single chromosome might become added to the normal complement, resulting in $2n + 2$. Obviously meiosis could be more normal in a $2n + 2$ individual than in one having $2n + 1$, and the condition might be perpetuated.

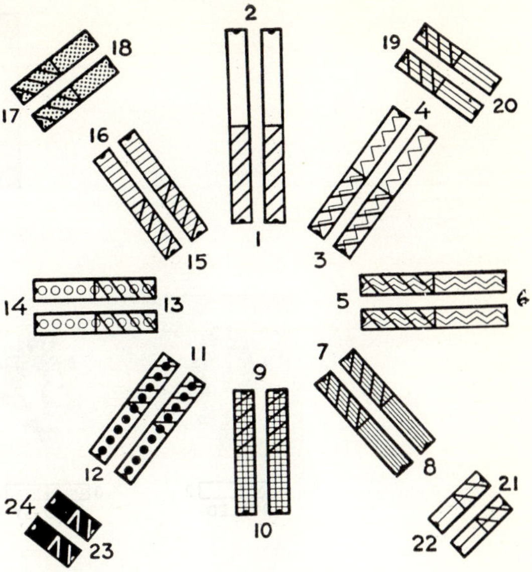

A general term for variations in the number of chromosomes is **ploidy.** For cases like those we have been discussing, involving the addition of one or more chromosomes or pairs of chromosomes but not the whole complement, the term used is **aneuploidy.** The evolution of many plant species appears to have progressed in this manner. Often related species or varieties are found to differ one from the other by one or a few pairs of

Fig. 20.1 Diagram of the twelve pairs of chromosomes of the Jimson weed. Each chromosome has been given a characteristic conventional marking, one half being distinguished from the other by shading and each end being given a number. Compare with Figures 20.2, 21.4, 21.5. *From Blakeslee in the Journal of Heredity*

chromosomes. Different members of the cabbage family, for example, have respectively 8, 9, 10, 11, 17, 18, 19, 27, and 29 pairs. Similar aneuploid series are known in tobacco, crocus, iris, violets, salvia, veronica, and other plant groups.

Although nondisjunction (and other processes to be discussed in Chapter 21) resulting in aneuploidy take place in nature at a low rate, the rate may be greatly speeded up by the application of the alkaloid colchicine. The announcements of the effect of colchicine in changing chromosome numbers were made in 1937 and 1938 by Blakeslee, Eigsti, Nebel, and others, and precipitated a new era in the study of chromosomes and indeed of evolutionary processes. The application of colchicine to seeds, young embryos, or growing shoots causes a failure of the completion of normal mitosis, with consequent aberrations in numbers of chromosomes in some of the resulting nuclei.

In addition to aneuploidy, the entire set of chromosomes may be duplicated as a result of colchicine treatment. This situation is in fact

NORMAL

| 1 [////] 2 | 3 [\\\/\/\] 4 | 5 [\\\\~] 6 | 7 [/////] 8 |
| ROLLED | GLOSSY | BUCKLING | ELONGATE |

| 9 [\\\\||||] 10 | 11 [••••] 12 | 13 [\\\ooooo] 14 | 15 [\\\\\|||] 16 |
| ECHINUS | COCKLEBUR | MICROCARPIC | REDUCED |

| 17 [\\\\] 18 | 19 [\\\\] 20 | 21 [\\\\] 22 | 23 [\\\\■] 24 |
| POINSETTIA | SPINACH | GLOBE | ILEX |

Fig. 20.2 Above, the capsule of a normal Jimson weed. Below, capsules of the twelve primary 2n + 1 forms. Each of these forms contains an extra chromosome of one set. The extra chromosome is shown in each case, with the name of the variant form beneath. The characters of the entire plant are affected by the additional chromosome. *From Blakeslee in the Journal of Heredity*

quite a usual result of the treatment, and results in **euploidy,** or as it is often called, **polyploidy.** Polyploidy is a general term meaning the replication of the whole set of chromosomes. Specifically, an individual having three of each kind of chromosome is spoken of as **triploid;** four of each kind, **tetraploid;** five of each kind **pentaploid;** and so on. The haploid number of chromosomes may be replicated as many as twelve or more times in some known species of plants.

Polyploidy, like aneuploidy, occurs in the wild, sometimes as a result of injury to a growing shoot, and appears to have been responsible for much of plant evolution. Polyploidy is rare in animals. The discovery that the application of colchicine will greatly speed up the occurrence of polyploidy has made it possible to test hypotheses of the evolutionary history of some plant species.

Polyploids arising from a duplication of the chromosome complement within the same species are known as **autopolyploids,** as contrasted with **allopolyploids** arising from hybridization of two species or genera with subsequent duplication of each chromosome complement. The reproduction of the two types will be significantly different because of the way in which each is formed.

Autotetraploids, for example, have four identical chromosomes of each kind. Hence in synapsis all four of each sort may come together, so that normal segregation does not necessarily take place. Often two chromosomes of each kind do go to each pole, but sometimes the segregation is three to one pole and only one to the other. Thus some of the gametes of an autotetraploid have chromosomes in excess, while others are deficient for certain chromosomes. Fertilization involving these gametes results in less viable or even inviable offspring. In this and other ways the fertility may be reduced. Autotetraploids are usually larger than the corresponding diploids in all their parts except height, and even the height is greater in some cases. Since each chromosome is duplicated, no specific character is affected more than others.

The reproductive situation is different in allotetraploids. Here the two diploid complements of chromosomes come from different species or even different genera; therefore, each chromosome has only one mate. Synapsis and segregation can be normal, and the new type may breed true with no reduction in fertility. Not all allotetraploids are completely fertile, however. Allotetraploids arise through hybridization, from the union of a haploid complement of chromosomes from each of two taxonomically different individuals, with subsequent doubling of the chromosomes in occasional gametes of the hybrid. Many if not most species hybrids are sterile, but in some cases a few diploid gametes are produced. When two such gametes unite, allo-

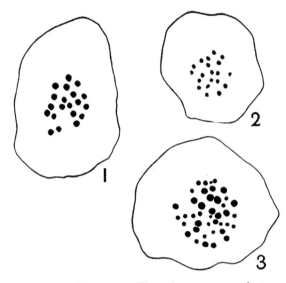

Fig. 20.3 The chromosomes of two species of horse chestnut and of a fertile new tetraploid species arising from the cross between them. 1, the twenty chromosomes of the haploid complement of *Aesculus pavia*. 2, the twenty chromosomes of the haploid complement of *Aesculus hippocastanum*. 3, the haploid complement of forty chromosomes of *Aesculus carnea* (the Pink Chestnut), a tetraploid new species containing all the chromosomes of both parent species. *From Skovsted in Hereditas*

tetraploids are produced, having characters different in many ways from either parent species.

In this way fertile new species may arise. In order for a tetraploid to breed true it must, as we have seen, produce only diploid gametes. In order for *any* polyploid species or variety to breed true it must have the chromosomes of each kind in even numbers, so that regular segregation can occur. Thus triploids, pentaploids, and other forms having each kind of chromosome present in odd numbers cannot breed true. A large amount of sterility results, with the production of some offspring having one or more chromosomes in excess of the normal number.

Triploids may come about through the union of a gamete from a tetraploid with a gamete from a diploid. Even though a triploid plant cannot breed true it may be propagated asexually if its phenotypic characters warrant its perpetuation.

Not only have many new autopolyploid and allopolyploid species and varieties been experimentally produced, but there is much evidence that they occur in nature, thus providing a potent factor in evolution. Only a few cases of new forms arising in nature through autopolyploidy have been substantiated, but many cases of natural alloploidy are known. Such forms have been recorded among the chestnuts, grasses, irises, roses, and others. The chromosomes of a natural allopolyploid are shown in Figure 20.3 and of an experimental allopolyploid in Figure 20.4.

We may cite cotton (*Gossypium*) as an illustration of the testing of a hypothesis regarding the evolutionary development of a genus of plants. The cultivated species of American cotton are known to have 26 pairs of chromosomes: 13 pairs of large ones and 13 pairs of small ones. The cultivated species of Old World cottons have 13 pairs of large chromosomes, and cultivated American cotton was long suspected to be an allotetraploid, with Old World cotton as one of its

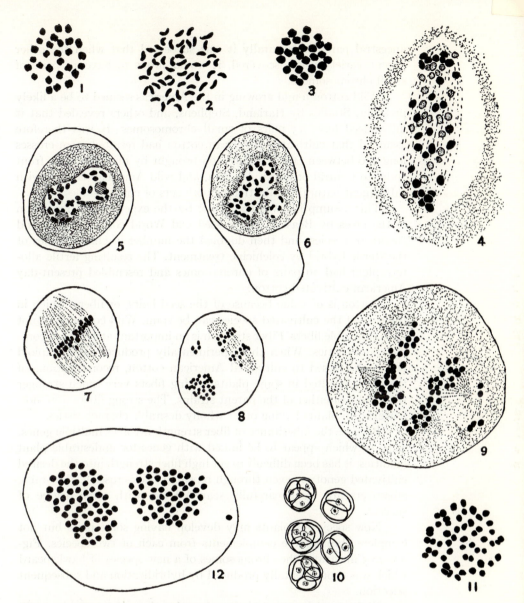

Fig. 20.4 The chromosomes of two species of foxglove and of a fertile new tetraploid species arising from the cross between them. 1, the haploid complement of 28 chromosomes of *Digitalis purpurea*. 3, the haploid complement of 28 chromosomes of *Digitalis ambigua*. 2, the 56 chromosomes of the hybrid between them. 4–10, the reduction division of the hybrid, showing the failure of normal reduction, thus producing gametes with 56 chromosomes. The union of such gametes produced in the F_2 some individuals with 112 chromosomes (56 haploid), which formed a fertile new tetraploid species producing gametes with 56 chromosomes (see 11 and 12). *From Buxton and Newton in the Journal of Genetics, courtesy of the Cambridge University Press*

ancestral parents. Naturally it was suspected that when the other parent variety was discovered, it would prove to have 13 pairs of small chromosomes.

Wild cotton found growing in the Americas seemed to be a likely prospect. Studies by Harland, Stephens, and others revealed that it did indeed have 13 pairs of small chromosomes. It was therefore assumed that cultivated American cotton had resulted from crosses long ago between Old World cotton brought by primitive man from India to Central or South America, and wild American cotton, with subsequent natural duplication of both sets of chromosomes.

This assumption was confirmed by the experimental repetition of the cross by Beasley. He crossed Old World cotton with a wild American species, and then doubled the number of chromosomes of the sterile hybrid by colchicine treatment. The resulting fertile allo-tetraploid had 26 pairs of chromosomes and resembled present-day American cultivated cotton.

Cotton is of value because of the seed hairs, or fibers, which in the case of the cultivated species can be spun. Wild cotton does not have spinnable fibers. Fiber strength is an important attribute of commercial varieties. When the experimentally produced allotetraploid was back-crossed to cultivated American cotton, recombinations of the genes resulted in some plants having fibers very much stronger than those of either of the parent strains. The strong fibers were not, however, in plants having other wholly desirable characteristics.

Because the inheritance of fiber strength involves multiple genes, some of which appear to be linked with genes for undesirable plant qualities, it has been difficult to get high fiber strength into the desired cultivated genotype even through repeated back-crossing. Favorable crossovers are being carefully searched for, with some degree of success.

New species of plants may develop having some pairs but not complete chromosome complements from each of two species. Figure 20.5 illustrates the chromosomes of a new species of hawksbeard which was experimentally produced by hybridization and subsequent selection.

Various cultivated varieties of garden flowers, vegetables, crop plants, berries, and fruit trees are polyploids. Stayman winesap, Arkansas, Baldwin, and Turley apples, for example, are triploids; McIntosh, Ontario, Hibernal, and Wealthy are tetraploids. Triploid and tetraploid varieties are known and cultivated among roses, hyacinths, tulips, lilies, wheat, oats, sugar cane, and others. Autotriploidy and tetraploidy in tomatoes are shown in Figure 20.6.

The expression of the genes varies among polyploids. In some instances one dominant gene may express itself completely in the

Fig. 20.5 Chromosomes of two species of hawksbeard and a new species produced after crossing them. *a*, the chromosomes of *Crepis setosa* (4 pairs). *b*, the chromosomes of *Crepis biennis* (20 pairs). *c*, the chromosomes of the partially sterile hybrid between them (24 chromosomes not paired). *d*, the chromosomes of the fertile new species which appeared in the fourth generation, containing ten pairs of chromosomes from *Crepis biennis* and two pairs from *Crepis setosa*. The two pairs from *setosa* are marked as in *a*. *From Collins, Hollingshead and Avery in Genetics*

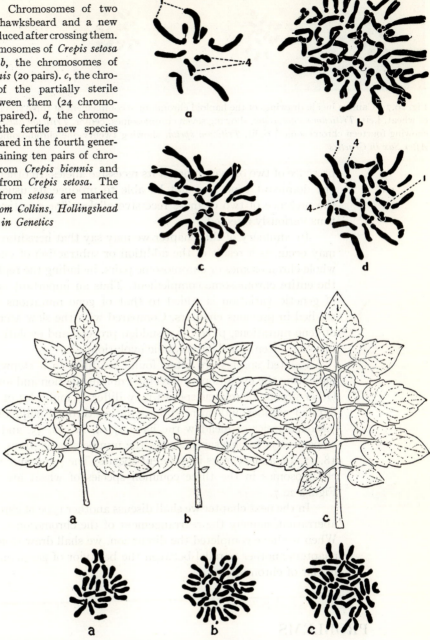

Fig. 20.6 Polyploidy in the tomato. Left, leaf and chromosomes of diploid (12 pairs); center, leaf and chromosomes of triploid (3 sets of 12); right, leaf and chromosomes of tetraploid (4 sets of 12). *From Jörgenson in the Journal of Genetics, courtesy of the Cambridge University Press*

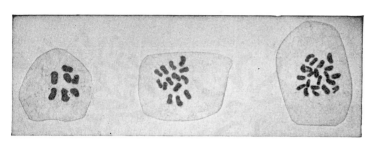

Fig. 20.7 Camera lucida drawings of the haploid chromosome complement of three species of wheat. Left, *Triticum monococcum*, showing seven chromosomes; center, *Triticum durum*, showing fourteen chromosomes; right, *Triticum spelta*, showing twenty-one chromosomes. *After Sax in Genetics*

presence of two or even more of its recessive alleles. In other instances one dominant gene may not be able to produce its usual effect in the presence of two or more recessive alleles. The genetic ratios are thus variously affected.

In summary of this chapter we may say that hereditary changes may occur as a result of the addition or subtraction of one or more whole chromosomes or chromosome pairs, including the replication of the entire chromosome complement. Thus an important new source of genetic variation is added to that of gene mutations which we studied in previous chapters. Compared with the slow accumulation of gene mutations, ploidy is a sudden process, and evolution by this means is often called cataclysmic evolution.

Related species are often found to differ in a stepwise series, indicating the evolutionary effects of nondisjunction and aneuploidy. Other groups of related species may differ in multiples of the basic haploid number, indicating differentiation through polyploidy. Thus various species of meadow rue have 7, 14, 21, 28, 35, and 42 pairs, respectively. In chrysanthemums the numbers range from 9 through 18, 27, 36, and 45 pairs in different species. The 7, 14, and 21 pairs of chromosomes in the three common species of wheat are shown in Figure 20.7.

In the next chapter we shall discuss another type of chromosomal aberration, namely the rearrangement of the chromosomal material. When we have completed the discussion, we shall draw from the two chapters another parallel between the behavior of genes and the behavior of chromosomes.

PROBLEMS

20.1 In the Jimson weed there are twelve pairs of chromosomes. Blakeslee has recorded the twelve possible $2n + 1$ types. How many different types are possible having an extra chromosome added to each of two sets, that is, $2n + 1 + 1$?

20.2 Tetraploid (4n) plants frequently occur in the Jimson weed. Starting with a 4n and a 2n plant as parents, how would you go about obtaining 2n + 1 plants?

20.3 Frequently two related species have the same number of chromosomes, yet are sterile when crossed. What explanation can you suggest for this?

20.4 Certain groups of closely related species have chromosome numbers which are respectively various multiples of a basic number. Other groups of closely related species have a continuous range of chromosome numbers. How may each of these conditions have come about?

20.5 Among the legumes the pea has seven pairs of chromosomes, while the broad bean has six pairs, one of which contains chromosomes twice the size of the others. What does this suggest as to the possible evolutionary relationships of these two species?

20.6 The various species of raspberries have 14, 21, 28, 42, and 49 chromosomes, respectively. The various species of sedges have 18, 30, 32, 38, 48, 50, 52, 54, 56, 58, 62, 64, 66, 68, 70, 72, 74, 76, 80, 82, 84, and

102 chromosomes, respectively. In which of these two groups has nondisjunction apparently occurred? In which has evolution progressed by means of polyploidy?

20.7 When one parent is blood group O and the other is group AB, the offspring consist of approximately equal numbers of group A and group B. A very occasional case is recorded, however, where a group O or a group AB child occurs. Aside from the possibility of illegitimacy, what might be the cause of such results?

20.8 Can you suggest any explanation as to why polyploidy is more common in plants than in animals?

20.9 In poultry, barring is due to a dominant sex-linked gene, B, nonbarring to its recessive allele, b. By crossing nonbarred males with barred females it is possible to tell the sex of chicks at hatching, since the males will normally be barred, the females nonbarred. If a breeder should find a few exceptions in such a cross, that is, a few nonbarred males and a few barred females, what might be the genetic explanation of these exceptions?

REFERENCES

BEASLEY, J. O., *Amer. Naturalist* **74**:285 (1940); *Jour. Heredity* **31**:39 (1940); *Genetics* 27:25 (1942).

BLAKESLEE, A. F., *Jour. Heredity* **25**:81 (1934).

BLAKESLEE, A. F., and AVERY, A. G., *Jour. Heredity* **28**: 393 (1937).

BRIDGES, C. B., *Jour. Exper. Zoölogy* **15**:587 (1913); *Genetics* **1**:1, 107 (1916).

BUXTON, B. H., and NEWTON, W. C. F., *Jour. Genetics* **19**:269 (1928).

CLAUSEN, J., KECK, D. D., and HIESEY, W. M. *Publ. Carnegie Inst. No.* 564 (1945).

COLLINS, J. L., HOLLINGSHEAD, L., and AVERY, P., *Genetics* **14**:305 (1929).

EIGSTI, O. J., and DUSTIN, P., *Colchicine in*

Agriculture, Medicine, Biology and Chemistry. Ames, Iowa, The Iowa State College Press (1955).

HARLAND, S. C., *Tropical Agriculture* **17**:53 (1940).

JÖRGENSON, C. A., *Jour. Genetics* **19**:133 (1928).

RICHMOND, T. R., *Advances in Genetics* **4**:213 (1951).

SAX, K., *Genetics* **7**:513 (1922).

SKOVSTED, A., *Hereditas* **12**:64 (1929).

STEBBINS, G. L., *Variation and Evolution in Plants.* New York, Columbia Univ. Press (1950).

STEPHENS, S. G., *Advances in Genetics* **4**:247 (1951).

CHAPTER TWENTY-ONE

Chromosomal aberrations II. Rearrangements of chromosomal material

In addition to the variations in chromosome numbers which were discussed in the preceding chapter, deviations are found to occur in the arrangement of the material of the chromosomes. Variations of this nature may result in unusual linkage relationships, in abnormal segregation ratios, and in phenotypic changes; and they may, like ploidy, be the basis for evolutionary differentiation.

One of the arrangement aberrations is **translocation.** Here a piece of one chromosome becomes broken off and attached to another chromosome, often of another pair. The most interesting thing about these translocations is that frequently they have been first detected genetically, then their cytological occurrence predicted from the genetic data, and finally observed under the microscope exactly as predicted.

For example, in a certain strain of Drosophila the genes from scarlet to roughoid in the third linkage group (see map, Fig. 11.2) were found by Muller to be linked to the genes in the second linkage group — an aberrant condition. The remaining genes from pink to minute $-G$ in the third linkage group remained independent of the genes in the second linkage group. The genetic evidence thus indicated that a large block of genes of the third linkage group had somehow become part of the second linkage group. Therefore, if genes are really carried in chromosomes, the cytological examination of the chromosomes should show a translocation of part of a chromosome. When the cytological examination was made (by Painter), one of the third chromosomes was found to be much shorter than usual, and correspondingly one of the second chromosomes was longer than usual

(Fig. 21.1). Thus the aberrant behavior of the genes was again found to be directly correlated with a corresponding aberration of the chromosomal arrangement.

In another case in Drosophila, Altenburg found that a number of second chromosome genes were unexpectedly sex-linked. This indicated the breaking of a piece of the second chromosome and its translocation to one of the sex chromosomes. Again cytological examination proved the prediction to be accurate. A part of one of the second chromosomes was seen to be attached to the end of an X-chromosome (Fig. 21.2).

In recent years many cases of translocations have been studied, particularly in plants. In some of them the first evidence of the translocation was from the unusual behavior of the genes. In these cases the cytological examination confirmed the genetic results. In other cases the translocation was first seen under the microscope and then confirmed by breeding tests. Translocations, then, furnish another proof of the chromosome theory of heredity, since in every case the comparison of cytological and genetic data shows that the genes are located in the chromosomes in the order which has been determined by the mapping.

The actual *spacing* of genes in the chromosomes, however, is shown by translocations to be somewhat different from that shown in the maps. Muller and Painter have found several cases where the translocated piece is proportionally smaller than would be expected judging from the number of genes involved. This and other evidence indicate that crossing over occurs more readily in some parts of the chromosome than in others, so that a unit of distance in one part of the map is not necessarily the physical equivalent of a unit in another part. The *order* of the genes as shown in the maps, however, is correct.

More frequently found than simple translocations are **reciprocal translocations,** that

Fig. 21.1 The chromosomes of a female Drosophila in which a translocation of part of one of the chromosomes of pair III to one of the chromosomes of pair II has occurred. The genetic findings gave the clue to the cytological findings. *After Painter and Muller in the Journal of Heredity*

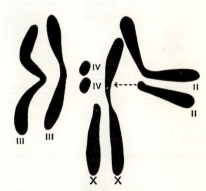

Fig. 21.2 The chromosomes of a female Drosophila in which a piece of a chromosome of pair II has been translocated to the end of one of the X-chromosomes. The genes on the translocated piece are found to be sex-linked instead of showing their usual linkage relationships. *After Muller and Painter in the American Naturalist*

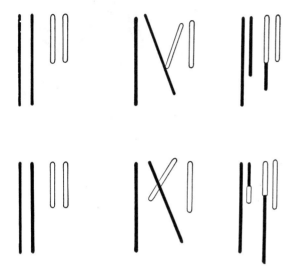

Fig. 21.3 Diagrams indicating how translocations may occur by the overlapping and breaking of chromosomes in the threadlike stage. Upper row shows breakage resulting in a simple translocation. Lower row illustrates how overlapping and breaking may result in reciprocal translocation. *Based on suggestions by various workers in translocation*

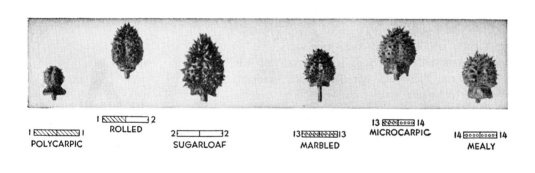

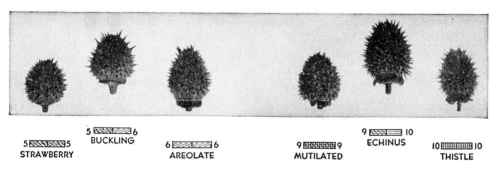

Fig. 21.4 Capsules of four of the primary $2n + 1$ forms of Jimson weed, with two secondary forms of each. The secondary forms each have one extra chromosome which has the two ends alike through reciprocal translocation. *From Blakeslee in the Journal of Heredity*

is, the exchange of parts by nonhomologous chromosomes. Crossing over is, of course, the exchange of material by two chromosomes, but it is the exchange of *homologous* parts of *homologous* chromosomes. Reciprocal translocation is the exchange of parts by two chromosomes belonging to different pairs. The results are of considerable importance in the production of new variations.

There is some doubt as to just how such reciprocal translocations come about. Some investigators believe that the chromosomes sometimes break into fragments during gametogenesis and then become attached in new combinations. Other investigators favor the hypothesis that translocations occur by overlapping or entanglement and subsequent abnormal breaking and nonhomologous exchange of parts. Figure 21.3 shows the latter view diagrammatically.

In the Jimson weed, as we have seen, the addition of an extra chromosome through nondisjunction produces a variation. Occasionally as a result of reciprocal translocation the two members of a pair of chromosomes exchange nonhomologous parts, resulting in a chromosome with two ends alike. A zygote containing such a chromosome without at least one normal mate would not be expected to form a living plant, since certain genes would be entirely lacking. As a third chromosome added to a normal pair, however, it does not kill the plant, but produces characteristic variations, depending on the set to which it belongs. Figure 21.4 shows some of these variations in the capsules of the plant. The chromosomes are marked as in Figures 20.1 and 20.2.

Reciprocal translocation (or **segmental interchange,** as it is sometimes called) explains many hitherto puzzling facts in the genetics of certain plants. It may be seen that in synapsis, if one chromosome of a pair were normal and the other were abnormal due to a reciprocal translocation, the pairing could not be complete or of the usual type, since only homologous regions undergo synapsis. Hence many of the queer synaptic configurations are explained. Rings of chromosomes, chains of chromosomes, and other peculiar formations owe their shape to the fact that homologous parts of the chromatin material are attracted to each other in synapsis, even though through reciprocal translocation they may be located in nonhomologous chromosomes. A relatively simple example of this is shown in the chromosomes of a particular race of Jimson weed in Figure 21.5. The formation of rings of chromosomes such as this is called **catenation.**

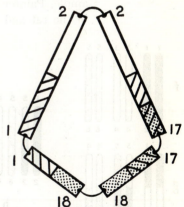

Fig. 21.5 Diagram of the catenation of chromosomes of the Jimson weed at the reduction division, due to reciprocal translocation. *From Blakeslee in the Journal of Heredity*

Translocations may be produced in the laboratory or greenhouse by subjecting plants to X-rays or other types of irradiation. The experimental production of translocations provides a method of studying the behavior of translocated chromosomes in crosses. Once this behavior has been learned (chain formation, ring formation, etc.) it is possible to identify translocations in natural populations by observing the maturation divisions of hybrids. By this means we know that reciprocal translocations do occur in natural populations and are undoubtedly responsible for a certain amount of evolutionary change. Many natural races of the Jimson weed, occupying different but sometimes overlapping geographical ranges, differ in reciprocal translocations, as shown by the fact that the hybrids exhibit varying degrees of catenation in gametogenesis. The F_1 hybrids between the standard American strain and Peruvian strain, for example, show in their maturation divisions two circles of four chromosomes each and eight synapsing pairs. A diagram of reciprocal translocation involving three pairs of chromosomes and resulting in a circle of six is shown in Figure 21.6. More detailed analyses of segmental interchange by means of the newly discovered technique involving giant chromosomes will be presented below. Suffice it to say here that translocations occurring in the wild have been reported in different races of a number of plant species and of several species of lower animals.

In addition there is indirect evidence that reciprocal translocations have occurred in the evolution of the higher animals. For example, Painter found that, while the amount of chromatin material in the rat and in the mouse was almost identical, nevertheless the

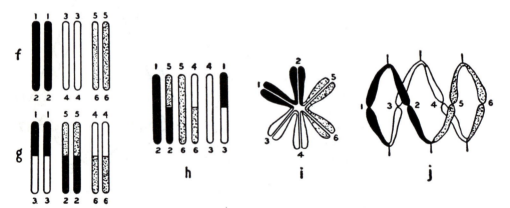

Fig. 21.6 Reciprocal translocation between three pairs of chromosomes. Normal chromosomes, f. Translocation homozygote, g. Translocation heterozygote, h. Chromosome arrangement at pairing stage, i. Catenation at the metaphase of the reduction division, j. *From Dobzhansky, Genetics and the Origin of Species, courtesy of the Columbia University Press*

distribution of the chromatin among the chromosomes was very different in the two species. It is probable that the rat and the mouse have diverged from a common ancestor through numerous translocations resulting in more and more sterility between the ensuing races and finally, as a result of mutations added to the translocations, the emergence of distinct species.

It will be realized that, in general, cytological observations and analyses of translocations are extremely difficult because of the very small size of chromosomes. In most animals and plants the chromosomes measure but a few micra in length (1 micron = 1/1000 millimeter = 1/25,000 inch). It would be most desirable to discover an organism having unusually large chromosomes of which detailed structure could be observed. This discovery was made, and strangely enough, the organism exhibiting the phenomenal chromosomes belonged to the very species about which most is known genetically, the fruit-fly, *Drosophila melanogaster*. Naturally we should expect many new facts about chromosomes and genes to be revealed in the study of these **giant chromosomes.** Before discussing these facts, however, it will be necessary to describe the giant chromosomes in detail, since they differ in many essential ways from ordinary chromosomes of the fly or, indeed, of any other organism.

In 1933 Professor Painter of the University of Texas and Drs. Heitz and Bauer of Germany independently reported the existence in the salivary gland cells of the larvae of Drosophila, and other flies, of chromosomes which are from 100 to 200 times longer than those of ordinary somatic or germinal cells and from 1,000 to 2,000 or more times larger in volume — truly giant chromosomes. Actually these investigators were not the first to see such chromosomes. The Italian cytologist Balbiani had described similar structures in the salivary glands of the midge larva *Chironomus* as early as 1881. Several other cytologists made similar observations, but the significance of their findings was apparently overlooked or forgotten until the rediscovery of the giant chromosomes. All available studies indicate that the giant chromosomes which are to be described for Drosophila are characteristic of the salivary gland cells and of certain other larval tissues of all of the Diptera or true, two-winged flies.

The larval salivary glands are a pair of transparent club-shaped organs attached by a common duct to the pharynx near the mouth of the larva, each gland comprising about 100 large cells. In preparing these glands for examination they are dissected out in saline solution and placed upon a microscope slide in a drop of acetocarmine stain. Applying a cover glass a preliminary examination of the stained cells may be made at this point, whereupon two of the many peculiarities of these cells are immediately apparent. In the first place, the cells

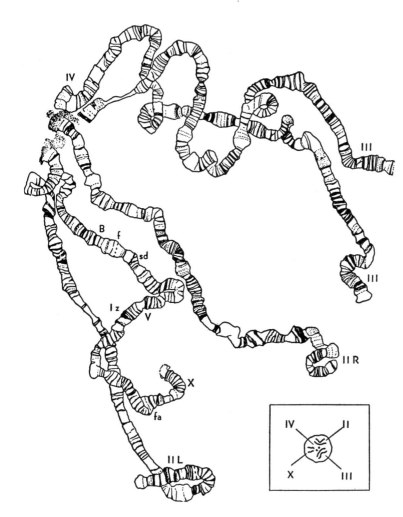

Fig. 21.7 Camera lucida drawing of the giant chromosomes in the salivary gland of Drosophila. In the small inset are the chromosomes of a normal female primary oöcyte, drawn to scale. *Adapted from Painter in Genetics*

have unusually large nuclei, and in the second place, chromosomes are visible in these nuclei even though the cells are not undergoing mitotic division but are apparently in the interphase. It will be remembered that the chromatin of ordinary interphase nuclei is in the form of a network in which no definite chromosomes can readily be discerned.

For a more detailed examination the glands are next smeared out on the slide by applying pressure to the cover glass. This disintegrates the cell membranes and nuclear membranes, thus allowing the chromosomes to float free in the flattened cytoplasmic material (Fig. 21.7). The stained chromosomes can now be examined under high magnification, as a result of which some additional peculiarities become apparent. The chromatin material consists of six ribbonlike "elements" of gigantic dimensions, all of them being attached to a dark-staining body called the **chromocenter.** All the elements are banded, being constructed of alternating discs or bands of dark-staining chromatin and light- or nonstaining protein material. The order and arrangement of the bands as well as of other morphological features are identical for any element observed in different cells or in different individuals. An unexpected feature, however, is the fact that there are only six such elements. Since *Drosophila melanogaster* has four pairs of chromosomes, we should expect to find eight chromosomes in a somatic cell such as a salivary gland cell. The apparent discrepancy is explained by two additional features which are not easily observable and which are not clearly indicated in Figure 21.7.

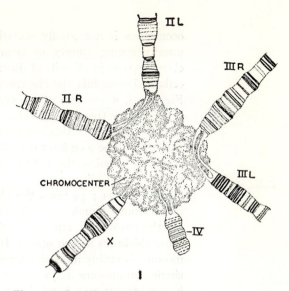

Fig. 21.8 Semidiagrammatic sketch showing the general orientation of the chromosomes about the chromocenter in the salivary gland of Drosophila. *From Painter and Stone in Genetics*

In the first place, each "element" in the salivary gland cell nucleus is actually a synapsed pair of chromosomes. Upon careful examination a fine dividing line can be detected throughout the entire length of each element, indicating a close band-to-band fusion of the two homologous chromosomes. Occasionally, too, excessive pressure in smearing the glands may cause the fused chromosomes to separate over part of their lengths, in which case the synapsis is quite obvious. Secondly, it may be demonstrated that four of the six elements represent respectively the two arms, right and left, of the two long V-shaped IInd and IIIrd chromosomes, these being connected through the chromocenter. Thus there are eight chromosomes, but these are synapsed into four pairs, the rod-shaped X- and IVth chromosome pairs being attached to the chromocenter at their ends, the V-shaped IInd and IIIrd pairs having their arms connected through the chromocenter (Fig. 21.8).

These two features are quite extraordinary and deserve some further comment. Synapsis of homologous chromosomes, it must be recalled, occurs normally in most species only in germinal cells, prior to the reduction division of the primary gametocytes, and not in mitotically dividing somatic cells. The occurrence of **somatic synapsis** in the salivary gland cells of dipterous larvae is thus an exceptional phenomenon as compared with other organisms. And yet its

occurrence is not wholly remarkable, for there seems to be an unusually strong affinity or synaptic tendency between homologous
chromosomes in all cells of dipterous flies. Thus in ordinary somatic
cells of Drosophila the chromosome mates lie close side by side (cf.
Fig. 21.2), whereas in other organisms they tend to repel each other
or to scatter themselves within the cell body (cf. Fig. 20.5). In the
salivary gland cells this synaptic urge is evidently carried to completion. As will be seen later it is this feature coupled with their gigantic
size which makes the salivary chromosomes of enormous value in
cytogenetic studies.

Figure 21.7 pictures the chromosomes in a salivary gland cell
taken from a female larva. The two X-chromosomes are synapsed as
are the autosomes, and the X element is therefore of essentially the
same thickness as the others. In male larvae, however, the X-chromosome is visibly more slender than the rest, since it represents but a
single chromosome and not a fused pair. The Y-chromosome, in fact,
is not present as a banded chromosome, but instead it makes up a
part of the chromocenter. Careful studies have shown that the chromocenter is constructed from the so-called inert regions of all four
pairs of chromosomes. It had previously been shown in genetic studies
that the Y-chromosome is quite inert, carrying comparatively few
genes, but that there are also inert regions of chromatin at the spindle
fiber ends of the X- and IVth chromosomes and between the right
and left arms of both the IInd and IIIrd V-shaped chromosomes,
which have their spindle fiber attachments in their middles. This
chromatin material making up the chromocenter is also banded, but
the chromomeres are much less distinct. The inert portions of the
various chromosomes are probably of somewhat different chemical
nature from the banded gene-bearing arms of the chromosomes, but
are essentially similar to each other, so that they all synapse together
in salivary gland cells forming a chromocenter.

Summarizing this description we may say that in the salivary
gland cells of larval flies the chromosomes are of enormous size, composed of an orderly sequence of bandlike chromomeres, synapsed
band-for-band in pairs, and in some species, are attached to a chromocenter constructed from their inert regions. Realizing the importance
of the new type of material for cytogenetic study, the first task which
confronted the Drosophila cytologist was that of preparing very
accurate drawings or "maps" of the four salivary chromosomes. A
short section of such a "map" is shown in Figure 21.9.

Much interest attaches to the question as to how the giant chromosomes arise, and although present information is somewhat incomplete and variable, the following description probably fits their
development in most species of flies. The entire number of cells in

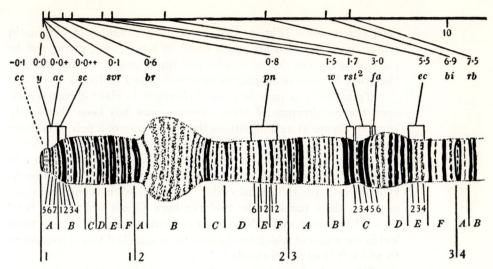

Fig. 21.9 Semidiagrammatic drawing of the left end of the X-chromosome in the salivary gland of Drosophila. The loci of some of the genes are shown in the brackets, and their positions on the crossover map are shown at the top of the figure. *From Emmens in the Journal of Genetics, courtesy of the Cambridge University Press*

the salivary gland is formed early in the embryonic development of the larva, and subsequently the cells enlarge without undergoing any divisions. Meanwhile, the chromosomes remain apparently in an attenuated prophase, each chromosome reduplicating itself several times, without separating, so that eventually many (in Drosophila probably 16, in other flies 32, 64, or even 300–500) strands come to comprise each chromosome of the synapsed pair. However, in addition to the fact that each chromosome is actually a bundle of chromonemata, a real growth process must also accompany the reduplication process, since the increase in chromosome volume is not 16-fold but 1,000–2,000-fold in Drosophila.

This hypothesis as to the origin and detailed structure of the salivary chromosomes is supported by several studies on living and stained glands of larvae of various ages and by the observation of longitudinal striations which extend between the bands throughout the entire length of

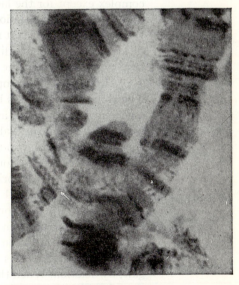

Fig. 21.10 Photograph of part of a giant chromosome in *Sciara coprophila*. The striations are considered by Metz to be artifacts produced by partial disorganization of the chromosome through stretching and local distortion. *From Metz in the Journal of Heredity*

each chromosome (Fig. 21.10). These bear granules of chromatin (chromomeres) which are quite small in some cases, giving rise to the appearance of dotted bands, and quite large in other cases so that they become confluent, forming solid discs or bands.

Translocations may be readily observed in giant chromosomes, once the architecture of these chromosomes has been thoroughly learned. Figure 21.12B illustrates the appearance of a pair of salivary chromosomes in one of which a translocation is present. The lower end of the pair of chromosomes shows the two members closely synapsed band for band, but the upper part illustrates the failure to synapse because the translocation has resulted in nonhomologous genes on these parts of the two members. Genes which have been shown by genetic methods to be translocated must then have their loci in the segment which can be seen to be attached to a chromosome to which it does not normally belong.

Often a broken piece of a chromosome does not become translocated to another chromosome, but remains free. If it does not contain the spindle fiber attachment-point, it is subsequently lost. In such a case we may have an individual which has a normal chromosomal complex except for the lack of a piece of a chromosome. Such a condition is known as **deletion.** If the missing piece be not too extensive, the individuals lacking it may live, especially in the heterozygous condition. Rarely can an individual exist with a similar part missing from both chromosomes of the pair.

An interesting example of a deletion in which the parallel cytological and genetic facts have been investigated is that of the loss of a gene in mice. In these animals the gene for normal gait, V, is dominant to the gene for waltzing gait, v. Waltzing mice are unable to run in a straight line and usually run about in small circles. Crosses between homozygous normal mice, VV, and homozygous waltzers, vv, result in normal offspring, Vv. In one such cross, however, a waltzing female was produced.

Gates, in whose laboratory this occurred, concluded that the gene for normal gait had been lost from this individual, either as the loss of the entire chromosome carrying this gene, by nondisjunction, or as the loss of a part of this chromosome including the gene for normal gait, by deletion. When the chromosomes were examined it was found that, in this mouse and others like it which it produced by suitable breeding, one member of one pair of autosomes was found to be only a quarter as large as its mate (Fig. 21.11). In normal mice the members of this pair of chromosomes were found to be equal in size.

This was the first case in which a deletion of part of a chromosome was shown actually to remove a gene from the organism. Since then many such cases have been studied in other organisms, and the

Fig. 21.11 Left, the twenty pairs of chromosomes of a normal mouse. The Y-chromosome is marked Y, and the members of the smallest pair of chromosomes are each marked s. Right, the chromosomes of a mouse which through fragmentation and deletion has lost part of a chromosome bearing the gene *V*. The remaining part of the chromosome is marked q; the small chromosomes and the Y-chromosome are marked as before. *After Painter in Genetics*

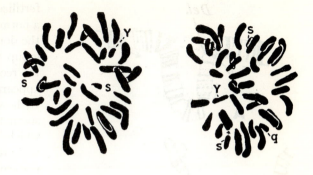

evidence from deletions, like the evidence from other chromosomal aberrations, points to the validity of the theory that genes are actually located in the chromosomes.

Deletions, like translocations, are readily detectable in giant chromosomes, and they provide extraordinary opportunities for the construction of actual cytological maps showing the locations of the many genes which are known in the various species of Drosophila. Genetic maps of these chromosomes (cf. Fig. 11.2) have, of course, been available for many years. These are based solely upon crossover percentages found in breeding experiments; their construction requires the assumptions of linear arrangement of the genes within the chromosome and of equal probability for breakage at any point along the length of the chromosome. By comparing the new salivary chromosome maps, based upon actual cytological observations, with the linkage maps, based solely upon breeding results, an excellent opportunity is afforded for testing these assumptions and thus for establishing in a most convincing fashion the entire chromosome theory of inheritance.

The location of gene loci on the salivary chromosome maps is made possible by examination of larvae which are heterozygous for certain chromosomal aberrations, that is, of larvae having one normal and one abnormal chromosome of a pair. Let us first consider the case of minute deletions, which are often produced by radiation and which have proved most helpful for the location of genes.

Let us suppose that a male fly homozygous for a long series of dominant third chromosome genes is treated with X-rays or some other form of radiation, and that as a result of this treatment a small segment of the IIIrd chromosome is removed and eliminated in one of the sperm cells. If this fly is mated to a female homozygous for corresponding recessive genes of the IIIrd chromosome, then eggs produced by this female will carry a IIIrd chromosome with a complete set of recessive IIIrd chromosome "markers." If the egg is

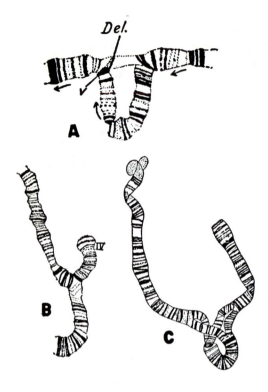

Del.

A

B

C

Fig. 21.12 Chromosomal aberrations in giant chromosomes. A, a deletion. B, a translocation. C, an inversion. *A, from Mackensen in the Journal of Heredity; B, from Painter in Genetics; C, from Tan in Genetics*

fertilized by a sperm which has received a normal IIIrd chromosome, then all of the dominant genes of the IIIrd linkage group will be present, so that none of the recessive characters can make their appearance in the resulting offspring. If, however, the egg is fertilized by a sperm that contains a IIIrd chromosome which has a deleted portion, then certain recessive genes present in the maternal chromosome III will have no alleles in the paternal IIIrd chromosome, and will thus assume "pseudo-dominance" and manifest their recessive phenotypes in the resulting offspring. Suppose that the genes A, B, and C are involved in this deletion, as evidenced by the unexpected appearance of the recessive characters of a, b, and c. Such a fly can now be mated to any normal fly and half of the resulting offspring will be expected to receive the deleted chromosome. In the salivary gland cells of these larvae the normal IIIrd chromosome will synapse band-for-band with its abnormal mate except for a buckle in the former, indicating a deleted segment in the latter (Fig. 21.12A). The buckled portion can be identified in the normal giant chromosome map, and the genes a, b, and c may therefore be placed on the map in this region.

Suppose that another fly derived from an irradiated parent shows unexpectedly the recessive traits of c, d, e, and f and the larvae possessing one such deleted third chromosome show a buckle involving a closely adjacent portion of the chromosome. This buckle may overlap the region of the first buckle by only a single band (Fig. 21.13). In this case, then, the gene c is localized to that particular band or to the achromatic material adjacent to either side of the band. The study of such **overlapping deletions** may thus lead to very accurate determination of gene loci in the actual chromosome maps.

Another chromosomal aberration is inversion, in which part of a chromosome is reversed with respect to the rest of the chromosome. Here the peculiarity is generally first noted by the genetic result, that

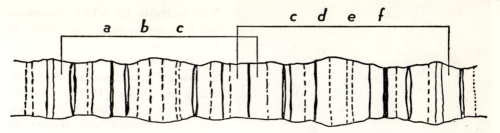

Fig. 21.13 Diagram illustrating the method of locating genes by means of over-lapping deletions. For explanation, see text.

is, the reversing of part of the normal map order within a linkage group. In ordinary chromosomes it is usually not possible to detect an inversion cytologically, but in one case in corn a genetic inversion was paralleled by the type of synaptic figure which would be expected after part of a chromosome was reversed (Figures 21.14 and 21.15).

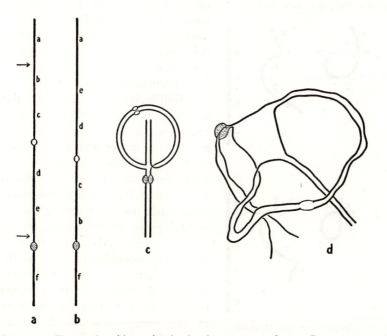

Fig. 21.14 The results of inversion in the chromosomes of corn, *Zea. a,* a normal chromosome with arrows indicating the points where inversion is to occur, resulting as in *b. c,* diagram of how a normal and an "inverted" chromosome might synapse so that homologous parts were in contact. *d,* drawing of an actual synapsis of two such chromosomes. This drawing was made from the preparation shown in Fig. 21.15. *From McClintock in Univ. of Mo. Exp. Sta. Res. Bull. 163*

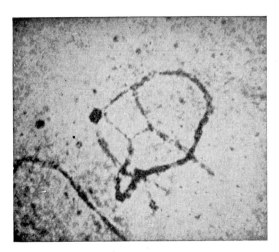

Fig. 21.15 Photomicrograph of the synapsis of a normal and an "inverted" chromosome of corn, *Zea*. Compare with Figure 21.14. *From McClintock in Univ. of Mo. Exp. Sta. Res. Bull. 163*

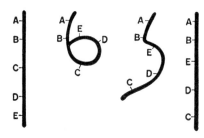

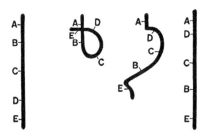

Fig. 21.16 Diagram of the methods by which inversions are thought to occur The upper row results in the inversion of one end of the chromosome; the lower row results in the inversion of central region, leaving ends as before. *Adapted from Serebrovsky*

The methods by which inversions are thought to occur are shown in Figure 21.16.

The giant chromosomes provide a remarkable way for quickly recognizing inversions. If one chromosome of a pair contains a section which is inverted with respect to the other, the two can synapse band-for-band only by forming a loop in which one member of the pair has an open loop and the other a twisted or closed loop. Figure 21.12C will make this clear. The genes which have genetically proved to be inverted must therefore have their loci in the looped portion. Overlapping inversions (and overlapping translocations as well) may thus be used in addition to overlapping deletions in limiting the loci of particular genes to short lengths of the chromosome.

Employing the methods just described as well as some other techniques, it has been possible to locate many genes rather accurately in each of the four chromosomes of *Drosophila melanogaster*. Figure 21.9 shows a portion of the salivary X-chromosome with the approximate loci of several genes as determined by cytological study. Above the drawing is the corresponding section of the linkage map for the X-chromosome as determined from crossover percentages. Two things are apparent in the comparison of these two maps: the order of arrangement of the genes is the same in both, but the relative distances between successive genes varies somewhat in the two maps. Thus the assumption of a linear arrangement of the genes in the chromosome is substantially upheld, whereas the assumption that breaks occur with equal probability at all points throughout the chromosome is apparently not quite true. It is evident therefore that a chromosome does have a greater tendency to breakage at some points than at others. Prior to the discovery of giant chromosomes, however, it was necessary in constructing linkage maps to adopt the foregoing assumption, not because it was *a priori* most probable but rather because it was the only logical one to adopt in the absence of detailed knowledge about the chromosome and its physical properties.

A map of the X-chromosome compiled by Bridges shows 1024 bands in the chromosome. Whether the genes are represented by the bands or fractions of them or by the achromatic regions between the bands, or indeed, whether the genes are actually discrete portions of the chromosomes or merely points of chemical linkage in complex protein molecules is a matter not yet determined.

Another study which has been greatly facilitated through the use of the salivary gland chromosomes is the study of comparative chromosomology, the comparison of chromosomes in different species or varieties. With ordinary chromosomes one may compare the number, sizes, and shapes of chromosomes in species or varieties which are judged from their external similarities to be closely related. Similarities, then, in these chromosomal features strengthen the indication of a common phylogenetic origin, and any differences which are found may suggest the possible mode of evolutionary divergence between the two forms. Further, if large numbers of similar mutations are known in both species, and if the linkage groupings show similarities, this may also suggest the identity of certain sections of the chromosomes in the two species. The construction of linkage maps and their comparison, however, requires a great deal of time and labor. Such comparisons can be made with much greater facility and accuracy with giant chromosomes, provided that hybrid larvae can be obtained. The salivary gland cells of hybrid larvae will contain in each pair one chromosome derived from each of the two parent species. If certain sections are homologous these will synapse together, showing their identity. In this manner the entire chromosomal architecture of one species may readily be compared with that of a second species with which it is cross-fertile.

Drosophila pseudoobscura and *D. miranda* are two species which are apparently very closely related, since they are so strikingly similar in all of their somatological characters that it is very difficult to tell them apart. Nevertheless, they deserve to be called separate species, since although they hybridize, their hybrids are sterile. Because of

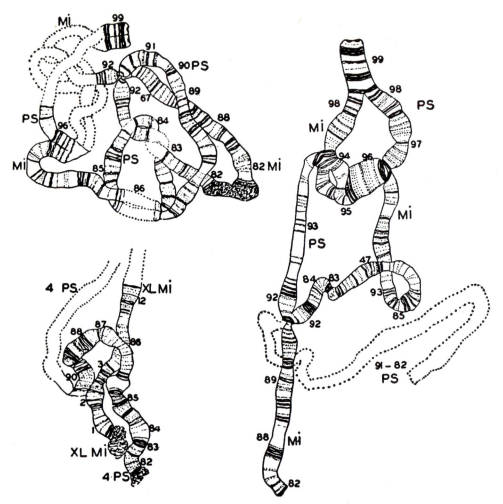

Fig. 21.17 Chromosome pairing in the salivary gland cells of the hybrid *Drosophila pseudoobscura* × *D. miranda*. Upper left, the fourth chromosomes; lower left, the fourth chromosome of *D. pseudoobscura* partly paired with the left arm of the X-chromosome of *D. miranda*; right, the fourth chromosomes. *From Dobzhansky, Genetics and the Origin of Species, courtesy of the Columbia University Press*

their similarities we would be led to assume that both species must possess essentially the same quantity and quality of germ plasm, or in other words, very similar gene assortments. This supposition is further supported by the fact that, in ordinary somatic cells, both species possess five pairs of chromosomes which are to all appearances identical. Yet if they were identical it is difficult to understand why the species hybrids should be sterile. By a study of the salivary gland chromosomes of the hybrids, Dobzhansky was able to adduce many interesting facts relevant to these questions.

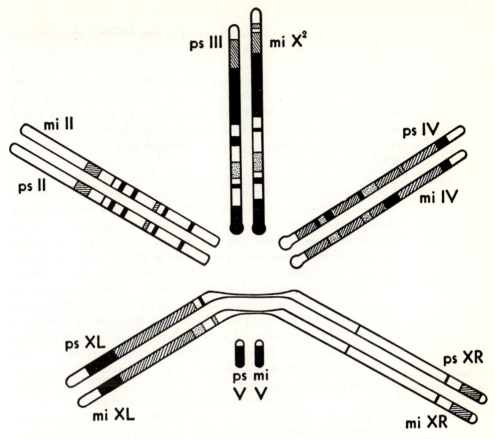

Fig. 21.18 A comparison of the gene arrangements in *Drosophila pseudoobscura* and *D. miranda*. Sections having the same gene arrangements in the two species are white; inverted sections, crosshatched; translocations, stippled; sections of which the homologues are not detectable in the other species, black. *From Dobzhansky, Genetics and the Origin of Species, courtesy of the Columbia University Press*

In the salivary gland cells of the hybrid larvae the chromosomes either fail to synapse or else do so only after undergoing extremely complex contortions, as shown in Figure 21.17. By carefully piecing together the chromosome homologies indicated by the abnormal pairing configurations, Dobzhansky was able to construct the chromosome models shown in Figure 21.18. The right arms of the V-shaped X-chromosomes in the two species are almost exactly alike, differing only in an inversion near the end and in two minute segments which are probably located in some other chromosomes in the one species, but as yet unidentified. The other chromosomes differ from each other quite extensively. Long inversions are quite common; genes which are adjacent in one species may thus be far apart in the corresponding chromosome of the other species. Other genes which are linked in the one species are found in two different chromosomes in the other, indicating that translocations have also been involved in rearranging the chromosomal structures. Still other segments have presumably become so jumbled through chromosomal aberrations that even abnormal synapsis is impossible, so that homologies cannot be determined. Thus the giant chromosomes of the hybrids reveal that, as anticipated, both species possess quite the same chromosome constituents, but these have been organized into radically different whole chromosomes.

In the primary gametocytes, pairing of the chromosomes is evidently a necessary mechanism for their accurate segregation into the secondary gametocytes. Normal pairing presumably could not take place in the primary gametocytes of any *pseudoobscura–miranda* hybrid, and it is probable that the spindle fibers are unable to disentangle the contorted conditions shown in Figure 21.17, so that no complete and therefore no functional gametes can then be produced. The extensive chromosomal reorganization may thus be the cause of the evolutionary separation of the two species. It is difficult to prove conclusively that any one plausible factor is the cause of sterility in a hybrid, but the finding of structural chromosomal difficulties in many such sterile hybrids is strangely suggestive. Provided that such proof can be found, it is then easy to explain evolution as a consequence of chromosomal aberrations. If a population of organisms becomes divided into groups, if different types of chromosomal rearrangements accumulate in the various groups, and if they possess selective value, then the groups will eventually come to differ so extremely in their chromosomal architectures that hybrids between them will no longer be capable of normal gametogenesis, and thus new species may come into existence.

Even more surprising is the possibility, realized by Dobzhansky, of predicting the occurrence in the wild of varieties of Drosophila which had never before been observed and of subsequently finding them and demonstrating the exact chromosomal configurations which were predicted. When two varieties are crossed in which the giant chromosomes of the hybrid larvae synapse to form an overlapping figure-8 loop, as shown in Figure 21.19, this indicates that the one variety with the chromosome order $AEHGFBCDI$ must have arisen from $ABCDEFGHI$ (or vice versa) by the occurrence first of the inversion $AEDCBFGHI$, followed by the overlapping inversion of the region $DCBFGH$. Such intermediate types of third chromosomes were unknown among the various subspecies of *D. pseudoobscura* but were later found in the wild after they had been predicted from the overlapping inversions found in the salivary chromosomes of hybrids obtained by crossing certain available varieties.

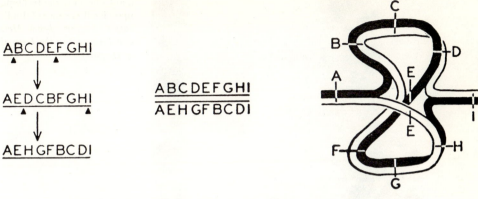

ABCDEFGHI

↓

AEDCBFGHI

↓

AEHGFBCDI

ABCDEFGHI
AEHGFBCDI

Fig. 21.19 Diagram of chromosome pairing in the salivary gland of an individual heterozygous for overlapping inversions. *From Dobzhansky, Genetics and the Origin of Species, courtesy of the Columbia University Press*

Another interesting contribution to our understanding of evolution is the discovery, originally made by Bridges, of the occurrence of numerous duplicated segments in the giant chromosomes. In the cytological maps there are several indications of identical series of bands, sometimes on the same chromosome, sometimes on non-homologous chromosomes. That they are actually identical is more convincingly demonstrated by the fact that the chromosome recoils upon itself or upon another chromosome so that the similar regions synapse band-for-band (Fig. 21.20). **Duplications** of this sort probably arise as a result of unequal crossing over of the synapsed chromosomes of primary gametocytes in such a way that one chromosome suffers a deletion and the other receives a duplication of a short segment. This method furnishes an obvious means of accumulating additional chromosomal material in an organism. Having once become homozygous, the duplicated portion can be transferred to other positions within the same chromosome or to a different chromosome, as a result of inversion or translocation. Recent work of Painter and others has revealed the fact that such duplications are by no means uncommon and may therefore be of great significance in the evolutionary origin of species.

One of the best known duplications in Drosophila is that resulting in the "bar-eye" condition. Bar-eyed flies have narrow slitlike eyes in place of the normal oval eyes, and the abnormality is inherited as though due to a sex-linked gene without dominance, heterozygous females having eyes of intermediate width. Sturtevant and Morgan demonstrated that the bar "gene" really is a short duplication. Bridges has confirmed this by cytological examination of the giant

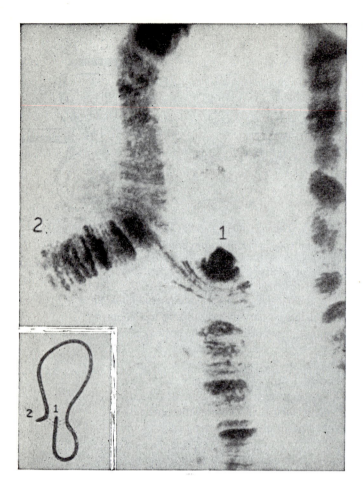

Fig. 21.20 Photograph of giant chromosome recoiling upon itself because of duplicated sections. *From Metz and Lawrence in the Journal of Heredity*

chromosomes, showing that the duplicated segment is in the region of the X-chromosome known as 16A (Fig. 21.21).

Homozygous bar-eyed females possess this segment twice in each X-chromosome, whereas normal females have it singly in each. By unequal crossing over in bar-eyed females it is possible to obtain the segment in triplicate, a condition which results in an even more extreme reduction in eye size, known as ultra-bar.

The bar-eye character also furnishes an example of another recently discovered principle of genetics, the **position effect.** This principle states that the effect of a gene depends not only upon its presence but also upon its position with respect to its neighboring genes. If, for example, we designate the duplication responsible for bar-eye as B, the genotypes of various individuals may be written as follows: BY, normal male; BBY, bar-eyed male; BBBY, ultra-bar male; BB, normal female; BB B, heterozygous bar-eyed female; BB BB, homo-

Fig. 21.21 Diagrams showing the duplications involved in bar-eye and ultra-bar-eye. For explanation, see text. *From Bridges in Science*

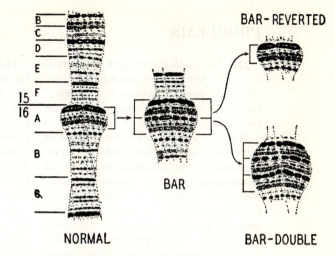

BAR-REVERTED

NORMAL

BAR

BAR-DOUBLE

zygous bar-eyed female; *BBB B* or *BBB BB*, heterozygous ultra-bar female, and *BBB BBB*, homozygous ultra-bar female.

In general, eye size decreases with the number of duplicated segments. The position of these segments on the chromosomes, however, is extremely important in producing the effect. Thus a male having two bar-eye segments on one chromosome (*BB*Y) has much smaller eyes than a female having one bar-eye segment on each of two chromosomes (*BB*). The eyes of an ultra-bar male (*BBB*Y) are much more reduced than those of a heterozygous bar-eyed female (*BB B*). Within the same sex the eyes of heterozygous ultra-bar females (*BBB B*) are smaller than those of homozygous bar-eyed females (*BB BB*), although the number of segments is the same.

Thus the effects of genes depend not only upon their number and kind but also upon their position. Other instances of position effects are coming to light, all indicating that the effect of a gene depends, to some extent, at least, upon the genes which it has for neighbors. An extension of this principle, involving the problem of "pseudo-alleles," will be discussed in Chapter 26.

The facts and principles presented in this and the preceding chapter lead to the formulation of one of the most important parallels between the behavior of genes and the behavior of chromosomes. It is the last of the parallels which we shall develop, and with it we may complete our list. It may be stated as follows: Genes occasionally behave in peculiar unexpected ways (abnormal ratios, unusual linkage relationships, genetic deficiencies, etc.). *In these cases the chromosomes are also found to be aberrant (ploidy, translocation, inversion, deletion, etc.).*

In the next chapter we shall summarize the parallels we have drawn between genetic and cytological observations.

PROBLEMS

21.1 Designating each pair of enlarged synapsed chromosomes in a salivary gland cell of a Drosophila larva as an "element," trace the history of an element back to the two parents of the larva.

21.2 In the microscopic examination of giant chromosomes, how would you interpret each of the following situations? A buckle in one of the two synapsed chromosomes of an element; a recoiling of an element upon itself in synapsis; a synapsis between two elements; a loop in an element.

21.3 Does the fact that the relative distances between successive genes are different in the genetic maps and the salivary maps invalidate the hypothesis that chromosomes carry the genes? How may this difference be reconciled with the chromosome hypothesis?

21.4 In what ways has the discovery and analysis of giant chromosomes strengthened the hypothesis that chromosomes carry genes?

21.5 Which, if any, of the following conceptions may prove helpful in explaining the position effects? The production of enzymes by genes; the chemical union of adjacent genes; the mere physical propinquity of genes. Can you suggest other helpful conceptions?

21.6 If the cytological examination of the maturation process in a plant reveals that the chromosomes undergo synapsis in the form of rings of chromosomes, what phenomenon would you suspect to have taken place in the plant?

21.7 Which would be expected to produce the more specific effect on the characters of an organism, a gene mutation or a chromosomal aberration? Why?

21.8 Of what advantage to the plant breeder is the fact that orange, apple, and many other fruit trees may be propagated asexually?

21.9 Do you think it possible that recessive lethal genes are really small deletions? Explain.

21.10 Would you call crossing over a chromosomal aberration? Give reasons for your answer.

21.11 If some of the sex-linked genes in a strain of Drosophila should suddenly give ratios and linkage relationships which were not sex-linked, what might you infer had occurred?

21.12 What further evidence would you need to prove your inference?

REFERENCES

BRIDGES, C. B., *Jour. Heredity* **26**:60 (1935); *Science* **83**:210 (1936).

DOBZHANSKY, T., *Genetics and the Origin of Species*. Columbia Univ. Press (1951).

EIGSTI, O. J., and DUSTIN, P., *Colchicine in Agriculture, Medicine, Biology and Chemistry*. Ames, Iowa, The Iowa State College Press (1955).

EMMENS, C. W., *Jour. Genetics* **39**:191 (1937).

GATES, W. H., *Genetics* **12**:295 (1927).

HEITZ, E., and BAUER, H., *Zeitschr. f. Zellforsch. u. mikr. Anat.* **17**:62 (1933).

MACKENSEN, O., *Jour. Heredity* **26**:163 (1935).

McCLINTOCK, B., *Univ. of Mo. Agr. Exp. Sta. Res. Bull.* **163** (1931).

METZ, C. W., *Jour. Heredity* **26**:491 (1935).

METZ, C. W., and LAWRENCE, E. G., *Jour. Heredity* **29**:179 (1938).

MULLER, H. J., and PAINTER, T. S., *Amer. Naturalist* **63**:193 (1929).

PAINTER, T. S., *Genetics* **12**:379 (1927); *Science* **78**:585 (1933); *Genetics* **19**:175 (1934); *idem* **20**:301 (1935).

PAINTER, T. S., and MULLER, H. J., *Jour. Heredity* **20**:287 (1929).

PAINTER, T. S., and STONE, W., *Genetics* **20**:327 (1935).

SAX, K., *Genetics* **7**:513 (1922).

SEREBROVSKY, A. S., *Amer. Naturalist* **63**:374 (1929).

STEBBINS, G. L., *Variation and Evolution in Plants*. New York, Columbia Univ. Press (1950).

STURTEVANT, A. H., and MORGAN, T. H., *Science* **57**:746 (1923).

TAN, C. C., *Genetics* **20**:392 (1935).

CHAPTER TWENTY-TWO

Proof that Mendelian genes are carried in the chromosomes

In the preceding chapters we have from time to time found parallels in the behavior of genes as seen in the results of breeding and the behavior of chromosomes as seen under the microscope. It may be well at this point in our study to review and summarize these parallels and to place them in their proper perspective in the general proof of the hypothesis that the genes are actually carried in the chromosomes.

If we reflect upon the general facts of reproduction, we find it possible to state a series of principles and inferences, in which the parallels which we have been discussing find their place. Let us list them in logical order.

I. **Genes are carried in the sperms or the eggs or both, since only these bridge the gap between generations.**

Although it is true that in some species the embryo develops within the body of the mother, so that it might be conceived that genes could be received from the mother in some other manner than through the egg, yet it is equally true that in other species the sperms and eggs are shed from the parents, subsequently uniting and developing independently of both parents. Moreover, the principles of heredity appear to be the same for all species.

II. **In general, within a species, the sperm and the egg contribute equally to the inheritance of genes.**

The evidence for this statement lies in the results of reciprocal crosses, where the F_1 is usually identical, whichever way the cross is made. Both the sperm and the egg, therefore, carry genes. There are certain exceptions to this rule, however. We have already discovered that the sex chromosome of the sperm may be different from that of the egg. Moreover, either a sperm or an egg may carry a chromosomal aberration making it different from the other. Both of these exceptions serve only to strengthen the hypothesis that Mendelian genes are carried in the chromosomes, however, since genetic and cytological parallels exist for them, as will be pointed out in principle V, below.

One more exception must be mentioned. In recent years evidence has been accumulating that the results of reciprocal crosses within a species are not always identical and that there is for some characters a maternal, hence cytoplasmic, transmission. This exception will be considered in detail in Chapter 25. The fact remains, however, that both the sperm and the egg carry Mendelian genes.

III. Although the egg has a relatively large amount of cytoplasm in addition to a nucleus, the sperm is practically all nucleus.

Such little cytoplasm as the sperm contains is left out of the egg when the sperm enters, and only the nuclei unite in the actual fertilization. It would appear, then, that the nucleus is the essential part of the gamete in regard to the transmission of the genes.

IV. Of the nuclear constituents, only the chromatin material appears to be accurately divided at mitosis and segregated during maturation.

Moreover, the chromatin material is formed into chromosomes with a constant and characteristic number and appearance for each species. The other constituents of the cell do not appear to undergo the same quantitatively accurate division and segregation.

V. A striking series of parallels occurs between the behavior of genes as seen in the results of breeding and the behavior of chromosomes as seen under the microscope.

The parallels are as follows:

1. Genes normally occur in pairs in the cells of the individual. *So do chromosomes.*

2. The two genes of each pair segregate in the formation of the germ cells. *The two chromosomes of each pair also segregate in the formation of germ cells.*

3. Certain genes assort at random. *Likewise certain parts of the chromatin material (that is, whole chromosomes) assort at random.*

4. Certain genes behave as though only one member of the pair were present in one sex (sex-linked genes). *Similarly only one member (or at least only one normal member) of one pair of chromosomes is present in the corresponding sex.*

5. Certain genes do not assort at random but occur in paired groups (linkage groups) which tend to be transmitted as units. *The chromatin material is also gathered into paired groups (chromosomes) which tend to be transmitted as units.*

6. The members of a linkage group do not stay completely together as a rule, but during maturation exchange with a definite frequency homologous members of the paired groups (genetic crossing over). *The pairs of chromosomes also exchange homologous parts of their lengths during the maturation of the germ cells (cytological crossing over).*

7. In certain cases genetic crossing over is more frequent in one sex than in the other. *In these cases chiasmata formation is proportionately more frequent in the sex which exhibits more crossing over.*

8. At the time of genetic crossing over, the genes are arranged in a specific linear order. *At the time of cytological crossing over, the chromatin material is in an attenuated linear arrangement.*

9. The number of linkage groups is as a rule definite and constant for any species. *In those species thus far studied the number of linkage groups is equal to, or at least never exceeds, the number of pairs of chromosomes.*

10. Genes occasionally behave in peculiar unexpected ways (abnormal ratios, unusual linkage relationships, genetic deficiency, etc.). *In these cases the chromosomes are also found to be aberrant (nondisjunction, translocation, deletion, catenation, ploidy, etc.).*

It would appear to be an inescapable inference from the above facts and principles that Mendelian genes are carried in the chromosomes. In Chapter 24 we shall consider the problems of the physical and chemical structure of genes, the nature of their mutations, and the means by which genes bring about the production of characters.

PROBLEM

22.1 Below are listed some facts about chromosomes and their behavior. Pick out the statements which are of direct use in proving the hypothesis that chromosomes carry the genes. Discuss the reasons why the remaining statements are not of direct aid in proving this hypothesis.

(*a*) Chromosomes are clearly visible only when stained.

(*b*) The chromosomes in any somatic cell may be of various lengths.

(*c*) The chromosomes in any somatic cell occur in pairs, with certain exceptions in the case of sex chromosomes and chromosomal aberrations.

(*d*) The members of a pair of chromosomes start to synapse at the end nearest the centrosome.

(*e*) The motive power for the movement of a chromosome from the equatorial plate to the pole of the spindle is apparently supplied by the spindle fiber.

(*f*) Each chromosome has only one spindle fiber attachment-point.

(*g*) At the time of synapsis the material of each chromosome is in an attenuated linear arrangement.

(*h*) The members of a pair of homologous chromosomes normally exchange equivalent parts during the maturation process.

(*i*) Chromosomes arrange themselves in a flat circle across the interior of the cell during the metaphase of mitosis.

(*j*) Each chromosome is imbedded during part of its life history in a translucent matrix.

(*k*) The two members of a pair of chromosomes segregate into separate cells during the maturation process.

(*l*) At certain times chromosomes may shorten and thicken by means of spiralling tightly upon themselves within the matrix.

CHAPTER TWENTY-THREE

The determination of sex

Sex is one of the fundamental qualities which we recognize in living things, particularly in the higher forms of life. Differentiation of races into two distinct sexes is universally found in all higher animals as well as in many plants and lower animals. It is striking to observe that the offspring of the same parents can show such great differences from one another as are exhibited by the two sexes. In the case of human beings, for example, these differences extend to practically every part of the body. The muscles, skin, skeleton, and blood are not usually thought of as showing secondary sexual characteristics, but the differences in these parts of the body are so distinctive that it is comparatively easy to distinguish between the sexes by examination of these individual parts. In addition to these structural differences there also exist a great many physiological differences, such as rate of metabolism, blood pressure, heart beat, and rate of respiration.

Two questions are involved in the problem of sex differences. First, why does one individual develop into a male, producing sperms, another individual into a female, producing ova? Second, why are different characteristics associated with the two sexes?

In regard to the first problem, that of primary sex determination, there have in the past been two prevailing theories. One theory, built around the discovery of sex chromosomes, stated that sex was unalterably determined by some internal chromosomal mechanism. The other theory, built around the demonstrated possibility of "sex reversal," stated that sex was determined by environmental factors such as food, light, metabolic rate, and others. Today we know that neither of these alone is adequate to answer the question of sex determination. As is so often the case in science, a merging of the valid essentials of two or more hypotheses has furnished a nearer approach to the truth.

As early as 1902 McClung suggested that the X-chromosome might be the determiner of sex. It was known at that time that the somatic cells of certain insects differ in the two sexes in regard to their chromosome make-up. The cells of females contain chromosomes in pairs, while in the cells of males one chromosome has no mate. This XO type of chromosome distribution we have already studied in Chapter 8. We have likewise seen that in some species the X-chromosome in the male may have a mate, different in appearance, known as the Y-chromosome. This arrangement is known as the XY type. Similarly we have investigated the ZW and ZO types which occur in birds, moths, and some fishes.

In the above types of chromosomal distribution we normally find a close association between sex and a particular chromosomal complex. Thus in Drosophila the males have XY, the females XX. As a result of maturation two kinds of sperms are formed in equal numbers with respect to these chromosomes, one kind having X and the other Y. Only one kind of egg is formed, containing X. If an egg is fertilized by an X-bearing sperm, a female (XX) results; if by a Y-bearing sperm, a male (XY).

So regularly does this type of sex determination occur that the belief grew that the sex chromosomes were the only requisite for the production of maleness and femaleness. (By a *male* is meant an individual which produces male gametes; by a *female* is meant an individual which produces female gametes. All other differences between the sexes are secondary in nature.)

One might be tempted to guess that the presence of the Y in the male is what determines its sex. You will recall, however, that in an animal such as Drosophila (XY type of sex determination), individuals occur which lack the Y. These are phenotypically males, and differ from normal XY males only in being sterile (see Chapter 8). You will also remember that a female may have a Y-chromosome. Individuals having two X-chromosomes are normal females and fully fertile whether or not they have a Y-chromosome. These observations would appear to exclude the possibility that the Y-chromosome plays any role in sex determination, although its presence is necessary for fertility in the male.

The question of sex determination by chromosomes, at least in the XY and XO types thus seems to rest upon the presence of one or of two X-chromosomes as the controlling factor. The only genetic difference between the sexes is that the male has a haploid set of sex-linked genes, whereas the female has a diploid set; there is no difference in the genes themselves.

It appears, therefore, that every individual possesses all the genes necessary for producing the characteristics of either sex, and that some mechanism causes one set of effects to be produced in each sex, while the other potential expressions of the same genes are suppressed. An explanation of sex determination, then, requires knowledge of the mechanism which shifts the expression of the genes in one direction or the other.

Much light has been shed on mechanisms of sex determination through the study of **intersexes.** As the name would suggest, these are individuals which are neither completely male nor completely female, but are phenotypically intermediate.

It has long been known that certain crosses between geographical races of a moth, *Lymantria* (in which the sex-chromosome formula is of the ZW type) regularly yield intersexes among the progeny. Goldschmidt suggested that the outcome of these crosses could be accounted for by supposing that genes for maleness, carried in the Z-chromosomes, vary in "strength" from race to race, and that there is similar variation in the strength of female-determining factors in the cytoplasm. Within any one race, the relative strengths of the male- and female-determining factors are so adjusted that the genes for maleness in *two* Z-chromosomes are sufficient to overbalance decisively the effects of the factors for femaleness in the cytoplasm; the male-determining genes of *one* Z-chromosome, on the other hand, are decisively outweighed by the effects of the cytoplasmic factors for femaleness. Thus, matings between individuals which belong to the same geographic race would give the customary one-to-one ratio of normal males and females.

If, however, a female from a race in which both male- and female-determining factors are relatively weak is crossed with a male from a race with "stronger" factors for both maleness and femaleness, the outcome may be different. The ZZ progeny from crosses of this type are phenotypic males, in agreement with their sex-chromosome constitution. But the ZW offspring are intersexes; according to Goldschmidt's theory, the female-determining factors in the hybrid (received from the "weak"-race mother in the cytoplasm of the egg) are not sufficiently strong to overbalance altogether the "strong" male-determining genes in the single Z-chromosome inherited from the father.

Goldschmidt has documented his quantitative theory of sex determination in Lymantria with an elaborate series of crosses involving more than a dozen different races, including crosses between races, backcrosses of hybrids to the parent races, crosses between F_1 hybrids of different derivation, etc. He has been able to arrange the various races in an order corresponding to the relative strengths of their sex-determining factors, as inferred from the degree of intersexuality (or absence of intersexuality) in hybrids from the various

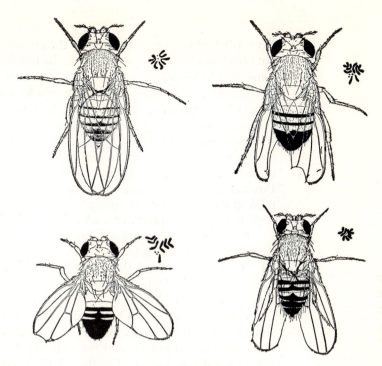

Fig. 23.1 Sex types in Drosophila. Upper left, normal female; upper right, intersex; lower left, supermale; lower right, superfemale. *Adapted from Bridges in the American Naturalist*

crosses; and having made crosses between races A and B (let us say) and between B and C, he is able to predict the results of crossing A and C. Goldschmidt's theory appears to provide an adequate explanation for the Lymantria case in its many ramifications. Because of the complexity of his experimental data, however, we shall not attempt to discuss them in detail.

The discovery of *triploid intersexuality* in Drosophila and the careful studies of this and related phenomena have clearly shown that there is also a quantitative basis for sex determination in this insect. In this case, however, it is the ratio of genes in the X-chromosome (female-determining) to genes in the *autosomes* (male-determining) that determines the sex of the individual.

Intersexes in Drosophila (Fig. 23.1, upper right) were first discovered in the course of linkage experiments by Bridges, who found several dozen of them in the progeny of a single mating. He noticed also among the normal progeny of the same mating that the segregations of certain mutant genes involved in the cross were aberrant. An analysis of these segregations, together with breeding tests of the brothers and sisters of the intersexes, led Bridges to conclude that the female parent must have been a triploid, with three sets of autosomes and three X-chromosomes.

Data on the distribution of segregating genes among the intersexes themselves indicated that they, too, had three sets of autosomes.

No sex-linked gene was involved in the cross, and the intersexes do not breed, so that genetic evidence on the number of their X-chromosomes was lacking. But if they had three sets of autosomes like their mother, their intersexual character would be hard to explain unless they differed from her in number of X-chromosomes. Bridges concluded, therefore, that the intersexual flies did not possess three X-chromosomes but, most likely, only two, with or without a Y-chromosome. Symbolizing a haploid set of autosomes by **A,** the chromosomal formula of the intersexes would be 3A 2X or 3A 2X Y. Progeny having these respective formulas could be produced by a triploid mother if, for example, a 2A egg with one X-chromosome is fertilized by an X-sperm, or a 2A 2X egg is fertilized by a Y-sperm.

Cytological examination confirmed the predicted chromosomal constitutions of the intersexes (the one shown in Figure 23.1 is 3A 2X). It also revealed that a number of their superficially normal sisters were triploid; this is of course what we would expect from the fertilization of 2A 2X eggs by X-bearing sperms.

From the fact that 3A 2X individuals in Drosophila are intersexes, whereas both 3A 3X and 2A 2X flies are female, we can see at once that the autosomes, and not only the X-chromosomes, play a role in sex determination. For the 3A 2X intersex differs chromosomally from the normal 2A 2X female only by the *addition* of a set of autosomes, and it differs from the triploid 3A 3X female only by the *subtraction* of a set of autosomes. It is also evident that the autosomes must influence development in a male direction, the X-chromosomes in a female direction.

The considerations just mentioned, along with the fact that 2A 1X Drosophila are male, led Bridges to suggest that sex in this animal is dependent upon the *ratio* of X-chromosomes to autosomes. If the value of the X/A ratio is 1, we have a female; if it is 1/2, we have a male. Flies with the formula 3A 2X have an X/A ratio of 2/3, or 0.67, which is *between* 1 and 0.5 and would therefore account for their intersexual character.

The *genic balance* theory of sex determination, as Bridges' theory is called, was quickly reinforced by additional discoveries in Drosophila. Tetraploid flies, 4A 4X, were soon found and, as would be predicted from their X/A ratio of 1, they are female. Flies of the formula 4A 3X have also been identified; consistent with the fact that their X/A ratio of 0.75 lies between 1 and 0.5, they are intersexual. Haploid Drosophila (1A 1X) do not exist, but occasional mosaic specimens occur with patches of haploid tissue, and when structures which differ in the two sexes are composed of haploid cells, the structures are of the female type.

Table 23.1 shows the effects of various degrees of balance between

Table 23.1. RELATION OF CHROMOSOME RATIOS IN *Drosophila melano gaster* TO SEX

X	A	X/A RATIO	SEX TYPE
3	2	1.50	"Superfemale"
4	4	1.00	Female (4n)
3	3	1.00	Female (3n)
2	2	1.00	**Female (2n)**
1	1	1.00	Female (n)
3	4	0.75	Intersex
2	3	0.67	Intersex
1	2	**0.50**	**Male**
2	4	0.50	Male
1	3	0.33	"Supermale"

X stands for the number of X-chromosomes, A for the number of haploid sets of autosomes. The formula 1X/1A has been found only in patches of tissue in otherwise diploid flies.

autosomes and sex chromosomes in the chromosomal types actually found in Drosophila. The "supermales" and "superfemales" included in the table, despite their names, are not superior to normal males and females in any respect; in fact, they are invariably feeble specimens with low viability. They were given their designations wholly on account of their chromosomal formulas.

We properly speak of *genic balance*, rather than chromosomal balance, in the determination of sex in Drosophila, because evidence that many genes are involved has been obtained from observations on the effects of extra fragments of chromosomes in the nucleus. Dobzhansky and Schultz have shown that when pieces of the X-chromosome obtained through breaking this chromosome by X-radiation are added to an intersex (3A 2X), there is a shift of characters in the female direction. The larger the piece of X-chromosome added, the greater the shift, a fact which indicates that sex-determining genes are present in various parts of the chromosome. This conclusion is further substantiated by the work of Pipkin, who added to intersexes very short sections of the X-chromosome, covering successively its entire length. No small section resulted in any more significant shift toward femaleness than did any other.

From the experiments just cited and from other experiments in which the effects of fragments of autosomes were studied, it is evident that the many genes normally involved in the determination of sex in Drosophila must have individually quite small effects. Nevertheless, mutation has occasionally given rise to a gene with powerful sex-modifying action. One gene of this kind, located in the third chromosome and called "transformer" (*tra*), when homozygous converts 2A 2X individuals into flies that, though sterile, are indistinguishable from ordinary *males* except for the reduced size of their testes.

We have seen that a variety of tests of the genic balance theory of sex determination have established its validity in Drosophila beyond much question. There is some evidence that it is also valid for at least a few other organisms (including both plants and animals) with XY, XO, ZW, or ZO sex-chromosome formulas. In the ZW or ZO type, of course, the theory would require the male-determining genes to be in the Z-chromosomes, the female-determining genes in the autosomes. Triploid intersexes of the formula 3A 2Z have, in fact, been found in several species of moths, including Lymantria. In the case of the latter, this finding does not necessarily contradict the theory proposed by Goldschmidt to account for *diploid* intersexes. It may well be that in Lymantria male-determining genes in the Z-chromosomes are balanced against female factors in both autosomes and cytoplasm.

There are many organisms, however, to which the genic balance theory, at least in its simplest form, is not readily applicable. Notable among these are various Hymenoptera (ants, bees, wasps, etc.). The fact that in the honeybee only females (workers and queens) come from fertilized eggs and that unfertilized eggs develop partheno-genetically into males (drones) was first noted by Dzierzon, a contemporary of Mendel. We now know that the same rule holds for numerous insects of the order Hymenoptera. The most thoroughly studied of these is the tiny parasitic wasp, *Habrobracon juglandis*.

In Habrobracon, since unfertilized eggs ordinarily develop into males and fertilized eggs into females, we find that males normally inherit only from their mothers, while females inherit from both parents. A cross of a female homozygous for the recessive gene c (cantaloup eyes), for example, by a male carrying the dominant allele for black eyes would be symbolized as shown below:

Parents	cc	$\times$	C
	cantaloup		black
	female		male
Offspring	Cc		c
	black		cantaloup
	female		male

We use a single gene symbol for the formula of a male, since the male is haploid and therefore possesses only one member of each pair of alleles.

But in Habrobracon *biparentally produced males also occur*, that is, some fertilized eggs develop into males. The biparental males have the diploid number of chromosomes but are usually sterile. They are found almost exclusively among the offspring of related parents.

We see at once that no theory of simple balance between sex

chromosomes and autosomes or between sex genes in the chromosomes and cytoplasmic sex factors can account for the occurrence of both haploid and diploid males together with diploid females. A theory that does account for this situation, however, has been developed by Whiting, based on his own extensive observations together with those of the Bostians, Grebs, Speichers, and others.

According to Whiting, the development of femaleness requires the action of *complementary sex factors, dependent on multiple alleles*. Every female is *heterozygous* for a pair of alleles each of which contributes some factor or substance not produced by the other. The contributions of *both* alleles are necessary for femaleness to develop, and in this sense the actions of the two sex alleles in a female are complementary.

To suggest how the sex genes act, we might represent the nine alleles thus far identified in the series by such symbols as $x^{aBCDEFGHI}$, $x^{AbCDEFGHI}$, $x^{ABcDEFGHI}$, etc., to $x^{ABCDEFGHi}$. Here the capital-letter superscripts, A through I, indicate factors which must *all* be present to produce femaleness. Each allele, you will notice, lacks one of the essential factors, as is indicated by the small-letter superscript in its gene symbol. But this notation is unwieldy, and each allele can be adequately represented by a symbol with a single small-letter superscript indicating the factor *which the allele lacks*, provided we clearly understand that all of the other factors are present. Hence, instead of the symbols listed above, we shall use simply x^a, x^b, x^c, ... x^i.

We see from the above that all diploid heterozygotes, such as $x^a x^b$, $x^a x^c$, $x^b x^c$, should be female, since any two different alleles together provide all of the female factors; but haploids, x^a, x^b, x^c, etc., always lack one or another of the factors for femaleness and would therefore be male. Diploids homozygous for any of the alleles, $x^a x^a$, $x^b x^b$, etc., moreover, would be male for the same reason, so that the occurrence of biparental males is accounted for.

You may wonder how such a theory came to be thought of and how it could be tested.

The idea of complementary sex alleles determining femaleness was first suggested by certain observations on *mosaic males*. These are males resulting from the development of unfertilized eggs in which *two* reduced (haploid) nuclei have been retained, instead of one. During development, some parts of the animal receive derivatives of one of the nuclei, and some receive derivatives of the other. Corresponding chromosomes of the two egg nuclei, through segregation of any alleles for which the mother was heterozygous, may of course carry different genes, in which case different parts of the adult wasp are of two genetically different kinds.

In mosaic specimens in which the dividing line between the

genetically different tissues passes through the sex organs, *the structure of these organs is frequently modified in a female direction.* Whiting suspected that the partial feminization was due to the combining (through diffusion into neighboring cells) of two substances, one of which was present in each kind of tissue. He thought it possible that the substances might be the respective products of two allelic genes (say x^a, x^b) for which the mother was heterozygous. He saw that if *all* females were heterozygous for a pair of alleles acting in this way, and all diploid (biparental) males homozygous for one or the other, the problem of sex types in Habrobracon would be in large part solved.

In its original form, Whiting's theory assumed only two alleles at the x locus; all females were taken to be $x^a x^b$, all males either x^a or x^b. A test of his hypothesis involved use of the fused gene (fu) — named for its effect on the antennal segments — which shows linkage with the sex-allele locus. According to the theory, matings between females heterozygous for fused, and fused males, would be of four types, as shown in Table 23.2. These matings fall into two groups

Table 23.2. THEORETICALLY POSSIBLE TYPES OF "TWO-ALLELE" MATINGS IN *Habrobracon* BETWEEN *Fufu* FEMALES AND *fu* MALES

Type	Female Parent	Male Parent	Expected Kinds of Daughters	
			Noncrossovers	Crossovers
1	$(Fu\ x^a)\ (fu\ x^b)$	$\times\ (fu\ x^b)$	$(Fu\ x^a)\ (fu\ x^b)$	$(fu\ x^a)\ (fu\ x^b)$
2	$(Fu\ x^b)\ (fu\ x^a)$	$\times\ (fu\ x^a)$	$(Fu\ x^b)\ (fu\ x^a)$	$(fu\ x^b)\ (fu\ x^a)$
3	$(Fu\ x^a)\ (fu\ x^b)$	$\times\ (fu\ x^a)$	$(fu\ x^b)\ (fu\ x^a)$	$(Fu\ x^b)\ (fu\ x^a)$
4	$(Fu\ x^b)\ (fu\ x^a)$	$\times\ (fu\ x^b)$	$(fu\ x^a)\ (fu\ x^b)$	$(Fu\ x^a)\ (fu\ x^b)$

Genes carried on the same chromosome are bracketed together in parentheses, as in Chapter 10.

which should have distinguishably different results. From one group of matings (Types 1 and 2 in the table) the majority of female progeny should be nonfused; the majority from matings of the second group (Types 3 and 4) should be fused. In actuality, every *Fufu × fu* mating *between related individuals* has been found to fall into one or the other group, yielding (roughly) either 90 per cent nonfused daughters and 10 per cent fused, or 10 per cent nonfused and 90 per cent fused. Matings which give results of this kind are called "two-allele" crosses.

But matings of *Fufu* females by *unrelated fu* males most often yield *approximately equal numbers of nonfused and fused daughters.* This finding, together with the fact that biparental males are rarely produced in outcrosses, suggested that there must be more than two alleles at the x locus. Outcrosses, more often than matings of related wasps, would involve a male whose sex allele differs from both of those present in the female. A cross of this kind (called a "three-allele" mating) would be, for example:

Parents	$(Fu \ x^a)(fu \ x^b) \times (fu \ x^c)$
Female Offspring	$1 \ (Fu \ x^a)(fu \ x^c) : 1 \ (fu \ x^b)(fu \ x^c)$

Note here the expected equality of nonfused and fused daughters, and also the fact that no biparental males can be produced from this kind of mating. The theory that there is a series of multiple alleles with complementary effects thus accounts adequately for all of the major peculiarities of sex determination in Habrobracon. To the wary student the theory may at first seem speculative. It has successfully stood up, however, under several critical tests which alternative hypotheses have failed to meet. One of these tests is the subject of Problem 23.10 at the end of this chapter.

The extent to which the theory just outlined will prove applicable to other animals that normally produce males from unfertilized eggs and females from fertilized eggs is as yet unknown. Wasps of three genera other than Habrobracon have been studied. There is evidence that the theory is applicable in the case of one of these; it has been shown not to apply in the other two. The results so far obtained by Mackensen in recent experiments on the honeybee are not decisive, but they point to the possibility that sex determination in that insect may involve the same mechanism as that which has been worked out for Habrobracon.

In our discussion of sex determination up to this point we have dealt with forms (Lymantria, Drosophila, Habrobracon) in which the sex of the individual is definitely established by its genotype. In these species, the direction of sexual development is not modified by variations in environmental factors. Drosophila *intersexes* provide a partial exception to this rule; higher temperatures during their development cause the phenotype to be shifted in the female direction, lower temperatures in the male direction.

There are other forms, however, in which no relation between genetic constitution and sex can be discovered. In numerous species of worms and mollusks, each individual ordinarily produces sperms at one stage in its life cycle, eggs at another. Thus, most oysters may undergo several alterations of sex during a lifetime. Other animals, such as the mollusk *Crepidula*, regularly begin life as males, later becoming and remaining females. A variety of environmental factors is known to influence the change. Forced activity, high temperature, and exposure to toxic substances tend to accelerate it; the proximity of females tends to delay it. In still other invertebrates, the common earthworm, for example, each individual possesses functional organs of both sexes throughout its reproductive life.

In the marine worm, *Bonellia*, the female is large with a long slender proboscis, while the male is minute and lives as a parasite in the female's uterus. The fertilized eggs develop as free-swimming larvae which later settle down and continue their development. Those larvae which settle on the sea bottom grow into females, while those which happen to settle on the long proboscis of a female (from which they subsequently migrate into the uterus) become males. It has been shown experimentally that the larvae which settle on a female proboscis have not already been determined toward males, but that any larva will become a male under these circumstances.

Among the vertebrates, two or three species of fish are complete hermaphrodites, each individual possessing the reproductive organs of both sexes. In most kinds of fish, however, the sexes are separate. In those that have been studied genetically, chromosomal or genic mechanisms of sex determination have been demonstrated, but the sex is not in all cases irreversibly fixed by the genotype, so that under certain environmental conditions sex reversal may occur. The same appears to be true of many amphibians. Frogs ordinarily have separate sexes, and there is evidence of an XY type of sex determination. In certain races, however, the tadpoles develop into approximately equal numbers of males and females only when reared at low or moderate temperatures; when reared at elevated temperatures, most or all develop into males regardless of their chromosomal constitution.

Among mammals, no hermaphrodite in the strict sense of the word (that is, an individual with a complete set of both male and female reproductive organs) has been found. It would, in fact, be virtually impossible to occur, because the reproductive organs of both sexes develop from the same embryonic rudiments. That is, the structures of the embryo which, in the male, develop into male reproductive organs are identical with the embryonic structures which, in the female, form the reproductive organs of that sex. In various mammals, however, including man, an occasional individual is born in which the development of these organs has been arrested or modified. The external sex organs then have an appearance that is, in one degree or another, intermediate between male and female; some parts would usually be identified as having a more or less male structure, others as more nearly female.

Persons exhibiting the developmental abnormalities just described usually have gonads wholly of one sex or the other, i.e., either testes or ovaries; these persons are called *pseudohermaphrodites*. Those who are found to possess a mixture of testis and ovary tissues are, somewhat misleadingly, called *true hermaphrodites*. In many cases the external abnormalities of human hermaphrodites can be repaired by surgery, and if the internal structures are properly developed, normal function may be possible. The diagnosis of the sex of a child at birth is usually, of course, based on external anatomy. Since frequently, in the case of pseudohermaphrodites, this does not correspond to the "primary" sex (the sex of the gonads), surgeons are sometimes faced with the problem of "transforming" into a female a person brought up as a male, or *vice versa*. The most widely publicized cases of surgical "sex transformation" in recent years, however, (for example, that reported by Hamburger and his colleagues) have involved not pseudohermaphrodites, but *transvestists*. These are persons whose reproductive organs are clearly either male or female, but who are psychologically afflicted with an obsessive desire to be of the other sex.

In plants it is common for the same individual to produce both microspores and megaspores, which in turn produce respectively male and female gametophytes and finally sperms and eggs. In a flower the cells nearer the outside develop into stamens and those nearer the center develop into pistils. It appears probable that sex here is determined largely by the position of the cell in relation to other cells of the flower.

In plants which produce microspores and megaspores in separate individuals, Schaffner, McPhee, and others have shown that the sex of the individual may be readily changed by the influence of environmental factors (light, mineral supply, etc.) upon food manufacture and other physiological processes within the individual. Even in the higher vertebrates sex reversal may occur, as we shall see.

We must conclude, then, that maleness and femaleness are evidences of an inherent capacity of all cells to react in either of two directions, one resulting in the manifestations of one sex, the other in the manifestations of the opposite sex. Moreover, "maleness" and "femaleness" are only specific degrees of a potentially continuous series of stages.

There is ample evidence that a gene may produce a conspicuous effect in one environment and be without any visible effect in a different environment. Or, as occurs commonly in all organisms, the influence of one set of genes may be expressed in one environment, the influence of another set in a different environment. With this in mind, we need find no contradiction in the fact that the control of sexual development may range all the way from rigid and irreversible determination by genes to complete dependence on environmental influences.

In the higher vertebrates the first effect of the chromosomal balance appears to be the initiation of the embryonic development of the primary sex organs or gonads (testes in the male, ovaries in the female), which in addition to being producers of gametes also produce

Fig. 23.2 A freemartin. This heifer was twin-born with a bull calf, and is sterile. Compare this figure with Figure 23.3.

Fig. 23.3 A cow which was twin-born with a bull calf. At the age of ten she had produced twelve calves, including several pairs of twins. Fertility in such an animal is a rare occurrence, but occasionally happens, apparently due to the fact that the blood vessels from the two embryos remain separate.

the sex hormones. The subsequent appearance of sex-differentiating characteristics is in large part controlled by the hormones, which prevent the expression of the characteristics of one sex and permit or stimulate the development of those of the opposite sex. Hormones are spread by the blood and lymph to all cells of the body and thus affect all sexual characters, both primary and secondary.

An excellent illustration of the early beginning of hormone effects is furnished when twin calves of opposite sex are born. Usually the female is sterile and shows a tendency toward male characteristics. This is explained by the fact that there is in such cases a blood connection between the two embryos in the uterus of the cow, and since the male hormone seems to be produced first, the female absorbs enough of it to prevent the normal formation of female organs (Figs. 23.2 and 23.3). It may be noted in passing that a similar situation does not occur in human beings.

By removing the gonads early in life and injecting the hormone of the opposite sex, it is possible to get an individual that appears and acts like the opposite sex, although genetically it is unchanged. In some animals it is possible to remove the gonads and engraft those of the other sex and achieve similar results. This has been done by Steinach in rats and by Finlay and others in the domestic fowl.

In birds the female contains a rudimentary testis-like growth that may enlarge and produce the male hormone if the functional ovary is removed or destroyed by disease. Because of this, old hens occasionally grow spurs, begin to crow, and assume other male characteristics. Crew reports one case of this kind in which a hen, at first normal and able to produce eggs, gradually developed the behavior and appearance of a rooster, mated with hens, and finally became the father of two chicks. In some amphibia, fish, and other lower vertebrates, spontaneous sex reversal is relatively common.

In insects and other invertebrates no sex hormones have been proved to exist, and the sex of each cell of the body appears to be dependent on the chromosomes of that particular cell. The gonads may even be completely removed without affecting the secondary sexual characteristics. It is therefore possible to get individuals with female tissue in one part of the body and male tissue in another, due to chromosomal abnormalities that occur during embryological development. Such individuals are called **sex mosaics,** or **gynandromorphs.** The relative amounts of male and female tissues may vary. One type of gynandromorph is bilateral, having one side of the body male and the other side female. Such an individual could be produced from a 2X zygote in which during early development one of the X-chromosomes from a cell was lost by an accident of mitosis. The cells deriving from this cell would have but one X-chromosome and would be male, whereas the cells retaining two X-chromosomes would be female. The proportion of male tissue would depend to some extent upon the stage of development at which the aberration occurred. If it were early enough the result might be a bilateral gynandromorph.

Gynandromorphs rarely breed, but an amusing case of sexual reaction has been reported concerning one of them. In Drosophila, during courtship, the male holds the wings over the body and vibrates them rapidly while the female spreads the wings to the side of the body. In one case when a bilateral gynandromorph was placed with other flies of both sexes, the male side reacted by vibrating the wing over the body and the female side spread the wing in typical female reaction.

Summarizing the problem of sex determination, we may say that sexuality appears to be a fundamental attribute of the higher animals and plants, that maleness and femaleness are specific degrees of expression of a continuous series of stages including intersexes, and that cells of the higher forms of life are potentially capable of reacting so as to produce any of these stages. The determination of which of these stages shall be produced is bound up both with numerous genes and with an environmental complex. In the higher animals the genic balance appears the more potent, since the usual variations in the environment have little or no effect. This is especially true in the vertebrates, where the initial effect of the genic balance is supplemented by the action of the hormones. In many plants the effect of the genes may not be expressed until late in the development of the individual, that is, in the flowers. In most plants the genic balance may be overthrown with comparative ease by changes in the environment. Inasmuch as other hereditary characters also show variations in the degrees to which one or another of them may be influenced by the environment, we must conclude that sex is not very different in its genetic nature from other inherited traits of the organism.

PROBLEMS

23.1 What sex ratio would be expected in the offspring of a hen which, through sex reversal, had become a functional male? Explain why you answer as you do.

23.2 In poultry silver is due to a dominant gene, S, gold to its recessive allele, s. These genes are sex-linked. If a silver hen were to undergo sex reversal and if it were then mated to a gold hen, what kinds of offspring would be expected and in what proportions?

23.3 Of what practical importance might the artificial determination of sex be in cattle? In poultry? In human beings?

23.4 If a method should be discovered for artificially determining sex in human beings by means of controlling the metabolic rate of the embryo, what cytological complications might result in later generations?

23.5 Why should the artificial determination of sex be more readily achieved in the higher plants than in the higher animals?

23.6 In human beings the sex ratio at birth is not one to one, but always shows an excess of males. Is this consistent with the chromosome determination of sex? Explain.

23.7 If there is 10 per cent crossing over between the loci of *fused* and the x-alleles in Habrobracon, what would be the expected percentages of fused and nonfused wasps among the *biparental males* produced by each of the types of mating in Table 23.2?

23.8 In Habrobracon reasonably large progenies of matings between a female and any one of her (haploid) sons always contain biparental males, even if the female herself was the offspring of a "three-allele" cross (e.g., $x^a x^b \times x^c$). Would a mating between a female and one of her brothers necessarily be capable of yielding biparental males if the female was the offspring of a three-allele cross?

23.9 Whiting designates the sex alleles of a particular one of his Habrobracon stocks (which we shall call Stock I) as x^a, x^b;

wasps of this stock carry the gene *veinless* (*vl*), recessive to normal-wing. When veinless females of Stock I, *vlvl xᵃxᵇ*, are crossed to normal-wing males of another inbred strain, Stock II, normal-wing sons are found among the progeny of every mating. When Stock I veinless females are crossed to normal-wing males of a third strain, Stock III, about half of the matings produce some normal-wing sons. When the same cross is made using normal-wing males from Stock IV, none of the matings yields any normal-wing sons. Explain.

23.10 According to Whiting's theory, if matings between wasps of two different stocks consistently fail to produce any biparental males, the two stocks must have different sex alleles, say $x^a x^b$, in one, $x^c x^d$ in the other. It appears that every F_2 male from crosses between two such stocks produces biparental sons in matings with females of one or the other parent stocks, but never in matings with females of both stocks. Explain.

23.11 Some stocks of Habrobracon do not carry any mutant genes. If we wish to detect biparental males from crosses between two such stocks, it is necessary to introduce a "marker" gene into one of them. The gene *lemon* (*le*, body color) carried in some Stock I ($x^a x^b$) wasps, is a convenient marker, because heterozygous *Lele* individuals are clearly distinguishable from both *lele* and *LeLe* (normal colored) specimens. The first step in introducing the lemon gene into wasps with say, $x^c x^d$ sex alleles is to cross a *Lele* $x^c x^d$ female to a lemon male of Stock I. Show that the genotype ratio among lemon males in the F_2 from this mating will be either 1 *le* x^c : 2 *le* x^a : 1 *le* x^d or 1 *le* x^c : 2 *le* x^b : 1 *le* x^d.

23.12 The different genotypes of the F_2 lemon males referred to in Problem 12.11 cannot, of course, be distinguished by inspection. If we mate a dozen or so of these lemon males to females of the constitution LeLe $x^c x^d$, the daughters from *some* of the matings will of course be Lele $x^c x^d$. How can we tell, by examining the other progeny, which matings these are?

REFERENCES

ALLEN, E., *Sex and Internal Secretions.* Baltimore, The Williams and Wilkins Co. (1939).

BRIDGES, C. B., *Science* **54**:252 (1921); *Amer. Naturalist* **56**:51 (1922); *ibid* **59**: 127 (1925); *Proc. Nat. Acad. Sci.* **11**:706 (1925); *Science* **72**:405 (1930).

CREW, F. A. E., *Sex Determination*, 3rd ed. New York, John Wiley and Sons (1954).

DOBZHANSKY, T., and SCHULTZ, J., *Proc. Nat. Acad. Sci.* **17**:531 (1931).

FINLAY, G. F., *Brit. Jour. Exp. Biol.* **11**:439 (1934).

GOLDSCHMIDT, R., *Proc. Nat. Acad. Sci.* **34**:245 (1948).

HAMBURGER, C., et al., *Jour. Amer. Med. Assn.* **152**:391 (1953).

MACKENSEN, O., *Genetics* **36**:500 (1951); *Jour. Hered.* **46**:72 (1955).

MARTIN, A., JR., *An Introduction to the Genetics of Habrobracon Juglandis Ashmead.* New York, The Hobson Book Press (1947).

McPHEE, H. C., *Jour. Agr. Research* **31**:935 (1925).

MORGAN, T. H., and BRIDGES, C. B., *Carnegie Inst. Wash. Publ.* **278** (1919).

PATTERSON, J. T., *Amer. Naturalist* **72**:193 (1938).

PIPKIN, S. B., *Univ. of Texas Publ.* **4032**:126 (1940); *Genetics* **27**:286 (1942).

SCHAFFNER, J. H., *Ohio Jour. Science* **19**:409; **20**:25 (1919); *Bot. Gazette* **71**:197 (1921); *Amer. Jour. Bot.* **9**:72 (1922); *Ohio Jour. Science* **22**:149; *Bull. Torr. Bot. Club* **50**:73 (1923); *Ohio Jour. Sci.* **33**:225, 323; *Amer. Naturalist* **59**:115 (1925).

WHITING, P. W., *Genetics* **28**:365 (1943).

CHAPTER TWENTY-FOUR

Genes and mutations

Variation is one of the most universal phenomena in nature. Rarely do we find two individuals of a species exactly alike. Sometimes the differences are large and striking, sometimes they are small and only detectable by careful measurement, but regularly differences are present.

Among the variations which we may observe in nature we find both hereditary and nonhereditary differences. The nonhereditary variations are those produced by gross changes in the environment, such as the results of differential feeding, humidity, light, training, and so on. Variations of this sort are frequently referred to as fluctuations. There is ample evidence that such "acquired characters" are not hereditary. In this chapter we are concerned with *hereditary* variations.

We have seen in previous chapters that hereditary variations may come about in various ways. Let us briefly summarize the methods by which they may occur.

In the first place, *mutations* may take place. A mutation is a change in a gene, potentially capable of being transmitted. A mutation may take place either in somatic tissue or in germinal tissue. If it takes place in somatic tissue it will not be sexually transmitted, of course, but it may be asexually propagated, particularly in plants. A dominant mutation in somatic tissue will produce an immediate effect; a recessive mutation ordinarily will not, unless both genes of the pair mutate simultaneously. Of course a recessive sex-linked mutation may produce an immediate effect in a male of the XO or XY type or in a female of the ZO or ZW type. A dominant mutation in germinal tissue may be directly transmitted and will produce an immediate effect in the ensuing generation. A recessive mutation in germinal tissue will not show up in succeeding generations until an individual happens to receive such a changed gene both through the sperm and the egg.

In the second place, *recombinations* may occur. That is, genes already present in certain combinations may through segregation and fertilization be united in new combinations producing new characters. Thus in Chapter 5 we found that crossing a black rat with a yellow one produced gray F_1 individuals. It is clear that the gray color is not the result of a new mutation but is due to the recombination of the genes which in the parental combinations produced black and yellow. Similarly in the F_2 of this cross there appeared some cream-colored rats. This new color again is not the direct result of a mutation but is due to a new recombination of the same two pairs of genes previously involved. The first appearance of many characters is due to recombinations of genes rather than to mutations which have just occurred.

In the third place, *chromosomal aberrations* may occur, producing changes which are hereditary. Nondisjunction, translocation, ploidy, and the rest are examples of such aberrations.

We have already sufficiently discussed two of the above methods of producing hereditary variations, namely recombinations and chromosomal aberrations. We have said very little, however, concerning mutations, confining ourselves thus far to the mere statement that they do occur. We may now inquire as to the nature and causes of mutations and indeed as to the nature of the genes themselves.

Until recently almost no answer could be given to these questions. Even today the answers are not wholly satisfactory. It has taken a great deal of careful, painstaking research on the part of many investigators to be able to give even the partial information which is at our disposal. A great deal more investigation must be undertaken before anything like an adequate understanding may be had. Yet when we marshal the facts which are available, we find that there is really a great deal of interesting and important material which bears upon the problem of the nature and causes of mutations and the structure of genes.

We may arrange the known facts in a series of statements, putting them in the form of principles whenever possible.

1. Most genes are exceedingly stable.

This applies both to normal "wild-type" genes and to genes which have arisen by mutation. The natural mutation rate is very low. Many species have remained much the same for long geologic ages. The brachiopods among animals and the sea-weeds and others among plants are examples of groups of organisms in which almost no changes are observed in present-day species as compared with fossils. Even in the laboratory among organisms chosen for their capacity to produce mutations, a high stability of genes is found. Muller, by means of cleverly devised experiments in Drosophila, has recently estimated that the mean life of a gene (that is, the average time elapsing without change in any particular gene and its descendants) approximates 100,000 years. This recent estimate is considerably lower than estimates made earlier by Muller and Altenburg, but is thought to be quite accurate on the basis of detailed observations and experiments. Allowing about ten generations per year in the life history of Drosophila, any particular gene would ordinarily undergo only one mutation while being transmitted through a million generations of individuals. Conversely, in a sample of a million gametes from any single generation only one mutation would be expected for any given locus.

Estimates of the mutation rates for several genes in man have been made. It is possible to do this by direct observation and a little mathematical calculation for dominant genes (which are recognizable in the heterozygous state) and for sex-linked recessive genes (which are recognizable when present only once — *hemizygous* — in males). Haldane has recently reviewed the results obtained by himself and others for the following genes: hemophilia, epiloia (a type of mental deficiency associated with tumors of the skin and brain), achondroplasia (a type of dwarfism), retinoblastoma (tumor of the retina of the eye), and aniridia (absence of the iris). The mutation rates for these genes vary between one and four per hundred thousand. These rates are about ten times as high as those found in Drosophila, *per generation*. Since, however, cell division and growth are so rapid in Drosophila, with its short life cycle, as compared with man, with his long life cycle, the *daily* rates are several hundred times as high in Drosophila as in man.

2. Different genes have different rates of mutation.

Certain genes are vastly more mutable than others, the mean life of some genes being only a few years. Stadler, using corn, was able to compare the mutation rates of several known genes. The results are shown in Table 24.1.

Table 24.1. Comparison of the Mutation Rates of Seven Genes in Corn. (*Data from Stadler*)

Gene	Gametes Tested	Number of Mutations	Average per Million Gametes
R	554,786	273	492.0
I	265,391	28	106.0
Pr	647,102	7	11.0
Su	1,678,736	4	2.4
Y	1,745,280	4	2.2
Sh	2,469,285	3	1.2
Wx	1,503,744	0	0.0

3. Mutations may occur at any point in the life history of an organism.

Fig. 24.1 Mutations at various stages of development. Above, two flowers of lavender Delphiniums, in which each dark spot is the result of a mutation from lavender to purple in a single cell. The spots are all approximately the same size, showing that the change in the color gene occurs at a definite stage in development Below, two flowers of the rose strain of Delphiniums, in which the spots vary from tiny dots to half a petal in extent, due to mutations which have occurred at various stages in development. *From Demerec in the Journal of Heredity*

They may occur either in somatic or in gametic tissue, but experimental evidence indicates that they occur with most frequency just before or during the maturation of the germ cells.

4. The rate of mutation in various genes may vary in different tissues or at different stages of development of the organism.

Demerec has found, for example, that the color genes rose and lavender in Delphiniums are each relatively unstable, mutating frequently to purple. The rose gene is uniformly unstable throughout the life cycle of the plant, while the lavender gene mutates only at very early and very late stages in the development of the plant (Figs. 24.1 and 24.2). In Drosophila certain genes are known which mutate only or largely during the maturation division, others which mutate only or chiefly in somatic cells, and still others which mutate in both germinal and somatic tissues.

Fig. 24.2 A mutation in Delphinium which occurred in the lavender gene at a very early stage in development, resulting in a flower spike that is half purple and half lavender. *From Demerec in the Journal of Heredity*

5. A mutation is a change in a gene, not the loss of the gene.

This is proved by the fact that, when a gene has mutated, the mutant gene may later change back to the original gene. Such "reverse mutations" are known in many species, although they are proportionately not so frequent as the mutations from wild type to mutant type. Losses of genes do of course occur, but such losses are deletions, a type of chromosomal aberration. True mutations are not losses of genes.

6. More than one change may occur in a given gene, producing multiple alleles, which, while usually affecting the same character in differing degrees, may affect different characters.

The fact that multiple alleles usually affect the same character, differing only slightly in the degree of their effect, indicates that very slight changes in the gene are responsible for the various alleles of a single gene. The mutations of one gene to its various alleles appear to occur quite independently of each other. In rare cases multiple alleles affect different characters. The members of one such set in Drosophila produce shortened wings, abnormal thorax, and a lethal effect, respectively.

7. The multiple allelic mutations of a given gene are not always in the same direction.

Mutations from a single gene may produce darker or lighter pigment, larger or smaller parts, a dominant or a recessive allele, etc.

8. The direction of mutation is, however, preferential, occurring more often in some directions than in others.

Many genes are known which mutate to a certain allele more frequently than to another.

9. The mutability and the preferential direction may themselves become changed through mutation.

In various species there have been demonstrated genes which increase the mutability of other genes.

10. The changes in genes appear to be chemical processes.

In some unstable genes the rate of change is high enough to be accurately measured, and from such data Demerec has adduced the following evidence for the chemical nature of mutations.

a. The end product of the change is always the same. There are no intermediate forms. The unstable rose gene of Delphinium, for example, always changes to its wild-type allele, which is purple, and the unstable lavender gene changes into its wild-type allele, which is also purple.

b. The change is not always a random process; it may be favored by certain tissues or it may even be limited to certain tissues, as outlined in Point 4. It would appear that a certain environment is necessary for a certain change to take place.

c. There have been found various genes which stimulate the rate of change in certain unstable genes, as outlined in Point 9. These genes appear to produce the favorable environment which is necessary for the change.

d. The process is a reversible one, as outlined in Point 5.

Demerec holds that these facts favor the conception that changes in genes are chemical changes.

11. Gross mutations are usually harmful to the organism.

This is to be expected, as the organism is a delicately adjusted mechanism, and a random change would more likely be deleterious than beneficial. The vast majority of gross mutations have been found to be detrimental to the continued existence of the individual or the species.

12. Mutations are usually recessive to the wild type.

Whether this is due to the more frequent occurrence of recessive mutations is a debatable question. Fisher has suggested that when a mutation first occurs it has an immediate effect in the heterozygous condition. Since most individuals carrying the new gene will carry it in the heterozygous condition, selection may act on these heterozygotes. They will vary, as all individuals do, and those most nearly like the wild type will have a better chance of survival than those tending towards the new mutation, if it is a deleterious mutation. If it is a beneficial mutation, the heterozygotes most nearly like the new mutation in its homozygous form will survive to the gradual exclusion of the old types, so that the new mutation in time becomes the "wild type." In either event, since the same mutations have presumably occurred repeatedly over a long period of time, the heterozygous individuals would through natural survival tend more towards the more viable or "wild type," until in time they closely resembled it. On this view we have the phenomenon of dominance as a result of evolution through natural selection and not because mutations in themselves tend to be recessive. Whatever the mechanism involved, however, the vast majority of mutations *are* recessive to the wild-type genes.

13. Mutations do not ordinarily occur in more than one gene at a time.

This indicates that, whatever is the cause of mutations, it is not a gross environmental cause affecting all genes alike.

14. Two identical genes at corresponding loci in a pair of chromosomes mutate independently, just as different genes do.

This, even more than the last point, indicates that the cause of mutations is a restricted, specific influence of some sort. Here are two genes of a pair, exactly alike, within a cell, so that they can hardly be more than a ten-thousandth of an inch apart, and yet one of them mutates and the other does not. Considerations such as this gave rise to the discovery of the possibility of the artificial production of mutations, as taken up in Point 17.

15. Mutations with slight effects are much more common than those with marked effects.

Multiple genes, in which the effect of a single added mutant gene is very small, are excellent examples of this point. Such multiple genes occur in the majority of crosses.

16. Mutations with no visible effects are the most common of all mutations.

Experimental evidence indicates that mutations with lethal effects, physiological and viability effects, are produced with great frequency in comparison with those which have visible effects. Such mutations, of course, are difficult to recognize, and it is only in carefully studied and well-known species that their frequency can be measured. The development by Muller of a method of recognizing their production led to one of the most important discoveries, the artificial production of mutations. This will be taken up in the following two points.

17. Radiation (X rays, radium rays, ultraviolet light, and others) may greatly increase the natural mutation rate.

This discovery marks one of the most significant advances in the study of genetics and evolution. For years geneticists tried in many ways to cause an artificial production of mutations. Experimental animals, particularly Drosophila, were subjected to variations in food, light, humidity, temperature, and other conditions of the environment, without any obvious production of mutations as a result. Even irradiation was tried with little result until Muller in 1927 announced that by a special technique he had been able to demonstrate the production of mutations in Drosophila by the use of X rays. Since then mutations have been produced in large numbers in many species of animals and plants by the use of various types of irradiation.

Muller's results were the climax of a long series of careful investigations on the nature of mutations, many of which led to some of the points already outlined. Among the facts which Muller had accumulated and which led to the discovery of the use of X rays in producing mutations were these. If two genes of a pair are as close together in a cell as alleles must be, and one mutates and the other does not, something which can affect one gene and not another similar one in close proximity must be the cause of mutations. High-energy radiation might conceivably produce such an effect.

Furthermore, Muller reasoned that, if he were to search for mutations following treatment with irradiation, lethal mutations would be the kind to look for, since in nature they are by far the most frequent.

Hence he devised a very clever method of recognizing lethal mutations. Ordinarily lethal mutations are difficult to recognize, since they seldom produce any visible effect. The method devised by Muller, now known to all biologists as the *ClB* method, is as follows.

In the X-chromosomes of Drosophila the following genes are known. *L* represents a dominant gene for normal viability, *l* denotes its recessive allele, which is a known lethal. *B* represents a dominant gene for bar eye, while *b* denotes its wild-type allele producing normal eye. There is also known on the X-chromosomes an inversion. Flies homozygous for the normal X-chromosome, or those homozygous for the inversion, will have normal crossing over in their maturation divisions, since the chromosomes can synapse gene for gene. A fly which contains the inversion in one X-chromosome but not in the other will, however, not have any crossing over in this pair of chromosomes. Thus the inversion can be so used as to enable us to locate a hidden recessive gene by means of a dominant "marker." Since the presence and absence of the inversion will behave in inheritance just as a pair of alleles, the inversion may be represented by *C*, the normal chromosome by *c*.

Muller produced a stock in which the females were heterozygous for the two genes and the inversion, having *ClB* on one chromosome and *cLb* on the other. They could live because the lethal *l* was covered up by its normal dominant allele *L*. Such females were mated to (*cLb*)Y males which had been irradiated. Of the female offspring the bar-eyed flies would carry *ClB* on one chromosome (from the mother) and *cLb* on the other (which was from the father and had consequently been irradiated).

These female bar-eyed flies were bred to normal males (*cLb*)Y and then the offspring examined. Reference to Figure 24.3 will show that half of the males will die because of the lethal received from the original female parent. The other half of the males receive the irradiated chromosome from the original male parent. If a recessive lethal had been produced at any locus on the X-chromosome by the irradiation, these flies would also die, since they would receive the lethal with no normal allele to cover it. Hence large numbers of flies may be examined for lethal mutations simply by looking for cultures with no males. When such cultures are found, it is because of a lethal produced in the X-chromosome of the irradiated male. It may be subsequently tested for and its linkage relations determined because the nonbar females in this generation would be heterozygous for it, since no crossing over can occur.

Following this technique, many lethal mutations resulting from irradiation were discovered. Once the proper dosage was known, large numbers of flies were irradiated and many *visible* mutations were dis-

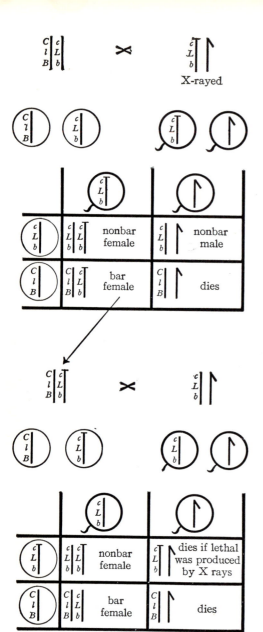

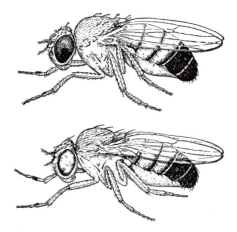

Fig. 24.4 Mutations produced in Drosophila by X rays. Above, a forked-bristle fly with normal eyes. Below, a normal-bristle fly with "spectacled" eyes, arising after irradiation from a race like the upper figure. The normal-bristle condition is thus a *reverse* mutation of the mutant "forked." The lower figure, then, represents one of the rare cases where two mutations have occurred at the same time. *From Patterson and Muller in Genetics*

Fig. 24.3 Diagram of the *ClB* method for detecting lethal mutations produced in the X-chromosome in Drosophila. Only the sex chromosomes are shown. The parental male (at the upper right-hand corner of the figure) is subjected to X rays. The irradiated X-chromosome is marked in the diagram with a horizontal line so that it may be followed through subsequent generations. In the second generation half the males will die because of the lethal *l* already present in the stock. If a lethal mutation was produced in the X-chromosome of the parental male by irradiation, the other half of the males in the second generation will also die. Cultures containing no males are easy to detect and indicate the production of a lethal mutation by the X rays.

covered due to the irradiation. Most of these were recurrences of mutations already known, but some of them were quite new. The rate of mutation was increased as much as 150 times by the irradiation. As in natural mutations, most of the changes caused by the X rays are recessive, most of them are lethals, and the majority of the visible mutations are deleterious. Again as in natural mutation it has been possible to bring about reverse mutation by the treatment, showing that the changes are not due entirely to losses (Fig. 24.4).

The mutation rate resulting from X rays is linearly proportionate to the dosage. It is apparently independent of the wave length. Moreover, it does not matter whether a given dosage is applied all at one time or in small fractions at different times.

Many chromosomal aberrations of the usual kinds are also found to occur as a result of X-ray exposure. Unlike mutation rates, however, the aberration rate is not usually linearly proportionate to the dosage but increases more nearly in proportion to the square of the dosage. Moreover, spreading the dosage over a longer time diminishes the number of interchanges. Thus it would seem that by the use of X rays all of the usual types of hereditary variations may be caused to occur with greatly increased frequency. The importance of this fact to the study of genetics and evolution can scarcely be over-estimated.

In other animals and in plants the application of X rays has also been found to produce mutations. Corn, wheat, oats, and barley among plants have responded to irradiation with a higher mutation rate (Figs. 24.5 and 24.6). In plants as in Drosophila many of the mutations produced by X rays are similar to those already known in nature.

Fig. 24.5 A mutation induced in barley by irradiation. Left, the mutant "vine"; right, a normal plant. *From Stadler in Scientific Agriculture*

Recent researches indicate that mutations may be similarly produced in microorganisms, including yeasts, molds, and bacteria. The changes produced in these forms are of such fundamental importance

Fig. 24.6 A mutation induced in barley by irradiation. Left, the mutant "twirled"; right, a normal plant. *From Stadler in Scientific Agriculture*

in the study of biochemical processes that a detailed discussion of them will be presented in Chapter 27.

Studies of Altenburg, Muller, Hanson, and Plough and Ives indicate that not only X rays but radium rays, ultraviolet light, and even heat may increase the mutation rate (Fig. 24.7). By exposing the larvae of Drosophila to high temperatures (just below the killing temperature) the mutation rate was increased to six times the natural rate.

Researches of Lea and Catcheside, and others, indicate that neutrons also produce mutations and chromosomal aberrations. Neutrons, however, produce a greater percentage of chromosomal aberrations than of gene mutations, while the reverse is true for X rays. This is thought to be due to the fact that **ionization** is dense along neutron paths, resulting in breakage, while it is not dense along the path of a fast electron, although it becomes denser in the tail of the path as the electron slows up.

Ionizing radiation is essentially that which in its passage through matter ejects electrons from the atoms through which it passes, thus ionizing the atom or radical, which is left positively charged and is called an **ion.** Ionizing radiations include α, β, and γ radiations of radioactive substances, X rays, protons, and neutrons. Ultraviolet light, which also can cause mutations, is not ionizing radiation. It can, however, cause **excitation,** which is still another way of dissipating energy in tissue and thus bringing about genetic effects. Excitation is the raising of an electron in an atom or molecule to a state of higher energy. X rays and other ionizing radiations also cause excitation, but this is far less effective in producing mutations and aberrations than is ionization.

Other physical agents such as electricity, ultra-short radio waves, supersonic radiations, electrostatic radiation, and high frequency alternating potentials have not resulted in increased production of genetic variation when tested.

The question of the mutagenic effects on the human species of exposure to ionizing radiation has been brought into dramatically sharp focus by the development of nuclear explosives (the "atom"

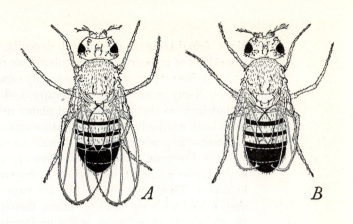

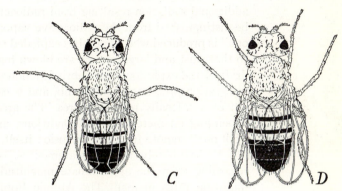

Fig. 24.7 Mutations in Drosophila resulting from radium irradiation. A, normal. B, rudimentary wing. C, miniature wing. D, small wing. These are true mutations and are inherited in regular Mendelian fashion. *From Hanson in the Journal of Heredity*

and "hydrogen" bombs, and the "U-bomb" exploded at Bikini in March 1954) and the increasing development of constructive applications of atomic energy. At the time of this writing, geneticists, physicists, medical men, and statesmen are acutely concerned with this question, and we may safely predict they will continue to be concerned with it for some time to come. The reasons for the intense interest in this problem are not hard to find.

(a) Ionizing radiations have been proved to accelerate the rate of mutation in every organism in which their genetic effects have been studied. These organisms include numerous kinds of insects, many species of seed plants, several yeasts, molds, bacteria and viruses, and mice. Since the genetic materials in the human species behave in every known respect like those of other organisms, we may safely assume that man's genes are similarly responsive to radiation.

(b) Insofar as mutations produce detectable effects, the effects are, as we have seen above, in the majority of cases harmful to the organism.

(c) Everyone is exposed to a certain amount of natural or "background" radiation; this comes from cosmic rays, local gamma radiations (emanating from mineral deposits, etc.), and from minute quantities of radioactive chemicals in our own cells.

(d) Many persons are occasionally exposed to ionizing radiations during X-ray examination or therapy, and some (radiologists, X-ray technicians, workers in industrial plants using radioactive materials) have been routinely exposed. Routine exposure will doubtless become commoner as peacetime uses of atomic energy become more prevalent.

(e) *Everyone, since 1945, has been exposed to radiation from radioactive vapors which become globally distributed after every nuclear-bomb explosion.* These are produced by the vaporization of the bomb itself and, mixed with air, tend to diffuse throughout the atmosphere, ultimately settling out more or less uniformly over the earth's surface.

(f) Many persons have been exposed (in some cases fatally) to additional radiation resulting from radioactive "fall out." This is to be distinguished from the radioactive vapor referred to above. "Fall out" is produced when a bomb is exploded relatively near the ground, so that dust and larger debris are blown high into the air by the updraft of the explosion. The debris is rendered radioactive by the disintegration products of the bomb, and is carried downwind, settling out over a locally restricted area. The area may be large or small, depending on meteorological conditions, and there may be intense "fall out" remote from the explosion itself.

Unfortunately, no clear statement is possible at the present time regarding even the approximate magnitude of radiation effects on mutation rates in man. The Atomic Bomb Casualty Commission, composed of outstanding American and Japanese scientists, made ingenious attempts to discover what genetic effects had resulted from the Hiroshima and Nagasaki bombings. Among many other data, they collected information on the sex ratio of children born to parents who had been in the bombed areas. They reasoned that if the radiation had produced a conspicuous increase in recessive lethal mutations on the X-chromosome, there should be relatively fewer males among the children whose mothers had been in the exposed areas, but whose fathers had not been exposed, than among children of exposed fathers and unexposed mothers. The findings of the Commission were inconclusive, however, apparently because so many other variables affect the sex ratio that it is almost hopeless to disentangle from them the possible effects of mutation in this kind of an investigation.

More recently, Macht and Lawrence have attacked the problem in another way. They sent questionnaires to 3000 radiologists asking for information regarding the outcome of their wives' past pregnancies; simultaneously they addressed the same inquiry to a control group of 3000 specialists in other fields. Some of the latter, they discovered, had experienced frequent exposure to X rays, so they made their comparisons between radiologists and "exposed" nonradiolo gists on the one hand, and the unexposed controls on the other. Perhaps their most interesting finding was that among children born to fathers in the exposed group there had been 6.0 per cent congenital malformations of one degree or another, as compared with 4.8 per cent among children of the unexposed controls. The differences are statistically significant, but some caution is needed in interpreting them because of possible sources of bias in the data.

Until a few years ago there had been little or no investigation of the mutagenic effects of radiation in any mammal because of the enormous scale on which the experiments must be conducted. Work on mammals has now begun in several laboratories, however, and preliminary reports on experiments carried out at the Oak Ridge National Laboratory have been published by W. L. Russell. His studies to date have involved more than 85,000 mice. Among Russell's early findings are (1) that X radiation conspicuously accelerates the mutation rate at a number of selected loci in the mouse; (2) that more than half of the detected mutations induced by radiation are lethal in homozygous condition; and (3) that the mutation rate induced in the mouse may be 15 times as great as that induced in Drosophila by comparable dosages.

Russell's conclusions from his preliminary findings are appropriately conservative, and he recognizes, of course, that to extrapolate from mouse to man is unwarranted. Nevertheless, referring to the "tolerances" or permissible exposures to radiation that are currently accepted as safe for the human species, he writes:

"The magnitude of the first generation effects already observed, with the doses used in these preliminary experiments with mice, indicates that if the present permissible weekly dose is to be kept, a total accumulated dose limit may have to be established to protect the individual from incurring too great a risk of damage to his offspring."

We have been unable here to do justice in any sense to the complex and important problems involved in assessing the mutagenic effects of radiation on man. We urge the student who is interested (and we think all should be) to read from time to time the excellent and authoritative nontechnical discussions of this problem which appear almost every month in the *Bulletin of the Atomic Scientists*.

18. Certain chemicals may also serve to increase the mutation rate.

For many years geneticists have attempted to discover chemical agents that would result in increased production of mutations, but negative results were obtained until the time of the Second World War. Compounds of copper, lead, iodine, ammonia, and other substances had been tried with no success.

During the Second World War Dr. J. M. Robson of England was engaged in a study of the effects of war gases. He noted that mustard gas burns were similar to X-ray burns, in that they healed with difficulty, tended to break down again after healing, and showed evidence of inhibited mitosis. These facts caused him to speculate that mustard gas might be effective in producing mutations, in a manner similar to the action of X rays. This possibility was tested by Auerbach with Drosophila, and a great increase in mutation rate was obtained. Other investigators have obtained positive results using the same and other chemicals on such widely separated forms as mice, plants, and bacteria.

Among the effective chemicals are the sulfur mustards, the nitrogen mustards, allyl isothiocyanate, ethyl urethane, phenol, and such cancer-producing chemicals as methylcholanthrene, dibenzanthracene, and benzyprene. Other chemicals which are also penetrating and toxic or which also cause blisters have not proved to be mutagenic. Among those tested with negative results are Lewisite, osmic acid, picric acid, chloracetone, dichloracetone, phenanthrene, pyrene, and azoxybenzene.

It is thought that those chemical agents which increase the mutation rate have a distribution of electrons such that they can transfer energy to specific loci on the chromosomes. Thus their mode of action in producing mutations would be similar to that of radiations. From a detailed knowledge of physical chemistry it should eventually be possible to predict which compounds would be mutagenic and which would not.

Like radiations, chemical mutagens act in an unspecific, random way on the chromosomes and genes. It has not yet been possible to predict what particular mutation or aberration will result from any given treatment.

The usual method of treatment with chemical mutagens is to keep the experimental organisms in an atmosphere containing a fine mist, or aerosol, of the solution of the chemical, although Strong's experiments on mice were by means of injecting the chemical directly into the body.

19. Genes are ultramicroscopic in size.

Various methods of estimating the size of genes have been used. In early work attempts were made to determine the volume of a chromosome, calculate the number of gene loci on it, and divide the volume by the number of genes. Even crude estimates of this sort made it clear that genes must be submicroscopic in size. Later methods include comparisons of the number of gene changes with the number of ions produced by a given X-ray dosage. One of the best methods (Muller and Prokofyeva) utilizes the giant chromosomes which we discussed in Chapter 22. Here the physical length of a given section of a chromosome can be directly measured and compared with the maximum possible number of breaks produced by X rays between detectable genes. All estimates agree that the gene is of sub-microscopic volume, probably within the range of size of large protein molecules. Thus, recent work of Lea and Catcheside in Great Britain indicates that the diameter of the gene is 4–8 millimicrons (a millimicron is a millionth of a millimeter, or about a twenty-five millionth of an inch).

The X-ray work indicates that each mutation produced by irradiation is the result of a direct hit by a photoelectron. This would favor the assumption that a gene is a single large organic molecule rather than a group of molecules.

In addition to the indirect evidence for the ultramicroscopic size of the gene, there is some direct evidence. Huettner finds that when dividing cells of Drosophila are stained with Feulgen stain, which colors only chromatin, the nucleus in the interphase is entirely clear. As the stages of mitosis take place, minute chromatin granules appear. These rapidly increase in size and number, so that the thread-like structure of long chromosomes is soon evident. In one definite position in the central region of the nucleus two small chromatin dots appear, which develop into a pair of small chromosomes. The rest of the granules are grouped in three regions and develop into three pairs of long chromosomes. Thus the gene strings have definite positions inside the nucleus, but they are visible only when enough of the chromatin matrix has been evolved by them to increase their size to the point of visibility.

20. Chemically, genes are most probably desoxyribose nucleic acids (DNA).

It is, of course, exceedingly difficult to get any direct chemical analysis of individual genes. Various investigators, including Watson, Crick, and their colleagues in England, and Mirsky and Ris in America, have analyzed isolated chromosomes and have found that they are largely made up of **nucleoproteins.** A nucleoprotein is a substance of high molecular weight, consisting of protein combined with nucleic acid. **Nucleic acids** are themselves of high molecular weight and are highly compounded (polymerized).

Two main groups of nucleic acids are known, taking their names from the sugar which is an essential part of each. **Ribose nucleic acids** contain ribose (a pentose sugar), while **desoxyribose nucleic acids** contain desoxyribose (a desoxypentose sugar). Ribose nucleic acid is generally confined to the cytoplasm and its inclusions, but desoxyribose nucleic acid is always found in the nucleus. We shall therefore focus our discussion on desoxyribose nucleic acid, the chemical structure of which has been so elegantly elucidated by the British workers.

A molecule of desoxyribose looks like this:

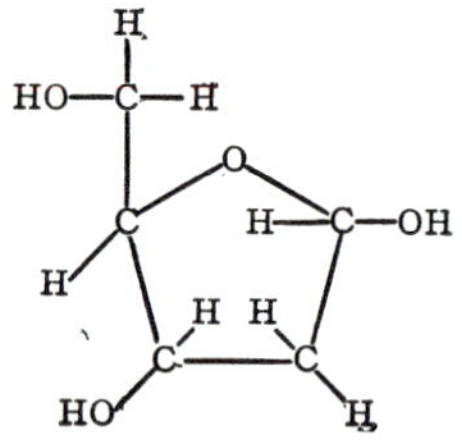

Such a sugar molecule may readily become attached to a **purine** (a molecule with a double ring consisting of five carbon atoms and four nitrogen atoms) or to a **pyrimidine** (a molecule with a single ring consisting of four carbon atoms and two nitrogen atoms). A sugar molecule attached to a purine or a pyrimidine is called a **nucleoside**, as shown below, left.

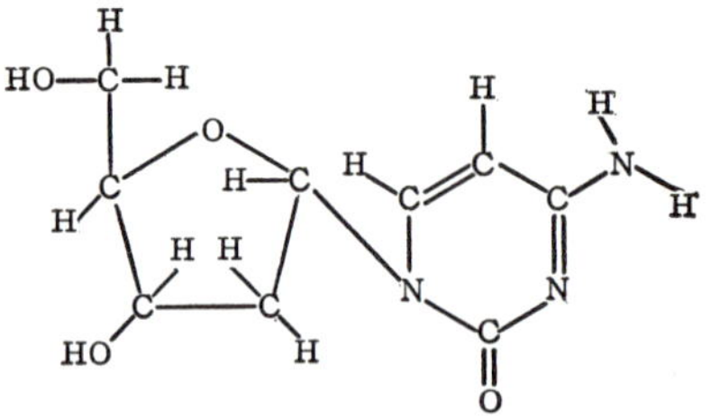

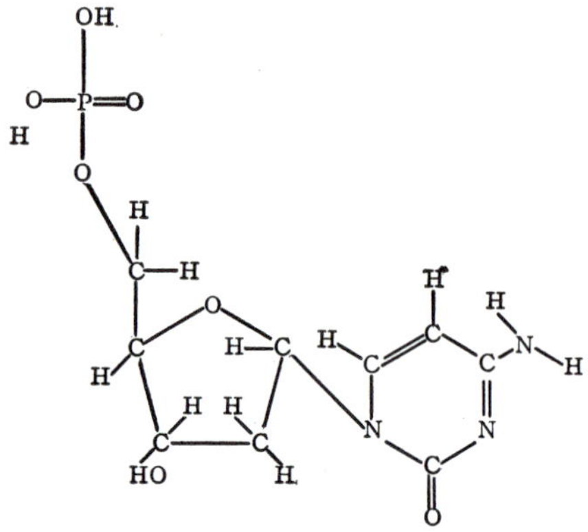

When the sugar of a nucleoside is attached to phosphate the molecule is called a **nucleotide**, as illustrated above.

The sugar of one nucleotide may be attached to the phosphate of another, and so on in regular sequence, forming long molecules. The alternating sugar and phosphate groups form a long, rather straight chain, with the purines and pyrimidines projecting out from the chain at right angles, thus:

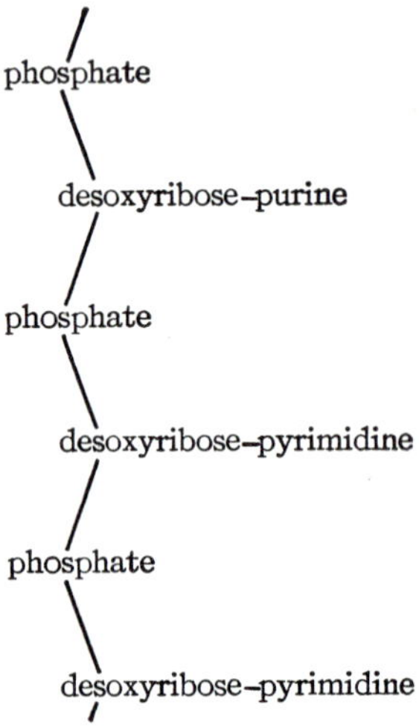

The DNA molecule consists of two such chains running parallel to each other but oriented in opposite directions. Each purine of one chain is attached to a pyrimidine of the other chain, forming a series of short cross-chains between the two long chains.

If you can imagine a ladder made of chains, you will have the general effect. Each of the two lengthwise chains of the ladder is made

phosphate

desoxyribose–purine

phosphate

desoxyribose–pyrimidine

phosphate

desoxyribose–pyrimidine

up of units of sugar and of phosphate, alternating one with the other along the length of the chain. The sugar in DNA is always desoxyribose. The long chains are thus fairly straight and quite regular. Since the two run in opposite directions, there is no distinctive top nor bottom to the molecule.

Each short cross-chain, or "rung" of the ladder, connects a sugar on one long chain with a sugar across from it on the other. Each cross-chain consists of one purine and one pyrimidine, loosely bonded together by hydrogen bonds. The general structure of a DNA molecule would therefore look like this:

```
      /                                                    \
  phosphate                                            phosphate
      \                                                    /
   desoxyribose–purine —— pyrimidine-desoxyribose
      /                                                    \
  phosphate                                            phosphate
      \                                                    /
   desoxyribose–pyrimidine —— purine-desoxyribose
      /                                                    \
  phosphate                                            phosphate
      \                                                    /
   desoxyribose–purine —— pyrimidine-desoxyribose
      /                                                    \
  phosphate                                            phosphate
      \                                                    /
   desoxyribose–purine —— pyrimidine-desoxyribose
      /                                                    \
```

Although there are many kinds of DNA, there are only two different purines and two different pyrimidines ordinarily found in them. The purines are adenine and guanine, and the pyrimidines are thymine and cytosine. Moreover, adenine is always joined to thymine to make a cross-chain, and guanine is always joined to cytosine.

There may be more cross-chains of one of the two types than of the other in any particular kind of DNA, but for every adenine there is always one thymine, and for every guanine there is always one cytosine. The order of the two kinds of cross-chains may likewise vary in different kinds of DNA; moreover, the cross-chains may be connected to the side chains now in one direction, now in the reverse direction. Figure 24.8 illustrates a diagrammatic model of a fragment of a molecule of DNA.

The DNA molecule is very long and thin, being less than a billionth of an inch across, and more than a thousand times as long as its diameter. Moreover, the whole molecule is coiled lengthwise, and we must imagine our chain ladder twisted so as to form a spiral staircase, with the rungs or steps remaining parallel to each other. Running through the center of the spiral (or more properly, *helix*) is a protein core.

There are, then, apparently only four basic units in the DNA molecule, namely, sugar (desoxyribose), phosphate, purines, and pyrimidines. Moreover, only two kinds of purines and two kinds of pyrimidines ordinarily occur. How, then, can there be enough kinds of DNA to account for all the kinds of genes and chromosomes? The

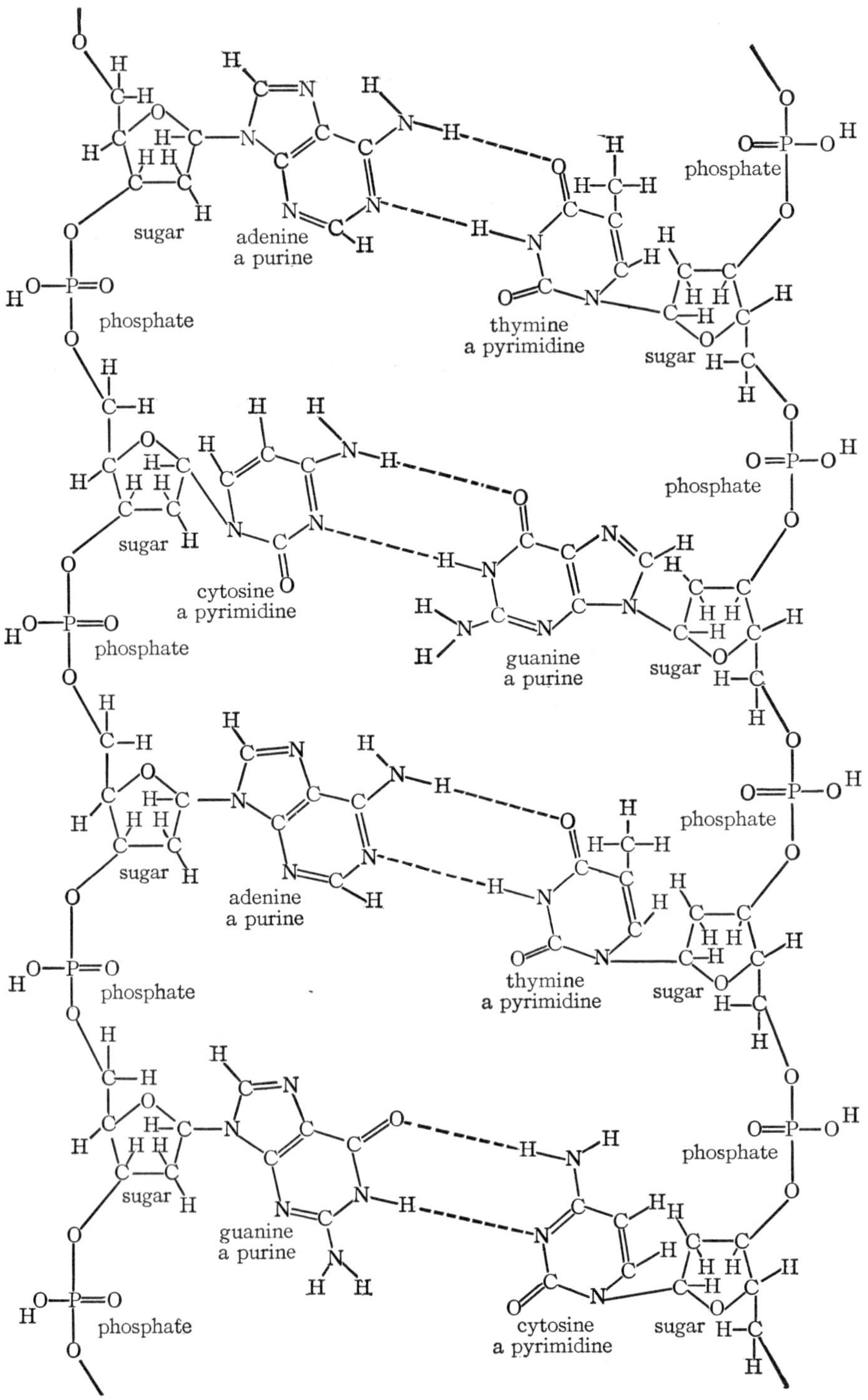
sugar
adenine
a purine
phosphate
thymine
a pyrimidine
sugar
phosphate
sugar
cytosine
a pyrimidine
phosphate
guanine
a purine
sugar
phosphate
sugar
adenine
a purine
phosphate
thymine
a pyrimidine
sugar
phosphate
sugar
guanine
a purine
phosphate
cytosine
a pyrimidine
sugar

answer probably lies in the fact that variation can occur in the relative numbers of adenine-thymine and of guanine-cytosine cross-chains; it can occur in the order in which these cross-chains appear, and it can occur in the direction in which each cross-chain is attached to the long chains. Because DNA molecules are very long, the permutations and combinations of these variations are tremendous.

It is not yet certain whether genes, like chromosomes, are nucleo-proteins or only the desoxyribose nucleic acids of the nucleoproteins. Evidence is appearing which indicates that true genic material is DNA. For one thing, it is found that ultraviolet light may induce mutations. Since only *absorbed* ultraviolet light can cause chemical change, it is important to know the wave lengths which are effective in inducing mutations. It is found that the effective wave lengths are those absorbed by DNA. Further evidence in favor of DNA as the material of the gene arises from the study of transformations and transductions in bacteria, which will be discussed in detail in Chapter 27.

It is obvious that genes are highly specific in function. We have already seen in connection with the blood groups that certain genes produce very specific antigens. It will be shown in succeeding chapters that genes frequently produce equally specific enzymes (chemicals that facilitate chemical reactions without themselves becoming used up in the process). Thousands of enzymes take part in the metabolic activities of living organisms, and many of the enzymes appear to be referable to single genes. The constructive potentialities of nucleic acids appear to be such as to provide that great diversity, nicety, and forcefulness of action which is characteristic of the gene.

21. Genes are able to duplicate themselves.

At each mitosis every gene reproduces itself. The manner of this self-propagation is clearly one of the fundamental problems of genetics, but as yet relatively little progress has been made toward its solution. It is now agreed that a gene duplicates itself not by growing and splitting but by building alongside itself a duplicate of itself. Moreover, when a gene mutates, it will build a copy of the new mutated form just as faithfully as it formerly copied the original form.

This unique ability of a gene to draw from the surrounding medium the various building blocks needed to duplicate itself and to impress upon them its own pattern, even when that pattern is a changed, or mutated pattern, is at the very center of the process of the evolution of life and life processes. The necessary building blocks for

Fig. 24.8 A model of a fragment of a molecule of DNA, constructed according to descriptions published by Crick, Watson, and others.

the formation of nucleoproteins are amino acids, purines, pyrimidines, and phosphates. It has been suggested that each chemical unit of a gene, such as a side chain or radical, attracts to itself a similar but uncombined unit available in the surrounding medium, and that these are held together in position against the gene while chemical union between the parts takes place, thus creating a replica of the gene. The problems of gene duplication are among the most challenging of those facing geneticists at the present time and will require the aid of biochemists and physicists for their complete solution.

Crick has proposed an interesting hypothesis of chromosome and gene duplication. It will be recalled that DNA is composed of two complementary chains of nucleotides, loosely bonded together, purine to pyrimidine, by hydrogen bonds (indicated by the dotted lines in Figure 24.8). These chains may separate at the hydrogen bonds and unwind from their helical twist. Each chain is a complement of the other, and when separated and unwound each chain may construct another complement of itself from the available building blocks in the protoplasm, so that there will be two long double chains (DNA molecules) where there was only one before.

Crick suggests that the formation of the new complementary chains begins as the old chains start to unwind, and that this formation is the force behind the continued unwinding of the original pair. Crick's article, listed in the references at the end of this chapter, should be read by all students of genetics.

The twenty-one points discussed above constitute the major facts at our disposal regarding genes and mutations. Individually many of them are of limited significance; taken together they form a unified and important body of knowledge upon which to build our conception of the gene and its behavior.

As to the origin of genes, we know very little, although it is tempting to speculate. Genes are assumed by some to be the most primitive living things. It is said that they were probably the first manifestations of life, growth, and reproduction, and that the complicated organization of cells developed first under the influence of genes — genes which presumably were originally free living entities.

An alternative hypothesis is proposed by Holmes. He suggests that perhaps genes, instead of representing primitive living bodies, are secondary products arising as the end result of a long series of exchanges between homologous chromosomes. He postulates that during the early stages of their evolution chromosomes may have consisted of similar material throughout. In different individuals of a species, chromosomes might have come to be composed of material of slightly different chemical constitution. As sexual reproduction evolved, and with it the mechanism of crossing over, chromosomes would gradually come to be composed of dissimilar material in their different parts through reciprocal exchange.

Through repeated crossing over during many generations these regionally different sections of the chromosomes would become more numerous and consequently smaller until they reached the minimum size or structure compatible with self-perpetuation. This would account for the linear arrangement of genes in the chromosomes.

Hypotheses such as the two just cited are interesting speculations, but it must not be forgotten that they are only speculations, and are not to be confused with the known facts and the reasonable inferences which make up the bulk of our knowledge of genes and mutations.

General conclusions

From the above facts, principles, and inferences, we may devise a working hypothesis as to the nature of the gene and the nature and cause of mutation. It will be understood that this hypothesis is by no means final. It may be revised at any time by the discovery of new facts, the search for which is continuing unabated in many laboratories in all parts of the world.

The gene, then, is pictured as a large complex organic molecule, or part of a molecule, occupying a specific place in a series of such molecules arranged in linear order. Each string of molecules composes the essential part of a chromosome, which at certain stages in cell division is visible due to the elaboration around the genes of a stainable matrix.

On this basis a mutation would consist of a rearrangement of the order, direction, or proportion of the cross-chains. The cause of these rearrangements is probably inherent in the molecular structure of the genes. Mutations may be regarded as the results of random inter- and intra-molecular rearrangements. They are, in other words, the results of isolated microchemical accidents, not individually controllable. As Muller has pointed out, such accidents would tend to occur with a fixed frequency under given conditions. He compares mutation to ordinary chemical reactions, in which the gross change from one substance to another really is the statistical resultant of a whole series of individually accidental molecular collisions; the rate of change as a whole is fixed and calculable.

Muller has carried this reasoning one step further. In the case of ordinary chemical reactions, we are interested not in any individual molecular effects because they are so numerous, but rather we think in terms of the total reaction. In the case of mutations, however, due to the great stability of gene molecules, each change that does occur becomes in its development and reproduction so magnified in importance that the individual molecular changes rather than the mass effect become the primary concern of geneticists.

There is some experimental evidence to indicate that, in addition to spontaneous molecular changes, natural radiation may under certain circumstances play some small part in the production of natural mutations. For example, Drosophila placed in an abandoned carnotite mine, where natural radiation was high, produced a greater proportion of mutations than those kept in a region where terrestrial radiation was low. Such instances, however, must be considered of minor significance in the total production of mutations.

PROBLEMS

24.1 In using the *ClB* method what would be the result if the irradiation should cause the gene *L* in the X-rayed *cLb* male to mutate to *l?*

24.2 Why is the X-chromosome more favorable for the study of the production of recessive gene mutations than are the autosomes?

24.3 Why is the X-chromosome more favorable for the study of the production of recessive lethal mutations than are the autosomes?

24.4 If a single recessive mutation occurs in the somatic tissue, what effect will it have upon the appearance of an individual?

24.5 What happens to a somatic mutation when the individual organism dies?

24.6 How may a recessive mutation produce a visible effect?

24.7 If a recessive mutation occurs in the fertilized egg, in what cells of the mature individual will the mutant gene be found?

24.8 Would the answer to the previous question be different if the mutation were a dominant mutation?

24.9 If a mutation occurs in one of the two cells into which the fertilized egg divides, in what cells of the mature individual would the mutant gene be found?

24.10 If a mutation occurs in one of the many somatic cells of a relatively late stage of development of an organism, in what cells of the mature individual will the mutant gene be found?

24.11 If a mutation occurs in a spermatogonium, what will be its history?

24.12 Suppose a Drosophila sperm containing a Y-chromosome fertilizes an egg containing an X-chromosome. The resulting zygote divides into two cells by mitosis, and in one of these two cells a gene on the X-chromosome mutates so that instead of causing the production of normal wing it causes the production of miniature wing. Assuming that the first cleavage division determines the plane of bilaterality, what will be the sex of the mature fly and what kind of wings will it have?

24.13 The Washington navel orange is characterized by a relatively smooth skin. Occasionally, however, a tree has a branch on which the oranges all have deeply corrugated, ribbed skin. If such a branch is used for grafting, the resulting grafted tree produces only ribbed fruit. The ribbed fruit is probably due to what cause?

REFERENCES

ALTENBURG, E., *Science* **78**:587 (1933).

AUERBACH, C., *Proc. Eighth Internat. Cong. of Genetics* **129**. Lund, Sweden, Berlingska Boktryckeriet (1949).

BEADLE, G. W., *Science in Progress* **6**:184. New Haven, Yale Univ. Press (1949).

BLACKWOOD, O., *Physical Rev.* **37**:1698 (1931); *ibid.* **40**:1034 (1932).

CATCHESIDE, D. G., *Advances in Genetics* **2**:271. New York, Academic Press, Inc. (1948).

CRICK, F. H. C., *Scientific American* **191**:54 (1955).

DEMEREC, M., *Jour. Genetics* **24**:179 (1931); *Jour. Heredity* **24**:369 (1933); *Proc. Eighth Internat. Cong. of Genetics* **201**. Lund, Sweden, Berlingska Boktryckeriet (1949).

FISHER, R. A., *The Genetical Theory of Natural Selection*. Oxford, The Clarendon Press (1930).

HALDANE, J. B. S., *Proc. Eighth Internat. Cong. of Genetics* **267**. Lund, Sweden, Berlingska Boktryckeriet (1949).

HANSON, F. B., *Jour. Heredity* **20**:277 (1929); *Physiol. Rev.* **13**:466 (1933).

HUETTNER, A. F., unpublished material quoted by DEMEREC, *Jour. Heredity* **24**: 369 (1933).

LEA, D. E., *Actions of Radiations on Living Cells*. Cambridge, England, Cambridge Univ. Press (1945).

LEA, D. E., and CATCHESIDE, D. G., *Jour. Genetics* **44**:216 (1942); *ibid.* **47**:10, 41 (1945).

LEVENE, P. A., *Jour. Biol. Chemistry* **48**:1191 (1921).

MACHT, S. I., and LAWRENCE, P. S., *Amer. Jour. Roentgenology* **73**:442 (1955).

MIRSKY, A. E., and RIS, H., *Jour. Gen. Physiol.* **31**:7 (1947).

MULLER, H. J., "Mutation." *Eugenics, Genetics and the Family* **1**:106. Baltimore, The Williams and Wilkins Co. (1923); *Science* **66**:84 (1927); *Proc. Int. Cong. Plant Sciences* **1**:897 (1929); *Amer. Naturalist* **64**:220 (1930); *Current Science*, Special Number on Genetics, March (1938); *Bull. Atomic Scientists* **11**:329 (1955).

MULLER, H. J., LITTLE, C. C., and SNYDER, L. H., *Genetics, Medicine, and Man*. Ithaca, Cornell Univ. Press (1947).

MULLER, H. J., and MOTT-SMITH, L. M., *Proc. Nat. Acad. Science* **16**:277 (1930).

MULLER, H. J., and PROKOFYEVA, A. A., *Proc. Nat. Acad. Science* **21**:16 (1935).

NEEL, J. V., and SCHULL, W. J., *The Effect of Exposure to the Atomic Bombs on Pregnancy Termination in Hiroshima and Nagasaki*. Washington, D.C., Publ. 461, Nat. Acad. Sci.–Nat. Research Council (1956).

NORDHEIM, L. W., *Bull. Atomic Scientists* **11**:253 (1955).

PATTERSON, J. T., and MULLER, H. J., *Genetics* **15**:495 (1930).

PENROSE, L. S., and HALDANE, J. B. S., *Nature* **135**:907 (1935).

PLOUGH, H. H., and IVES, P. T., *Proc. Sixth Int. Cong. Genetics* **2**:156 (1932); *Proc. Nat. Acad. Science* **20**:268 (1934).

ROTBLAT, J., *Bull. Atomic Scientists* **11**:171 (1955).

RUSSELL, W. L., in *Radiation Biology* (A. Hollaender, ed.) **1**:825. New York, McGraw-Hill Book Co. (1954); *Bull. Atomic Scientists* **12**:19 (1956).

STADLER, L. J., *Sci. Agr.* **11**:645 (1931); *Univ. of Mo. Bull.* **300**:77.

STRONG, L. C., *Proc. Eighth Internat. Cong. of Genetics* **486**. Lund, Sweden, Berlingska Boktryckeriet (1949).

CHAPTER TWENTY-FIVE

Cytoplasmic inheritance

One of the major conclusions drawn from genetic research of the past half century has been that traits are determined, insofar as genetic differences provide the effective variables, by self-duplicating, mutable genes located at specific points in the chromosomes. The evidence for this conclusion was summarized in Chapter 22.

In recent years, however, various observations and experiments have been made which suggest that some genetic variability is the result of self-duplicating, mutable units located not in the chromosomes but in the cytoplasm. Such units are apparently transmitted only by means of the cytoplasm, and therefore since only the egg ordinarily contributes cytoplasm to the zygote, the inheritance, in higher animals and plants at least, is maternal.

One type of cytoplasmic transmission, plastid inheritance in plants, has long been known, but it was until recently considered an isolated and unique example. A discussion of plastids will serve to introduce the general problem.

Plastids are cytoplasmic bodies occurring in certain cells of plants. Normal plastids contain (or can produce in the presence of light) chlorophyl, the green coloring matter which is involved in the process of photosynthesis. They are self-duplicating bodies which are distributed *more or less at random* to the two daughter cells when a plant cell divides, in contrast to nuclear genes which are distributed *in an exact orderly fashion* by the segregation of chromosomes.

Not all plastids in higher plants contain or can produce chlorophyl. We have already discussed in several places albinism, in which the plastids are defective and no longer synthesize chlorophyl, so that the cytoplasm appears white. Albinism is usually the result of a typical recessive gene mutation, so that a seedling homozygous for the mutated gene is completely white, while one not having the gene in homozygous form is completely green. Here the gene mutation seems to have resulted in the production of a physiological condition unfavorable to normal plastid development, and the mutant gene is transmitted in the usual Mendelian manner.

In some cases, however, a different type of transmission occurs, not involving chromosomal segregation. In certain strains of four-o'clocks, for example, colorless plastids are found as well as green ones, but both types occur in the same plant and even in the same leaf. Such leaves are variegated, that is, irregularly blotched green and white. Sometimes a whole branch is white, containing only colorless plastids in its tissues. Again, a whole branch may be green, containing only colored plastids.

When flowers on a white branch are pollinated with pollen from a green branch, the resulting offspring are all white. When flowers on a green branch are pollinated with pollen from a white branch, the resulting offspring are all green. Whichever way the cross is made, the offspring resemble only the mother in regard to leaf and stem color.

Since the plastids are contained in the cytoplasm and since ordinarily no cytoplasm is brought in by the sperm at fertilization, it appears that the transmission in such instances is purely cytoplasmic and non-Mendelian. Similar behavior has been recorded in corn, beans, sorghum, and many other plants. A photograph of striping in sorghum, in which the transmission is purely maternal, is shown in Figure 25.1.

In cases like those just mentioned it is supposed that a mutation has taken place in the plastid itself. Since in this view plastids are self-duplicating mutable units controlling characters, they or some parts of them are sometimes referred to as plastogenes.

Other examples of cytoplasmic inheritance have been coming to light, some of them with far-reaching implications in biological theory

Fig. 25.1 Striping in sorghum. This form of striping is transmitted only through the female line, the male parent playing no part in the inheritance of the character. *From Karper in the Journal of Heredity*

and even in medicine. In deciding whether transmission is really cytoplasmic, care must be taken to exclude other possibilities. For example, as will be pointed out in Chapter 26, certain characters of the plant or animal are already determined in the cytoplasm of the egg, under the influence of the Mendelian genes of the mother. Effects such as these can be ruled out by various procedures such as transplantation experiments and repeated back-crossing.

There are now on record a number of clear cases of cytoplasmic transmission in addition to plastid inheritance. These include certain structural characters in mosses, sterility in various plants, size and shape differences in the evening primrose, pathogenicity in rusts, color in wasps, sensitivity to carbon dioxide in Drosophila, and a number of characters in the protozoan Paramecium. Some of the examples mentioned are instances of purely maternal inheritance, others are cases where there seems to be an interaction of a Mendelian gene and a unit or units in the cytoplasm, but all involve cytoplasmic transmission.

The researches of Sonneborn and his collaborators with Paramecium are of especial importance in understanding cytoplasmic inheritance, and a brief account of some of them will be given here. Although many of the characters of this unicellular organism are controlled by genes carried in the chromosomes in the nucleus, other characters are apparently cytoplasmically determined. Such cytoplasmic determiners are often called **plasmagenes.** One kind of plasmagene in Paramecium has been shown to be self-reproducing and capable of mutation. This kind of plasmagene depends for its maintenance and reproduction on nuclear genes, however, and is therefore not completely autonomous. A description of this plasmagene and its action will illustrate the general developments in this very new area.

Genes are traditionally named with Roman letters: a, b, c, and so on. The convention has arisen of naming cytoplasmic determiners with Greek letters such as alpha, beta, gamma. The plasmagene most thoroughly studied in Paramecium is one called "kappa." When it is present in the cytoplasm in sufficient concentration it results in the production of an extra-cellular antibiotic agent called paramecin. This substance will kill Paramecia of certain strains known as "sensitives," although it does not affect those strains which produce it, known as "killers."

Kappa can be maintained in an individual and its progeny only when the dominant gene K is present in the nucleus. Thus individuals of genotypes KK and Kk may be killers; those of genotype kk are always sensitives. However, the mere presence of gene K in the nucleus does not insure the presence of kappa. Kappa must come from pre-existing kappa by its own self-duplication.

The modes of reproduction of *Paramecium aurelia* are varied and complicated. These animals may reproduce asexually by simple fission, in which case all the individuals of a single line of descent will be genetically identical except for mutations which may occur. They may also reproduce sexually, but in two different ways. In one mode of sexual reproduction two individuals of opposite mating type come together and exchange one of the two micronuclei which each animal possesses. These nuclei are diploid during most of the life of the individual but become haploid before mating by maturation divisions. Moreover, of the eight haploid nuclei resulting from the maturation of the two micronuclei, only one survives, and this one divides mitotically to form two. The two haploid nuclei of each mating partner are thus identical within the individual. When the two animals separate after mating they have become identical for all their nuclear genes because of the exchange. If the cytoplasmic bridge between the two mating individuals persists for less than three minutes, no cytoplasm is exchanged, but if it persists longer, cytoplasm as well as nuclei may be exchanged.

The second type of sexual reproduction involves only one parent. In this type, known as autogamy, the two micronuclei undergo maturation divisions, but seven of the eight resulting haploid nuclei degenerate, leaving one. This one divides mitotically, forming two identical haploid nuclei, just as happened previous to mating in the description given in the preceding paragraph. But instead of the individual mating with another Paramecium, its own two haploid nuclei fuse, forming a homozygous diploid nucleus, which then by mitosis divides to form two.

Because of these varied modes of reproduction, it is possible to manipulate Paramecium in such a way as to combine any cytoplasm with any desired gene. Thus by proper manipulation it is possible to replace gene K by its allele k in a killer animal. When this is done the animal gradually loses its kappa and becomes sensitive. If now the original K is brought back into the cell by suitable crossing, it cannot recreate kappa, and the individual will remain sensitive.

A killer individual must, then, contain both the gene K and a suitable concentration of kappa. The concentration necessary to make an individual a killer is from several hundred to about 1000 kappa particles. The reproduction of plasmagenes is not necessarily correlated with the rate of cell division, so that by suitable control of the cultural conditions it is possible to bring the concentration of kappa to any desired level and maintain it there. When a killer animal with several hundred kappa plasmagenes is so manipulated as to reduce its supply of kappa, it first stops producing paramecin, although remaining resistant; it then becomes sensitive, although retaining gene K.

Now these facts show a remarkable similarity to a series of discoveries in regard to cancer. In mice, for example, there are strains in which practically every animal develops mammary cancer; others in which almost no animal does. Crosses between these strains indicated that the inheritance of the tumors was largely maternal, hence extrachromosomal. Further studies by Bittner indicated that the transmission was largely on the basis of some substance, probably a virus, in the mother's milk.

Recent research by Heston and his colleagues indicates a strong resemblance between the milk agent in mice and kappa in Paramecium. For example, the maintenance of the milk agent is dependent upon certain genes in mice just as that of kappa is dependent upon the gene K in Paramecium. Again, certain noncancerous strains of mice have the requisite genes but lack the milk agent, just as certain sensitive strains of the protozoan may have K but lack kappa. In addition, the transfer of the milk agent through milk from foster mothers to mice having the cancer genes but lacking the milk agent will result in these animals maintaining the milk agent and transmitting it, just as in Paramecium, killer strains can be produced by adding kappa to a strain having gene K but lacking kappa. Finally, Heston and his colleagues showed that it was possible to maintain the milk factor at low concentration with no resulting cancer, just as Sonneborn had been able to do with kappa and the resulting lack of production of the antibiotic paramecin.

The above facts raise the question as to the fundamental differences, if any, between plasmagenes and viruses. Both are located outside the chromosomes; both are self-duplicating, but only in the requisite genotype; both are mutable and reproduce the mutated form; both result in definite characters. If they differ at all, it would appear to be in the conceptions that plasmagenes are transmitted by a type of heredity and are normal cell constituents, while viruses are transmitted by infection and are abnormal, pathogenic cell dwellers. Darlington, Haddow, Sonneborn, and others have speculated on these facts. It has been pointed out that what is a virus in one species or variety may be a plasmagene in another, in the same way that thiamine is a necessary vitamin for man but is normally synthesized by certain plants and is thus not a vitamin for them.

For example, a plasmagene in one variety of potato acts as a pathogenic virus when transferred to another variety. Other examples both in plants and in animals are known. It may be then, as Darlington suggests, that a virus is merely a plasmagene in the wrong host. Recent research appears to indicate, however, that a virus particle may contain several genes. This discovery complicates the hypothesis of the equivalence of plasmagenes and viruses. The genetics of viruses will be discussed in more detail in Chapter 27.

On the basis of facts such as these there has been formulated the plasmagene theory of cancer. This theory involves the production of cancer by somatic mutations of plasmagenes, resulting in the release of the ordinary inhibitions regulating cell growth and division. The various known carcinogenic agents would, on this theory, either make the cells more receptive to foreign plasmagenes (viruses) or cause mutations of native plasmagenes.

On the plasmagene theory of cancer the lag between the application of the cancer-producing chemical and the appearance of the cancer would be readily explained. When a few particles of kappa are introduced into a Paramecium lacking kappa but having K, the kappa increases gradually under proper conditions. When it reaches the level of several hundred particles, the cell becomes a killer instead of being sensitive. It may very well be in cancer that the mutated plasmagene must slowly increase to the critical cellular concentration requisite for cancer manifestation.

The older theory of the gene clearly requires modification. There is no reason now to doubt the existence of cytoplasmic units: mutable, self-duplicating, and capable of controlling the development of characters. Specific, localizable, Mendelian, chromosomal genes and specific extra-nuclear determiners, some of which are localizable in visible cytoplasmic structures, must both be taken into account in formulating a complete description of the hereditary basis for characters.

As was pointed out at the beginning of the chapter, cytoplasmic inheritance due to plasmagenes such as kappa and to viruses such as the milk agent is known in a variety of organisms. Yet there is no assurance at present that all examples of cytoplasmic inheritance have the same physical basis and result from the same mechanism. Indeed, Sonneborn's investigations already show fundamental differences in the mechanism even within Paramecium. The differences are largely concerned with the extent of the dependence of the physical basis of cytoplasmic inheritance on nuclear genes. The significance of these differences and the explanation of the examples that differ from kappa are still not fully understood. Whatever the explanation turns out to be, it seems likely that it will throw much light on the problem of how cells that are identical in genes, such as the cells of the various tissues in higher animals, can remain persistently different in structure. This leads directly to the problem of the roles of genes and cytoplasm in the control of developmental differentiation, a subject to be considered in the next chapter.

PROBLEMS

25.1 When flowers on a variegated branch of the four-o'clock are self-pollinated, the offspring may have green or variegated or white leaves. How do you account for these results?

25.2 What offspring would you expect from flowers on a variegated branch pollinated with pollen from a green branch? With pollen from a white branch?

25.3 It has been suggested by some writers that nuclear inheritance affords greater opportunities for genetic variation than does cytoplasmic inheritance because of the possibility of recombination in the former. Criticize this statement in the light of the information gained from the preceding problems.

25.4 Can we discriminate between nuclear inheritance and cytoplasmic inheritance on the basis of the mere presence or absence of recombination? Would the occurrence of Mendelian ratios aid the discrimination?

25.5 Correns concluded from his study of the inheritance of leaf color in the four-o'clock that the whitening of all or of part of the leaf was due to a sort of disease carried by the cytoplasm. Can we discriminate between his interpretation and an explanation based on cytoplasmic inheritance?

25.6 All strains of the King Edward potato possess the paracrinkle virus, which has no apparent effect on the King Edward potato but shows its effects when transmitted to certain susceptible strains by grafting. Is paracrinkle virus a normal or abnormal constituent of the King Edward potato? Why is it classified as a virus? Can we readily distinguish between virus transmission and cytoplasmic inheritance?

25.7 In Habrobracon (a wasp) the females are diploid, the males haploid. There is a dark strain and a light strain in this species. When these strains are crossed, the diploid F_1 females are intermediate, but there is a difference depending on whether the mother was light or dark. When the mother was light, the F_1 females are significantly lighter than the F_1 females from dark mothers. This difference persists in the haploid sons of these females and also in their daughters when the F_1 females are

crossed to males of both sorts. Suggest an explanation of the color inheritance.

25.8 Cytoplasmic inheritance is frequently characterized by differences in the results of reciprocal crosses. Such differences may also be observed in sex-linkage, and in inheritance due solely to maternal genotype. (See Chapter 26 and problems 26.3, 26.4, and 26.5 for a discussion of such inheritance.) What crosses would you make to distinguish between cytoplasmic inheritance and sex-linkage?

25.9 What crosses would you make to distinguish between cytoplasmic inheritance and inheritance due to maternal genotype?

25.10 Geranium plants may have green, variegated, or white leaves. When the flowers of plants with green leaves are self-pollinated, the offspring have green leaves. When the flowers of plants with white leaves are self-pollinated, the offspring have white leaves. Reciprocal crosses between plants with green leaves and plants with white leaves produce offspring with variegated leaves. Considered by themselves, can these results be interpreted on a Mendelian basis?

25.11 When flowers of geranium plants with variegated leaves are self-pollinated, all the offspring have variegated leaves. What bearing does this additional information have upon your previous conclusion?

25.12 Can the results of these geranium crosses be interpreted on the basis of cytoplasmic inheritance with transmission through both pollen and egg?

25.13 Can we then consider difference in results from reciprocal crosses as essential criteria of cytoplasmic inheritance?

25.14 Drosophila are normally anesthetized by a short exposure to CO_2 gas, but recover with no ill effects. One strain, however, was found to be killed by such exposure. When sensitive females are crossed to resistant males, the F_1 are always sensitive. When resistant females are crossed with sensitive males, most of the F_1 are resistant, though some, in varying proportions, may be sensitive. (The sperm in Drosophila may bring in small amounts of cytoplasm.) Sensitive females were then crossed to resistant males in which each of the autosomes was marked by a dominant gene. The sensitive F_1 males containing these three dominant genes were crossed to resistant females. Some of the offspring were sensitive and some were resistant, but the response was independent of the segregation of the genes. The male offspring which showed all three of the marker genes had no chromosomes or parts of chromosomes from the original sensitive grandmother, since there is no crossing over in male Drosophila. Yet some of these males were sensitive. Suggest an explanation for the transmission of sensitivity.

25.15 Snapdragons may have green or variegated leaves. Reciprocal crosses between two varieties produce F_1 plants with green leaves and F_2 plants approximately $\frac{3}{4}$ of which have green leaves and $\frac{1}{4}$ have variegated leaves. Can these results be interpreted on a Mendelian basis?

25.16 Do these results necessarily preclude a possible role of the cytoplasm in the determination of leaf color in the snapdragon?

25.17 Certain hereditary differences (in antigenic type) in Paramecium have so far been ascribable only to difference in the cytoplasm. Do these results necessarily preclude a possible role of the nucleus in the determination of these differences?

25.18 On the basis of the answers to the two preceding questions, what logical inference might be drawn as regards the roles of nuclear and cytoplasmic elements in heredity?

25.19 Most hereditary traits have been shown to be nucleus-controlled, and relatively few have been shown to depend on genes inherited through the cytoplasm. Do these observations prove that the chromosomes are the major bearers of genes, or could they equally well indicate greater genetic variability in nuclear genes than in cytoplasmic genes?

25.20 Would any difference in degree of genetic variability between cytoplasmic and nuclear inheritance be necessarily ascribed to differences in mutability of the genes involved, or might they equally well suggest that mutations in one class of genes are less apt to be lethal to the individual carrying them than are mutations in another class of genes?

25.21 In view of the nature of the evidence required for the critical demonstration of cytoplasmic inheritance, is it reasonable to suppose that investigators have paid less attention to this mechanism of hereditary transmission than they have to the genes and chromosomes?

REFERENCES

BITTNER, J. J., *Amer. Jour. Cancer* **35**:90 (1939).

CASPARI, E., *Advances in Genetics* **2**:1 (1948).

DARLINGTON, C. D., *Nature* **154**:164 (1944).

HADDOW, A., *Nature* **154**:194 (1944).

HESTON, W. E., DERINGER, M. K., and ANDERVONT, H. B., *Jour. Nat. Cancer Inst.* **5**:289 (1945).

LEDERBERG, J., *Heredity* **2**:145 (1944).

LINDEGREN, C. C., *The Yeast Cell, Its Genetics and Cytology*. St. Louis, Educational Publishers, Inc. (1949).

RHOADES, M. M., *Cold Spring Harbor Symposia on Quantitative Biology* **11**:202 (1946).

SONNEBORN, T. M., *Quart. Bull. Indiana Univ. Med. Center* **9**:51 (1947); *Advances in Genetics* **1**:263 (1947); *Amer. Scientist* **37**:33 (1949).

CHAPTER TWENTY-SIX

Genes and development

Between the presence of the genes in the chromosomes and the appearance of the developed characters in the individual organism there exists a gap which is not yet thoroughly understood. How can a gene or a group of genes influence the development of a character? What is the connection, for example, between a gene that affects spotting and the appearance of spots on an animal? How do the genes result in color blindness or a blue eye or a bald spot? Do genes have anything to do with such fundamental characters as the presence of a stomach or a backbone? Questions such as these inevitably occur to the thoughtful student of heredity.

The older view that the individual was preformed in miniature in the egg, and that it became an adult simply by enlarging, has had to be discarded. Observation and experimentation have disproved such a hypothesis, particularly the observations of Driesch and others that in many animals the artificial separation of the cells in the very early stages of development can result in the production of a complete, though small-sized, embryo from each of them.

The growth and development of an individual from an egg involves a gradual differentiation, an increase of diversity. Such development is spoken of as **epigenesis,** in contrast to preformation. While preformation of a miniature adult in the egg is no longer accepted, we must keep in mind that the egg does have a definite set of genes, to which are added by fertilization another set from the sperm. In this sense certain parts of the egg and zygote are preformed. The development of the embryo from the zygote is, however, epigenetic in nature.

Following fertilization, the fertilized egg divides into two cells by mitosis, then each of these into two, and so on until a ball of cells is formed. There may be at this time many hundreds of cells, enclosing a hollow central space. This hollow ball of cells is called a **blastula.** It consists of a single layer of cells.

Soon the single-layered condition is converted into a double-layered condition by indentation of one side of the blastula. This may be accomplished by a slower rate of growth of the cells of one side as compared with those of the other. The two layers thus formed are termed *ectoderm* and *endoderm*, and from them will develop definite structures of the organism. A third layer, the *mesoderm*, is soon formed between them, derived partly from each of the other two.

From these three layers, by outpocketing, indentation, folding, and other manifestations of disproportionate growth rates, the various organs of the embryo will develop. During the process of development, the cells which will compose different tissues and organs undergo *differentiation*, that is, they become very different from one another in appearance and in function. Some become muscle cells, others epithelial cells; some become functionally specialized to transmit impulses, others to secrete hormones, and so on. Since we know that the cells of different tissues and organs in the same individual very commonly (though not invariably) contain precisely the same chromatin material, we cannot in general attribute the differentiation of cells to a differential sorting out of the genes among them in the course of embryologic development.

Modern work in experimental embryology suggests that initial differences in the protoplasm of the egg (which are known to exist) may affect the activity of the genes, which in turn affect the protoplasm, thus initiating and perpetuating a series of reciprocal reactions by means of which gradual differentiation occurs.

The original differences in the egg are differential gradients set up under the influence of the environment (gravity, pressure, distribution of the yolk, access of the various parts of the egg to oxygen, etc.). The genes give to the egg and the embryo a certain capacity to respond differentially to definite stimuli such as these environmental variables. Thus the normal development of an embryo must depend both upon a normal environment and a normal make-up of genes. Abnormalities in either of these will result in abnormal development.

An illustration of the fact that primary differentiation is an effect of external factors as well as of genes is found in the results of crosses between two species of sea-urchins, *Cidaris* and *Lytechinus*. When eggs of *Cidaris* are fertilized by sperms of *Lytechinus*, the resulting embryo develops as a typical *Cidaris* larva, forming its two-layered condition in about twenty hours as *Cidaris* does, not in nine hours as *Lytechinus* does. Thus for the first twenty hours the egg controls development rather than the sperm. At about twenty hours, however, the first effects of the genes contributed by the sperm become apparent, since the production of the third layer (mesenchyme) is like that of *Lytechinus*.

The important and interesting thing to note is that the time at which the genes contributed by the sperm begin to take effect is the time when the ratio of cytoplasm to nucleus in each cell becomes that which is characteristic of the species. The egg because of the inclusion of yolk is larger than other cells of the body. As it divides, forming the embryo, the immediately resulting cells do not enlarge, so that eventually by successive divisions they are reduced to the size characteristic of the species. From this point on, the cells enlarge before again dividing. At this point the ratio of cytoplasm to nucleus in each cell is a definite and characteristic ratio, and at this point the genes contributed by the sperm begin to act.

It may very well be then, as pointed out by Huxley and deBeer, that the genes of the embryo begin to act at the time of the reversion of the cytoplasmic-nuclear ratio to its initial value. Previous to this the differentiation has been largely dependent upon external factors, which act by setting up gradients in the egg and embryo. There is a difference of gradient, for example, between the protoplasmic or animal pole of the egg and the yolk or vegetative pole. There is an exterior-interior gradient, since cells or parts of cells in direct contact with the external world are not affected in the same way as cells removed from external contact. There is a dorso-ventral gradient, dependent in some instances upon the point of entry of the sperm.

The early differentiation in a developing embryo, then, seems largely brought about by the structure of the cytoplasm of the egg, which is formed into differential gradients imposed primarily by the external environment. As development proceeds and the embryo gradually becomes an adult, characteristics appear as a result of the production of genic substances in differential gradient fields.

Bridges has suggested that, when a gene reproduces itself prior to cell division, the *autocatalytic process* giving rise to the new gene involves the production of chemical by-products. The raw materials used in reproduction of the gene are derived from the cytoplasm. As the new gene is formed a series of chemical by-products returns to the cytoplasm, which is then of different chemical content than formerly. The various by-products may react with one another and the resulting products react again, setting up long chains of chemical variations.

The autocatalytic reactions would be very much the same at each cell division. In addition to this kind of genic action, Bridges suggests that there may be a *heterocatalytic* action, which could readily vary from stage to stage in development. The heterocatalytic action is also assumed to be enzymatic in nature, that is, the genes or certain surface areas of the genes act as *enzymes* or *catalysts*, absorbing specific protoplasmic substances in definite proportions and causing interactions between them.

This type of action could well be different at various stages of development, inasmuch as certain materials, such as yolk, might become exhausted and new ones become available through food and the building up of progressively different compounds. New chemical arrangements, acting in varying environments brought about by the position of particular cells in the tissue mass and the resulting variations in gradients, according to this hypothesis, would produce differentiation. The chemical products or enzymatic action of a particular gene may produce a certain result or perhaps no result in one gradient or in the presence of one set of chemicals and a totally different result in another gradient or in the presence of new chemicals.

Beyond question, then, we must visualize development as a continual reaction between chemical constituents of the protoplasm and chemical products and enzymatic action of the genes, occurring in varying metabolic gradients.

The fact that at least one of each kind of chromosome (except the relatively inert Y-chromosome) is necessary for development was suggested in Chapter 21. Further proof of this is found in experiments performed by Boveri in which sea-urchin eggs were fertilized by two sperms. As a result of the entrance of two sperms into the egg, two spindles are formed, and the $3n$ number of chromosomes arrange themselves on these. As always happens in mitosis each chromosome divides, and thus $6n$ chromosomes are distributed among the four resulting cells. Each cell may thus contain, on the average, $6n/4$, or $1.5n$, chromosomes.

Since we know that an individual with the haploid or n number of chromosomes can develop, it might be expected that *any* cell receiving as many chromosomes as the haploid number could develop. (The four cells of a developing sea-urchin's egg may be easily separated and allowed to develop separately. In a normal zygote they develop into small larvae.)

In the case of an egg fertilized by two sperms, however, not every cell receiving as many chromosomes as the haploid number develops; only some of them. The reason is that *any* group of chromosomes totalling n in number is not sufficient to bring about development. Only a group containing *at least one of each kind* of chromosome can produce development.

Calculation of the chances of any particular cell receiving at least one of each kind of chromosome has been made (cf. Huxley and deBeer), and the calculations have been compared with the actual results obtained by allowing all the cells to develop separately. The observations of the proportion of cells which were able to undergo development proved to be in complete accord with the calculated probabilities. Thus we may conclude that genes are quite necessary in development, and probably at least one of each kind of gene is essential. Moreover, it seems clear that, whatever gradients may be set up in egg or embryo by environmental causes, these gradients are established in a cytoplasm that is already under the influence of genic action.

The ways in which genes may act in affecting characters are many and varied. Genes may so affect the cytoplasm of the egg as to produce early and far-reaching changes, or they may affect the final gradient (and thus the development) of a structure appearing late in differentiation. They may slow up development in general, or they may retard it at a critical period. They may modify the direction or the plane of cell division. They may produce an enzyme at a particular stage of development, or they may fail to produce it. Examples of some of these postulated actions are given below.

Color is one of the most interesting characters to study from the standpoint of genetic development because it is extremely variable within many species and because we know something of the chemistry of color and color formation. The *melanin* colors of animals (black, brown, red, and yellow, and their various shades) are known to be formed by the oxidation of colorless *chromogens*. The reaction requires one or more *enzymes* to bring it about. In a test tube we may add, for example, the enzyme *tyrosinase* to the colorless amino acid *tyrosin* and produce a dark melanin pigment. Other amino acids may also act as chromogens and be converted to colored substances by oxidation in the presence of an appropriate oxidase (enzyme bringing about oxidation).

Wright has suggested a hypothesis regarding the action of genes on the production of color in mammals, which adequately accounts in a general way for most of the observed facts. He assumes two enzymes capable of oxidizing chromogen to various degrees. Enzyme I is necessary for any color production. Acting alone on chromogen it produces yellow or red. Enzyme II is supplementary to enzyme I and has no effect alone. Acting together the enzymes oxidize the chromogen to the point where a very dark color results. After an enzyme has accomplished its catalytic action, it dissociates itself from the converted compound and is available for further activity.

Genetic evidence indicates that certain genes control the presence or absence of one or the other enzyme, other genes control the relative amount of one or the other, and still other genes control the potency of a particular enzyme. The various combinations of these genes will affect color in various ways. The gene for albinism, for example, probably prevents the development of enzyme I. The restriction gene prevents the development of enzyme II, at least in the epithelial cells. The gene for brown reduces the potency of enzyme II, and so on. Figure 26.1 will help to make this clear.

The researches of Scott-Moncrieff and of Lawrence and Scott-Moncrieff have resulted in much specific knowledge concerning gene control of plant pigments. An interesting example of the various effects of such genes is found in the autotetraploid *Dahlia variabilis.* Here we find a gene, *B,* producing cyanin (one of the anthocyanins, the principal red, blue and purple plant pigments), and a gene, *I,* producing apigen (a flavone pigment). Since *Dahlia variabilis* is an autotetraploid, we may have one, two, three, or four of each of these genes *B* and *I* in any individual. Increasing numbers of the genes *B* and *I* produce, in addition to cyanin and apigen, pelargonidin, another anthocyanin; and finally, as the numbers of these genes increase further, the flavone is suppressed. The following selected genotypes and their phenotypes express these relationships:

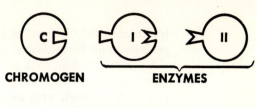
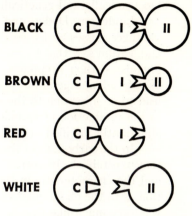

Fig. 26.1 A hypothesis for the genetic development of color in mammals. Above is shown diagrammatically a chromogen (C), which is colorless, but which may in the presence of enzymes be oxidized into pigment. Enzyme I is basic for all color production and acting alone on chromogen produces yellow or red. Enzyme II has no effect by itself, but when acting in addition to enzyme I carries the reaction to black. A few of the possible combinations of these enzymes with chromogen are shown in the lower part of the figure. Small symbols indicate an enzyme of reduced potency. *Adapted from Wright in the Journal of Heredity*

bbbbiiii no pigment (white flowers)
Bbbbiiii cyanin (chocolate flowers)
bbbbIIii apigen (ivory flowers)
BbbbIIii cyanin and apigen (purple flowers)
BbbbIIIi cyanin, apigen, pelargonidin (magenta flowers)
BBbbIIii cyanin, pelargonidin (carmine flowers)

The most important advance in biochemical genetics occurred, however, when Beadle and his co-workers realized that the practicability of artificially inducing mutations by irradiation or chemical treatment made it possible to attempt the large-scale study of the genetics of microorganisms. It was clear that the vital chemical reactions of metabolism took place within cells and that genes might in some way direct or control these reactions. It would therefore be profitable to work with an organism which could be studied both biochemically and genetically.

Lindegren, Dodge, and others had already demonstrated the advantages possessed by yeasts and molds in genetic analysis. Beadle and Tatum saw that by inducing large numbers of mutations in such organisms, their peculiarly favorable genetic potentialities might be used to advantage in biochemical studies. Such studies might in turn lead to an approach to the solution of the problem of how genes act in the production of specific characteristics. These hopes have been abundantly justified in recent years.

In the early days of the study of genetics, the geneticist was content to establish the correlation between the gene in the chromosome and the characteristic in the individual, without raising much question as to the chain of events which connected the two. The attitude was very much like that of the traveler who boards the Miami train in New York, confident that he will step out at the Miami station, but actually knowing very little about the physical-chemical principles of the Diesel engine or the intricacies of the switching and signaling systems that will get him there.

Today, however, the question of genic action in the development of finished characters is uppermost in the minds of geneticists, and biochemical genetics is leading the attack on this front.

The bread mold, *Neurospora*, is of especial importance for biochemical genetic studies for a number of reasons. First, the larger part of its life cycle, as in other lower plants, consists of a structure (the gametophyte) in which the cells are haploid, that is, they contain but one of each pair of chromosomes, and thus one of each gene pair. In one sense all the cells of the mold correspond to the gametes of an animal. Thus any gene may produce its effect in the cells of the mold; there is no complication of dominance or recessiveness; and the commonly observed Mendelian ratio will be one to one.

Second, there is a diploid generation (the sporophyte) in the life cycle of the mold, in which the chromosomes and genes are in pairs; but this is limited to a single cell-generation. Its occurrence, however, makes it possible to cross two haploid strains, recombine the genes, and map the chromosomes.

Third, and extremely important, the bread mold, unlike man, is capable of synthesizing all the purines, pyrimidines, and amino acids which it needs for its development, and all the "vitamins" but one. In other words the mold can live and grow on a basic medium containing merely a source of energy and carbon; a suitable source of nitrogen, such as ammonium salts; a source of inorganic elements such as salts supplying calcium, phosphate, sulfur, potassium, and iron; and the one vitamin which the mold cannot make, namely biotin, one of the B-vitamins. From this basic medium Neurospora can synthesize at least 20 amino acids, many vitamins, purines, pyrimidines, and nucleic acids, and other substances which go to make up the mold.

Beadle and his colleagues knew that irradiation caused mutations and that the mutated genes were usually inactive, or at least less active, in carrying out the particular functions which they formerly controlled. They reasoned that irradiation of Neurospora spores might be expected to inactivate genes which controlled the metabolism of one or another of the various substances built up by the mold from the basic medium. If this occurred it should be possible to deduce, from the change thus brought about, the role of the unmutated, normal gene.

Accordingly, asexual spores of Neurospora were irradiated and then allowed to germinate in a normal culture of the opposite sex, thus achieving a cross. The sexual spores resulting from the cross were grown individually on complete media containing all the substances necessary for growth and functioning of the mold. This, of course, was to insure that the mutations, if any, would be preserved. After obtaining a profuse vegetative growth, part of each culture was transferred to the minimal medium. If it grew there, no mutation interfering with the production of essential substances had occurred. If it did not grow on the minimal medium, a mutation had apparently taken place preventing the synthesis of some vitamin, amino acid, or other necessary building block.

About one or two cultures out of every hundred irradiated showed inability to grow on the minimal medium. It was then necessary to discover what particular substance was no longer being synthesized by the mold. A culture was therefore tried on a minimal medium to which all the known vitamins had been added and another on a minimal medium to which all the amino acids had been added.

If the culture then grew in the presence of vitamins but not in the presence of amino acids, it was evidence that this strain had lost the ability to produce some one of the vitamins which it formerly could produce. If it grew in the presence of the amino acids but not of the vitamins, it had lost the power to synthesize some amino acid. If perchance it grew on neither culture, it had lost the power to synthesize some necessary substance other than the known vitamins or amino acids.

Suppose a particular treated strain will grow on a minimal medium supplemented with vitamins, but not on a supplement of amino acids. It is then necessary to determine just which vitamin is no longer synthesized. The strain is then tried on a series of minimal media, each supplemented with one vitamin, such as riboflavin, niacin, thiamin, and so on. In this way the strain is found to be incapable of synthesizing a particular specific substance.

Next it must be determined whether or not the change is connected with a gene. This is done by crossing the new strain with an opposite-sexed untreated strain. If the two strains differ by a single gene mutation, half of the resulting spores will give rise to the original kind of mold and half to the new kind.

Tests of hundreds of thousands of spores have revealed many mutations as a result of irradiation, each mutation making the mold incapable of synthesizing a particular substance. For example, various mutated strains cannot make, respectively, vitamins B_1, B_2, B_6, niacin, choline, inositol, pantothenic acid, or p-aminobenzoic acid. Other strains can no longer synthesize one or another of the amino acids phenylalanine, leucine, valine, isoleucine, arginine, proline, lysine, tryptophane, threonine, ornithine, citrulline, and methionine. Still others cannot build specific purines or pyrimidines, substances which go to make up nucleic acids, the principal components of chromosomes, and probably of genes.

At this point the union of genetics and biochemistry becomes apparent. Genetic research discloses the fact that each failure in synthesis is the result of a single gene mutation. Biochemical research makes it clear that each failure is the result of a lack of a specific enzyme. In general, each step in the chemical reactions occurring in the cells of living organisms takes place under the influence of a specific enzyme and in the absence of the enzyme either will not take place or will proceed at such a slow rate as not to be very effective.

Furthermore we know, due to the work of Sumner and those who followed him, that all the enzymes that have been adequately purified and analyzed are proteins. We also know, as a result of the researches of Mirsky and his colleagues, that chromosomes consist of, or at least contain, proteins.

It is not difficult, then, to accept Beadle's suggestion that the genes serve as permanent models in the images of which enzymes are constructed. Enzymes are very specific, and it seems highly probable that each enzyme is referable to a single gene. In other words the genes appear to direct the production of specific enzyme proteins, and these in turn control specific chemical reactions.

On this hypothesis a mutation, either natural or induced, is thought of as being an alteration in the chemical arrangement of the molecule. The mutated gene, in its reproduction, duplicates itself in its altered form just as faithfully as it previously copied its original form. This is one of the foundation stones of evolution. Furthermore, the molecule after mutation is usually inactive, or at least less active, in catalyzing the particular reaction which it formerly brought about.

Practical applications of this knowledge have been many. Such forms as *Neurospora* can be used in bio-assays, for determining qualitatively and quantitatively the presence of individual vitamins, amino acids, and other substances. Moreover, the steps in the syntheses of such substances can be worked out and the precursors identified. In this way there have been discovered, for example, the steps leading from ornithine through citrulline to arginine, and those proceeding from anthranilic acid to indole, followed by condensation with serine, resulting in trypotophane. Research along similar lines is in active progress at the present time, involving many biosynthetic processes and making use of other organisms such as yeasts and bacteria.

Examples of the production of traits through the genic control of biochemical reactions are not lacking in man. It was first demonstrated by Fölling that among the inmates of institutions for the mentally defective, some individuals may be found who excrete in the urine about a gram per day of an abnormal metabolite, phenylpyruvic acid. This substance is a derivative of phenylalanine, which is one of the indispensable amino acids in our diet. Phenylpyruvic acid is never excreted by normal individuals.

Phenylalanine is handled by the cells in various ways (see Figure 26.2). Some of it goes to make up our body proteins. Some of it is converted to tyrosine and eventually to melanin. Some of it is oxidized to phenylpyruvic acid by replacing its amino group with an oxygen atom. The phenylpyruvic acid is then normally degraded by successive steps through parahydroxyphenylpyruvic acid, 2,5-dihydroxyphenylpyruvic acid, homogentisic acid, and aceto-acetic acid to carbon dioxide and water. Each of these steps requires the action of a specific enzyme. All these enzymes are produced by normal individuals.

Those persons suffering from phenylketonuria, however, cannot convert phenylalanine to tyrosine. Lacking the requisite enzyme, these individuals cannot carry phenylalanine through the steps shown in the left hand column of Figure 26.2, and the phenylalanine piles up and saturates the blood and other tissues of the individual. Excess amounts of phenylalanine and its derivative, phenylpyruvic acid, are excreted in the urine. This disturbance of metabolism is invariably associated with mental deficiency, and certain concomitant characteristics such as light hair and skin and accentuated reflexes are commonly observed.

Fölling, Jervis, Penrose, and others have clearly demonstrated

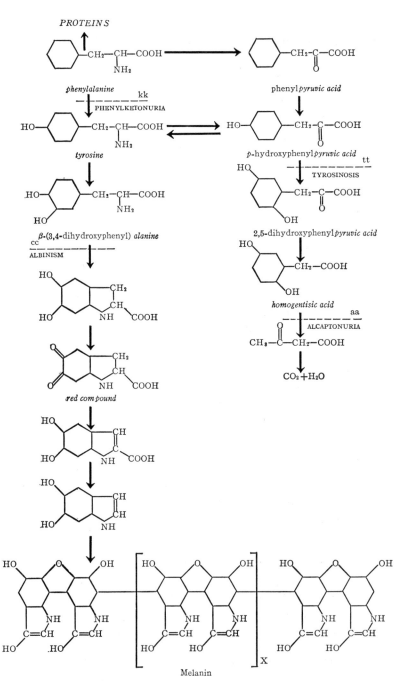

Fig. 26.2 Metabolism of phenylalanine in man. Dotted lines indicate the points at which the chain of steps may be stopped because of the lack of an enzyme, as a result of the homozygous state of a mutant gene. The mutant genes concerned are c, the gene for albinism; k, the gene for phenylketonuria; t, the gene for tyrosinosis, and a, the gene for alcaptonuria. *Based on the researches of Garrod, Haldane and others*

that phenylketonuria is the result of a single autosomal gene substitution, and that the mutant gene fails to provide the enzyme which its normal allele provides.

Other metabolic anomalies in man are similarly conditioned. If the conversion from phenylalanine to tyrosine is made, tyrosine is further converted by a series of biochemical steps through 3,4-dihydroxyphenylalanine to melanin, which is the pigment of our skin, eyes, and hair. Normally pigmented persons produce all the enzymes necessary to make each of these steps, but an occasional individual inherits in homozygous form a mutant gene (the gene for albinism) which fails to produce a requisite enzyme. Melanin is therefore not formed, and the individual is an albino. The enzyme involved has generally been thought to be the one acting on 3,4-dyhydroxyphenylalanine, as shown in Figure 26.2, but some recent investigations suggest that it may be the enzyme acting on tyrosine.

Figure 26.2 also illustrates the biochemical blocks resulting in two other human anomalies. In the right hand column it will be observed that parahydroxyphenylpyruvic acid may not be converted to the 2,5-dihydroxy form, in which case the individual has tyrosinosis (an extremely rare condition). If this step is carried out, another mutant gene, that for alcaptonuria, will, if present in the homozygous state, result in the absence of the enzyme necessary to degrade homogentisic acid to aceto-acetic acid. The ensuing disease, alcaptonuria, is marked by the excretion of homogentisic acid in the urine, which then turns black on exposure to air or if alkalis are added. Alcaptonuria is often harmless; but it is potentially a severe disease and may be marked in later life by a type of diffuse degenerative arthritis.

Not only is amino acid metabolism subject to breaks in the chain of reactions, but lipid and carbohydrate metabolisms are also interfered with by lack of appropriate enzymes. Carbohydrate metabolism is being extensively studied with yeasts by Lindegren and others. Again, recent research is providing examples in man.

Normal individuals carry glycogen through glucose-1-phosphate and glucose-6-phosphate to glueose and H_3PO_4. Those having Von Gierke's disease, however, fail to produce the enzyme phosphorylase and so do not degrade glycogen, which thus piles up in the liver, heart, kidneys, and other organs during infancy, causing characteristic symptoms. Other derangements of carbohydrate metabolism, such as diabetes, pentosuria, and fructosuria, are also the results of gene mutations.

Turning to lipid metabolism, an interesting human example is Tay-Sach's disease, in which the affected infant becomes blind, paralyzed, and mentally deficient and invariably dies within a short time. Here the oxidation of the lipid sphyngomyelin, which takes place in normal individuals, fails to occur. Many other examples, such as failure to metabolize kerasin in Gaucher's disease or cholesterol in xanthomatosis, could be cited.

Each of the human diseases listed above results from the lack of a specific enzyme, and each is genetically the result of a single mutated gene substitution. Genetics thus provides additional evidence for the growing belief in a one-to-one correspondence between gene and enzyme. It will be recalled from Chapter 24 that the researches of Lea and Catcheside indicate that on the basis of ionization effects, genes appear to have diameters of 4 to 10 millimicrons. Molecular weights range from 500,000 to 1,000,000. These values fall within the size and weight ranges of enzymes.

The one-to-one relationship between gene and enzyme probably also applies to other protein products of the gene, such as the antigens discussed in Chapter 13 in connection with the blood groups. It should be pointed out here, however, that there are inherent in biochemical genetics not only implications in regard to the understanding of particular diseases and anomalies but also of the organism as a whole. It is not too much to hope that the day will arrive when the genetic basis for the complete metabolic processes of man may be built into a single mosaic. Since several of these inherited metabolic derangements, such as Tay-Sach's disease, epilepsy, and phenylketonuria, involve severe mental defects, it is also within the range of possibility that the study of biochemical genetics will make it possible to specify the entire nervous and mental make-up of an individual in terms of measurable inherited metabolic activities.

It is relatively easy to understand how one gene, acting through an enzyme, can result in a restricted effect, such as eye color, but it is more difficult to comprehend at first glance a wide-spread fundamental effect such as the complete syndrome of Tay-Sach's disease. Presumably the magnitude and extent of the effect depend at least in part on the time during development at which the gene exerts its influence. The requisite substrate may be available for an enzyme as early as in the fertilized egg. On the other hand, the substrate may not be built up until many antecedent reactions have occurred.

To return to the analogy of the train which we used a few pages back, let us suppose that you have boarded a train in New York. Just outside the Pennsylvania station is a switch. If it is thrown one way, you will end up somewhere in the south, possibly Miami; whereas if it is thrown the other way you will end up in the west, perhaps Chicago. A simple switch acting at an early stage of your journey can make a tremendous difference in the outcome.

Assume now that the switch has been thrown so as to send you south. It is now determined that you will not proceed west, but there is yet the opportunity of ending up at, let us say, either Miami or New Orleans. The positions of various switches along the route will determine this, but at least you will end up in the south as opposed to the west.

Let us assume, however, that you finally approach Miami. Just outside the Miami station is another switch, similar in its intrinsic action to the others. But whether this switch is thrown one way or the other will make only the specific and relatively slight difference as to whether you arrive on track 1 or track 2 of the Miami terminal.

Thus an early-effective gene such as the recessive determiner for Tay-Sach's disease, which fails to produce the enzyme necessary for the oxidation of the lipid sphyngomyelin, may result in profound physical and mental disturbances. On the other hand, the recessive gene which fails to form the enzyme necessary for the production of pigment in the iris, acting very specifically and at a relatively late point in the development of the eye, may make only the difference between being brown-eyed and being blue-eyed.

Up to this point we have spoken of mutations as though they resulted in the failure to produce an enzyme or in a diminution of its activity. To be sure this is frequently the case; and for this reason many mutations have harmful or lethal effects, because the various enzyme systems have been subjected to natural selection and as a result the wild-type systems are delicately adjusted mechanisms.

Evidence is accumulating, however, that a mutation does not necessarily result merely in the failure to elaborate the enzyme formerly produced, but may cause the production of a new enzyme, likely to be related to the original enzyme but performing a new function in metabolism. The phenotypic effect of the mutant gene is then not merely that caused by the lack of the old enzyme but an effect resulting from whatever conversion may be accomplished by the new enzyme.

As long as a mutant gene can become homozygous only at the expense of the original gene (that is to say, the genotype aa necessitates the absence of A), the acquisition of a new function implies the loss of the old one. Presumably evolutionary progress could result more readily if a mechanism existed by means of which new functions could be added while the old ones were maintained.

A mechanism of this sort would involve the addition of new loci. Polyploidy has already been discussed as a source of new loci. Another mechanism which is being actively investigated is duplication. The giant chromosomes of wild-type individuals of various species of Diptera, for example, show many small "repeats" of single bands. These are interpreted as being duplications of single genes in such a way that the old gene and its duplicate lie very close together on the chromosome: so close, in fact, that crossing over between them occurs in only one or a few instances out of ten thousand. (It should be noted that this figure is still far above the usual mutation rate.) Duplications of this sort may have become established in other organisms as well as in the Diptera.

A small amount of crossing over has shown that in several instances what had been considered to be a single locus with multiple alleles was in reality two or more very closely linked loci of which the genes affected the same trait. It will be recalled that ordinary linked genes do not, as a rule, affect the same characteristic (cf. page 289). The finding of a number of examples of closely linked genes (originally thought of as multiple alleles) acting on the same trait would seem to imply more than coincidence. These cases are now interpreted as involving closely adjacent duplicate loci (sometimes triplicate or higher replicas) in which genes which were once identical have diverged in function by mutation. Such genes are designated **pseudoalleles,** and their common descent is considered to be the cause of their similarity of action.

Thus Lewis has worked with a series of mutations in Drosophila which affect the thorax in various ways. One of the mutations is *bithorax (bx)*, which in homozygous state causes the anterior portion of the metathorax to resemble the anterior portion of the mesothorax. The mesothorax of the Diptera bears the wings; the metathorax has small appendages (halteres) instead. In bithorax flies the halteres of the metathorax become winglike.

Another mutation is *bithoraxoid (bxd)* which in homozygous state causes the *posterior* portion of the metathorax to resemble the posterior portion of the mesothorax, plus a metathoracic-like modification of the first abdominal segment. The change may proceed so far as to result in the production of a pair of legs on the abdominal segment, in addition to the three pairs normally developing on the thorax.

Linkage studies between these mutations and known marker genes indicate that the two mutant genes occupy the same locus. They should then be alleles, forming with the wild-type gene a series of three multiple alleles, and crosses between the two mutants should result in one mutant type or the other or an intermediate between them. The F_1, however, proves to be wild type, suggesting that *two* pairs of factors are involved and that each mutant is bringing into the cross the dominant which the other one lacks. Nevertheless the F_2 is produced in a one-factor ratio, as would be expected if the genes are actually alleles.

The dilemma is solved by raising enough F_2 individuals to permit the observation of occasional crossovers (2 or 3 in 10,000). The genes involved, then, are not multiple alleles but are located at closely adjacent linked loci. The double recessive (*bx bxd*) (*bx bxd*) shows the effects of both genes. In addition, both types of double heterozygote (*Bx bxd*) (*bx Bxd*) and (*Bx Bxd*) (*bx bxd*) are, as expected, wild type.

This latter point, involving the equivalence of the two types of double heterozygote, was mentioned because it serves to introduce another phenomenon which occurs frequently among pseudoalleles: the position effect. The two types of double heterozygotes do not always both produce the wild type. For example, a third locus involved in the bithorax series contains the mutant gene for *postbithorax* (*pbx*). Individuals homozygous for *pbx* have the posterior portion of the metathorax modified to resemble the posterior portion of the mesothorax, but the abdomen is not affected.

Ordinary mapping techniques place *pbx* at the same locus as *bx* and *bxd*. Crosses involving *pbx* and *bxd* again tell the story, but not quite as quickly as in the previous example. *The hybrids between postbithorax flies and bithoraxoid flies are like the postbithorax parent*, indicating that *pbx* and *bxd* are indeed alleles. The F_2 are produced in a one-factor ratio at first, but the observation of many thousands of offspring provides evidence of a small amount of crossing over. The *pbx* locus proves to be closely adjacent to the *bxd* locus, but on the opposite side from *bx*.

The cross between postbithorax and bithoraxoid is, then, a two-factor cross involving closely linked genes, and can be indicated as (*Bxd pbx*) (*Bxd pbx*) $\times$ (*bxd Pbx*) (*bxd Pbx*). The genotype of the F_1 is (*Bxd pbx*) (*bxd Pbx*). Note that these flies, because of the way in which the cross was made, are in the repulsion phase (sometimes called the *trans* phase). Since each mutant brought to the cross the dominant gene which the other one lacked, the question logically arises as to why the F_2 did not exhibit the wild-type phenotype. An approach to the answer is made when the coupling or *cis* phase of the double heterozygote is produced, namely (*Bxd Pbx*) (*bxd pbx*). These flies *do* show the wild-type phenotype.

Obviously a position effect is involved, since both types of double heterozygotes have exactly the same genes. In one case, however, both dominant genes are on the same chromosome of the pair, and in the other case they are on opposite chromosomes.

The explanation of the position effect apparently lies in the biochemical sequence controlled by the genes. It is probable that gene *Bxd* causes the production of an enzyme which converts some compound (C_1) to another (C_2). C_2 is then converted by *Pbx* to C_3, which is necessary for the development of the wild type. A mutation to *pbx* means that C_2 will not be converted to C_3. C_2 will then accumulate, resulting in postbithorax. A mutation to *bxd* will prevent the conversion of C_1 to C_2, and C_1 will accumulate, resulting in bithorax.

In the *cis* phase, the wild-type genes *Bxd* and *Pbx* lie close together on the same chromosome. When C_2 is formed by *Bxd*, it will be immediately available to be acted on by *Pbx*, which is closely adjacent. The sequence in the *cis* phase may be diagramed as follows, using greatly enlarged small sections of the chromosomes:

The wild-type phenotype will result. But suppose now that C_2 is not diffusible, so that it must be produced in very close proximity to gene *Pbx* if *Pbx* is to act on it. If *Bxd* and *Pbx* are on opposite chromosomes (*trans* phase) this condition would not be met; C_2 would not be available to *Pbx*, and would not be converted to C_3. The resulting phenotype would be postbithorax. This situation may be diagramed as follows:

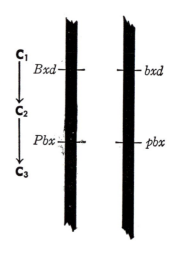

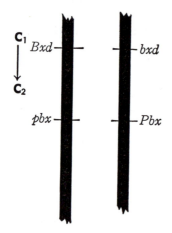

The necessity for certain compounds and the enzymes which act upon them to be produced in close proximity to each other appears to be a reasonable explanation of the position effect. Further instances of pseudoalleles have been described in Drosophila and in several other organisms. Position effects, that is different phenotypic expressions of the *cis* and *trans* phases, seem to be the rule in pseudoallelism. The organisms concerned are as widely varied as corn, cotton, fungi, mice, and pigeons.

Cytological evidence for the duplicate-gene (pseudoallelism) hypothesis is available in some instances. Thus in the bithorax series just described the loci have been located on the giant chromosomes, and the region shows repetition of a band at that point. Other cases of pseudoallelism in Drosophila, such as Star-asteroid and Stubble-stubbloid are also correlated with "repeats" in the giant chromosomes. In other organisms the cytological evidence is not always readily available, but the genetic evidence all points to pseudoallelism.

Thus in various organisms, sets of genes which were originally considered to be sets of multiple alleles have proved to be nests of closely linked genes affecting the same trait, and therefore presumably derived one from the other by duplication and subsequent mutation. It is obvious that new concepts of evolutionary development are opened up by these discoveries.

Although no case of psuedoallelism has been established in man, the Rh blood type genes, which were discussed in Chapter 13 on the basis of alternative hypotheses of multiple alleles and linked genes, may prove to be an instance of this phenomenon.

The control of hormone production by genes has already been mentioned in connection with sex determination. Evidence that hormones or hormone-like substances may control other developmental processes in invertebrate animals and in plants as well as in the vertebrate animals is rapidly coming to hand. Studies by Beadle and Ephrussi have shown that the developing eyes of Drosophila produce at least two hormones which are necessary for the production of pigment in the eyes themselves. One of these hormones is conditioned by the vermilion gene, the other by the cinnabar gene, and the two are apparently sequentially related in a chain reaction.

Both hormones are lacking in vermilion flies, one of them is lacking in cinnabar flies, and both are present in wild flies and are necessary for the development of the normal wild-type eye color. That the substances are diffusible and hormone-like is shown by transplantation experiments. It has also been shown that at least one of these substances can be effectively administered with food.

The inheritance of shape has also provided material for the study of the effects of genes on development. In gourds the elongate, spherical, and disk shapes have been shown by Sinnott and Durham to depend upon simple genes, but these genes could be analyzed only when the *relative* growth rates in length and breadth were studied rather than the separate or absolute growth rates. Here the genes act in at least two ways. One of these controls the plane of cell division in growing tissues, so that cell division is more frequent in one plane than in the other. The other method of genic action is by the localization or restriction of growth to particular parts of the growing tissues. When the genes are analyzed in these terms, the heredity of shape may be expressed in simple monohybrid and dihybrid ratios.

The chemical activities of genes in their control of metabolism and development are being actively studied in many laboratories. Molds, yeasts, and bacteria are favorite experimental organisms in such studies, although higher plants as well as animals are receiving their share of attention. The use of bacteria in the study of genetics is quite new, but there are already so many interesting and suggestive facts emerging from the study of bacterial genetics that the following chapter will be devoted to a discussion of these topics.

It is to be expected that a unified set of principles involving genetics, embryology, and biochemistry will gradually be evolved. In the meantime we may summarize present knowledge by stating that a complete complement of chromosomes as well as a normal environment is necessary for development; early differentiation is probably effected primarily by gradients imposed from without upon a cytoplasm already under the control of genes; later differentiation takes place through interactions of genic substances in differential gradients, the whole process being a continuous one of reciprocal reactions between genes and cytoplasm in progressively differing gradient fields; and finally the action of genes may take the form of the production of antigens, hormones, and especially enzymes, with the consequent elaboration of reactive chemical substances, establishment of specific metabolic rates, or modification of the plane or frequency of cell division in localized areas.

An interesting viewpoint has recently been presented by Goldschmidt. This viewpoint holds that the whole concept of the gene as a hereditary unit of separate existence is obsolete. On the basis of the position effects, Goldschmidt proposes to substitute, for the idea of a string of individual genes which we call a chromosome, the concept of a large chain molecule of complex arrangement. If, as seems certain from the standpoint of chemistry, the chromosome is a long nucleoprotein molecule, then it is the real unit of heredity responsible for the production of the normal "wild type." The changes which we call mutations would then be merely stereoisomeric rearrangements of the normal molecule, and the point at which a stereoisomer occurred would be a so-called mutant "gene."

Mutations and chromosomal aberrations would on this hypothesis be but position effects, and so-called "wild-type" alleles would not exist. The complex chain molecule (the chromosome) would be the real unit of heredity, and "genes" would be merely chemical points of reference on such a molecule.

Goldschmidt points out that in order to have complex molecules of this type, highly specific organizers are necessary. For the nature of these he goes to the work of Bergmann, who has stated that the only known substances capable of doing this work are the intracellular proteinases, which both hydrolyze and synthesize the protein molecule.

While this concept is revolutionary, it leads to attractive speculation. Its final acceptance by geneticists must await further data, both genetic and biochemical.

PROBLEMS

26.1 What methods can you suggest, other than those outlined in this chapter, by which genes may influence the development of characters?

26.2 In poultry a lethal gene is known, which in the heterozygous condition results in Creeper fowls. Embryos homozygous for the dominant gene usually die at about 72 hours of incubation, at which time they are greatly retarded in development as compared with normal embryos of the same age. Landauer and Dunn have shown that when strains of Creeper fowls related only very distantly are crossed, the embryos homozygous for the dominant gene may live beyond 72 hours, even nearly to hatching time. How may this be explained?

26.3 The eggs of silkworm moths are sometimes oval, sometimes spindle-shaped. All the eggs laid by any one female are the same shape. Females from a strain in which only oval eggs are produced will lay oval eggs even if mated to a male from a strain in which only spindle-shaped eggs are produced. Conversely, females from a strain in which only spindle-shaped eggs are produced will lay spindle-shaped eggs even if mated to a male from a strain in which only oval eggs are produced. What appears to be the genic action in this case?

26.4 If we assume a pair of genes O and o, in silkworm moths, so that OO and Oo females lay oval eggs, while oo females lay spindle-shaped eggs, what sort of eggs would be produced by the F_1 females in a cross between an OO male and an oo female? What kinds of eggs would be produced by the various F_2 females?

26.5 The larvae of some strains of silkworm moths are striped, the larvae of other strains are not striped. The cross beween a moth from a strain having striped larvae and one having nonstriped larvae always results in striped larvae, no matter which strain furnishes the male parent. In the F_2 the ratio is always 3 striped larvae:1 nonstriped larva. Taking into consideration these facts and the facts given in Problem 26.3, what is indicated as to the relative time of effective action of the genes from the sperm? How do these conclusions compare with others mentioned in this chapter?

26.6 Several mutant strains of Neurospora cannot synthesize methionine (an amino acid necessary for growth). By supplying methionine to the medium, all these strains will grow, but by supplying methionine or one or another of the substances thought to be precursors of methionine, the strains may be differentiated. These substances are homocysteine, cystathionine, and cysteine. One mutant, for example, will develop only if methionine is added to the medium. Another will grow if either methionine or homocysteine is added, but not if either of the others is provided. A third strain grows upon the addition of methionine, homocysteine, or cystathionine, but not if cysteine is added. A fourth strain will grow if any one of the four is provided in the medium. What appears to be the change in activity associated with each of these mutant genes?

26.7 Using the information in Problem 26.6, what is the likely sequence of biochemical steps in the synthesis of methionine?

REFERENCES

BEADLE, G. W., *Science in Progress*, 5th Series 166 (1947); 6th Series 184 (1949).

BEADLE, G. W., and EPHRUSSI, B., *Genetics* **22**:76 (1937).

BEADLE, G. W., and TATUM, E. L., *Proc. Nat. Acad. Sci.* **27**:499 (1941).

BERGMANN, M., *Proteins and Proteolytic Enzymes.* Harvey Lectures (1935–1936).

BOVERI, T., *Ergebnisse über die Konstitution des Zellkerns.* Jena (1904); *Zellenstudien* **6** (1907).

BRIDGES, C. B., *Sex Determination.* In *Sex and Internal Secretions*, edited by Allen. Baltimore, The Williams and Wilkins Co. (1939).

EPHRUSSI, B., *Amer. Naturalist* **72**:5 (1938).

GOLDSCHMIDT, R., *Physiological Genetics.* New York, the McGraw-Hill Book Co. (1938).

HALDANE, J. B. S., *The Biochemistry of Genetics.* London, George Allen and Unwin, Ltd. (1954).

HUXLEY, J. S., and DEBEER, G. R., *The Elements of Experimental Embryology.* Cambridge, The Cambridge University Press (1934).

LANDAUER, W., and DUNN, L. C., *Jour. Genetics* **23**:397 (1930).

LAWRENCE, W. J. C., and SCOTT-MONCRIEFF, R., *Jour. Genetics* **30**:155 (1935).

LEDERBERG, J., *Genetics* **32**:505 (1947).

LINDEGREN, C., *The Yeast Cell, Its Genetics and Cytology.* St. Louis, Educational Publishers, Inc. (1949).

MIRSKY, A. E., and RIS, H., *Jour. Gen. Physiol.* **31**:7 (1947).

MORGAN, T. H., *Embryology and Genetics.* New York, Columbia University Press (1934).

"Pseudoalleles and the Theory of the Gene," a symposium by M. M. Green, E. B. Lewis, J. R. Laughnan, Clyde Stormont and S. G. Stephens. *Amer. Nat.* **89**:65–122 (1955).

SINNOTT, E. W., and DURHAM, G. B., *Bot. Gazette* **87**:411 (1929).

STONE, W. S., WYSS, O., and HAAS, F., *Proc. Nat. Acad. Sci.* **33**:59 (1947).

TATUM, E. L., and BEADLE, G. W., *Growth* **6**:27 (1942).

WAGNER, R. P., and MITCHELL, H. K., *Genetics and Metabolism.* New York, John Wiley and Sons (1955).

WRIGHT, S., *Jour. Heredity* **8**:224 (1917); *Physiol. Rev.* **21**:487 (1941).

CHAPTER TWENTY-SEVEN

The genetics of bacteria and viruses

In 1945, on the occasion of reviewing a new book on bacterial cytology, Beadle entitled his review "Do Bacteria Have Genes?" Thus nearly half a century after the development of Mendelian genetics it was still debatable whether hereditary transmission in bacteria occurred in a manner similar to that of sexually reproducing forms of life.

In recent years, however, the development of new methods of studying both cytology and hereditary transmission in bacteria has progressed very rapidly. Many research workers are now convinced that the genetics of bacteria is essentially similar to that of higher organisms. It would be nice to be able to state that nuclei and chromosomes have been unequivocally shown to exist in bacteria by direct observation. Unfortunately not all workers in the field are convinced that these structures have actually been seen. Probably all workers are convinced, nevertheless, that nuclei and genes actually do exist in microbes, and some find evidence that the genes are organized into chromosomes. Figure 27.1 illustrates what are regarded by many as nuclei and chromosomes in bacteria.

There are many good reasons for believing that genes occur in bacteria. These organisms grow and divide, each division resulting in two daughter cells which are like each other and like the parent cell in many different traits. Bacteria can be characterized by numerous specific qualities, such as the shape of the cell and the arrangement of cells into colonies; the presence of capsules or flagella; the capacity to form pigment and to ferment carbohydrates; the ability to carry out specific biochemical reactions such as the synthesis of vitamins, amino acids, purines, pyrimidines, nucleosides, and nucleotides; the presence of specific antigens; the susceptibility to drugs, antibiotics and viruses; and the virulence of the organisms.

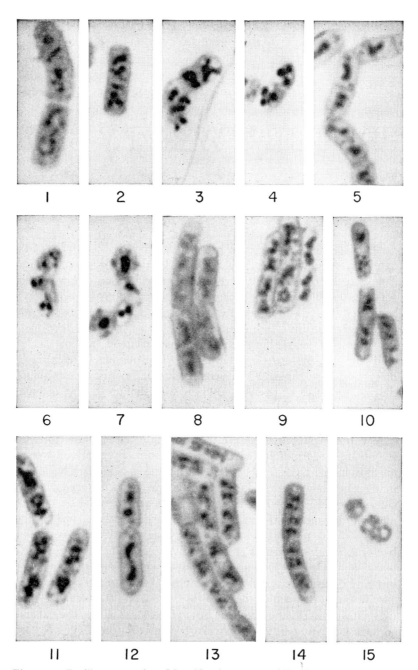

Fig. 27.1 *Bacillus megaterium*. Magnification ✕4800. All cells fixed with osmium tetroxide except Figure 8, stained with Azure A–SO₂ stain, and dehydrated in freezing alcohol.

1 — Early prophase. Chromosomes as contracting threads.

2 — Binucleate cell. Middle prophase. Chromosomes as short rods.

3 — Middle and late prophase. Upper nucleus, chromosomes as short rods; lower nucleus, chromosomes as paired granules.

4 — Prometaphase (unipolar metaphase). Binucleate cell. Three chromosomes in each nucleus appear as dense contracted granules. In lower nucleus centriole is visible.

5 — Prometaphase. Chromosomes densely contracted. Single centriole has appeared. Upper nuclei indicated show anaphase stages.

6 & 7 — Metaphase. Dense chromosomes on metaphase plate lying between centrioles.

8 — Acetic acid fixation. Indicated nuclei. Metaphase and anaphase. Upper nucleus in metaphase with both centrioles evident; lower nucleus in anaphase.

9 — Polar view of metaphase. Chromosomes as paired granules.

10 — Early anaphase. Chromosomes separating toward poles.

11 — Later anaphases with chromosomes separating toward polar centrioles. Spindles evident. In upper nucleus chromosomal bridges evident.

12 — Arrested anaphases due to cold shock. Attenuated configurations characteristic.

13 — Numerous anaphases in synchronized culture produced by cold shock.

14 — Telophase stages. Nuclei reorganizing.

15 — Three interphase nuclei. Chromosomes as tangled attenuated threads. *Courtesy of Dr. Edward D. DeLamater*

A single bacterium may divide and the resulting cells redivide at the rate of one cell generation every half hour. It can, for example, pass through 24 generations in a period of twelve hours, giving rise to more than eight million individuals. The fact that practically all these organisms are identical with the original parent cell in all their many characteristics is strong evidence that there is some precise and accurate division of genetic determiners in a fashion similar to that which we have found to occur in higher forms. It is logical to assume on this basis that bacteria have genes which duplicate themselves, the duplicate genes then separating into the daughter cells at cell division.

Compelling evidence for the existence of bacterial genes arises, however, when it is realized that mutations occur in bacteria in a manner similar to that in higher organisms. The mutant genes are transmitted just as faithfully as were the original genes. Mutations occur in all the traits listed above, and a mutation in one gene is independent of a mutation in other genes. Mutations may occur spontaneously, in the absence of extraordinary environmental influences, but their occurrence may be speeded up by the same agents that are known to increase mutations in higher forms, namely, X rays, ultraviolet light, nitrogen mustard, and other mutagenic agents. There is some indication that reverse mutations also occur, suggesting that the original changes are true mutations and not losses or deletions.

The natural mutation rate varies for different traits, and sometimes for the same trait in different strains, but it is remarkably constant for any particular trait in a particular strain. The rates for bacterial mutation range from one in 10,000 to one in 10,000,000,000 per cell per generation.

The above facts on bacterial mutations, coupled with the increasing evidence that bacteria do possess nuclear structures which are distributed in a precise manner to daughter cells, make the assumption of the existence of genes in bacteria highly valid. We shall proceed on this assumption.

Bacteria may be grown in many ways. One commonly used method consists of growing them in flat glass dishes called Petri dishes. The dishes are supplied with a culture medium on which the organisms may grow, and which provides necessary nutrients. Nutrient agar is frequently used, consisting of a mixture of beef extract, peptone, distilled water, and agar sterilized to insure its freedom from microorganisms at the start. Bacteria may be poured or spread on the agar in the culture dishes, which are then covered; and the growth of the organisms into colonies may be observed. By careful techniques a single bacterial cell may be placed on the culture medium. The resulting colony will consist exclusively of descendants of this single individual. Such a colony is called a clone.

The majority of bacterial cells appear to be haploid, containing only one of each kind of gene. Since there are practically no reduction divisions or fertilizations, the usual tools of the geneticists, namely hybridization, segregation, and recombination, are seldom available in the study of heredity in bacteria. The occurrence of many interesting mutations, however, provides a point of departure which has proved to be of great interest and of practical value to medicine, public health, agriculture, and industry.

When living bacteria are placed on a plate containing nutrient culture medium, growth and multiplication take place. After a slow start (the lag phase), the rate of division becomes constant and remains so for a time until eventually it slows down and becomes stationary, even stopping entirely unless the culture is re-plated on fresh medium. In the ordinary course of a colony, a single cell may give rise to more than a hundred million descendants. This is enough to permit the occurrence and possible establishment of several mutations, especially those which ordinarily occur in frequencies greater than one in a hundred million.

Some mutations are readily visible to the naked eye (Figure 27.2). Thus it is usual in certain bacterial species to find that the colonies are moist, round, and glossy with even margins; these are referred to

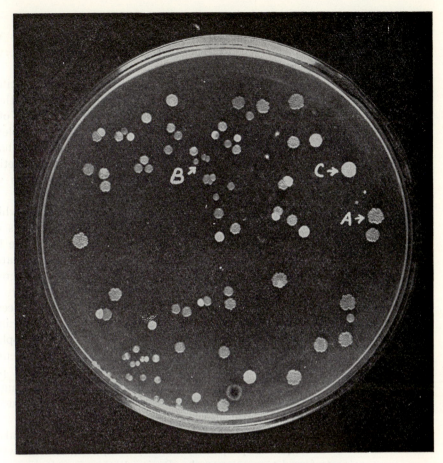

Fig. 27.2   A culture of *Nocardia corallina*, showing colonial mutants. The normal colonial morphology of this organism is pigmented, rough (A). Mutants occur which may be pigmented, smooth (B), or white, rough (C). *Courtesy of Dr. J. Bennett Clark*

as "smooth" or S type colonies. They usually have a high degree of virulence, which seems to be associated with antigens in the polysaccharide capsules that are characteristic of smooth forms. Individual smooth cells, however, may mutate to a "rough" or R form. Rough colonies developing from an R type cell are dry, flat, and wrinkled with irregular margins. The antigenic capsule is lacking, and virulence is absent or greatly reduced. The mutation is transmitted to the descendants.

Still other variations in colonial morphology are known, such as the "mucoid," or M type, in which the colony is moist, round, and of a slimy or gummy consistency due to the presence of mucopolysaccharides in the capsules. Like the S type, M type bacteria are usually highly virulent.

Some bacteria produce pigments, and the colonies may be brightly colored. Mutations in pigments are readily observed and may be used for study.

Numerous mutations known in bacteria are not identifiable by simple inspection; for these, tests must be made. Many of these have proved to be of fundamental importance to the development of genetic theory. They have helped, for example, to elucidate problems such as the chemical structure of genes and how genes act. They have even provided us with some new and surprising methods of genetic transmission, such as transformation and transduction, which we shall discuss presently.

Bacteria are usually grown on a complete medium which provides all the building blocks necessary for the synthesis of their protoplasm. Most bacteria can, however, synthesize these building blocks from a minimal medium. It has been demonstrated that *Escherichia coli*, a parasite of the human intestine, can grow on a minimal medium made up of glucose, KH_2PO_4, K_2HPO_4, sodium citrate, $MgSO_4$, and $(NH_4)_2SO_4$. From these simple substances *E. coli* will build all the necessary sugars, phosphates, vitamins, amino acids, purines, pyrimidines, and the other ingredients of its protoplasm.

It will be recalled from the preceding chapter that Neurospora, which can normally grow on a simple minimal medium, produces mutations which require some preformed substance (vitamin, amino acid, etc.) for growth. In a similar manner bacteria produce mutations of these kinds.

The "wild-type" parent cells which will grow on minimal medium are called **prototrophs,** and mutant cells requiring some growth factor are referred to as **auxotrophs.** By irradiating *E. coli*, permitting the colonies to develop on complete medium, and then plating part of each colony onto minimal medium, auxotrophic mutations may be discovered by their inability to develop on the minimal medium. It is then necessary, by adding various substances to minimal media, to discover which substance cannot be synthesized by the auxotroph. Many shortcuts and refinements of technique have been developed by bacteriologists for discovering auxotrophs, and the interested reader is referred to the references at the end of this chapter.

Among the biochemical building blocks which cannot be synthesized by individual auxotrophic strains are phenylalanine, tyrosine, tryptophan, threonine, methionine, proline, arginine, cystine, leucine, lysine, glutamic acid, glutamine, histidine, isoleucine, homocystine, biotin, thiamin, pantothenic acid, *p*-aminobenzoic acid, nicotinamide, pyridoxin, pyrimidines and purines.

Each of these metabolic deficiencies is considered to be the result of a mutation in a single gene. Their existence, coupled with the fact that the deficiency may show up soon after the mutation occurs, provides genetic evidence for the belief that bacterial cells are haploid, containing only one gene of each kind. Additional evidence for this belief is to be found in the manner in which bacterial cells respond to ionizing radiations. In sexually reproducing organisms we have seen that biochemical mutations are recessive. In order to be expressed, therefore, the mutant gene must either be in the homozygous state in a diploid cell, as albinism in man, or it must be in a haploid cell, as in the biochemical deficiencies in the haploid stage of Neurospora. When mutations of this sort are produced in bacteria by irradiation, the mutation is expressed in all the cells of the colony arising from the affected individual. It will be recalled that only one gene mutates at a time. If bacterial genes were normally in pairs, the mutation would not be expressed until it had an opportunity to become homozygous, and then it would appear in a genetic ratio or proportion.

Occasionally a mutation does fail to show up until some cell generations after it is presumably produced by some mutagenic agent such as irradiation. This lag may be due to the fact that the normal gene before mutating has already produced enough of some necessary enzyme or substrate to last for a time before being exhausted. The lag may in some cases be the result of the occurrence of multinucleate cells among bacteria. A mutation in one gene would not express itself in a multinucleate cell, since the unmutated allele in the other nucleus or nuclei could carry out the normal reaction and would thus show dominance. The mutation would not show up until the mutant gene occurred in a haploid cell, or until all the nuclei of a multinucleate cell carried the gene.

On the assumption that there might be an occasional sexual phase in bacteria, Tatum and Lederberg grew mixed cultures of auxotrophs which differed in regard to several mutations, and searched for recombinations among the offspring. To obtain individuals having more than one mutation, *E. coli* were irradiated, the mutants were then in turn irradiated, and so on until various strains were developed each of which had several mutations. In one attempted cross, for example, a strain which required methionine and biotin for growth but which could synthesize leucine, thiamin, and threonine was grown in culture along with a strain which could synthesize methionine and biotin, but which required leucine, thiamin, and threonin.

On a minimal medium, neither of these strains could grow for very long, but if there should be any sexual fusion of cells of the two strains, recombination might occur, resulting in some cells which had all the dominant genes and could synthesize all the substances. Prototrophs of this nature did actually occur at the rate of one in ten million. It is highly unlikely that these could be due to reverse mutation, since to produce a prototroph two simultaneous mutations would be required in one strain and three in the other.

By enriching the minimal medium with one or a combination of the various substances required by the parent strains, all possible combinations of characters were detected among the offspring. Thus some individuals could synthesize biotin, methionine, leucine, and threonine but not thiamin. Moreover the various recombinations occurred in proportions which indicated that the genes are linked and that crossing over had occurred in a regular and understandable fashion.

These results strongly suggest that occasionally, perhaps once in some million times, two bacterial cells come together in sexual fusion and form a diploid zygote, which subsequently undergoes reduction division with the segregation of genes into the daughter cells, which are again haploid. This type of genetic behavior has been demonstrated only for *E. coli*, but may be found to occur in other species. So far the evidence for it is only indirect, based on the genetic data, and no one has ever observed its occurrence under the microscope. Using the genetic data, a provisional chromosome map of *E. coli* has been prepared (Figure 27.3).

Auxotrophic mutations have proved of practical value in determining the sequence of the biochemical steps in the synthesis of various substances and thus in the identification of intermediate compounds which may be used to make possible a reaction which would otherwise not occur. Auxotrophs are also of practical use in the assay of various biologicals such as vitamin and amino-acid preparations. By culturing the appropriate auxotrophs on media to which the material to be tested has been added, the vitamin content, for example, of a particular commercial preparation may be readily measured and standardized.

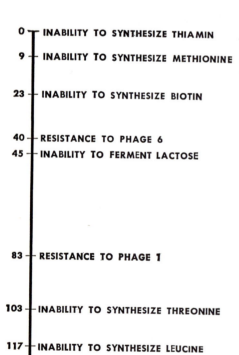

0	INABILITY TO SYNTHESIZE THIAMIN
9	INABILITY TO SYNTHESIZE METHIONINE
23	INABILITY TO SYNTHESIZE BIOTIN
40	RESISTANCE TO PHAGE 6
45	INABILITY TO FERMENT LACTOSE
83	RESISTANCE TO PHAGE 1
103	INABILITY TO SYNTHESIZE THREONINE
117	INABILITY TO SYNTHESIZE LEUCINE

Fig. 27.3 A provisional chromosome map of *Escherichia coli*, based on determinations by Lederberg.

Another property of many bacteria is the ability to ferment specific carbohydrates. Bacteria, by the fermentation of inexpensive carbohydrates, produce valuable commercial solvents such as acetone and ethyl alcohol. They produce many commercial acids, including lactic, acetic, tartaric, oxalic, and butyric. Through their fermentations bacteria aid in the production of such foods as cheese, butter, vinegar, coffee, and sauerkraut. Part of the manufacture of linen, leather, synthetic rubber, and other products depends on bacterial fermentation. Many yeasts and molds have similar fermenting abilities, and some are of even more importance than bacteria in some of the above reactions.

Many mutations are known which affect the fermentation abilities of bacteria. In some instances the mutation may endow the cell with the ability to ferment a carbohydrate which it could not previously affect. In other instances the cell may lose a fermentative capacity which it formerly possessed. Mutations have been noted, among others, in the ability to ferment lactose, galactose, maltose, xylose, arabinose, and mannitol.

Bacteria also vary as a result of mutation in their resistance or susceptibility to drugs and antibiotics. The mutations are undirected, that is, they can occur in the absence of the drug or antibiotic to which sensitivity is altered. By testing large populations with an agent which is ordinarily anti-bacterial, some resistant cells or clones will be found, and this characteristic generally proves to be genetically transmitted. The natural occurrence of such mutations is of very real practical importance to medicine, since wide-spread treatment with an anti-bacterial agent often permits the selective growth and development of resistant strains. Thus in many instances drugs and antibiotics become less effective as resistant strains become prevalent in the population. As one method of avoiding this, it has been suggested that two antibiotics at a time be used. Since mutations are independent events and resistance is specific, the likelihood of the occurrence of two mutations, conferring resistance to both substances, is very remote.

Mutations conferring resistance to streptomycin or to isonicotinic acid hydrazide may be of various kinds, some resulting in low degrees of resistance and others in high degrees. Apparently different genes with different potencies are involved. In contrast, high resistance to most antibiotics is reached only by a series of mutational steps, each increasing resistance by a certain amount, but no mutation being known which confers high resistance by itself.

Because resistant mutations may occur in the course of treatment of a patient, antibiotics are usually given at a high concentration, since a low concentration could permit the development of slightly resistant mutants, which could subsequently lead to mutation to higher resistance, and so on in a stepwise manner. Such stepwise mutations are known to occur in regard to penicillin, neomycin, terramycin, aureomycin, and others.

The extreme to which mutations affecting resistance may go is illustrated by the fact that some bacteria become not only resistant to streptomycin, but actually become dependent upon it for growth and reproduction.

Changes in virulence may also occur as a result of mutation. The change associated with the presence of an antigenic capsule in smooth or mucoid types, and its absence in rough types, has already been mentioned. Virulence may also be related to the production of toxins, hemolysins, or other substances harmful to cells or to tissues. Mutations affecting all these characters have been observed, and nonvirulent strains of various ordinarily pathogenic bacteria are known.

In addition to the smooth, mucoid, or rough colony types, variations in antigenicity may be associated with other morphological differences which may be discovered by various techniques, especially by the use of obliquely transmitted light for microscopic examination. This technique has resulted in the discovery of many morphological traits which were formerly undetected and which, with the altered virulence, develop because of the basic activity or lack of activity of some mutant gene.

It has been repeatedly stressed, both in this chapter and in preceding chapters, that mutations occur at random and are undirected. We come now to a unique phenomenon which takes place in bacteria and provides evidence that under certain conditions specific genetic changes can be induced at will. The phenomenon is known as **transformation.**

The studies on transformation have been carried out largely in pneumococci, although a few instances have been observed in other kinds of bacteria. A pathogenic strain of pneumococcus always has a capsule surrounding the cell. The capsule is composed of a polysaccharide. Nearly 100 strains are known, each of which has its own polysaccharide, specific in regard to chemical composition and consequent antigenicity. These properties of the capsule are transmitted from generation to generation, and each type remains specific, apparently not mutating to other S types.

An S type may, however, mutate to an R form, which has no capsule, lacks specific antigenicity, and is not virulent. An R form apparently does not spontaneously mutate back to S. When S cells are injected into mice they cause infection, the severity depending on which type of S is used; the injection of R cells does not result in an infection.

Various investigators, of whom Griffith was the first, have shown that if R cells are injected into mice, and along with them are also injected S cells which have been killed by heat, the R cells will change to encapsulated S cells and will cause infection. The interesting thing about the phenomenon is that the derived living S cells are always of the same type as that of the dead S cells which caused the change.

If, for example, S cells of type II mutate to the R form, and if these R cells are injected into mice along with heat-killed S cells of type III, the resulting live S cells into which the R cells are transformed will be of type III, not of type II. It was later shown that this same result could be obtained in culture media. The transformed cells henceforth produce offspring only of the new transformed type, and continue to do so in the absence of the transforming material.

It has been found that a particular substance of the heat-killed S cells is responsible for the transformation. Avery, MacLeod, and McCarty have proved that the transforming substance is the highly polymerized desoxyribose nucleic acid (DNA) of the cells. An extract of DNA from the donor cells will produce the same result as the use of the killed cells themselves. Capsule transformations of this sort have been produced in several different species of bacteria. In addition, drug resistance and changes in colonial morphology have been brought about by transformation.

The use of DNA from a donor strain differing from the recipient strain both in capsule type and in drug resistance results in the separate transformation of individual recipient cells, some being changed in regard to capsule type and some in respect to resistance.

The facts regarding transformations suggest that gene material, in the form of particles of DNA, can penetrate bacterial cells and can become incorporated into the genetic material of the cell, possibly replacing homologous genic material on a host chromosome. In this way the genotype of the transformed cell is changed, somewhat as though a mutation had occurred; but in transformation the change can be specified and directed.

The preparations of DNA which have been experimentally employed to produce transformations are highly purified, containing no more than two hundredths of one per cent of protein, if indeed they contain any. This fact suggests that the genetic material itself may be desoxyribose nucleic acids rather than the more complex nucleoproteins. Although the possible presence of small amounts of protein in the extracts has not been ruled out in the experiments just cited, the work with viruses, which will now be discussed, tends to support the suggestion.

Closely akin to transformation is another phenomenon causing genetic change in bacteria: the phenomenon of **transduction.** In the case of transformation, it will be recalled, DNA penetrates the host cell and becomes incorporated into the genotype of the host, possibly by replacing homologous genic material. In transduction, a similar replacement occurs, but the DNA is carried from one bacterium into another by bacteriophage, which penetrates the host cell. The bacteriophages are those viruses which attack bacteria. Viruses are organisms very much smaller than bacteria, which can invade living cells and can reproduce within the cells and only within cells. Like bacteria, some viruses are "virulent" and some are not. "Virulent" bacteriophages reproduce within all infected bacterial cells to the point where they ultimately lyse (burst) the cells releasing the many phage progeny. So-called "temperate" phages do not kill all the host cells, but live within many of them, establishing a symbiotic relationship.

Bacteriophages, which are less than one tenth of a micron in size, can be visibly observed by means of the electron microscope. Some are spherical, some have ovoid or spherical heads with attached tails. Phages may be isolated by filtration, and a suspension of phage may be added to a culture of bacteria. When phage is added to a strain of phage-sensitive bacteria, a few phage-resistant mutants among the bacteria are usually found. The spontaneous mutation rate to phage resistance is about one in one hundred million.

In Salmonella (the typhoid group of bacteria) Zinder, Lederberg, and others have demonstrated that phages may carry particles of the genetic material of bacteria from one bacterial cell to another. When the lysate (the material resulting from the bursting of bacteria by bacteriophage) from a strain of bacteria is filtered and applied to another strain which differs in its genetic traits, the recipient strain will acquire some of the characteristics of the donor strain. The new traits become a part of the genetic endowment of the recipient strain, and are transmitted to descendants. Each trait is acquired independently of others, and any genetic trait of Salmonella may be thus transduced by a particle of phage. Temperate phages are used in the tests so that not all the recipient cells will be killed.

Experiments thus far seem to indicate that the material which is transduced is DNA, as in transformation, but that it is incorporated from the donor into the phage and later released into the recipient. Thus, as in transformation, individual genes may move from one bacterial cell to another by a process quite different from sexual fusion and cell division. How the new gene actually becomes a part of the genetic material of the recipient cell is not completely understood, but it probably does so by replacing a homologous gene during chromosome reduplication in a manner analogous to crossing-over. Phages are composed of both protein and DNA, but only the DNA appears to enter bacteria, the protein being left outside. This is a further indication that, although chromosomes are composed of nucleoprotein, the genic material itself may be only DNA.

Thus at a low level of life we find a new possibility for the exchange of genetic material and even, perhaps, for the formation of species in bacteria.

As a final point of interest, it may be added that viruses themselves have their own mutations and hereditary transmission. Bacteriophages undergo mutation in regard to host specificity, rapidity of lysing of the host, and biochemical activity. Moreover, when two different strains of phage are grown together, exchange of genetic material can occur between them in a manner suggesting that sexual fusion and segregation may occasionally occur in addition to vegetative reproduction. The evidence clearly indicates that a phage particle may have several genes, and Catcheside concludes that the minimum number of genes in a phage is thirty to fifty.

Thus the same principles of genetics which were first found to apply to multicellular organisms have been extended to man at one extreme of the development of life and to the simplest known organisms at the other. Even filterable viruses are composed of several genes and transmit them to progeny, sometimes by a process akin to sexual reproduction. Moreover, the study of the genetics of bacteria and viruses is opening up new vistas of the chemical and physiological basis of the ultimate units of heredity, and indeed of life itself.

PROBLEMS

27.1 When a population of bacteria susceptible to penicillin is inoculated into a nutrient medium containing a high concentration of penicillin, colonies never develop. When, however, a population of bacteria susceptible to streptomycin is inoculated into a nutrient medium containing a high concentration of streptomycin, a few colonies develop and the organisms in these colonies continue to grow and reproduce. Using only these results, what can you conclude as to the spontaneous occurrence of mutations resistant to each of the antibiotics?

27.2 When a population of bacteria susceptible to penicillin is inoculated into a

medium containing a *low* concentration of penicillin, a few colonies develop and grow. What additional conclusion can you now draw?

27.3 How might you obtain bacteria resistant to high levels of penicillin?

27.4 Auxotrophic mutants have been found in bacteria, in which the organisms cannot synthesize tryptophan (an amino acid). However, not all "tryptophanless" mutants are found to be alike when the precursors of tryptophan are provided in the medium. Some will grow only if tryptophan itself is provided, others will grow if either tryptophan or indole is provided, and still others will grow if tryptophan, indole, or anthranilic acid is provided. What can you say as to the probable action of the individual mutant genes?

27.5 What information does the preced-ing problem offer as to the probable se-quence of steps in the synthesis of trypto-phan?

REFERENCES

BRAUN, W., *Bacterial Genetics*. Philadel-phia, W. B. Saunders Co. (1953).

CATCHESIDE, D. G., *The Genetics of Micro-organisms*. London, Sir Isaac Pitman and Sons, Ltd. (1951).

HOTCHKISS, R. D., *Jour. Cellular and Comp. Physiol.* **45,** suppl. 2:1 (1955).

LEDERBERG, J., editor, *Microbial Genetics*. Madison, University of Wisconsin Press (1951).

OGINSKY, E. L. and UMBREIT, W. W., *An Introduction to Bacterial Physiology*. San Francisco, W. H. Freeman and Co. (1954).

ZINDER, N. D., *Jour. Cellular and Comp. Physiol.* **45,** suppl. 2:23 (1955).

CHAPTER TWENTY-EIGHT

The mutant gene in man

Throughout the preceding pages we have found evidence that human beings are subject to the same fundamental laws of heredity as are other living organisms. We have analyzed, from chapter to chapter, this or that condition in man as an example of a particular type of hereditary behavior. Deaf-mutism, color blindness, hemophilia, the blood groups, baldness, and others have been discussed, and their mode of inheritance described.

The number of heritable characters in man which have been investigated runs into the hundreds. For some of these characters the hereditary basis has been accurately analyzed. For many of them, however, the type of inheritance is only vaguely understood, either because of the lack of a sufficient number of available family histories or because of the impracticability of using the experimental method in studies of human heredity.

Although the same laws of heredity apply to man as to other organisms, we must remember that human beings are capable to a large extent of controlling their own environment. The result may be a profound modification of the *expression* of a gene. Such modification does not, however, obviate the *fact* of the genetic nature of any hereditary condition, nor does it change in the least the *potentiality* or the *mode* of its transmission. For example, a man may inherit the recessive sex-linked gene which will ordinarily result in hemophilia. Yet, by his undergoing treatment with one of the globulin fractions of the blood, the appearance of the symptoms of the disease may be effectively prevented. To all appearances such a man is non-hemophilic. Yet he will transmit the gene that conditions hemophilia in just the same way as though he were himself an active bleeder.

Conversely, a man may through inheritance have the usual structure of the ear and the nerves supplying the ear, thus having the usual ability to hear. He may, through disease or accident, become deaf. Yet he will transmit the potentiality of normal ear development, just as though he himself had never become deaf.

Let us keep clearly in mind the fact that any finished character is the cooperative result of hereditary and environmental influences. One or the other influence may in certain circumstances appear negligible, but the dual nature may always be demonstrated. These statements furnish the answer to the question so frequently asked about a human characteristic: "Is it due to heredity or to environment?" Neither genes nor environmental influences can be solely responsible for any character. Let us illustrate this statement.

We may arrange variable characters roughly in a series depending upon the relative influence of variability in hereditary or in environmental factors upon them. At one extreme would be those in which environment is the effective variable influence, heredity being so similar in all the individuals studied as to play no part in the observed variations of the character. Such a trait is measles, with regard to which everyone, so far as we know, inherits a susceptibility. Therefore whether or not a person contracts measles depends entirely upon the environmental contact with the causative agent. At the other extreme would be characters in which heredity is the effective variable influence, no environment of sufficient potency to alter the expression of the genes being readily available at present. The blood groups are characters of this sort. Any person inheriting the gene for antigen A, for example, develops antigen A in his cells regardless of environmental influences, and the antigen is not developed if the gene is not inherited.

Between these two extremes lie many characters, in the production of which may be found variations in both the heredity and the environment. In diphtheria, for example, Hirszfeld has shown that the susceptibility is dependent upon a simple recessive gene and immunity upon its dominant allele. Yet infection with the causative agent is necessary before the disease may be contracted. Thus in a given population all of whom were exposed to the bacillus, those who inherited an immunity would not contract the disease, while those who inherited the susceptibility would develop it. Here the heredity would be the variable influence. In another population where all the individuals happened to inherit susceptibility but only some were exposed, those exposed to the germ would have the disease while those not exposed would not have it. Here the environment would be the variable influence. Thus one investigator might conclude that diphtheria was the result of hereditary influences, while another investigator might with equal logic conclude that environment was responsible.

The point is, of course, that both hereditary and environmental influences are at work in the development of any character. The fact that we can alter the expression of the hereditary character must not be used as an argument against the concept of a hereditary background. In the above example we can make a person artificially immune to diphtheria by means of toxin-antitoxin even though he inherits susceptibility. This does not alter the fact that he inherited the susceptibility nor does it change the fact that he will transmit the susceptibility. The fact that a causative agent is known for a condition or that the condition may be modified or cured does not invalidate the assumption of a hereditary as well as an environmental influence in the production of the condition. Conversely, the fact that an abnormality is known to be genetically determined does not mean that it cannot be alleviated or controlled by the requisite environmental manipulation.

We have become accustomed to speaking of a character as "hereditary" when variations in the character are caused mainly by differences in the genetic make-up. While this is the common use of the word, it must be realized that "hereditary" is a relative term, all characters, as stated above, being limited by hereditary and environmental influences. As we have found again and again in these pages, our knowledge of the nature of the hereditary basis of any character begins only when we find evidence of mutations affecting it.

Human beings possess all the basic biological conditions that are subject to the laws of heredity in other organisms. They reproduce sexually, their physiological processes are similar to those of other animals, and most important of all, they have a chromosomal mechanism comparable in all respects to that of other living things.

When the principles of heredity were discovered, tested, and finally understood in experimental plants and animals, it was inevitable that the interest and attention of geneticists should be drawn to the study of these phenomena in man. Today there exists a body of men and women whose chief interest in research lies in the study of the transmission of genes for diverse characteristics from generation to generation in human beings. The data obtained in these researches are gathered from careful studies of families, often in their homes, sometimes from hospital observations, and sometimes from laboratory tests of individuals and their relatives.

One result of such studies has been the increasing realization of the importance of human heredity in the affairs of everyday life. So important has this knowledge become to the physician, the social worker, and the psychologist that courses in medical genetics have been inaugurated in various medical schools, and studies of human heredity have been incorporated into curricula of sociology, social administration, and psychology.

Our knowledge of human heredity has now reached the point where specific practical applications have been developed. These include first, genetic prognosis, that is, giving advice on prospective marriages and prospective families; second, diagnosis, on the basis of the family history, of conditions difficult to identify accurately by other means; third, instituting preventive measures against certain diseases on the basis of the known genetic background; fourth, testing paternity, and other medico-legal problems, on the basis of the various blood groups; and fifth, evaluation of eugenic programs for the protection and improvement of society, a problem which can be scientifically approached only with an intelligent understanding of the basic genetics.

Taking up these practical applications in order, let us consider first genetic prognosis in prospective marriages and prospective families. The geneticist, physician, or social worker is frequently asked, "What are the chances that this trait in my family will develop in my children?" Sometimes the question concerns a desirable trait such as musical ability, intelligence, or curly hair; sometimes the question concerns an unwanted character such as deafness, feeble-mindedness, or epilepsy.

Several preliminary steps are necessary before such a question can be answered. First, the trait must be carefully observed and properly described and identified. Variations within a trait are often genetically different. Second, literature on human heredity must be consulted in order to learn what may have been already discovered about the mode of inheritance of the trait. Third, the family history of the person seeking aid must be carefully charted in order to discover whether or not the inheritance of the condition is similar in this family to that of others recorded in the literature. Fourth, the potential effects of the environment on the trait must be reviewed, and the probable environment in which the trait will develop must be specified. With all these facts in hand it is often possible to give accurate estimates of the chances of the reappearance of the character in the family.

A young husband and wife were recently referred to a medical genetics laboratory, having just lost their first child from infantile amaurotic idiocy. This is a condition in which mental failure, paralysis, blindness, and finally death occur in early infancy. The diagnosis had been made by a competent physician. This trait is known to be the result of an autosomal recessive gene, unaffected by ordinary environmental variations, so that it was possible to tell the parents that the chance of another child developing the same condition was one in four.

Several days later the father returned to the laboratory in good spirits. He had been thinking over what he had learned and had made a discovery. Since the condition was due to a recessive gene, he reasoned, and since the chance of its appearing was one in four, and since furthermore the first child had actually developed the abnormality, it followed that the next three children would have to be free from the disease. A little reflection on the principles of probability outlined in Chapter 7 will make it clear that this was false reasoning, and that the chance of one in four still applies to each subsequent child.

The second practical application of a knowledge of human heredity, diagnosis, is of particular importance to the physician. It has repeatedly been shown that the alert physician may occasionally make a difficult diagnosis on the basis of the family history. An interesting example of this application reported by Macklin is the case of a child whose skin was very dry, whose hair was sparse, and whose teeth had failed to develop. The child had fever and was taken to a physician. The diagnosis was under-activity of the thyroid gland, and the child was placed on thyroid medication.

The treatment only made the child worse and a consulting physician was brought in. This doctor made a study of the patient's family and learned that one of the parents and several other relatives had defective tooth development and defective body temperature controls. On this basis he identified the condition as the dominant hereditary form of ectodermal dysplasia, a trait which involves hair and tooth deficiencies as well as the total absence of sweat glands. Thyroid administration was stopped, since it had been as harmful a type of therapy as could well have been devised. Because of the lack of sweat glands, the child was already suffering from defective temperature control. Thyroid increased the metabolic rate, thus causing the temperature to become even higher. Here the study of the family history and the knowledge of the genetic nature of the dysplasia gave the clue to the correct diagnosis of the child's condition.

The third practical application of a knowledge of heredity in man, the instituting of preventive measures, is again largely a medical application. It is frequently possible to prevent the appearance of hereditary abnormalities and diseases in the relatives of a patient. When a person with a genetic condition consults a physician, the relatives may be examined by means of certain laboratory tests, in search of the early preclinical signs of the disease. Where these are found, preventive measures are instituted. It might be argued that this could be done without any knowledge of genetics, and so it could, were it possible to examine everyone in the world for every illness that he might some day have. Since this is not feasible, it becomes important to do the feasible thing, that is, to search for preclinical signs where they are most likely to be found, namely, in the relatives of patients with genetic conditions.

A good example of the value of genetics in prevention is furnished by a blood anomaly known as hemolytic icterus. In this condition the spleen becomes enlarged and holds many red blood cells from the circulation, gradually destroying them. The final result is jaundice and anemia and frequently death from a crisis. Prompt removal of the spleen may save the life of the patient.

Since hemolytic icterus is inherited on the basis of a dominant autosomal gene, it may be expected to appear in half the offspring of a person with the condition. It is therefore valuable to examine such offspring, looking for the early preclinical signs of the disease. These early signs are observable in the laboratory and include certain changes in the size, shape, reactions, and relative abundance of the various types of blood cells. When these are found, the spleen may be removed at once as a preventive measure, thus removing the possibility of subsequent death from this dangerous trait. Already many lives have been saved by such preventive measures. Similarly lives have been saved in incipient cases of pernicious anemia, hypertension, diabetes, certain types of cancer, and other genetic conditions.

The fourth application, the investigation of disputed paternity and the identification of individuals, was discussed in connection with the blood groups in Chapter 13. This application is becoming of increasing importance, and more and more states are providing laws for the precise use of such tests, which have already prevented many potential miscarriages of justice.

The fifth application, the evaluation of programs of eugenics for the protection and improvement of society, will be reserved for Chapter 29.

Now how do we dare to make such practical applications to human life? What right do we have to give advice, to diagnose, to institute preventive measures, and to enter courts of law, on genetic grounds? The answer is, of course, that back of such practical applications is a thoroughly scientific knowledge of the mutant gene in man. A discussion of the basic facts about mutant genes will not only provide the technical background for the applications under discussion, but will review for us in their proper setting many of the principles discussed individually in earlier chapters.

Let us, then, turn our attention to the various relationships of the mutant gene in man. Knowledge of some of these relationships is quite necessary, and knowledge of all of them is desirable, before attempting practical applications in regard to the trait conditioned by any gene. We may classify the basic relations of the mutant gene under three main headings: spatial relations, ontogenetic relations, and phylogenetic relations (Table 28.1).

Taking these relations up in order, we may logically ask about

Table 28.1. THE MUTANT GENE IN MAN

I. SPATIAL RELATIONS

A. Absolute location
1. On an autosome (autosomal)
2. On the nonhomologous portion of the X-chromosome (sex-linked)
3. On the nonhomologous portion of the Y-chromosome (holandric)
4. On the homologous portions of the X- and Y-chromosomes (incompletely sex-linked)
B. Relative location with respect to any other gene not an allele
1. On a chromosome of another pair (independent)
2. On a chromosome of the same pair (linked)
a. On the same chromosome of the same pair in any given individual
b. On the other chromosome of the same pair in any given individual

II. ONTOGENETIC RELATIONS

A. Manifestations with respect to its alleles
1. Dominant
2. Recessive
3. Intermediate
4. Dominant in one sex, recessive in the other (sex-influenced)
B. Manifestations with respect to another set of alleles
1. Epistatic
2. Hypostatic
3. Additive
4. Multiplicative
5. Indifferent
C. Penetrance
1. Similar in both sexes
a. Complete
b. Reduced
2. Different in the two sexes
3. Restricted to one sex (sex-limited)
D. Expressivity
1. Similar in both sexes
a. Constant
b. Variable
2. Different in the two sexes
E. Viability produced in an individual having the gene
1. Similar in both sexes
a. Complete
b. Reduced
c. Eliminated (lethal)
2. Different in the two sexes

III. PHYLOGENETIC RELATIONS

A. Frequencies of the gene and its alleles
1. Constant
a. With genotypic equilibrium (under a system of random mating)
b. Without genotypic equilibrium (if the lack of equilibrium is due to assortative mating)
2. Changing
a. Due to mutation pressure
b. Due to selection pressure
c. Due to random genetic drift
d. Due to combinations of a, b, and c
B. Frequencies of the genotypes formed by a gene and its alleles
1. Constant (in equilibrium)
2. Changing (not in equilibrium)
a. Due to changing frequencies of the gene and its alleles
b. Due to assortative mating
c. Due to migration

the spatial relations of a gene. We inquire both as to its absolute location and as to its relative location with respect to any other gene not an allele. As to its absolute location, it may be autosomal, that is, located on one of the twenty-three pairs* of autosomes (Fig. 28.1). Such genes, of course, give no evidence of association with sex in

* Recent investigation suggests that man may have only 46 chromosomes, of which only 22 pairs are alike in male and female.

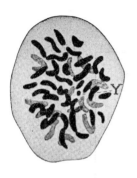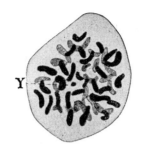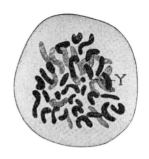

Fig. 28.1 The chromosomes of man. Above, three views of the chromosomes in the cells (spermatogonia). Below, the chromosomes lined up in 24 pairs (see footnote page 421) in the order of size, those from the male in the upper row, those from the female in the lower row. The sex chromosomes are at the extreme right in each row. Note the two X-chromosomes in the female row; one X-chromosome and one Y-chromosome in the male row. *From Evans and Swezy in Memoirs of the University of California*

transmission. Autosomal inheritance has been thoroughly discussed in previous chapters and requires no further comment here. The number of well-established autosomal genes in man runs into the hundreds.

Instead of being in an autosome a gene may be located in the sex chromosomes, in which case there are three possible regions in which it may be found. It has been shown by Koller and Darlington that there are three distinct portions of the sex chromosomes in mammals. The three portions are as follows: first, a part of the X-chromosome homologous with a corresponding part of the Y-chromosome, the two parts synapsing in maturation and forming chiasmata; second, a portion of the X-chromosome non-homologous with any part of the Y-chromosome; and third, a portion of the Y-chromosome nonhomologous with any part of the X-chromosome. The nonhomologous portions do not synapse during the maturation process (Fig. 28.2).

In human beings genes have been found to occur in each of the three regions. Best known as well as

ORDINARY SEX-LINKED GENES

HOLANDRIC GENES

INCOMPLETELY SEX-LINKED GENES

X

Y

Fig. 28.2 Diagram of the human sex chromosomes, showing the three regions in which genes may be located.

longest known are those in the nonhomologous portion of the X-chromosome. We call them sex-linked genes, and their behavior was discussed in Chapter 8. More than thirty such genes are known in man, variously affecting the eyes, the skin, the muscles, the nerves, the glands, and the blood (Fig. 28.3 and Table 28.2).

Advice to families carrying sex-linked mutant genes can be fairly specific. The men in the family who are free from an unwanted trait conditioned by one of these genes do not have the gene, and of course cannot transmit it, and may safely marry. Some of the apparently normal women in such families may, however, carry the recessive sex-linked gene and thus have sons in whom the character will develop. The daughters of an affected father will *all* be carriers. The sisters of an affected man whose father was normal have an even chance of carrying the gene, while the nieces have one chance in four of being carriers. Affected men cannot transmit the gene to their sons, since the X-chromosome carrying the mutant gene goes only to daughters, the sons receiving the Y-chromosome.

In addition to the sex-linked genes in the nonhomologous portion of the X-chromosome, there are genes in the nonhomologous region of the Y-chromosome. Such genes are spoken of as *holandric*. The transmission

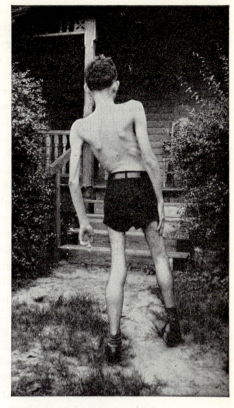

Fig. 28.3 Progressive muscular dystrophy, a trait here conditioned by a recessive sex-linked gene.

Table 28.2. Some Human Traits Dependent upon Sex-Linked Genes*

Red-green color blindness	Myopia
Hemophilia	Defective iris
Thrombasthenia	Pseudohypertrophic muscular dystrophy
Optic atrophy	Peroneal atrophy
Nystagmus	Ichthyosis
Microcornea	Keratosis
Megalocornea	Anhidrotic ectodermal dysplasia
Day blindness	Alopecia congenita
Night blindness	Epidermal cysts
Retinal detachment	Distichiasis (double eyelashes)
Microphthalmia	White occipital lock of hair
Albinism restricted to the eyes	Defective hair follicles
Coloboma iridis	Defective tooth enamel
Glaucoma of the juvenile type	

* Many of these traits have alternative forms dependent upon autosomal genes.

will be from an affected father to all his sons, and the trait conditioned by such a gene will not occur in women. Evidently mutations do occur in the nonhomologous region of the Y-chromosome in man, but those with noticeable effects are of excessive rarity. Thus, a single pedigree exists exhibiting clearly holandric inheritance of an otherwise unknown abnormality, ichthyosis hystrix gravior. The affected individuals in early infancy develop horny scales over the whole body with the exception of the face, palms and soles. In the one family in which it has been found, the condition was transmitted by affected males to all of their sons through six generations. There is a similarly unique pedigree of hypertrichosis of the ears in which Y-chromosome inheritance is clearly indicated. A type of keratosis, characterized by small, hard, nonpainful nodules on the hands and feet has been reported in one pedigree which strongly suggests Y-chromosome transmission. And in one pedigree of a much less rare (and quite trivial) anomaly, webbed toes, holandric inheritance appears to be involved, although in most families this abnormality is transmitted without limitation to the male sex.

The third kind of hereditary behavior associated with the sex chromosomes involves genes located on the homologous portions of the X- and Y-chromosomes. Such genes are spoken of as incompletely sex-linked. They will behave as ordinary autosomal genes except for one thing: about half the families in which the father carries the gene will contain more affected sons and unaffected daughters than would be expected on the basis of autosomal inheritance, while the other half will contain more affected daughters and unaffected sons.

Crossing over of incompletely sex-linked genes can occur in both sexes, but in women it merely transfers the gene from one X-chromosome to the other, while in men it shifts the gene from the X- to the Y-chromosome or vice versa, so that a differential sex ratio of affected offspring is produced.

There are nine or more pathological conditions in man which, with varying degrees of assurance, can be attributed to incompletely sex-linked genes (see Haldane 1936, 1944; Kaliss and Schweitzer; Snyder and Palmer). The traits resulting from these genes are total color blindness, xeroderma pigmentosum (a skin disease), epidermolysis bullosa (malignant skin blisters), Oguchi's disease (a type of blindness), spastic paraplegia (a neuro-muscular defect), hereditary hemorrhagic diathesis (a blood dyscrasia), retinitis pigmentosum (another type of blindness having two allelic genes involved), and a type of cerebral sclerosis (a mental defect).

Thus a mutant gene in man may have its absolute location in any one of four general regions: in an autosome, in the nonhomologous portion of the X-chromosome, in the nonhomologous portion of the

Y-chromosome, or in the homologous portions of the sex chromosomes. Next we may inquire as to the relative location of a gene with respect to any other gene not an allele. Two nonallelic genes may both be located in chromosomes of the same homologous pair, in which case they belong to the same linkage group; or they may be located in chromosomes of different pairs, and hence show independent segregation.

In order to test whether or not two pairs of genes are linked, we must of course study the amount of recombination between them. This is difficult to do in man, partly because the low frequency of many mutant genes in human populations means that we are seldom able to find two of them in the same family and partly because we cannot use experimental matings in man. Some progress has been made in the mapping of human chromosomes, however, in spite of these difficulties.

To begin with, it is obvious that the thirty or more sex-linked gene pairs in man must be linked with one another, since they are all carried in the homologous part of the X-chromosome. Since the mutant alleles are rare, very few cases of two in the same family have been observed. Nevertheless, enough instances of the simultaneous transmission of the genes for hemophilia and for red-green color blindness have been studied to establish the linkage between them; crossing over is in the neighborhood of 10 per cent.

In the case of the incompletely sex-linked genes, crossing over can always be studied in males between an incompletely sex-linked gene and the junction of the homologous and nonhomologous regions of the sex chromosomes. The technique of analyzing the linkage strength in such cases is rather specialized, but from such analyses have come the first chromosomal maps of human beings (Fig. 28.4). We should emphasize, however, that at the present time these maps must be regarded in large part as provisional.

Specialized techniques have also been developed for studying autosomal linkage in man. As would be expected, because of the large number of chromosome pairs, most of the genes studied have been independent of each other. As we pointed out in Chapter 10, there are at the time of this writing just two instances of autosomal linkage which we may regard as safely established. One of these involves the Rh locus and a gene for elliptocytosis; the other is linkage between the O A B locus and a gene causing a malformation known as the nail-patella syndrome (onycho-arthrodysplasia).

Next we may investigate the ontogenetic relations of the mutant gene. These include the manifestations of the gene with respect to its alleles and with respect to other genes which are not alleles. Ontogenetic relations also include the penetrance of the gene, its expres-

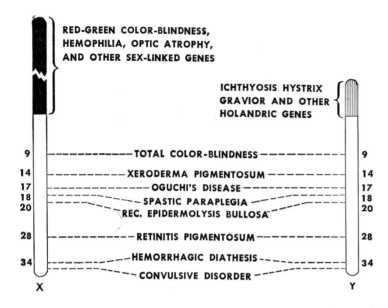

RED-GREEN COLOR-BLINDNESS,
HEMOPHILIA, OPTIC ATROPHY,
AND OTHER SEX-LINKED GENES

ICHTHYOSIS HYSTRIX
GRAVIOR AND OTHER
HOLANDRIC GENES

9	TOTAL COLOR-BLINDNESS	9
14	XERODERMA PIGMENTOSUM	14
17	OGUCHI'S DISEASE	17
18	SPASTIC PARAPLEGIA	18
20	REC. EPIDERMOLYSIS BULLOSA	20
28	RETINITIS PIGMENTOSUM	28
34	HEMORRHAGIC DIATHESIS	34
	CONVULSIVE DISORDER	

X   Y

Fig. 28.4 Maps of the human sex chromosomes. While this book was in press, the evidence for partial sex linkage was reanalyzed by more critical methods than were previously available [Morton, N. E., *Amer. J. Hum. Genet.* 9:55 (1957)]. The data suggesting partial sex linkage were found in every instance to fall short of statistical significance. The occurrence of this phenomenon in man, therefore, while possible, is as yet unproved.

sivity, and the viability produced in an individual having the gene.

With respect to its own alleles a mutant gene may be dominant, recessive, or intermediate. It may be dominant in one sex and recessive in the other, in which case the resulting trait is said to be sex-influenced. With respect to another pair of genes, a mutant gene may be epistatic, hypostatic (the converse of epistatic), or indifferent. In the case of multiple genes it may be additive or multiplicative in its effect. The ontogenetic relations of the gene have been thoroughly discussed in preceding chapters and need not be elaborated here.

In the study of heredity in man we frequently find that what appears to be the same trait will be inherited in one family on the basis of an autosomal dominant gene, in another as due to an autosomal recessive gene, and perhaps in a third on the basis of a sex-linked gene. Possibly such instances represent separate similar mutations, perhaps they indicate translocations and position effects. Careful observation sometimes reveals variations between the differently inherited forms of the same trait, while in other instances no differentiation can be made in the character even though more than one type of genetic behavior has been clearly demonstrated in various families.

In giving advice to families it is therefore important to know not only the diagnosis of the trait but also the family history of the person seeking advice. Only in this way can the ontogenetic relations of the mutant gene considered be discovered and the genetic prognosis properly made.

Next we shall discuss the remaining ontogenetic relations, namely penetrance, expressivity, and viability. Penetrance is a statistical con-

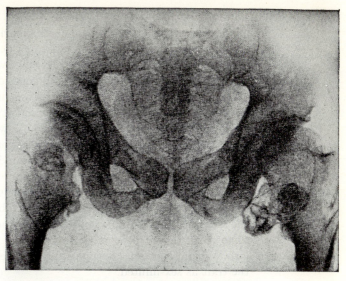

Fig. 28.5 X-ray of the pelvic region of a man suffering from multiple cartilaginous exostoses. Note the growths on the femur heads.

cept of the regularity with which a gene produces its effect. If a dominant gene produces a trait in every individual carrying it or if a recessive gene produces a trait in every individual homozygous for it, we say the gene has complete penetrance. If, however, some individuals fail to manifest the trait even though having the gene in the required homozygous or heterozygous state, we say that the gene has reduced penetrance.

The reduced penetrance may be due to the residual heredity, such as epistasis or other inhibiting effects, or it may be the result of environmental inhibition. The penetrance of human genes is difficult to establish with assurance, except in cases of dominant genes with high penetrance. The blood group genes, for example, appear to have complete penetrance. Every individual who inherits a gene for a specific agglutinogen develops that agglutinogen. On the other hand some genes give evidence of having reduced penetrance. Thus, diabetes insipidus (not to be confused with the far commoner and more familiar diabetes mellitus), a condition symptomatized by the discharge of enormous quantities of urine, is found in numerous pedigrees in which it is clearly dependent on a single dominant gene. But in several of the pedigrees there is a "skip," that is, an individual whose father or mother exhibited the condition and some of whose children are affected also, but who himself is free from it. In these pedigrees, the gene shows very high, but not quite complete penetrance. Systematic studies by Levit and Pessikova, however, have indicated that high penetrance for this gene may be the exception, rather than the rule. In pedigrees of families with multiple exostoses (cartilaginous tumors of the long bones, usually benign, but occasionally becoming malignant, Fig. 28.5), "skips" in otherwise apparently dominant transmission are relatively frequent, particularly among females. Penetrance of the gene may be lower than 75 per cent in women; in men it is considerably higher. Obviously genes with complete penetrance are the easiest to study, but since all genes do not have it, the degree of penetrance should be stated for each gene if it is known.

The differentiation between a dominant gene with low penetrance and a recessive gene is difficult, since both will appear sporadically in pedigrees. Statistical methods have been worked out, however, which make use of data such as the relative abundance of affected siblings, parents, offspring, and other relatives of affected individuals.

Penetrance may be equivalent in both sexes, or it may be higher in one than in the other. Pyloric stenosis (obstruction of the orifice of the stomach), for example, appears to be due to a recessive gene with some reduction in penetrance in boys but much more reduction in girls. When penetrance is completely reduced in one sex, we speak of the trait as sex-limited.

Another ontogenetic relation of the mutant gene is its expressivity. When the trait produced by a gene is variable from individual to individual, we speak of the gene as having variable expressivity. Many genes have rather constant expressivity, regularly producing a definite degree of the characteristic. Other genes do not have this constant expressivity.

Myotonic dystrophy, for example, is named for its nervous and muscular manifestations. But very commonly associated with these is a unique type of cataract. In pedigrees in which this condition occurs, the same dominant gene produces the disabling neuromuscular symptoms of the disease — with cataract in some cases, without it in others — in about 60 per cent of the individuals who inherit it; in the remainder, it results in cataract alone, sufficiently severe in some to seriously impair vision, in others so slight as to be imperceptible except on meticulous examination.

An "allergic diathesis" has also been attributed to a dominant gene, variously manifested as asthma, vasomotor rhinitis, atopic dermatitis, or hay fever (Schwartz 1953). Here again the variations may be due to the residual heredity in some cases, to the environment in others. A knowledge of the variable manifestations of a gene is essential to instituting preventive measures in relatives of an affected person.

Among the ontogenetic manifestations of a gene is the viability which results in an individual possessing it. Some genes do not noticeably decrease the length of life. Others, like the gene for hemophilia, definitely reduce the chances of living out a normal span. Still others are lethal in the homozygous state. Many lethal genes are known in man.

Finally, we discuss the phylogenetic relations of the mutant gene. These include the frequency of a gene and of its allele in the population and the frequencies of the genotypes produced by a gene and its allele. Phylogenetic relationships of a gene are relatively unimportant in laboratory genetics, where the emphasis is placed on experimental matings in which the genotypes are known or can be detected. Therefore we have had no need to discuss them in previous chapters. They become extremely important, however, in natural populations. The study of human inheritance is in large part a study of population genetics.

Perhaps the most important concept in population genetics is that of equilibrium. One of the commonest misconceptions in genetics is that a character dependent upon a dominant gene will in time increase in proportion in a population merely because of the dominance. This does not happen. As long as all genotypes in the population have equal opportunities of producing offspring, a dominant gene will not ordinarily change in frequency with respect to its recessive allele, but the frequencies of the two alleles will remain constant from generation to generation. Under a system of random mating the frequencies of the genotypes produced by a mutant gene and its allele will likewise remain constant.

Consider a pair of alleles T and t. In a given population most of the genes of this pair at this locus may be T alleles, with t alleles making up only a small fraction of the total. Or it may be the other way around, so that t alleles make up a larger proportion of the genes of this pair. If 70 per cent of the alleles of this pair are T alleles and 30 per cent are t alleles, we say that the frequency of T is 0.7 and the frequency of t is 0.3. The gene frequencies of different genes may differ in the same population, and the frequencies of the same gene may vary from population to population. The variation in frequency may range from 0 to 1, these being only limiting values.

It is easy to show that in the absence of disturbing factors, the relative frequencies of T and t alleles, as well as the relative frequencies of TT, Tt, and tt zygotes, tend to remain constant from generation to generation. Factors which may upset the constancy include, of course, selection (i.e., differential reproduction by different genotypes) and mutation; in a quite small population, the gene frequencies are likely to be shifted by a phenomenon known as *genetic drift*, even in the absence of selection or mutation. Assortative mating and inbreeding alter the relative frequencies of TT, Tt, and tt zygotes but in themselves do not affect the equilibrium between the frequencies of T and t genes.

We shall see later how some of the disturbing factors listed in the preceding paragraph may affect gene and zygote frequencies. But first it is necessary to understand the tendency toward equilibrium which is inherent in the Mendelian mechanism. Considering our pair of alleles T and t, let us represent the proportion of T genes in the population by p and the proportion of t genes by q. Then, since genes at this locus are either T or t, p + q must equal 1. Of the sperms produced by the men in the population p will contain T, and q will contain t. Likewise the proportion of eggs containing T will be p, and of eggs containing t will be q. The random union of sperms and eggs in the population would thus be as shown in the diagram.

SPERMS: EGGS:	p (T)	q (t)
p (T)	p² (TT)	pq (Tt)
q (t)	pq (Tt)	q² (tt)

It can be seen that TT individuals will occur in the population in the proportion p², Tt individuals in the proportion 2pq, and tt individuals in the proportion q². To prove that this ratio of p²(TT) : 2pq(Tt) : q²(tt) is truly an equilibrium ratio, let us see what proportions of T and t gametes would be produced by this generation. The TT individuals will produce only T gametes, while half of the gametes produced by the Tt individuals will contain T and half will contain t. The proportion of T gametes will thus be $p^2 + \frac{1}{2}(2pq) = p^2 + pq = p(p + q) = p$. Likewise t gametes will be produced in the proportion $q^2 + \frac{1}{2}(2pq) = q^2 + pq = q(q + p) = q$. Thus this generation will again produce T and t gametes in the ratio p : q, and the gene frequencies are the same as in the preceding generation. Necessarily the zygotic frequencies will consistently be reproduced in the ratio p²(TT) : 2pq(Tt) : q²(tt). It is also apparent that in a population to which the foregoing derivation applies (large, random mating, and without mutation or selection) there is a predictable relation between the frequency of heterozygotes and the frequencies of the two homozygous classes: the heterozygote frequency is always equal to twice the square root of the product obtained by multiplying together the frequencies of dominant and recessive homozygotes ($2qp = 2\sqrt{p^2 \times q^2}$). This important relation is known as the *Hardy-Weinberg equilibrium*.

We will best understand what the Hardy-Weinberg equilibrium means, and at the same time we shall be able to test its validity, by examining some actual data, such as those in Table 28.3. The data relate to frequencies of the M, MN, and N blood groups, as found in samples of various populations. You will recall from Chapter 13 that the presence of either or both of the M, N antigens can be detected serologically. Consequently, the frequencies of heterozygotes given in column (b) are actually observed frequencies, as are those of the two homozygous classes; and the gene frequencies (p' is the

Table 28.3. COMPARISON OF OBSERVED FREQUENCIES OF HETEROZYGOTES WITH ESTIMATED FREQUENCIES BASED ON THE HARDY-WEINBERG EQUILIBRIUM

Population Sampled	Number in Sample	Genotype Frequencies			Gene Frequencies		Estimated Frequencies of Heterozygotes ($= 2p'q'$)
		(a) MM	(b) MN	(c) NN	p' ($= a + \frac{1}{2}b$)	q' ($= c + \frac{1}{2}b$)	
Navahos	361	.845	.144	.011	.917	.083	.152
Rwala Arabs	208	.575	.367	.058	.758	.241	.365
Finns (Karjala)	398	.457	.432	.111	.673	.327	.440
Swedes	1200	.361	.470	.169	.596	.404	.481
Poles	600	.282	.490	.228	.527	.473	.499
Australian Aborigines	372	.024	.304	.672	.176	.824	.290

frequency of the M allele, q' that of the N gene) are, in effect, actual counts of the relative numbers of M and N alleles in each sample. The column $2p'q'$ gives the frequencies of heterozygotes *predicted from the Hardy-Weinberg formula* on the basis of the observed gene frequencies. If we compare the predicted frequencies in this column with the frequencies of heterozygotes actually found, column (b), we see that the agreement is remarkably good; in only one case do the observed and predicted values differ by as much as 0.01. We do not always find agreement as good as this, but we do find it in the overwhelming majority of all populations that have been studied.

One of the many sets of data on the M, N blood groups not included in our table relates to a sample of 1100 Japanese in Tokyo. The frequency of the MM genotype was 0.324; of MN, 0.472; and the NN frequency was 0.204. Can you apply the methods we used in Table 28.3 to find out how closely the observed frequency of heterozygotes compares with the frequency which would be predicted by the Hardy-Weinberg rule?

If we can be confident of the validity of the Hardy-Weinberg rule, we have a way of estimating the frequency of heterozygous carriers of *recessive* genes. Remember that q stands for the frequency of the recessive allele, and that q^2 is the frequency of recessive homozygotes. It is obvious, then, that to find the value of q (which we cannot in this case observe directly) we need only take the square root of the frequency of recessive homozygotes. With this as a beginning, we can readily answer such a question as: What are the chances that you are heterozygous for the albino gene? Say that one person in 10,000 is an albino (*aa*). Then $q^2 = 0.0001$, so that q, the frequency of the gene *a* must be $\sqrt{0.0001}$, or 0.01. The frequency of its normal allele, A, is of course p($= 1 - q$), or 0.99. The estimated frequency of heterozygous *Aa* individuals in the general population is therefore 2 × 0.99 × 0.01($= 2pq$), or very nearly 0.02. Hence the chance that an individual picked at random from the population is an *Aa* heterozygote is about 1 in 50 — probably rather higher than you would have guessed.

Misunderstandings of equilibrium and its implications are all too frequent in discussions of human inheritance. Examples of false statements based on lack of knowledge of equilibrium are the following: "Albinism is due to a recessive gene, *which explains why it is so rare*." "Left-handedness occurs in 25 per cent of the population, *which indicates that it is a Mendelian recessive*." Neither statement is correct.

A recessive trait may be common or rare in a population, depending upon whether the recessive mutant gene is common or rare. This in turn will depend upon the past history of the population in terms of mutation, selection, migration, system of mating, and population size.

"Lobster claw," a mutation in which the human hand has only two large fingers, is in some families dependent upon an autosomal dominant gene, yet the recessive normal five-fingered condition is common and the "lobster claw" rare (Fig. 28.6). "Lobster claw" will not become common just because this mutant gene is dominant. A recent prize-winning essay on mental health contained the statement: "We are indeed lucky that the mental disorders are not dominant traits, or we would all be insane by now, according to the laws of heredity." This is a glaring misunderstanding of the principle of equilibrium. It is important to recognize and reject fallacies such as this.

The discerning student will at once realize that human "races" are populations in the sense in which the term has been used in this chapter. Insofar as differences between races are conditioned by genes, these differences come about largely as a result of variations in the frequencies of the alleles from race to race. Most of the known human alleles are represented to some extent in all racial groups which have been studied. It is conceivable that a certain allele might not be represented at all in a particular population, but it is probable that such circumstances are uncommon within the human species. Races differ in the *frequencies* of various alleles, and obviously it would be most unlikely that any one race would have high frequencies of all the desirable genes or that any race would have high frequencies of all the undesirable genes.

We are now ready to consider some of the conditions under which gene and zygote frequencies *do* change. The problem is of considerable interest, because the whole process of evolution depends to a major degree upon extensive shifts in gene frequencies. Mutations occur, and the mutant genes may be eliminated from the population, or they may gradually increase in frequency at the expense of their respective alleles. If a given allele at any locus spreads through an entire popula-

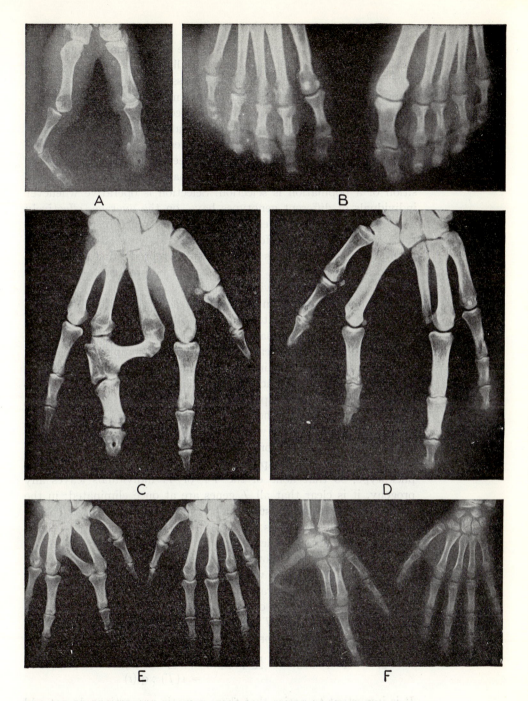

Fig. 28.6 Roentgenograms of typical "lobster claw" (A), and of variations of the condition which occasionally occur (B–F). *From Graham and Badgley in the American Journal
of Human Genetics*

tion, it is evident that other alleles at the same locus must be elimi-nated in the process. Obviously, if initially rare mutant genes at a sufficient number of loci become widely disseminated through a popu-lation, the phenotype of the population must become substantially altered, and transformation into a new species may be under way. In human populations consideration of the rates at which gene frequen-cies may shift under various circumstances is relevant to the evalu-ation of eugenics programs, as we shall see in the next chapter.

One of the factors which obviously may alter the genetic compo-sition of a population is selection. Selection is operative whenever individuals of different genotypes have, on the average, effectively different reproductive rates. An effective difference in reproductive rate may result from differential fertility, differential viability, or both. Thus an individual's effective rate of reproduction is zero if he produces no progeny; but it is also zero if he produces a dozen off-spring, none of whom survives to maturity.

The effects of selection can be most readily computed for the case of selection of maximal intensity, when all individuals of one pheno-type are completely eliminated from the breeding population in every generation. The simplest case is that involving complete dominance.

Suppose we start again with a population produced by gametes among which the frequencies of the alleles T and t are p_0 and q_0, respectively. (The subscripts are used to distinguish the frequencies in this generation from the frequencies which will be found in sub-sequent generations, and which we shall designate as p_1, q_1; p_2, q_2; etc.) The zygotic proportions will be, as we have seen above, $p_0^2(TT)$: $2p_0q_0(Tt)$: $q_0^2(tt)$. If complete selection acts against the dominant phenotype, so that none of the TT or Tt individuals leaves any progeny, it is clear that all T genes are at once eliminated; in the absence of mutation, all subsequent zygotic generations will consist exclusively of homozygous recessives.

Consider, on the other hand, the results of complete selection against the *recessive* phenotype. If all tt zygotes are eliminated from the breeding population, what remains will consist of TT and Tt individuals only, in the ratio $p_0^2(TT)$: $2p_0q_0(Tt)$. As we know, the TT individuals will yield only T gametes, while half of the gametes from the Tt's will carry T and half will carry t. Hence the effective breeding population will produce gametes in the ratio

$$[p_0^2 + \tfrac{1}{2}(2p_0q_0)](T) : \tfrac{1}{2}[2p_0q_0](t) = p_0[p_0 + q_0](T) : p_0q_0(t)$$
$$= 1(T) : q_0(t)$$

It is important to notice that these gametic proportions do not add up to unity but to $(1 + q_0)$. If we wish to compare them with the gametic frequencies of the preceding generation, p_0 and q_0 (which *do* add up to unity), we must express them as fractions of the total gametic population. To do this we divide by the total, $(1 + q_0)$, and this gives us the gene frequencies resulting from one generation of selection:

$$\frac{1}{1 + q_0}\ (T) : \frac{q_0}{1 + q_0}\ (t) \tag{1}$$

The new frequency of the t allele, which we may conveniently designate as q_1, is therefore given by the formula $q_1 = \dfrac{q_0}{1 + q_0}$.

Thus if we start with a population in which there are, say, 36% tt individuals (so that $q_0 = \sqrt{0.36} = 0.6$), complete selection against tt homozygotes will give us $q_1 = \dfrac{0.6}{1.6} = 0.375$; and there will be only 14% tt zygotes $[q_1{}^2 = (0.375)^2 = 0.1406]$ formed in the next generation. If the same selection is applied for another generation, we may compute q_2 in exactly analogous fashion: $q_2 = \dfrac{q_1}{1 + q_1} = \dfrac{0.375}{1.375} = 0.273,$ and the number of tt zygotes $(q_2{}^2)$ has become reduced to about 7.5% of the total zygotic population.

If we have to compute the effect of complete selection over any large number of generations, the repeated application of the method used in the preceding paragraph becomes tedious. It is very simple, however, to derive a formula with which we can immediately predict the value that q will have after 5, 500 or any number of generations of complete selection. The student will find in the Appendix to this Chapter (page 452) the derivation of this formula, and of an equally simple one that tells us *how many generations* of selection would be required to accomplish a specified reduction in the value of q. This permits us to answer such a question, for example, as this: If one person in 10,000 is an albino, *aa*, (i.e., $q^2 = 0.0001$) and no albinos were to reproduce henceforth, how many generations would it take before the frequency of albinism would be reduced to 1 in 40,000 $(q^2 = 0.000025)$? To answer this, use formula (A3) of the Appendix, $n = \dfrac{1}{q_n} - \dfrac{1}{q_0}$, writing 0.005 for q_n and 0.01 for q_0; the solution may surprise you!

The same kind of question (over a much more limited range, however) can be answered by consulting the graph in Figure 28.7. On this graph we can see at once approximately how many generations are needed to effect any specified reduction in q^2. Suppose we wish to know how many generations of complete selection it would take to reduce the frequency of recessive homozygotes from 10% to 1%. The graph shows that reduction of q^2 from 0.9999 (its first plotted value) to 0.10 is almost accomplished in two generations, and that reduction from 0.9999 to 0.01 requires nine generations. The difference between these two values of n, $9 - 2 = 7$, gives the number of generations required for q^2 to change from 0.10 to 0.01.

A striking characteristic of the action of complete selection is readily apparent in Figure 28.7. A reduction of q^2 from approximately 100% to 10% is nearly accomplished in two generations; but it requires seven generations to effect a reduction from 10% to 1%, 22 generations to reduce q^2 from 1% to 0.1%, and 68 generations to reduce it from 0.1% to 0.01%. It is seen, in fact, to be generally true that *the rarer a recessive trait becomes, the less effective is any further selection against it.*

Complete selection against a recessive homozygote, or *lethal selection* as it is sometimes called, is a phenomenon of some consequence in population genetics. Genes with recessive lethal action (Chapter 3) are subject to selection of this intensity, provided the lethality is expressed before sexual maturity. In man a considerable number of genes are known which, when homozygous, effectively prevent reproduction, either by causing death before puberty or by producing sterility. Among these are the genes for the infantile type of progressive muscular dystrophy, a congenital form of severe ichthyosis, and a malignant type of epidermolysis bullosa. The pathologic traits in man which can be attributed to the homozygosity of a pair of genes with recessive lethal action are individually quite rare; the homozygote frequency (at birth) is in almost every case 1 in 10,000 or lower.

Although in any animal species there is a fairly large number of mutant genes which may be classed as recessive lethals, an overwhelmingly larger number of mutants have much less drastic effects on viability or fertility. It is therefore necessary to consider the effects of *partial selection* as well as complete selection in approaching problems of population dynamics. Consider the case in which *tt* genotypes may survive and reproduce but are inferior in viability or fertility (or in both) to *TT* and *Tt* zygotes; the surviving progeny of a given number of *tt* zygotes might be only 95% as numerous, for example, as the surviving progeny of the same number of phenotypic dominants (*TT* and *Tt* zygotes). The consequences of a situation of this kind can be worked out by essentially the same procedures as we used in analyzing the effects of complete elimination of recessive homozygotes.

We start, as before, with the zygotic population produced by $p_0 T$ gametes and $q_0 t$ gametes, viz., $p_0^2(TT) : 2p_0q_0(Tt) : q_0^2(tt)$. Instead of eliminating *all* of the *tt* zygotes, however, from the effective breeding population, we eliminate only a fraction, k. This leaves *TT*, *Tt*,

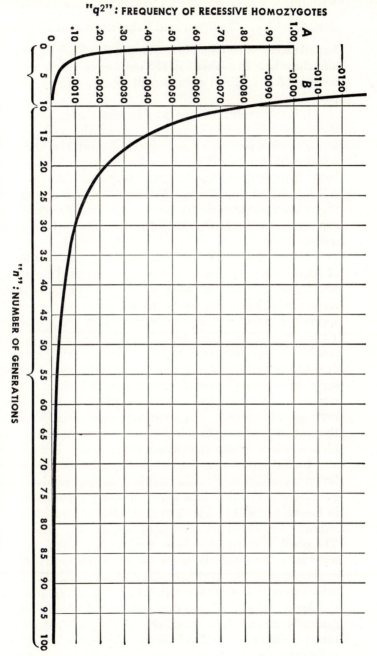

Fig. 28.7 The abscissal distance between ordinates at any two values of q² shows the time, in generations, required to change the frequency of recessive homozygotes from the higher to the lower value of q², when complete or lethal selection operates against them.

and *tt* individuals in the ratio $p_0^2(TT) : 2p_0q_0(Tt) : (1 - k)q_0^2(tt)$. With this as a start, you should be able to derive for yourself the relation, $q_1 = \dfrac{q_0 - kq_0^2}{1 - kq_0^2}$. If you need help, however, the derivation of this formula too will be found in the Appendix of this Chapter, where we also show how to evaluate n, the number of generations required to accomplish a specified reduction in gene frequency, for the case of partial selection.

It is extremely important at this point that we understand clearly the meaning of k. This is commonly called the coefficient of selection acting against recessive homozygotes. We can also think of it as the *selective disadvantage* of the recessive homozygote as compared with individuals showing the dominant phenotype. A concise definition, which is far less complicated than it may at first appear, would state that k is *the average deficit in net reproductivity of recessive homozygotes, expressed as a fraction of the net reproductivity of the dominant phenotype.*

All that the above definition really means is, that if the intensity of selection acting against recessives is indicated by a coefficient of selection of k = 0.05, say, then phenotypic dominants and recessives, respectively, instead of producing the same average number of offspring per parent will, on the average, yield progeny in the ratio of $1 : (1 - k)$, orhere, 1.00 : 0.95. In slightly different words, a given number of recessives born in any generation will be represented by $(1 - k)$, or 95%, as many progeny as have been produced by the same number of phenotypic dominants. (We should understand, of course, that the counts of parents and progeny are made at the same stage of development — at birth, say, or at sexual maturity.) When the coefficient of selection is unity, k = 1, we have the case of complete selection against recessives which has already been discussed.

Under partial selection, when the value of k is around 0.1 or lower, we find that the reduction in q or in q^2 resulting from two or even a dozen generations of selection is very slight indeed. The graph in Figure 28.8 will enable us to determine, at least roughly, the time required for partial selection to accomplish any given change in q^2. The graph is plotted for direct reading only when the coefficient of selection is 0.01, that is, when the net reproductive rate of the recessives is 99% that of the dominant phenotypes. If you will examine the formula on which the curve is based, however, (formula (A 6) in the Appendix) you will see that with partial selection the number of generations needed to effect any given gene-frequency change is proportional to $1/k$ — that is, *the time required is inversely proportional to the intensity of selection.* Thus we may read directly from the graph that to reduce q^2 from 0.15 to 0.01 would take about 900 generations

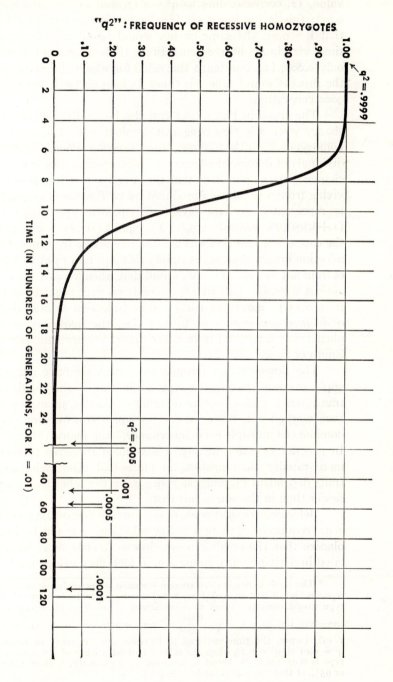

Fig. 28.8 The abscissal distance between ordinates of height q_0^2 and q_n^2 shows time (in hundreds of generations) required to change q^2, the frequency of recessive phenotypes, from one value to the other when the coefficient of selection is .01.

(the difference, in hundreds of generations, between the abscissal value, 12, corresponding to $q^2 = 0.15$, and 21, the abscissa at $q^2 = 0.01$); this is for $k = 0.01$. If selection is five times as intense, so that $k = 0.05$, the same change would be effected in one fifth the time, viz., in about 180 generations. If the coefficient of selection is only 0.001, i.e., one tenth the value for which the graph is plotted, the process would take ten times as long as for $k = 0.01$, or about 9000 generations.

The graph in Figure 28.8 can also be used to determine rates of change when selection is against dominants, that is, when recessive homozygotes, on the average, leave *more* surviving progeny than individuals of dominant phenotype. Algebraically this is equivalent to changing the sign of k, so that the effective breeding population surviving from a generation produced by p_0 T gametes and q_0 t gametes is represented by the zygotic frequencies $p_0^2(TT) : 2p_0q_0(Tt) : (1 + k)q_0^2(tt)$, instead of $p_0^2(TT) : 2p_0q_0(Tt) : (1 - k)q_0^2(tt)$, as was the case when selection was against recessives. In terms of the slow-selection graph, this means simply reading from right to left, instead of from left to right. Thus we found that when k was $+ 0.05$ (selection against recessives) about 180 generations were required to reduce q^2 from 0.15 to 0.01; when $k = - 0.05$ (selection against dominants), q^2 is *increased* from 0.01 to 0.15 (i.e., the frequency of dominant phenotypes is reduced from 0.99 to 0.85) in approximately the same length of time.*

The slow-selection formula and graph we have presented here apply, of course, to only one type of inheritance: single-pair autosomal transmission with complete dominance. Analogous expressions have been worked out, however, for sex-linked transmission, incomplete dominance, multiple-gene inheritance, and many other situations. In general, selection against a sex-linked recessive proceeds much more rapidly than against an autosomal gene; selection against traits dependent on multiple genes is, on the other hand, very much slower than in the single-pair case.

Before we consider some of the implications of the rates at which gene frequencies shift under slow selection, it would be well to emphasize that the conditions which were tacitly or expressly postulated in deriving our formula are, in fact, very inadequately satisfied

* The equivalence is close enough for most purposes but is not exact. A net reproductive deficit of 0.05 (i.e., 1/20) among individuals of dominant phenotype would correspond not to a coefficient of selection of $- 0.05$ acting upon recessives but to a k of $\frac{- 0.05}{1 - 0.05}$ or, very nearly, $- 0.0526$; ($1/20 \div 19/20 = 1/19$). Hence, the time required to increase the frequency of recessives from $q^2 = 0.01$ to $q^2 = 0.15$ when the selective disadvantage of the dominant phenotype is 0.05 would be about 0.05/0.0526 (quite exactly, $1/20 \div 1/19 = 19/20$) or 95% of that computed for $k = - 0.05$.

by natural populations. For example, the intensity of selection, as measured by k, has been treated as constant from one generation to the next; actually, the intensity of selection against any one genotype often varies markedly with changes in external environment. Recurrent mutation, nonrandom mating, and the effects of limited population size have not been taken into account. Perhaps most important of all we have considered selective advantage or disadvantage in terms of the situation at a single locus; as a matter of fact the fitness of an organism, even in a stable environment, is never determined by the presence or absence of one particular allele (except in the case of some lethal genes) but is a function of the genotype as a whole. We shall briefly consider below some of the factors which were ignored in the derivation of the slow-selection formula. Extensive analysis of the whole problem will be found in the works of Fisher, Haldane, and Sewell Wright which are cited at the end of this chapter.

In spite of the oversimplifying assumptions involved in its derivation, formula (A6), with its graphic evaluation in Figure 28.8, does inform us, to a first approximation, of a number of important characteristics of selective processes in Mendelian populations. It is evident, for example, that it would take an inordinately long time for a new mutant gene to replace its allele throughout a population at such selective intensities as are commonly encountered, corresponding, say, to values of k from 0.01 to 0.05. On the other hand we can also see that the process of selection if unopposed is inexorable: given enough time, a persistent selective advantage of even 0.001 (one tenth of one per cent) must result in the spread of a new mutant through any large population.

There is little doubt that a great part of adaptive evolution in the plant and animal worlds has been a consequence of the spread of genes with individually rather low selective advantages. The geologic time available for the requisite gene-frequency shifts can be shown to be adequate. To take only one index of the evolution of the horse, for example, there has been roughly a 50-inch increase in height from the ancestral Eohippus to the modern Equus. But this has taken place over a period of some 50,000,000 years, involving 10 to 20 million generations. On the basis of known mutation rates among animals generally it is easy to show that there has been ample time for the appearance of a sufficient number of mutant genes affecting height to serve as an adequate reservoir of variability for selection to act upon; and that there has been ample time for genes at *several hundred loci* — which individually might produce a height increment of but one tenth of an inch — each to be spread through more than 99% of the population, even if each of them on the average had a selective advantage in the neighborhood of only one per cent.

On the other hand the rate of selective action, in terms of individual generations, should make it apparent that no appreciable adaptive evolution in the biologic sense could have taken place in our own species within historic or near-historic times. Such major changes in ways of life as have been seen among mankind in the past 5000 or 10,000 years must therefore reflect primarily social, rather than biologic, evolution.

Finally, information regarding rates at which genes producing advantageous effects may be disseminated by selection makes it possible to compare the effectiveness of selection with that of recurrent mutation in accomplishing evolutionary shifts of gene frequencies.

It is not difficult to determine the rate at which allelic frequencies are affected by recurrent mutation. If m is the mutation rate from t to T (i.e., the fraction of t alleles which mutate to T in each generation), a zygotic population produced by p_0 T gametes and q_0 t gametes will yield gametes in which the frequencies of T and t alleles after mutation are in the ratio $[p_0 + mq_0](T) : [q_0 - mq_0]\,(t)$. Hence, $q_1 = q_0 - mq_0 = (1 - m)q_0$. In each following generation the new value of q will again be reduced by a fraction, m, of itself, so that we shall have for consecutive values of q:

$$q_1 = (1 - m)q_0$$
$$q_2 = (1 - m)q_1 = (1 - m)^2 q_0$$
$$q_3 = (1 - m)q_2 = (1 - m)^3 q_0$$
$$\cdot$$
$$\cdot$$
$$\cdot$$
$$\cdot$$
$$q_n = (1 - m)^n q_0 \qquad (2)$$

The successive values are seen to form a geometrical progression, and the value of q_n can readily be obtained from (2) by writing it in logarithmic form: $\log q_n = n \times \log (1 - m) + \log q_0$. From this we can get at once:

$$n = \frac{\log q_n - \log q_0}{\log (1 - m)} \qquad (3)$$

which tells us the number of generations it would take for the frequency of t alleles to be reduced from q_0 to q_n in consequence of recurrent mutation from t to T. A slightly simpler expression gives the value of n to a very close approximation and has the further advantage of showing an analogy with the slow-selection formula (Appendix [A6]), viz., that the time required to effect a given change in gene frequency is inversely proportional to the mutation rate; this formula, which we shall not undertake to derive here, is:

$$n = \frac{2.30}{m} (\log q_0 - \log q_n) \qquad (4)$$

If we wish to assess the evolutionary significance of mutation pressure, we need to consider how long it would require a recurring mutant to replace its allele more or less completely throughout a population. We might compute the value of n, for example, required to reduce the frequency of t from $q_0 = 1$ to $q_n = 0.1$ $(q_n^2 = 0.01)$; this would mean *increasing* the frequency of the T allele from zero to a level at which it would appear in 99% $(= 1 - q_n^2)$ of the population. By formula (4) we find that $n = \frac{2.3}{m} [0 - (-1)] = \frac{2.3}{m}$. For a mutation rate of 0.00001 (one mutation from t to T in 100,000 gametes in each generation) this would give n = 230,000; for a mutation rate of 0.0001 (one in 10,000), n = 23,000 generations. If we consult the slow-selection graph (Fig. 28.8), we find that the same effect would be accomplished in about 2,100 generations of selection with k = 0.01, and 21,000 generations, therefore, with k as low as 0.001. Now a mutation rate in the neighborhood of 1/100,000 to 1/50,000 appears to be characteristic of some of the most rapidly mutating loci in human chromosomes; a rate of 1/10,000 is extraordinarily high. On the other hand an intensity of selection corresponding to k = 0.01 is a rather modest one, and it seems fairly certain that most, if not all, genes have coefficients of selection as high as 0.001 or higher. These considerations allow us to conclude that the evolutionary significance of gene mutation lies primarily in its providing the materials for selection and other processes to act on; as compared with selection, mutation pressure must be of negligible consequence in the dissemination of genes through populations.

Generally speaking, mutation is a reversible process, and at many or most loci we may expect mutations to occur in both directions, i.e., from T to t as well as from t to T. At any given locus mutation rates to and from a particular allele may be about the same or they may differ in any degree. It is evident that the higher the frequency of one allele, say T, becomes, the more numerous will be the mutations from T to t. If T has an initially low frequency but is gradually increasing as a result of mutations from t to T, this process simultaneously diminishes the supply of t alleles available for mutation to T. We might expect that a point would ultimately be reached at which mutations from T to t would be just as numerous, in any generation, as mutations in the reverse direction. The frequency of the T allele would then cease to increase or, what is the same thing, the respective frequencies of T and t alleles would be in equilibrium. That reversible mutation does cause gene frequencies to tend toward an equilibrium point is readily proved. And you will see in the Appendix of this

Chapter (page 455) that it is also easy to show that equilibrium is reached *when the frequencies of T and t are proportional to the respective rates at which they originate by mutation.* That is, if in each generation a fraction, m, of *t* alleles mutate to *T*, and a fraction, m', of *T* alleles mutate to *t*, then mutation will cease to have any effect on the relative frequencies of *T* and *t* when

$$\frac{p}{q} = \frac{m}{m'}$$

If selection and mutation are both operative on a particular pair of alleles, it should be obvious that their effects will reinforce each other when the predominant mutation rate is in the direction of the allele which is also favored by selection; and that they will oppose each other when the converse is true. In the latter event, an equilibrium can again be predicted. For the case of complete selection against recessives, equilibrium is reached when $q^2 = m'$ (see Appendix, page 455). That is, when mutation to a recessive gene is opposed by complete selection against the recessive homozygote, the mutant gene tends to spread until q^2, the frequency of the *tt* homozygotes, is equal to the mutation rate from *T* to *t*.

Procedures like those used to determine the equilibrium between complete selection and mutation can be used also to find equilibria between mutation and slow selection. It will be found that in the case of slow selection against recessives an equilibrium is expected when $q^2 = m'/k$; for selection against phenotypic dominants, equilibrium is reached when $p^2 + 2pq = 2m/k$ where, it should be noticed, $p^2 + 2pq$ is the total frequency of dominant phenotypes (*TT* and *Tt*).

The estimate of mutation rates in man has in part been made possible by consideration of such equilibrium conditions as we have just discussed. The method, unfortunately, is not reliably applicable to deleterious autosomal recessives in human populations. In order to apply it properly we must have some assurance that mutational and selective processes are in at least approximate equilibrium at the time our gene-frequency estimates are made. Now the equilibrium conditions we have derived are those for a random-mating population. Equilibrium conditions may equally well be computed for a population with any specified amount of inbreeding. But if the amount of inbreeding decreases, the frequency of any deleterious autosomal recessive will begin to increase toward a new equilibrium because there are now relatively fewer of the recessive alleles in homozygous condition and therefore fewer exposed to adverse selection. Progress toward the new equilibrium is, however, extremely slow. We have good evidence that in recent generations the amount of inbreeding, in Europe and America at least, has been diminishing: there are fewer consanguineous marriages now than in the past. But we do not know how long this process has been going on; consequently, while we can be fairly sure that most or all deleterious autosomal recessive genes are below equilibrium frequency, there is no way of telling how far they fall short of it.

On the other hand the extent to which selection acts on infrequent *sex-linked* recessives is hardly affected by changes in the amount of inbreeding, because selection in this case acts chiefly through affected males and therefore does not depend on homozygosis of the deleterious allele. There is good reason to believe that the gene for hemophilia, for example, is at or near its equilibrium frequency; in this instance, therefore, we are justified in estimating mutation rate from gene-frequency data.

If k is the coefficient of selection acting against hemophilics, we may say that a fraction, k, of all *h* alleles carried by males is lost in each generation. But only one third of all X-chromosomes and therefore only about one third of all *h* alleles are carried by males; hence k/3 of the total *h* genes in the population are lost, per generation, as a result of selection. If p and q are the respective frequencies of *H* and *h* alleles, the reduction in frequency of *h* is kq/3. For equilibrium to obtain, this reduction must be compensated by the mutation of kq/3 *H* alleles to *h* in each generation. Thus, under the assumption that equilibrium has been reached, we conclude that m′ (the mutation rate from *H* to *h*) = kq/3. On the basis of life expectancy data on hemophilics, Haldane estimates their net fertility to be about $\frac{1}{4}$ of normal; that is, their selective disadvantage is k = $\frac{3}{4}$. The population frequency of hemophilics at birth (which is also an estimate of q, the gene frequency) appears to be somewhere between 0.00004 and 0.00017. Hence the mutation rate, m′, is probably between 0.00001 and 0.00004 or between 1 in 100,000 and 1 in 25,000 per X-chromosome per generation.

Thus far we have been discussing gene-frequency dynamics in populations under the pretense that the populations were infinitely large; that is to say, we have ignored whatever effects *sampling errors* might have upon our computations. Errors of sampling (or perhaps better, sampling *fluctuations*) constitute a characteristic of the Mendelian mechanism as inherent as any of its other properties, and in populations of limited size it can be shown that they may have some rather surprising effects.

More often than not, what appear to be very large natural populations — millions of individuals spread over an extensive continuous territory — are in fact composed of numerous local and more or less self-contained breeding units. If each of these units is completely self-contained and there is no intermigration among them, the gene-frequency dynamics of each is determined by its own size and mating pattern. If there is a certain amount of intermigration, the evolution of the whole super-population depends in very major ways on the numbers in the individual subgroups, as well as on the extent to which intermigration occurs. We shall consider here the effect of the size-factor only in the population of an *isolate*, i.e., a breeding unit which does not exchange members with other groups.

It is important to recognize that the effective breeding population of an isolate is not the same as the apparent population size. The *effective breeding number* is determined by *the number of mating individuals who are progenitors of a subsequent generation*. In many temperate-zone insects, for example, local populations may number in the tens or hundreds of thousands toward the end of the summer, but as few as one in a thousand may survive the winter's hibernation to carry on the population in the ensuing spring; in such a case it can be shown that the effective breeding population in the long run is more closely dependent on the small numbers that survive the winter than on the enormously larger numbers that appear later in the year.

Populations of the human species numbering in the hundreds of millions have continuous distributions over large areas of the earth's surface. There are, however, countless isolated rural groups which contribute only an occasional emigrant to the outside world; their *apparent* populations may each comprise only one or a few hundred individuals, and their effective breeding numbers are of course still smaller. Even in urbanized regions mating contacts are significantly restricted by geographic distance, social class, religious affiliations, and other factors. The mating pattern of modern Europe and America, in fact, is essentially that of a large number of partial isolates. Dahlberg has very roughly estimated, from the frequencies of various types of consanguineous marriages, that the average effective mating number of the quasi-isolates lies somewhere between 400 and 3000. It should be obvious that in earlier centuries the sizes of mating groups must have been appreciably smaller than now. Archeologic evidence indicates that neolithic human communities through central Europe were commonly composed of only 25 to 35 households (Gordon Childe), and most subhuman primates appear to live in groups comprising from a dozen to a few score individuals. It seems a rather plausible inference that a great part of primate evolution has been accomplished in populations with very small effective mating numbers.

In order to understand why population size is a factor of major importance in determining the distribution and movements of gene frequencies, we need to consider briefly certain elementary principles of *sampling*. This discussion will be an outgrowth of the principles of probability which were taken up in Chapter 7, and of the principles of statistical analysis discussed in Chapter 15.

When we toss a coin ten or a dozen or a hundred times, the results we get represent a *sample* from what may be thought of as an infinite *source of supply*. In the supply source the frequencies of heads and tails (for an ideal or perfect coin) are exactly equal; we shall indicate this in a convenient notation, by writing $\hat{p} = \frac{1}{2}$ (or 0.50), $\hat{q} = \frac{1}{2}$ (or 0.50), *using $\hat{p}$ and $\hat{q}$ to designate frequencies* (of heads and tails, respectively) *in the infinite supply source*. Frequencies of heads and tails in a sample (composed of any given number of tosses) drawn from the supply will be designated by p_i and q_i. Values of p_i (or of q_i) in different samples drawn from the same supply will of course tend to fluctuate around the supply value, $\hat{p}$ (or $\hat{q}$).

Now, if we were to toss an ideal coin a million times, it would be surprising if the frequency of heads, p_i, which we turned up should exceed or fall below the supply frequency of heads, $\hat{p} = 0.50$, by as much as 0.002.* But if we should toss the coin only four times, say, it would occasion little surprise if the frequency of heads in the sample should be only 0.25 (i.e., one head in four tosses) — a divergence of 0.25 from the supply value $\hat{p} = 0.50$ — or even if we turned up no heads ($p_i = 0$) or all heads ($p_i = 1$), reflecting divergences of -0.50 and $+0.50$, respectively, from the supply frequency. The probabilities of obtaining the various possible values of p_i in a sample of four tosses are, as we should recall from Chapter 7, given by the successive terms in the expansion of the binomial $(\hat{p} + \hat{q})^n$, in this case $[\frac{1}{2}$ (heads) $+ \frac{1}{2}$ (tails)$]^4$; it will be convenient to have this expansion before us in tabular form (Table 28.4). We may read this table as showing (for example, from right to left) that there is 1 chance in 16 of turning up

Table 28.4. Probabilities of the Various Possible Combinations of Heads and Tails in Four Successive Tosses of a Coin

No. of heads in sample:	4	3	2	1	0
No. of tails in sample:	0	1	2	3	4
Probability of obtaining a sample with indicated numbers of heads and tails:	$(\hat{p}^4)$ $\frac{1}{16}$	$(4\hat{p}^3\hat{q})$ $\frac{4}{16}$	$(6\hat{p}^2\hat{q}^2)$ $\frac{6}{16}$	$(4\hat{p}\hat{q}^3)$ $\frac{4}{16}$	$(\hat{q}^4)$ $\frac{1}{16}$
p_i (= frequency of heads in sample):	1	0.75	0.50	0.25	0
q_i (= frequency of tails in sample):	0	0.25	0.50	0.75	1

* This is due to the fact that the standard error (see Chapter 15) of a binomial frequency is, for large samples,

$$\sqrt{\hat{p} \cdot \hat{q}/n} \text{ — here, } \sqrt{(0.50)(0.50/1,000,000)}, \text{ or } 0.0005;$$

and the chance is less than 1 in 100,000 that a frequency in a sample will diverge from the supply frequency in either direction by as much as four times its standard error. This method of computing the likelihood of divergences is not applicable to small samples, and for these we shall use another procedure.

no heads ($p_i = 0$), 4 chances in 16 of turning up one head ($p_i = 0.25$), and so on.

Now the genes in the sperm and ova, respectively, which actually participate in the formation of zygotes, may quite properly be regarded as representing finite samples drawn from what are, in effect, infinite sources of supply (*all* of the spermatogonia and oögonia which *might* have contributed participating gametes). From this viewpoint suppose we consider the extreme case of a human mating population which consists of just two individuals, one male and one female, who produce two children.* Suppose each of the parents is heterozygous, *Tt*. In the supply source of the gametes (the combined parental gametogonia), the gene frequencies are therefore $\frac{1}{2}(T):\frac{1}{2}(t)$; this is the same as writing $\hat{p} = 0.50$, $\hat{q} = 0.50$. A sample of 4 genes drawn from this supply will compose the genotypes of the two children; hence the probabilities of getting the various possible frequencies of *T* and *t* genes in the progeny generation are the same as those shown in Table 28.4 (simply read "*T*" for "heads," "*t*" for "tails"). We see at once that the gene frequencies, p_i and q_i, in the sample which we are most likely to obtain (probability $= \frac{6}{16}$) are the same as the gene frequencies $\hat{p}$ and $\hat{q}$ (each $= 0.50$) in the parental supply. But we must also notice that a gene frequency in the progeny generation is somewhat more likely to diverge from the parental gene frequency than it is to duplicate it. There are 6 chances in 16 that there will be two *T* alleles and two *t* alleles in the sample, which would mean that the progeny would exhibit the same gene frequencies as the parents; but there are $1 + 4 + 4 + 1 = 10$ chances that there will be 0, 1, 3, or 4 *t* alleles among the four genes drawn to produce the progeny, i.e., that q_i will be 0, 0.25, 0.75, or 1. These possible and moderately probable values of q_i diverge by -0.50, -0.25, $+0.25$, and $+0.50$, respectively, from the supply value, $\hat{q} = 0.50$. In any very large gene sample, on the other hand, sampling fluctuations even approaching these magnitudes would be simply out of the question, as we have seen in our consideration of the million coin tosses; even in a sample of 100 genes (where the S.E. of $\hat{q} = 0.50$ is 0.05), they would be practically impossible (although in samples of this size we would find q_i's quite frequently ranging down to 0.40 or up to 0.60); and in samples of 2500 we would not very often encounter a q_i below 0.49 or above 0.51.

We may conclude from the discussion in the preceding paragraph

* Strictly speaking, the kind of sampling involved in our illustration would be found only in a random mating population of *monoecious* individuals in which self-fertilization and cross-fertilization occurred with equal facility. The principles illustrated, however, are identical with those which would obtain in a dioecious species, and the quantitative results in the dioecious case would be only negligibly different from those in the model described.

that (1) *in large populations* (numbering in the thousands) *sampling fluctuations are likely to result in only negligible shifts in gene frequencies from generation to generation;* while (2) *in small populations* (of a few hundreds or smaller) *radical alterations in gene frequencies are to be expected as a consequence of sampling fluctuations alone*, i.e., in the absence of selection, mutation, or other disturbing factors.

An equally significant feature of the sampling mechanism we are concerned with lies in the fact that *the sample of genes drawn from the parental generation's supply in turn generates the supply from which a new sample will be drawn when the progeny generation reproduces.* Thus, if sampling fluctuations result in drawing from the parental supply 3 T alleles and 1 t allele, the sample values $p_i = 0.75$ and $q_i = 0.25$ are the gene frequencies of the progeny population; when the progeny population reproduces, these now become the frequencies in the *supply* which furnishes the gene sample that will constitute the next generation, i.e., we have now, $\hat{p} = 0.75$, $\hat{q} = 0.25$. If this generation again comprises a sample of just four genes, the probabilities of obtaining the various possible frequencies of T and t alleles are therefore given by the terms in the expansion of $[0.75(T) + 0.25(t)]^4$, or $[\frac{3}{4}(T) + \frac{1}{4}(t)]^4$, as shown in Table 28.5.

Table 28.5. PROBABILITIES OF THE VARIOUS POSSIBLE FREQUENCIES OF T AND t ALLELES IN A GENE SAMPLE OF 4, DRAWN FROM A PARENTAL SUPPLY IN WHICH $p = 0.75$, $q = 0.25$

No. of T alleles in sample:	4	3	2	1	0
No. of t alleles in sample:	0	1	2	3	4
Probability of obtaining a sample with indicated numbers of T and t alleles:	(p^4) $\frac{81}{256}$	$(4p^3q)$ $\frac{108}{256}$	$(6p^2q^2)$ $\frac{54}{256}$	$(4pq^3)$ $\frac{12}{256}$	(q^4) $\frac{1}{256}$
p_i (= frequency of T alleles in sample):	1	0.75	0.50	0.25	0
q_i (= frequency of t alleles in sample):	0	0.25	0.50	0.75	1

Here we see again that the gene frequency in a sample is more likely to diverge from the frequency in the parental supply (148 chances in 256) than to duplicate it (108 chances in 256).

Over many generations, sampling fluctuations may have cumulative effects of considerable magnitude. Change in gene frequency resulting from sampling fluctuations is known as *genetic drift*. Genetic drift can lead to the spread of a new mutant gene through a small population until every individual is homozygous for it (*random fixation*), or in many more cases, to the loss of a new allele before it has had a chance to spread appreciably or at all (*random extinction*).

What appears to be an effect of genetic drift may be seen in the distribution of the antigen-A (blood group) allele among American Indian tribes. These tribes, for the most part, have constituted relatively small self-contained mating units for as long as their history is known and probably for as long as they have inhabited this hemisphere. Among other peoples, where it is usually not possible to delimit comparable mating isolates, the frequency of the A gene invariably ranges between 0.15 and 0.30. In about one quarter of the American Indian tribes which have been adequately investigated, however, the frequency of the A allele is below 0.05, i.e., very much lower than in other parts of the world; in about ten per cent of the tribes, on the other hand, the frequency of A ranges from 0.50 to 0.60 — the *highest* values known anywhere. It seems probable that the prehistoric immigrants who were the ancestors of our modern Indians possessed a frequency of the A gene in the neighborhood of 0.20. If their descendants have in fact lived for long periods in rather small isolated mating units, the concept of genetic drift would lead us to expect a situation like that which we now find. In a considerable proportion of the isolates, we would expect the gene frequency to have drifted downwards to extinction or near-extinction of the A allele; and we would expect that in a smaller proportion (as is the case) the frequency would have attained aberrantly high values.

We might reasonably suspect, from the striking gene-frequency changes in small populations that can be accomplished by genetic drift (sampling fluctuation) alone and from the negligible shifts attributable to the same phenomenon in large populations, that the directive effects of *selection* would be less in small populations than in large ones. This proves to be the case. It can be shown, in fact, that in populations numbering a few dozen or score of mating individuals, *the direction of gene-frequency shifts at any locus is in large part independent of the relative selective values of the alleles; unless the intensity of selection is quite high, fixation or extinction of an allele depends almost exclusively on genetic drift. In large populations, on the other hand, even a very low intensity of selection overrides the effects of random fluctuation, and the direction of gene-frequency shift is determined altogether by selection or by the interaction of selection and mutation.*

Whether genetic drift or selection dominates the direction of gene-frequency changes is not merely a matter of the ratio between population size and intensity of selection; the direction depends in a complex way on the dominance relations between the alleles involved, on mutation rate, and on the mating system of the population. But as a very rough generalization, it may be said that the direction of gene shift is virtually unaffected by coefficients of selection in the neighborhood of k = 0.01 in a population of two or three dozen mating individuals and only slightly affected in populations numbering around 100, whereas in populations of several hundreds, genetic drift is likely to be of little or no significance in comparison with selection of the intensity indicated. Coefficients of selection around k = 0.001 are nearly without effect in populations of several hundred mating individuals but are often decisive in determining gene-frequency changes in populations of thousands.

The effects of migration and hybridization on gene-frequency distributions are, in a sense, the reverse of those of genetic drift. Matings of members of one population with migrants from another (and *vice versa*) should obviously tend to reduce genetic differences between the two groups, whereas the tendency of genetic drift is to increase the differences. If intermigration is on a sufficiently large scale, it would ultimately amount to a merging of the two populations into one. In the particular case that members of an expanding population tend to spread out over large distances from their center of concentration, a kind of gene-diffusion may occur, resulting in the establishment of a *cline* (more specifically, a *genocline*), i.e., a geographic gradient in the frequency of a particular gene. The distribution of the antigen-*B* allele in the populations of Asia and Europe seems to afford a rather clear illustration of this phenomenon. The *B* gene has its highest frequency (0.25 and above) in the peoples of central Asia; toward the periphery of the Asiatic continent it declines to around 0.20, and it tends to be still lower on the eastern coast and the coastal islands. If we go westward from central Asia into and through Europe, we find a systematic trend toward lower and lower frequencies of the *B* allele. In eastern Europe its value centers around 0.15, in central Europe around 0.10, and still lower average frequencies are found in the west.

The situation just described is easily explicable if we assume that the *B* allele first became prevalent, through genetic drift, in a small central Asiatic population which subsequently expanded greatly in size and by large-scale emigrations spread the gene through the rest of Asia and into Europe. The assumption finds historical support in the migratory conquests of the Huns, Avars, and other Mongoloid peoples. Some of them are known to have invaded China as early as 400 B.C. and to have occupied extensive areas until they were driven back about 600 years later. During the next thousand years several Mongoloid invasions of Europe occurred (e.g., under Genghis Khan), and the invaders penetrated well into central Europe. It seems a reasonable hypothesis that the various invading hordes introduced the *B* allele into indigenous populations of Europe and Asia which had previously not possessed it. The absence of the *B* gene among the earlier inhabitants of these areas would imply either that they were descended from initially quite small groups in which the allele was lost through genetic drift or, perhaps more plausibly, that their progenitors had separated from an ancestral human stock before the *B* allele had become established. Interesting support for the theory we have outlined is found in the situation of the Basque peoples in France and Spain. On both anthropometric and cultural grounds, the Basques appear to be more nearly representative of the neolithic inhabitants of Europe than any other living group, i.e., they appear to have been the least affected by non-European contacts. Consistent with this is the finding that they have also the lowest frequency of the B allele (about 0.02) found anywhere in Europe.

The processes of mutation, selection, and genetic drift together with intermigration and hybridization among groups can very adequately account for all or very nearly all of the phenomena of animal evolution in terms of Mendelian mechanisms. As we have seen, the relative importance of the various processes differs, depending on such conditions as population size, individual and group mobility, and the intensity of selective factors in the environment. From this we may reasonably infer that the mode of evolution has been rather different in different groups of animals and even in the same group at different times in its history. Studies of natural populations, both in the field and in the laboratory, and re-evaluation of paleontologic data in the light of the theoretic implications of the Mendelian mechanism are just now beginning to indicate, in broad outline, the nature of gene-frequency dynamics, that is, the character of evolutionary patterns.

In this chapter we have examined briefly the various basic relations of the mutant gene with especial reference to human populations. Upon such a scientific foundation are based the practical applications of which we have spoken. With the further growth of our basic knowledge of human heredity, we may confidently expect the development of added practical uses of this knowledge and of a deeper understanding of the problems of man's individual, social, and economic welfare.

APPENDIX

I We wish to find q_n, the frequency of an autosomal recessive gene after n generations of complete selection against recessive homozygotes.

We can do this most easily by considering the change in the value of the ratio, p/q, from one generation to the next. We have already learned (page 435) that if we start with a population in which the frequencies of T and t gametes are p_0 and q_0, respectively, the gametic frequencies after one generation of complete selection are

$$p_1 = \frac{1}{1 + q_0}, \quad q_1 = \frac{q_0}{1 + q_0}$$

Hence,

$$\frac{p_1}{q_1} = \frac{1}{1 + q_0} \div \frac{q_0}{1 + q_0}$$

or,

$$\frac{p_1}{q_1} = \frac{1}{q_0}$$

The *change* in the ratio p/q which results from a single generation of complete selection is, of course, $p_1/q_1 - p_0/q_0$. Since $p_1/q_1 = 1/q_0$, we may write

$$\frac{p_1}{q_1} - \frac{p_0}{q_0} = \frac{1}{q_0} - \frac{p_0}{q_0}$$
$$= \frac{1 - p_0}{q_0}$$
$$= 1$$

or, more concisely, $\Delta\left(\dfrac{p}{q}\right) = 1$. This means simply that the ratio of T to t alleles increases by 1 in any single generation of complete selection against recessive homozygotes. Obviously the ratio will increase by 2 in two generations, by 3 in three generations, and by n in n generations. Hence we may write

$$\frac{p_n}{q_n} = \frac{p_0}{q_0} + n$$

If we substitute for p_n and p_0, respectively, $(1 - q_n)$ and $(1 - q_0)$, this becomes

$$\frac{1 - q_n}{q_n} = \frac{1 - q_0}{q_0} + n$$

$$\frac{1}{q_n} - 1 = \frac{1}{q_0} - 1 + n$$

so that

$$\frac{1}{q_n} = \frac{1}{q_0} + n \qquad (A\ 1)$$
$$= \frac{1 + nq_0}{q_0}$$

Now by simply inverting the fractions on the two sides of the equation, we obtain

$$q_n = \frac{q_0}{1 + nq_0} \qquad (A\ 2)$$

The application of this formula may be illustrated with the problem which was solved on page 435 by other means: The initial frequency of tt individuals was 36%, and $q_0 = 0.6$; after two generations of selection we would therefore have, by formula (A 2), $q_2 = 0.6/2.2 = 0.273$, and q_2^2 is 0.075, as before. But with the formula, we can compute the effects of selection for 10, 20, or 100 generations just as easily as for two generations. Thus, for n = 20 (and $q_0 = 0.6$), we find

$$q_n = 0.6/13 = 0.046,$$

and the frequency of tt individuals has been reduced to $(0.046)^2$, or about 0.2%.

II Quite often we wish to know how many generations of selection will be required to produce a specified reduction in the frequency of a gene, rather than how great a reduction will be accomplished in a given number of generations. This question can readily be answered for the case of complete selection. For it follows directly from equation (A 1) above, that if

$$\frac{1}{q_n} = \frac{1}{q_0} + n$$

then,

$$n = \frac{1}{q_n} - \frac{1}{q_0} \qquad (A\ 3)$$

With formula (A 3) we may answer such a question as: How many generations of complete selection will be required to reduce the frequency of tt zygotes from 36% to 1%? Here $q_0 = 0.6$, $q_n = 0.1$, whence n = 1/0.1 − 1/0.6 = 8.33. Eight generations, then, would almost effect the required reduction, while nine generations would more than accomplish it.

III To determine the effects of *partial* selection, in which a fraction, k, of the tt

zygotes are eliminated in each generation, we start, as noted on page 436, with the population of zygotes produced by $p_0 T$ gametes and $q_0 t$ gametes, that is, a population in which the zygotic frequencies are

$$p_0^2(TT) : 2p_0q_0(Tt) : q_0^2(tt)$$

If we eliminate a fraction, k, of the tt zygotes from the effective breeding population, this leaves TT, Tt, and tt individuals in the ratio

$$p_0^2(TT) : 2p_0q_0(Tt) : (1 - k)q_0^2(tt)$$

The p_0^2 (TT) individuals produce only T gametes, and half of the gametes from the Tt's (i.e., $1/2 \times 2p_0q_0$, or p_0q_0) also carry T; similarly, $p_0q_0 t$ gametes are produced by the Tt individuals and $(1 - k)q_0^2 t$ gametes by tt's. Thus one generation of partial selection results in the production of gametes in the ratio:

$$[p_0^2 + p_0q_0](T) : [p_0q_0 + (1 - k)q_0^2](t)$$
$$= p_0(T) : [p_0q_0 + q_0^2 - kq_0^2](t)$$
$$= p_0(T) : [q_0 - kq_0^2](t)$$

Here again, in order to have the gametic proportions expressed as fractions of unity, we must divide through by their sum, $p_0 + q_0 - kq_0^2$ or $1 - kq_0^2$. The new gene frequencies are then

$$\frac{p_0}{1 - kq_0^2} (T) : \frac{q_0 - kq_0^2}{1 - kq_0^2} (t),$$

so that the frequency of the t allele, after one generation of partial selection is given by the formula

$$q_1 = \frac{q_0 - kq_0^2}{1 - kq_0^2} \qquad \text{(A 4)}$$

IV An expression which will enable us to predict the effects of partial selection over a large number of generations cannot be derived completely by algebraic methods, but the first step in the derivation is one which is already familiar: We must find $\Delta(q)$, the change in the value of q in a single generation. This is simply the dif-

ference between q_1 and q_0, expressed in terms of q_0:

$$q_1 - q_0 = \frac{q_0 - kq_0^2}{1 - kq_0^2} - q_0$$
$$= \frac{- kq_0^2 + kq_0^3}{1 - kq_0^2}$$

or, $$\Delta(q) = \frac{- kq^2(1 - q)}{1 - kq^2} \qquad \text{(A 5)}$$

When k is quite small (say 0.05 or less) the value of $\Delta(q)$ is sufficiently low for it to be treated by techniques of the calculus as a so-called *differential* (an infinitesimal increment), to which the process of integration can be applied.* This process, in effect, gives us the approximate sum of any number of successive values of $\Delta(q)$ without the necessity of computing them individually and therefore is a way of finding the total change in q over any specified number of generations. After integration has been performed, we finally obtain the following rather complicated-looking expression as the formula for slow selection.

$$n = \frac{1}{k}\left[\frac{1}{q_n} - \frac{1}{q_0} + \log_e \frac{1 - q_n}{q_n} \right.$$
$$\left. - \log_e \frac{1 - q_0}{q_0} \right] \qquad \text{(A 6)}$$

* For those who have a modest acquaintance with the calculus, the whole derivation should be quite easy to follow. We simply treat (A 5) as a differential equation, writing $\frac{dq}{dt} = \frac{- kq^2(1 - q)}{1 - kq^2}$. Separation of the variables gives

$$dt = \frac{- (1 - kq^2)dq}{kq^2(1 - q)},$$

so that $\int_0^n dt = - \frac{1}{k}\int_{q_0}^{q_n} \frac{(1 - kq^2)}{q^2(1 - q)} dq$. Integration between the indicated limits gives

$$n = \frac{1}{k}\left[\frac{1}{q_n} - \frac{1}{q_0} + \log_e \frac{1 - q_n}{q_n} - \log_e \frac{1 - q_0}{q_0} \right.$$
$$\left. - \log_e \frac{1 - q_n}{1 - q_0}. \right.$$

When k is small the quantity outside of the brackets, $\log_e \frac{1 - q_n}{1 - q_0}$ is negligible in comparison with the remainder of the expression, and it has been ignored in formula (A 6).

V To show that reversible mutation causes gene frequencies to tend toward an equilibrium point, and to find what this point is, we may consider a population in which the gene frequencies for any given generation are $p_0(T) : q_0(t)$. If the rate of mutation from t to T is m and the reverse rate — from T to t — is m', the frequency of t alleles will be *decreased* by the amount mq_0 through mutations from t to T and will be *increased* by $m'p_0$ through mutations from T to t. Conversely, the frequency of T alleles will be decreased by $m'p_0$ and increased by mq_0. The allelic frequencies, as changed by mutations occurring in one generation, will therefore be

$$[p_0 - m'p_0 + mq_0](T) : [q_0 - mq_0 + m'p_0](t),$$

so that the new value of q is

$$q_1 = q_0 - mq_0 + m'p_0$$

We have then, for the *change* in q during one generation,

$$q_1 - q_0 = (q_0 - mq_0 + m'p_0) - q_0$$
$$= -mq_0 + m'p_0$$
or, $$\Delta(q) = -mq + m'p$$

Now the condition for equilibrium between the frequencies of T and t is that there should be *no further change* in their respective values; this is the same as saying that $\Delta(q)$ must equal zero. The condition is satisfied when $(-mq + m'p) = 0$; that is, when $m'p = mq$, or $p/q = m/m'$. We leave it for the student to solve this equation for q (start by substituting $1 - q$ for p); he will find that the equilibrium value of q is $m'/(m + m')$.

VI We wish to find the equilibrium value of q^2, the frequency of recessive homozygotes, when recurrent mutation of T to t is opposed by complete selection against tt zygotes.

We saw on page 435 that complete elimination of recessive homozygotes results, in one generation, in a change of the allelic frequencies from $p_0(T) : q_0(t)$ to

$$\frac{1}{1 + q_0}(T) : \frac{q_0}{1 + q_0}(t)$$

Mutation from T to t at rate m' would change this ratio (assuming reverse mutation negligible or nonexistent) to

$$\frac{1}{1 + q_0} - \frac{m'}{1 + q_0}(T) : \frac{q_0}{1 + q_0} + \frac{m'}{1 + q_0}(t)$$

From this it is seen that $q_1 = \dfrac{q_0 + m'}{1 + q_0}$,

whence the change in q resulting from a single generation of the opposing actions of selection and mutation is

$$q_1 - q_0 = \frac{q_0 + m'}{1 + q_0} - q_0$$
$$= \frac{m' - q_0^2}{1 + q_0}$$
or, $$\Delta(q) = \frac{m' - q^2}{1 + q}$$

Recalling that equilibrium is attained when $\Delta(q) = 0$, we set $\dfrac{m' - q^2}{1 + q} = 0$. Hence, at equilibrium, $m' - q^2 = 0$, and $q^2 = m'$.

PROBLEMS

28.1 Discuss some of the possible interactions of hereditary and environmental influences in the decay of teeth.

28.2 In studying the hereditary basis

for goiter what attention should be paid, if any, to the environment of the persons studied?

28.3 Suppose that a definite germ were to be discovered as the cause of cancer. Would this do away with the possibility of a hereditary basis for the susceptibility to cancer? Discuss thoroughly.

28.4 It is sometimes stated that if a hereditary basis were established for any human abnormality or disease, medical research on that condition would be of no use and could make no further progress. Is this attitude justified? Discuss question.

28.5 How might the study of identical twins be of value in investigating the hereditary basis for susceptibility to tuberculosis?

28.6 On what biological grounds would you expect human beings to obey the same laws of heredity as experimental animals?

28.7 Of what advantage to the student of human heredity would be the discovery of a pair of identical twins who had been separated at birth and reared apart?

28.8 If such separated identical twins should be quite different in regard to the expression of a certain character, what would you conclude as to the relative effects of genetic and environmental variation in the production of the character?

28.9 If separated identical twins should be strikingly similar in a certain character in spite of differences in their environments, what would you conclude as to the relative influences of environmental and genetic variation in its production?

28.10 In this and the next three problems assume that feeblemindedness is the result of the homozygous state of a single autosomal recessive gene. Assume further

that feeblemindedness occurs in about one half of one per cent of the population (for convenience in taking square root, use the figure 0.0049). Disregard possible effects of mutation and assume random mating in regard to this trait. What is the frequency of the gene involved? What effect on the frequency of the gene would be brought about by five generations of sterilization of all feebleminded individuals? What effect would this have on the incidence of the trait?

28.11 How many generations of sterilization would it take to reduce the frequency of the trait from the initial value of 0.0049 to 0.001? To 0.0001?

28.12 If only one tenth of the feebleminded were sterilized each generation, what would be the effect on the frequency of the trait of five generations of sterilization, again assuming an initial frequency of 0.0049? What would be the effect of fifty generations of such sterilization? How long would this degree of sterilization take to reduce the frequency of the trait from 0.0049 to 0.001?

28.13 If mating in regard to feeblemindedness were not random but assortative, would this fact hasten or retard the reduction of its incidence by sterilization?

28.14 If feeblemindedness were the result, not of one recessive gene but of ten, each contributing equally to feeblemindedness and all ten necessary for the complete expression of the trait, would selection against the trait have a greater or less effect over a given number of generations than in the case of a single gene?

REFERENCES

BOYD, W. C., *Southwest J. Anthropol.* **3**:32 (1947).

CANDELA, P. B., *Human Biol.* **14**:413 (1942).

CHILDE, G., *What Happened in History.* New York, Penguin Books, Inc. (1946).

DOBZHANSKY, Th., *Genetics and the Origin of Species.* 2nd ed., New York, Columbia Univ. Press (1941).

DUNN, L. C., and DOBZHANSKY, Th., *Heredity, Race, and Society*. New York, New Amer. Library of World Lit., Inc. (1946).

FISHER, R. A., *The Genetical Theory of Natural Selection*. Oxford, the Clarendon Press (1930).

GLASS, B., *Advances in Genetics* **6**:95 (1954).

GRAHAM, J. B., and BADGLEY, C. E., *Amer. Jour. Hum. Genet.* **7**:44 (1955).

HALDANE, J. B. S., *Annals of Eugenics* **7**:28 (1936); *Jour. Genetics* **41**:141 (1941); *The Causes of Evolution*. New York, Harper and Bros. (1932); *New Paths in Genetics*. New York, Harper and Bros. (1942); *Proc. Eighth Internat. Cong. of Genetics* 266. Lund, Sweden, Berlingska Boktryckeriet (1949).

HARRIS, H., *An Introduction to Human Biochemical Genetics*. New York, Cambridge Univ. Press (1953).

HOGBEN, L. T., *Genetic Principles in Medicine and Social Science*. New York, Alfred A. Knopf (1932).

KALISS, N., and SCHWEITZER, M. D., *Genetics* **28**:78 (1943).

KOLLER, P. C., *Proc. Roy. Soc. Edinburgh* **57**:194 (1937).

KOLLER, P. C., and DARLINGTON, C. D., *Jour. Genetics* **29**:159 (1934).

LEVIT, S. G., and PESSIKOVA, L. N., *Proc.* *Maxim Gorky Med.-Gen. Research Inst.* **4**:157 (1936).

LI, C. C., *Population Genetics*. Chicago, Univ. of Chicago Press (1955).

MACKLIN, M. T., *Jour. Assn. Amer. Med. Colleges*, September (1933).

MULLER, H. J., LITTLE, C. C., and SNYDER, L. H., *Genetics, Medicine, and Man*. Ithaca, Cornell Univ. Press (1947).

NEEL, J. V., and SCHULL, W. J., *Human Heredity*. Chicago, Univ. of Chicago Press (1954).

SCHWARTZ, M., "Heredity in Bronchial Asthma," *Opera ex Domo Biol. Hered. Humanae Univ. Hafn.* **29**(1952).

SIMPSON, G. G., *The Meaning of Evolution*, New Haven, Yale Univ. Press (1949).

SNYDER, L. H., *Bull. N.Y. Acad. Med.* **22**:566 (1946); *Milbank Mem. Fund Quart.* **24**:367 (1947); *Proc. Eighth Internat. Cong. of Genetics* 446. Lund, Sweden, Berlingska Boktryckeriet (1949).

SNYDER, L. H., and PALMER, D. M., *Jour. Heredity* **34**:207 (1943).

SORSBY, A. (editor), *Clinical Genetics*. St. Louis, C. V. Mosby Co. (1953).

STRANDSKOV, H. H., *Amer. Naturalist* **76**:156 (1942).

THOMASEN, E., "Myotonia," *Opera ex Domo Biol. Hered. Humanae Univ. Hafn.* **17** (1948).

WRIGHT, S., *Evolution* **2**:279 (1948).

CHAPTER TWENTY-NINE

Eugenics

Throughout the preceding pages we have seen that many human traits, both mental and physical, have definite hereditary components. From the standpoint of society some of these traits are desirable, others undesirable. To the thoughtful student many questions are likely to arise. Is the genetic composition of the human species changing? If so, at what rate and in what direction, and what, if anything, should be done about it? One of the first students to give attention to these and similar questions was the versatile British scientist, Sir Francis Galton (1822–1911).

Galton was strongly impressed by Darwin's explanation of evolution through natural selection. He reasonably concluded that man, as well as other animals, must be subject to evolutionary processes; and he felt that the time had come for man to undertake the conscious direction of his own evolution. From about 1870 until the end of his life, Galton spent the greater part of his energies urging that public attention should be given to this problem. It was Galton who coined the term **eugenics,** which he defined (in 1904) as "the science which deals with all influences that improve the inborn qualities of a race; also with those that develop them to the utmost advantage."

The formation of the Eugenics Society in 1908 by Galton marked the beginning of eugenics as an organized movement in England. A similar society had been founded in Germany a few years earlier, and during the next several decades the movement attracted many followers, especially in England, Germany, and the United States. A substantial number of independent organizations have been established in these and other countries for the dissemination of eugenic ideas and the promotion of eugenic policies.

In the early years of the eugenics movement and to a large extent down to the present time, the programs espoused by eugenists have placed almost exclusive emphasis on measures which they believe would improve the *genetic* composition of the human species, or which, at the least, would prevent or retard its deterioration. Until quite recently, little or no effort was made to promote environmental improvements which might permit more effective *expression* of existing genotypes.* The methods of genetic improvement proposed by the orthodox eugenists have, naturally enough, centered around the application of conscious selection to human reproduction. That is, eugenists would encourage reproduction by those whom they consider to possess superior genetic endowment, and discourage or prevent reproduction by those of inferior genotype.

Unfortunately, the knowledge of basic principles in human genetics which was available to the early eugenists (and to many of their followers) was woefully incommensurate with the tasks which they set themselves. There was inadequate comprehension of the distinction between phenotype and genotype, and the complexity of interactions between hereditary and environmental factors was little understood.† Methods for predicting the effectiveness of selection under different circumstances, such as we have outlined in the previous chapter, were nonexistent; and the vital relation between gene frequency and the efficacy of selection was, of course, not even suspected.

Unfortunately, too, it was almost inevitable that a movement whose program predicated the evaluation of innate superiority and inferiority should attract many persons with strong prejudices regarding the special status of their own race, nation, or social group. It is undeniable that the constructive aims of eugenics have drawn into the movement many who have been motivated by exclusively altruistic considerations; but it is equally undeniable that the eugenics movement has been severely handicapped throughout its history by adherents who have been more conspicuous for enthusiasm than for critical acumen. As early as 1908 Galton himself pointed out: "A danger to which these [eugenics] societies will be liable arises from the inadequate knowledge joined to great zeal of some of the most active among their probable members. It may be said without minc-

* There is perhaps some significance in the fact that when eugenics was formally defined on the occasion of founding the Eugenics Laboratory at the University of London, the second part of Galton's earlier definition which we have quoted above was dropped. Eugenics was now defined as "the study of agencies under social control that may improve or impair the racial qualities of future generations, either physically or mentally." In this context, "racial" means "hereditary."

† That Galton recognized some of the difficulties here is indicated by his statement that: "Man is so educable an animal that it is difficult to distinguish between that part of his character which has been acquired through education and that which was in the original grain of his constitution."

ing words, with regard to much that has already been published, that the subject of eugenics is particularly attractive to 'cranks.'"

The foregoing discussion indicates that we should hesitate at accepting without careful analysis the claims and recommendations that are presented in a large portion of the eugenics literature. It also suggests why professionally trained geneticists, on the whole, have given relatively little support to eugenic theories and programs. A number of prominent geneticists in fact, including T. H. Morgan, H. S. Jennings, Th. Dobzhansky, L. C. Dunn, Lancelot Hogben, J. B. S. Haldane, H. J. Muller, and J. V. Neel, have been explicitly critical, with varying degrees of vigor, of substantial portions of orthodox eugenic doctrine. The criticisms leveled against the eugenics movement by these and other geneticists are undoubtedly in large part justified, inasmuch as many who write as eugenists even today have not assimilated modern advances in genetic knowledge, particularly in the highly relevant fields of developmental and population genetics. Thus, the deficiencies which Galton recognized in the eugenics movement at its inception, and which we have called attention to above, are still perceptible in extensive areas.

There is, however, another side to the picture. In recent years, at least a few of those connected with the eugenics movement have taken cognizance of progress in the field of human genetics since Galton's time and have largely dissociated themselves from both the naïveté and the prejudices of the orthodox eugenists. Frederick Osborn, notably, has repudiated the unscientific social-class bias and racial prejudice in eugenics which, he points out, were natural developments of the class-conscious society of Galton's England and the race consciousness in the United States during the extensive immigrations in the early part of the present century. He has, moreover, recognized more clearly than most other eugenists the interconnection of hereditary and environmental factors in the determination of phenotype; consequently, an essential element in his program is the amelioration of environmental conditions which in many sections of our society tend to prevent the full expression of socially valuable genetic potentialities. Thus, among measures which Osborn regards as promising are:

> Community efforts, such as cooperative nurseries, providing frequent relief and relaxation for mothers; cooperative medical services for families; reduction of medical costs for middle income groups.
> Greater assurance of scholarships for intelligent children in large families; a changed basis of scholarships for graduate students and others now often restricted as to marriage.
> Tax reduction favoring parents of large families, especially in-

come tax changes whereby exemptions are more closely related to the actual cost of rearing children.

Provision of adequate maternity leave, with salary, for teachers and others employed in public and institutional service.

These are suggestions with which probably few geneticists could quarrel. It should be noted, however, that acceptance of these measures would probably be based primarily on an opinion that they are in themselves socially desirable, that is, that they would improve the social effectiveness or *phenotypic* "quality" of our population, whether or not they might in the long run affect its genetic composition. Thus, the validity of these and other measures would be assessed by the geneticist on the basis of what observable *effects* might be expected from them, rather than on the merits of their *intention*, which is, according to Osborn, "to modify the conditions of modern society in such a way that the distribution of births will be favorable to the improvement of inherent human capacities from one generation to another."

It is too early to predict the extent to which eugenics groups on the whole are likely to have their views modified by the results of modern research in developmental and population genetics. In the meanwhile, it is desirable that we scrutinize their programs with considerable critical care. In particular we should consider what *quantitative* results might be expected, if the various proposals should be put into effect, in terms of reduction in frequency of undesirable genotypes or increase in frequency of desirable ones. Only by considerations of a quantitative nature can we judge whether the potential gains are likely to outweigh possibly undesirable side-effects of the programs proposed.

In broadest terms, the programs of eugenists have been of two general kinds, designated as **positive eugenics** and **negative eugenics,** respectively. Positive eugenics involves attempts to establish a selective advantage for desirable genotypes over undesirable genotypes, by encouraging an *increased* birth rate among the desirable group; negative eugenics seeks the same results through *reducing* the birth rate in the undesirable group. Positive eugenic measures would therefore tend to accelerate population growth as a whole, while the methods of negative eugenics would tend to retard it. *Provided that the same definitions of desirable and undesirable are used in each case, any effect on the genetic composition of the population* (i.e., on the population frequencies of different genotypes) *would be the same whichever line of attack was employed.*

We shall consider some of the possibilities and limitations of negative eugenic measures first, because the advocates of these measures have on the whole been more vocal, and often more extravagant in their claims, than those whose primary efforts have been in the direction of positive eugenics.

The specific methods proposed for minimizing the production of undesirable genotypes have ranged from recommending the wider use of voluntary birth control by individuals presumed to possess undesirable genotypes to advocating the compulsory sterilization * of persons believed to fall in this category. The vigor with which the more extreme proposals have been urged is reflected in the fact that, between 1907 and 1931 thirty states in this country passed statutes either requiring or permitting the sterilization of various classes of defectives. The intentions of the statutes, as implied in the wording of the legislation, are said by Landman to be "eugenic" (usually also "therapeutic") in almost every instance. In the majority of the laws, sterilization is made compulsory for certain cases. Enforcement of these laws, however, has on the whole been very lax.

The various sterilization laws in this country list, in all, some two dozen classes of defectives to which they are applicable; many of these classes are subject to sterilization in only one or two states, however. The only conditions which are very widely stated as grounds for sterilization are idiocy, imbecility, feeblemindedness, insanity, and epilepsy, and these are included in virtually all of the statutes. It is important to notice that very rarely, if ever, does a statute designate as grounds for sterilization any specific defect which we know to be a genetic entity; quite on the contrary, the conditions for which sterilization is prescribed represent broad classes of defects, the causal factors of which on the whole we know little about.

It will perhaps be profitable for us to discuss briefly each of the major categories of conditions for which sterilization is recommended or required under the statutes mentioned above. We should take into consideration, first, the extent to which genetic factors appear to be involved in the etiology of these conditions; and, second, the effect on the genetic composition of the population which we might expect from systematic sterilization of individuals exhibiting these various conditions. Three of the categories listed (idiocy, imbecility, and feeblemindedness) concern *mental deficiency*, i.e., retarded intellectual

* Sterilization, as usually performed, is an operation which permanently prevents parenthood, without in any sense "unsexing" the individual subjected to it. In the male, it is a very minor operation, entailing little discomfort, and performed in a very few minutes under local anaesthetic. It consists merely of cutting and tying off the ducts which carry the sperm. After sterilization the patient has normal feelings and desires, has not lost any organ nor had any nerve supply or blood supply changed. He is not in any sense "mutilated." He has simply had the normal passage of the sperm shut off, and can no longer become a parent.

In the female the operation is a little more complicated because the abdomen must be opened in order to tie off and cut the Fallopian tubes which conduct the egg cell from the ovary to the uterus. It is not, however, any more serious than a simple operation for appendicitis.

development or *subnormal intelligence*. An adequate consideration of these conditions demands that we digress long enough to inquire what is meant by intelligence, how it is measured, what is known regarding the involvement of genetic factors in the determination of intelligence level, and how such genetic factors as may be involved appear to be distributed in the population.

Intelligence in the abstract is not easy to define, although most of us in a general way are in agreement as to what it means. It can perhaps be designated roughly as facility in making use of past experience to adjust to new situations. Since the new situations may be of various types (e.g., a problem in arithmetic, a crossword puzzle, a social emergency) many psychologists have questioned whether there is such a thing as *general intelligence*, which implies equivalent facility in adjusting to situations of all types. Some have suggested that instead there are a number of special abilities which can be measured more or less independently of one another, and that any evaluation of general intelligence must be a kind of weighted average of these. Still others find evidence that both general and special factors are discernible in intelligent behavior. Perhaps we shall be on safest ground if we follow the advice of Penrose and regard at present the existence of general intelligence as only a convenient hypothesis. It is well to remember, he suggests, that the facts are the test scores, and that to be really precise we should speak of the ability of each subject on a given test rather than of his "intelligence level."

A variety of mental tests has been devised to measure intelligence, the most widely used individual tests being the Stanford revision of the Binet-Simon tests. The tests generally consist of a series of questions or problems of increasing difficulty. In order to avoid as much as possible the effects of different degrees of familiarity with the test materials on the part of different subjects tested, an effort is made to utilize either material which is presumed to be equally unfamiliar to all subjects or material which is common to the experience of everyone to whom the test is applied. This requirement is obviously almost impossible to meet, and there is ample evidence that it has not been adequately satisfied except for subjects of relatively homogeneous cultural and educational backgrounds.

Intelligence tests were originally designed for children of school age, and they have been standardized by administering them to large numbers of children in each age group. The average score attained by ten-year-old children, for example, establishes the norm for the ten-year age-group, and *any* child who makes this score, whether he is 6, 10, or 15 years old chronologically, is said to have a *mental age* of 10. In general, it has been found that children whose mental age, determined in this fashion, is in advance of their chronologic age do better in their school work and on the average are more successful in intellectual activities of diverse kinds than children whose mental and chronologic ages coincide ("average" children). The converse is true of children whose *mental age* is lower than their age in years. It is well to keep in mind that the validity of intelligence tests rests ultimately on this observation.

Quite early in the history of intelligence testing it was discovered that children whose mental age was 6 when they were chronologically 8 years old, would *on the average* exhibit a mental age of about $7\frac{1}{2}$ when they became 10 years old, and a mental age of 9 when they became twelve. It appears then, that the *ratio* of mental age (as determined by these tests) to chronologic age tends to remain constant; in the illustration given, it is 3:4 or 0.75, regardless of chronologic age. This ratio multiplied by 100 (merely to get rid of the decimal) is known as the *intelligence quotient* or I.Q. Thus, to find the I.Q. of a child, we simply divide his mental age by his chronologic age and multiply by 100; if an eight-year-old child has a mental age of 6, his I.Q. is $100 \times \frac{6}{8} = 75$; a child of the same chronologic age, with a mental age of 10 has an I.Q. of $100 \times \frac{10}{8}$ or 125.

Difficulties arise when we try to compute I.Q.'s for persons beyond the childhood years because after about age 15 there is relatively little general improvement in the abilities which are measured by most of the standard intelligence tests. For this reason, in computing adult I.Q.'s from mental ages determined by Binet tests (and some others) the chronologic age used as the divisor is more or less arbitrarily taken as 15 (formerly 16 was generally used). In the latest (1937) revision of the Stanford-Binet, special adjustments are provided for computing I.Q.'s of individuals between ages of 13 and 18.

It should be obvious from the way the intelligence quotient is defined, that the average I.Q. in the general population should be 100. The average I.Q. among college students is about 115 or 120. Table 29.1 shows the frequencies of different I.Q.'s found in a sample of 884 Scottish children (aged 9 to 12), together with certain commonly used descriptive terms which are roughly applicable to the respectively designated I.Q. levels. These data are based on one of the very few almost perfectly representative population samples ever tested; frequencies need not be the same in the U.S., for which no comparably representative data exist. The designations attached to the different I.Q. classes must be recognized as rather arbitrary, and they are intended to be suggestive only. There is no magic dividing line at I.Q. 110, for example, above which one automatically achieves "superiority" and below which no superior person is found; nor does I.Q. 90 sharply separate normal from dull.

Table 29.1. I.Q. Levels: Frequencies and Commonly Applied Designations *

FREQUENCY (%)	I.Q.	DESIGNATION
4.7	140 or over	"near genius" or "genius"
	130–139	"very superior"
21.2	110–129	"superior"
48.6	90–109	"normal"
24.2	80– 89	"dull"
	70– 79	"borderline"
1.3	50– 69	"moron" — mentally deficient
	25– 49	"imbecile" — mentally deficient
	0– 24	"idiot" — mentally deficient

* Frequency data from 1935–37 Scottish survey, after Rusk.

The three categories listed at the bottom of the scale require special comment. The *mentally deficient* are those whose level of intelligence is so low that they require some degree of supervision in performing some or all of the everyday activities ordinarily expected of adults in our society. *Idiots* are persons who have failed to develop mentally beyond the level usually attained by a child of about two years of age. Like most two-year olds, they are unable to guard themselves against ordinary physical dangers and cannot adequately perform even such operations as eating and dressing. *Imbeciles* are those whose intelligence develops beyond this level, but does not exceed that of an average six- or seven-year old; they are capable of guarding themselves against common physical dangers, and can feed and dress themselves, but are incapable of earning their own living.

Morons have been defined as persons who are incapable of managing themselves under conditions requiring judgment or involving much competition, but who, under supervision, may become at least partially self-supporting; they have also been defined as those who cannot receive proper benefit from ordinary elementary schools but who may be benefited in special classes. Adults whose mental ages are between eight and ten are generally classifiable as morons, but it should be obvious that diagnosis of mental deficiency at this level must be based primarily on social competence. We can be fairly sure that anyone with an I.Q. below 60 will require supervision, and therefore be classifiable as a moron. But, depending in part on their temperaments and in part on the environments in which they find themselves, some individuals with I.Q.'s over 70 may have to be considered in the moron category, while others, with I.Q.'s of 65 or even lower may be sufficiently self-reliant to escape this classification.

At one time the I.Q., largely because of its observed constancy, was regarded almost reverentially as a measure not merely of an individual's intellectual ability at the time he was tested, but of the hereditary capacity or potentiality for intellectual development which he had possessed from birth or conception. Insofar as educational differences were shown to affect intelligence-test scores, it was felt that the tests were defective, and that further refinement would eliminate the disturbing effects of environmental influences. It is now quite generally recognized, however, that if measurements of intellectual ability or intelligence are to have any practical meaning, they must measure what an individual can do with the experience he has had up to the time of testing. I.Q. differences may indeed reflect genetic differences in neural organization or the like when the subjects tested have closely comparable backgrounds in respect to education and intellectual stimuli of various sorts. But it has become quite clear that the degree to which hereditary factors are concerned in the determination of the I.Q. is something to be investigated rather than categorically assumed.

In the past 25 years numerous efforts have been made to discover the relative importance of hereditary and environmental factors in determining intelligence-test scores.* Investigations in this field, no matter how carefully carried out, are extremely difficult to make foolproof. Consequently their results have aroused a great deal of discussion (frequently referred to as the "nature-nurture" controversy) which has not yet altogether died down. We cannot undertake here a detailed evaluation of any of these studies; but we shall try to indicate their general character and what seem to be the broad conclusions that we may safely draw from them.

One of the best known nature-nurture studies is that of Newman, Freeman, and Holzinger which deals primarily with separately reared identical twins. In order to understand the reasoning behind this study, we must recall that twins are of two kinds.

The commoner type of twins, *fraternal* (or, more technically, *dizygotic*) twins, results from the independent fertilization (by separate sperm) of two ova that have been released from the mother's ovaries during the same ovulatory cycle. In effect, then, they are simply sibs that happen to be conceived together and born together. From a genetic standpoint they are no more alike (and no more different) than ordinary brothers, sisters, or brother and sister born at different times, and they are as often as not of opposite sex. Physically, too, they resemble each other to about the same degree as ordinary sibs, when allowances are made for age differences among the latter.

* The more important studies are summarized, with much valuable critical comment, in the volume by Anastasi and Foley and the two Yearbooks of the National Society for the Study of Education listed in the references at the end of this chapter.

Identical (or *monozygotic*) twins, on the other hand, result from the splitting of a *single* zygote during its early stages of development. That is, *both* members of an identical twin pair are derived from a single fertilized ovum. Consequently, they are of identical genetic constitution, and are necessarily of the same sex. Physically, identical twins are often almost indistinguishable, but not "identical" in the strictest sense of the word. In fact, the physical resemblance between two members of an identical twin pair is on the average of the same degree as that found between the right and left sides of a single individual.

Intelligence tests have been given to a large number of identical twins, and the average intra-pair difference in I.Q. (i.e., the average I.Q. difference between the two members of respective pairs) is no greater than the average difference found when a single individual is tested on two different occasions (about 6 or 7 points on the I.Q. scale). These results relate, of course, to cases in which both members of respective twin pairs were reared in the same household, and therefore under closely similar environmental conditions. Data of this sort cannot, of course, tell us whether the close resemblance of the twins in I.Q. is to be attributed wholly to their identical heredity, wholly to their common environment, or partly to each. It occurred to Newman and his collaborators that if they could examine identical twin pairs whose members had been separated from each other since early infancy, they might get at least a partial answer to this question. If increased intra-pair differences in I.Q. should be found in such cases, their magnitude might be a measure of the degree to which environmental factors are involved in determining test-intelligence. If the I.Q. differences between separated identical twins (even when they were reared in widely differing environments) should be no greater on the average than the differences found between members of identical twin pairs reared together, it would indicate that environmental factors have little or no effect on the development of test-intelligence.

Unfortunately, identical twins are relatively uncommon to begin with (only about one birth in 300 is a monozygotic twin birth), and identical twins which have been separated since infancy or early childhood are very rare indeed; it took Newman nearly ten years to locate just 19 pairs. Other investigators have reported psychologic studies of one sort or another on 5 or 6 additional pairs, but since their data are not comparable in certain essential respects to those obtained in the Newman series, we shall not include them in the present discussion.

In the Newman study there was found an average intra-pair difference of 8.2 ± 1.6 in the I.Q.'s of the 19 pairs of separated identical twins. This is larger than the average intra-pair difference of 5.9 which was found for identical twins reared together, and smaller than the average difference of 9.9 seen in like-sexed fraternal twin pairs; but, in view of its relatively large standard error (see Chapter 15) it cannot be statistically distinguished from either of these values.

At first glance, these findings seem to afford no basis for a suspicion that environmental differences play any appreciable role in determining I.Q. level. We might be tempted to infer that at most the differences in environment between members of separated identical pairs do not result in I.Q. differences any larger than those referable to genetic differences between fraternal twins. And this, in fact, is frequently cited as a general implication of the Newman, Freeman, and Holzinger results. But a conclusion based only on the *average* I.Q. differences found in the separated identicals fails to take into account the magnitude of the intra-pair differences in environment. To determine the extent to which environmental differences may affect the development of test intelligence, it does not suffice that members of identical twin pairs should be reared merely in *separate* environments; it is necessary that their respective environments should be measurably *different* in respect to factors which we might reasonably suspect of having an influence on I.Q. As a matter of fact, the environments under which the two members of a separated pair were reared were generally, in the present material, not strikingly dissimilar. In the majority of cases, the two twins were adopted into homes of comparable socio-economic and cultural status and were given rather similar educational advantages.

Table 29.2 shows the I.Q. differences found in the individual twin pairs related to ratings of intra-pair differences in educational and social environments, respectively. The ratings are composites of independent estimates by five judges, and the scale of ratings runs from 5, which would indicate a minimal intra-pair difference in environment, to 50, which would indicate the largest possible environmental difference. It will be observed that most of the environmental difference ratings were well under 25, which might be regarded roughly as the average difference which the judges would expect to find between two homes simply picked at random.

When we examine the data arranged in this fashion we may see at once that there appears to be at least a rough parallelism (technically, a *correlation*) between the amount of rated difference in environment and the difference in intra-pair I.Q. Moreover, if we consider only about the upper third of the table, which includes all of the cases where any substantial environmental difference was noted, we observe that the I.Q. differences in these cases are quite frequently

Table 29.2. Differences between Members of Identical Twin Pairs Separated in Infancy or Early Childhood (*From Newman, Freeman, and Holzinger,* **1937.**)

(A) Pairs arranged in order of intra-pair differences in educational environment.			(B) Pairs arranged in order of intra-pair differences in social environment.		
Pair No.	Rated Diff. in Educ'n'l Environment	Diff. in Binet I.Q.	Pair No.	Rated Diff. in Social Environment	Diff. in Binet I.Q.
11	37	24	8	32	15
2	32	12	18	31	19
18	28	19	1	27	12
4	22	17	7	27	−1
12	19	7	5	26	4
1	15	12	11	25	24
17	15	10	4	15	17
8	14	15	17	15	10
3	12	−2	3	15	−2
14	12	−1	14	15	−1
5	11	4	10	15	5
13	11	1	2	14	12
10	10	5	19	14	9
15	9	1	9	14	6
7	9	−1	12	13	7
19	9	−9	13	13	1
16	8	2	16	12	2
6	7	8	6	10	8
9	7	6	15	7	1

(A minus sign before an **I.Q.** difference indicates that the twin in the more highly rated environment had the lower **I.Q.**)

of considerable magnitude: an I.Q. difference of 12 points, for example, corresponds to the difference in mental-test level between an average 14- and an average 12-year-old child; a difference of 24 points corresponds to the difference in level between an average child of 14 years and a child of ten.

It can readily be shown in spite of the small numbers involved, that the I.Q. differences associated with moderately large differences in environment are, from a statistical standpoint, significantly in excess of I.Q. differences found among identical twins reared together. Among the latter, only about 10 per cent reveal differences as large as 12 points in Binet I.Q. If we take the top six of the separated twin cases, we find that five of them in Part A of the Table, or four in Part B differ in I.Q. by 12 or more points. If, on the other hand, we should test six pairs of *unseparated* identical twins chosen at random, there would be a chance of less than 1 in 500 that as many as four of them would show intra-pair I.Q. differences of this magnitude. (If instead of the top six pairs in the Table, we use the top four or five or seven for our significance test, the result will be essentially the same.) Thus we have a substantial basis for inferring that under sufficiently diverse environments, appreciable differences in I.Q. may develop from identical genotypes, and that these differences may be at least of the same order of magnitude as those which are characteristically found between fraternal twins (or between siblings) who have been reared in the same environment.

At the same time, we should remember that, on the whole, identical twins who are reared in separate households, provided the environmental differences between these households are not remarkable, tend to resemble each other rather more closely than fraternal twins reared together. This gives us strong reason to believe that genes also play an appreciable role in determining phenotypic intelligence. It should be noted, however, that none of these data permits us to estimate *how much* of the total variability in I.Q. found in the population at large is referable to genetic differences and how much must be attributed to the action of environmental factors. Moreover, these data cannot give us any clue to the mode of transmission of whatever genes may be involved.

Other important studies which have shed light on the nature-nurture problem have made use of foster or adopted children, comparing them in respect to I.Q. with their own parents and sibs on the one hand and their foster parents and sibs on the other. Investigations of this type have been reported by Freeman, Holzinger, and Mitchell; Burks; Leahy; Skodak and Skeels; and others. We shall not attempt individual summaries of these. In general, they tend to confirm the conclusions we have drawn from the twin studies, viz., that intellectual development as measured by intelligence tests is significantly affected by both genetic and environmental factors, and that differences in environment, even when not extreme, may account for differences in I.Q. of 15 or 20 points, or even more.

The data from the foster-children studies (as was the case with the results of the twin investigations) do not provide a basis for apportioning the relative importance of hereditary and environmental factors in determining the variability in intelligence of the general population. Burks is often quoted as inferring from her material that "the total contribution of heredity in determining I.Q. is probably not far from 75 or 80 per cent." While the quotation is correct, it is worth noting that Burks' estimate involves a rather complicated analytic procedure at several stages of which assumptions have to be made in lieu of actual information. Making somewhat different assumptions (and as far as can be judged, equally reasonable ones) Woodworth concludes from the same data that the contribution of hereditary factors to I.Q. variability is in the neighborhood of 50 per cent, rather than Burks' 75 to 80 per cent. *The really important point, however, is that whichever of these estimates is valid* (if either), *its applicability is limited to the particular material which was investigated.* We have already seen in the twin studies that *observable influence of environmental factors on the development of the I.Q. depends on the range of environment which is sampled.* If the separated twins had all been reared under sufficiently similar conditions to merit environmental-difference ratings of 15 or below, we should not have perceived any effects of environment at all. If, on the other hand, the ratings had all ranged from 25 to 50, it is reasonable to suspect that the effects of environmental differences would have been more conspicuous than they appeared in the sample studied. The same principle applies to the foster-child studies. The greater the homogeneity of the environment provided by the foster homes the smaller will be the discernible share of the environment in determining the variability in I.Q. among the adopted children, and the larger will be the relative significance of hereditary differences. Foster homes are, in fact, required to meet certain socio-economic and cultural standards. Thus the environments they provide are by no means a representative sampling of the total range of environment existing in the general population. Consequently, any estimate of the relative contributions of genetic and environmental factors to the variability of intelligence among foster children is likely to assign greater relative importance to heredity and less to environment than would be appropriate for the population at large.

While what we have learned from the nature-nurture studies does not allow us to make a quantitative assessment of the respective roles of heredity and environment in determining the population variability of test-intelligence, it does help us to understand certain aspects of the distribution of I.Q.'s in various sections of the population.

Intelligence tests have rarely been administered to representative samples of adults in this country or any other. But school children have been rather extensively tested. One of the more consistent results of these tests is the finding of significant differences among children drawn from different socio-economic (or occupational) levels. Results of a typical survey (Haggerty and Nash, 1924) of nearly 7000 elementary school children in rural New York are shown in Table 29.3.

Table 29.3. AVERAGE I.Q.'S OF CHILDREN CLASSIFIED ACCORDING TO FATHERS' OCCUPATIONAL LEVEL

OCCUPATIONAL GROUP	AVERAGE I.Q. OF CHILDREN
Professional	116
Business and clerical	107
Skilled trades	98
Semi-skilled	95
Farmers	91
Unskilled labor	89

It is suggested from time to time that class differences in intelligence such as are shown in Table 29.3 are a reflection of differences in the genetic composition of the various groups. It is conceivable, of course, that a certain amount of genetic differentiation may have occurred: the abler children of skilled workers may enter clerical occupations, for example, and the least competent may become unskilled laborers. This would involve shifts which would tend to be mutually compensatory among the intermediate occupational levels, but which might in the long run tend toward differentiation in genetic composition between the uppermost and lowermost occupational classes. On the other hand, since the selection involved would be based on phenotypes and concerns a character which we have just seen is fairly sensitive to environmental influences, we would expect the process to be a very slow one. When we consider that our present social stratification hardly goes back more than a century or two, it seems rather unlikely that there has been time for appreciable genetic stratification to occur, even if there are selective factors acting in the manner suggested.

On the other hand, the demonstrable dependence of I.Q. development upon environmental factors, and especially on such factors as are associated with educational facilities and cultural stimuli, appears adequate to explain in large part, if not altogether, the observed socioeconomic differentials in test intelligence. An hypothesis based on this dependence receives additional support when we realize that I.Q. differentials of magnitude comparable to those associated with socioeconomic differences are also found between rural and urban populations and, further, that there are similar regional differences associated with differences in public expenditures on schools. Scotland is perhaps the only country in which a marked rural-urban difference in average test intelligence has not been found; it is also a country in which remarkably uniform educational facilities are provided in all areas. There are ample data, both for the United States and elsewhere, which show that isolated populations in very depressed regions (e.g., in certain mountain villages) yield average intelligence-test scores that are abysmally low. It is of interest to note that in one of these areas in which representative samples of several thousand school children were tested in 1940, following a considerable improvement in economic, social, and educational conditions, the average I.Q.'s (for comparable age groups) were more than 10 points higher than they had been a decade before (Wheeler).

We may now reasonably consider the probable eugenic implications of the sterilization laws cited on p. 462, which include idiocy, imbecility, feeblemindedness, insanity, and epilepsy as their major grounds for sterilization. We shall take up idiocy and imbecility together, and then discuss the higher grades of mental deficiency.

Several specific (although individually quite rare) types of idiocy and imbecility are known which, at least in some cases, have a definable genetic basis. The systematic studies of Sjögren, for example, establish beyond much doubt that the preponderant majority of cases of juvenile amaurotic idiocy (see p. 418) are contingent upon the homozygosity of a fully penetrant recessive gene. A single-recessive basis for all or nearly all cases of phenylketonuric amentia (see p. 389) appears to be equally well established. On the other hand, there is good evidence that the idiocy associated with microcephaly ("pinheadedness," Fig. 29.1) is transmitted as a simple recessive, but only in a fraction of the families in which it occurs. In addition, a rather extensive variety of individual pedigrees has been reported in which idiocy or imbecility appears to have a sex-linked basis. The only instances

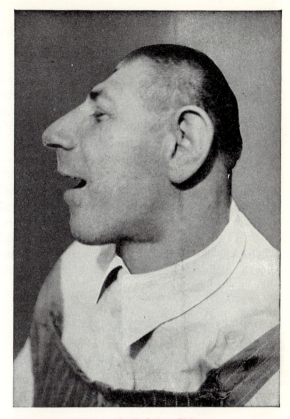

Fig. 29.1 A Microcephalic Idiot. This man is 30 years old, with a mental age of one year. He has a sister like himself. *Courtesy Dr. Leon Addis*

in which mental defect of these grades is associated with dominant transmission seem to be those in which it occurs as an occasional manifestation of a syndrome such as epiloia (p. 350).

Microcephaly, referred to above, appears to be without a discernible genetic basis in perhaps a majority of the families in which it occurs. There is direct evidence that pelvic X-radiation during early pregnancy may result in the birth of a microcephalic child, and it seems probable that a variety of antenatal accidents may have a similar result. *Mongoloid* idiocy or imbecility originally received its name because some of its more common symptoms, e.g., a relatively round head, a flat face, the presence of epicanthic folds which cause the eyes to appear oblique, give a somewhat oriental appearance to its victims. A furrowed tongue is frequently found (Fig. 29.2). A single member of a sibship is affected about 100 times as often as two sibs, and it has not been possible to discover whether genetic factors are significant or not in the etiology of the condition. It is evident, however, that intra-uterine (i.e., prenatal) environmental conditions play a significant role, since the incidence of mongolism varies strikingly in children born to mothers of different ages. Among children born to mothers below age thirty-five, fewer than one in a thousand are mongoloid idiots; the frequency of mongoloid births increases with maternal age, gradually at first then rather rapidly, until among children of mothers aged 45 to 50, two or three per cent (i.e., 20 to 30 per thousand) exhibit the condition; the incidence may be still higher for maternal ages beyond fifty. Other environmental factors which are known to be sometimes responsible for cases of idiocy and imbecility are syphilitic and certain other infections during embryonic life and cerebral injury occurring at birth. Cretinism, (Fig. 29.3) is a condition involving inadequate production of thyroxin by the thyroid gland; symptoms include dwarfing and mental deficiency which is often of idiot or imbecile grade. The condition may be improved, and under some circumstances completely alleviated by the administration of thyroid extract. It occurs sporadically in various environments, but it is *endemic* (i.e., it has a widespread distribution in the population) in some regions, e.g., in certain valleys of the Swiss Alps and in the Pyrenees, where there is a deficiency of iodine in the soil. Iodine is an essential constituent of thyroxin, and an inadequate amount of it in the diet results in signs of thyroxin deficiency (simple goiter, myxedema, and in extreme cases, cretinism). It may be that genetic factors are involved to some extent in the etiology of sporadic cretinism, but there is no doubt that its concentration in endemic areas is primarily a consequence of lack of iodine. In fact, the addition of an iodine supplement to the diet in a number of these areas has had remarkable effects in decreasing the incidence of cretinism, and of other hypothyroid conditions as well.

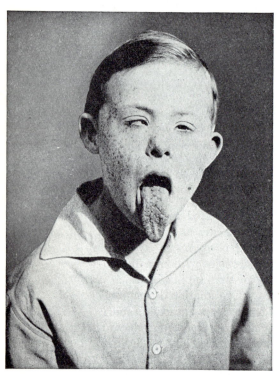

Fig. 29.2 A Mongolian Idiot. This boy is about 10 years old, with a mental age of three. Note the furrowed tongue, which is characteristic of this condition. *Courtesy Dr. Leon Addis*

Fig. 29.3 Cretins.
The three boys in
the picture are from
left to right 21, 16,
and 28 years of age.
Each has a mental
age of three. *Cour-
tesy Dr. Leon Addis*

Thus we see that the categories of idiocy and imbecility include
a wide variety of conditions. Some of these are properly attributable
in most or all cases to simply transmitted genetic factors; others may
sometimes have a genetic basis, sometimes not; still others may be
primarily contingent upon environmental factors; and finally, in some,
both genetic and environmental factors may be significantly involved.
It is difficult, however, to see any rational basis for the sterilization
of idiots and imbeciles on eugenic grounds even in individual cases
where there is strong presumption that their defect is primarily
genetic. The simple reason for this is that idiots practically never
and imbeciles only occasionally reproduce at all.

The third category of mental deficiency which is included in most
of the sterilization statutes is "feeblemindedness." In the United

States, the term as ordinarily used covers all grades of mental deficiency; occasionally, however, it is restricted to include only the higher grades of the mentally deficient, i.e., those designated in Table 29.1 as *morons;* in England, this is the customary usage.

The problem of the higher grade mentally deficient is a very complex one. One aspect is the difficulty of definition, especially at the upper levels of the class, which we have already discussed. Partly because of uncertainties of definition and partly because no adequate survey data are available, the total number of morons in our population cannot be stated, except within rather broad limits. The frequency of mental deficiency of all grades has been competently estimated (Doll) as between one and two per cent (Osborn cites estimates of "at least two per cent"); and in these groups morons constitute the overwhelming majority, being almost certainly at least 2 or 3 times as numerous as idiots and imbeciles combined.

Morons, in contrast to idiots and imbeciles, *are* able to reproduce. The excessive fecundity which is popularly attributed to them is, however, largely mythical, as was discovered by the authors of the famous Wood Report (1929) in Great Britain and reiterated in 1934 by the Committee of the American Neurological Association for the Investigation of Eugenical Sterilization. The myth of prodigal fertility among morons arises no doubt from the occasional families which contain 10, 12, or more children and are sufficiently spectacular to distract public attention from the nearly or altogether infertile marriages, which in the experience of the Wood Committee, were very much more numerous than the excessively prolific ones. Practically all of the systematic data which are adduced in support of the high fertility of morons are, in fact, data on *the size of families in which morons are found*, rather than on the fecundity of the morons themselves. Data of this kind are subject to certain recognized biases and they fail completely to take into account marriage and mortality rates, both of which must be considered in any valid estimate of net reproductivity. Data bearing directly on net reproductive rate as related to test-intelligence level are almost nonexistent. It is known, of course, that the net fertility of college graduates (who almost always have I.Q.'s in excess of 115) is much lower than that of other population groups; but little or nothing is known of the actual fertility of others of the same I.Q. level in different strata of society. Nevertheless, there is a good deal of indirect evidence to suggest that in general net fertility does tend to increase with decreasing I.Q. level. But, as Penrose shows, there is equally good basis for being fairly certain that maximal fertility is reached at I.Q.'s somewhere in the neighborhood of 80 or 90, and that it *declines* rather rapidly below this intelligence level. (As we shall soon see, the likelihood that this is the case is one of the factors limiting any *eugenic* effects which might be anticipated from sterilization among the moron group.)

Our knowledge of the genetic factors which may be involved in mental deficiency of the moron level is practically nil. Some of the rare recessive genes which usually produce imbecility or idiocy may on occasion result in a milder degree of mental deficiency, and a few conditions dependent on dominant genes with variable manifestation sometimes (about 10 per cent of the time in the case of neurofibromatosis) involve high-grade deficiency. But as this manuscript goes to the printer no specific genes have been identified which are characteristically associated with moron-level mentality. Morons frequently are found several to a family, of course, but the majority of the familial cases occur among socio-economically depressed groups, so that it is generally impossible to be sure whether hereditary or environmental factors are primarily to blame. In contrast, idiocy and imbecility (where we know that at least a portion of the cases have a clear-cut genetic basis) are distributed rather evenly throughout the population without regard to social class or economic level.

It is quite probable that hereditary factors are to some extent involved in the etiology of the milder degrees of mental deficiency. But the question of how and to what extent they are involved is in much the same state of uncertainty as the question of the respective roles of genetic and environmental determinants of intelligence differences in general. In fact, the two questions are quite probably in large part the same, that is, the genetic and environmental interactions involved in the differentiation of morons from cases of borderline and average intelligence may very well be largely of the same sort as those responsible for individual differences in intelligence at higher levels.

The twin data assembled by Rosanoff, Handy, and Plesset are representative of the kind of evidence we have which may bear specifically on the problem of high-grade feeblemindedness. However, this material includes not only a substantial proportion of cases which on the basis of I.Q. alone would ordinarily be classed as borderline but also a number of very low-grade defectives. Among 126 monozygotic twin pairs of which one member was feebleminded by Rosanoff's criteria, the other was similarly deficient in 115, or 91 per cent; among 101 like-sexed dizygotic pairs with at least one feebleminded member, the other was feebleminded in only 61 per cent of the cases.

The observation that in 9 per cent of the monozygotic pairs only one member was affected is adequate demonstration that feeblemindedness is not exclusively determined by genetic factors. The fact that both members of a monozygotic pair were affected in 91 per cent of the cases while both members of a dizygotic pair were deficient in only 61 per cent suggests that genetic factors, nevertheless, are also significantly involved. This inference is based on the assumption that the two members of a dizygotic twin pair share a common environment to the same degree as do the members of a monozygotic pair. This assumption, especially in regard to psychologically significant aspects of the environment, is, we must confess, open to some question: the psychologic environments of two identical twins may quite well be more alike in important respects than the environments under which the respective members of a fraternal twin pair develop. In so far as we may assume equally similar intra-pair environments for identical and fraternal twins, however, the difference in the respective frequencies of doubly affected pairs in the two types of twins must be attributable to the segregation of genetic factors in the production of the dizygotic pairs. Finally, several investigators have found that doubly affected pairs of *ordinary sibs* constitute only about 15 per cent of all sib pairs in which at least one member is feebleminded. Genetically, of course, the difference between two sibs is on the average of the same magnitude as that between the members of a dizygotic twin pair. Hence, when we find that feeblemindedness in both members of dizygotic twin pairs is three or four times as common as in both members of pairs of ordinary sibs, we are inclined to infer that such differences of environment as are found at different times *within the same household* are sufficient to have major effects on mental development at the levels involved in these studies. Some authors, however, interpret the data as suggesting that twin pregnancies themselves involve intra-uterine conditions favoring the development of deficient mentality.

From the preceding discussion it appears safe enough to conclude that both genetic and environmental factors are significant in the etiology of feeblemindedness of higher grades. But it is evident (as in the case of intelligence level in general) that we do not at present have any valid basis for estimating the relative degree to which the two kinds of factors are implicated. In particular, we have no information regarding either the population frequencies of the relevant genetic factors or the mechanisms of their transmission.

We come now to the question of possible grounds for sterilizing feebleminded individuals of the moron level. While there are, as we shall see below, a number of plausible arguments both for and against sterilization of morons, there is at the present time little or no valid basis for sterilizing them on *eugenic* grounds if this implies (as orthodox eugenists would generally insist) that eugenic measures are those which appreciably improve the *genetic composition* of the population. For, as we have seen in the last chapter, in order to predict the effects of phenotypic selection on the distribution of genotypes, it is necessary to know *the frequencies of the relevant genes* and *how they are transmitted* (autosomal or sex-linked) as well as their *ontogenetic relationships* (dominance relations, penetrance, nature of interactions, etc.).

Information of the kind just indicated is needed; in fact, to predict even the *direction* of the effects which will result from phenotypic selection. In some genetic situations phenotypic selection may have no effect at all. This would be true, for example, if one attempted to increase the proportion of Blue Andalusians in a flock of poultry to more than 50 per cent by culling all black and splashed-white birds. In other situations selection against a given phenotype can actually *increase* the frequency of the genes or gene interactions responsible for the phenotype. Thus in a population in which the gene r (see Chapter 13) has a frequency of about 0.6, as it appears to have among the Basques, the failure of infants with erythroblastosis to survive tends progressively to increase the frequency of the r allele; under these conditions, it can be shown that the frequency of erythroblastosis will actually increase for about 80 generations (2000 years!), although ultimately it will tend to diminish. Perhaps genetic situations of this sort are relatively unusual; but it is not unusual to find characteristics, especially of a quantitative nature, which are contingent upon multiple-gene interactions, where the expression of the genotype is to a large extent dependent on environmental factors. In these situations phenotypic selection may be effective in the expected direction, but its effects can be so slow (depending on the number of genes involved, their sensitiveness to environmental influences, and the degree of heterogeneity in the environment) as to be imperceptible within any historic time span.

Now the question of the sterilization of morons is clearly a controversial one. This fact implies that the problem is not in black and white, with *all* the valid arguments on one side; a sensible decision on the question therefore must involve weighing the *relative* merits of opposing arguments. This demands *quantitative* evaluation. It is frequently argued either explicitly or implicitly (as by urging legislation on eugenic grounds) that sterilization would have eugenic value, in the sense of improving the genotypic quality of the population, merely because there is evidence that genetic factors are *involved* in the etiology of mental deficiency. This argument is misleading unless it is made clear that our genetic knowledge is inadequate to tell us whether the improvement can be substantial enough to overbalance all countervailing arguments or whether it will be so minute as to be completely overshadowed by even incidental objections to a sterilization program.

As a matter of fact, it can be shown on purely empirical grounds that sterilization of morons on a large scale probably *would* reduce their phenotypic frequency in the population. The best available estimates suggest that from 10 to 20 per cent of morons are the offspring of parents one or both of whom are likewise mentally deficient. This would imply (provided no changes in relevant environmental factors take place) that sterilization of *all* morons before they reproduce might diminish by from one tenth to one fifth the incidence of morons otherwise to be expected in the next generation — representing reduction from a frequency of approximately 20 per thousand to 16 per thousand to make the estimate as generous as seems reasonably possible. *Progress of this sort beyond the first generation cannot be predicted.*

A sterilization program that reached even approximately 100 per cent of the class to which it is intended to apply, however, would be a miracle of efficiency, even if the class were one whose members could be readily and unequivocally diagnosed. In view of the uncertainties of borderline cases, even 50 per cent efficiency in carrying out this particular program would be rather remarkable, and it is fairly safe to assume that the cases most likely to escape sterilization would be those near the borderline levels of intelligence. But, as we have already seen, it is precisely at these levels (where diagnostic difficulties are greatest) that fertility appears to be higher than among the more readily diagnosed lower-I.Q. group. Consequently, anything short of 100 per cent efficiency in carrying out the program would mean that proportionately fewer of the more fertile than of the less fertile morons would be sterilized. Hence, it would appear to be more than generous to estimate that a program intended to sterilize all morons would, in practical application, perhaps reduce their population incidence from 20 per thousand to 18 per thousand. That is, the sterilization of about one and a half million morons might mean a diminution in the next generation of about 300,000 in the aggregate number of morons in the United States. But (on the basis of the presumptive initial incidence used for our estimate) there would still be a possible 2,700,000 left, and we have no way of telling what further reduction could be achieved by a continuance of the program.

It should be emphasized that the results suggested above are those which might be expected from an *all-out* effort. The advocates of sterilization in California are proud of the record of enforcement of the sterilization laws in that state, where more than 30,000 sterilizations (approximately a third of them on the feebleminded) have been performed since 1910. To be effective to the degree of phenotypic reduction suggested above, sterilization of morons throughout the U.S. would have to be accomplished at from 3 to 6 times the California rate.

That a reduction by one tenth in the number of phenotypic morons in our population would be a desirable accomplishment no one would deny. And one might easily argue that if a program of sterilization can accomplish such a reduction it makes no difference whether it is represented as a *eugenic* measure which promises genetic improvement in the population or not. But it does make a great deal of difference. Specifically, it is a matter of major importance whether the predicted results are achievable because the sterilization program would remove a significant share of "defective" genes, or because it would prevent an appreciable number of children of normal genetic potentialities from being born into environments which would doom a substantial proportion of them to intellectual inferiority. If the former is the case, it could be argued that preventing the morons from reproducing (whether by sterilization or segregation) is a rational procedure. But if the second alternative is the correct one, sterilization is neither a rational nor an economical approach to the problem; rather, the emphasis should most profitably be on the amelioration of unfavorable environmental conditions. At the present time, we have no evidence which permits us to decide between the two alternatives or between either one and a combination of the two. Consequently, any argument for a program for the eugenic sterilization of the feebleminded which purports to be demonstrable on genetic principles is essentially spurious. Moreover, propaganda for such a program is likely to be successful only by focusing public attention on the allegedly irremediable genetic basis of mental deficiency. And such propaganda is likely to be iniquitous to the extent that it diverts attention from the necessity for investigating nongenetic factors which may be of equal etiologic significance and of very much greater potential significance from a preventive standpoint.

There are, of course, arguments for and against sterilization other than those based on eugenic grounds. Respecting these, the student of genetics can speak with only a layman's knowledge. It would be well for him (and others) to bear in mind, however, that the alternative to sterilization is not *laissez faire* but institutional segregation.

It is sometimes argued, for example, that the feebleminded should be sterilized, regardless of eugenic considerations, because they are not sufficiently responsible to be fit parents. Probably most of us would agree with the latter part of this statement, but we might feel that for those who are clearly lacking in responsibility supervision would be desirable (both from their own standpoint and that of society), so that segregation rather than sterilization would be indicated. It may be noted here that in general sterilization should not be necessary in institutionalized cases to prevent reproduction because segregation itself ordinarily accomplishes this end. It is often urged that sterilization of institutionalized females would be a humane procedure in any case because patients could be allowed more frequent leaves from their institutions without risk of becoming pregnant; and cases are cited of pregnancies contracted during leaves or paroles. Unless it is shown, however, that cases of this sort are more than occasional in their occurrence they hardly constitute any substantial argument for the *routine* sterilization of institutionalized females.

Finally, the weightiest noneugenic argument cited in favor of sterilizing the mentally deficient is an economic one, and eugenists themselves use this argument rather extensively in addition to their eugenic thesis. There is indeed considerable expense involved in the maintenance of state institutions for the feebleminded and other deviate groups in spite of the fact that only a small proportion (probably less than 10 per cent of the feebleminded) is institutionalized. But the total cost of maintaining welfare institutions altogether represents only a small fraction of a per cent of the state's gross expenditures. It is not for a geneticist to say whether this is exorbitant or not. Certainly most mental hygienists would feel that ten times the current outlay needs to be spent on mental institutions.

The saving that would appear to ensue from sterilization *as a substitute for institutionalization* is, moreover, in large part illusory. As was pointed out by the Committee of the American Neurological Association, "placing a case . . . of feeblemindedness in an institution does not necessarily increase the cost of caring for him. It may be just as costly to care for him, financially, and more costly from the standpoint of social disorder and familial suffering, in his own home." In their opinion, when a patient is placed in an institution, "the social order is enhanced and the family can go about their life business with more effectiveness and greater comfort."

It would seem evident, even to a layman, that sterilization of those who are currently outside of institutions would not reduce the expense of maintaining those inside, and that we need institutional facilities for a far larger number of the feebleminded than can now be accommodated, as well as better facilities for those who are now within institutional walls. It might be better overall economy to divert to these ends whatever costs a blanket sterilization program might entail.

Nothing that has been said should be construed to reflect adversely upon the validity or value of *genetic prognosis* (see p. 418) in individual cases. The point is mentioned here, because the prediction of risk in such cases is frequently referred to as *eugenic* prognosis. In many circumstances it is possible to advise prospective parents of the likelihood that a future child will be defective in one way or another. It is the parents' right in these cases to be apprised of the risk involved, and to weigh the risk against their desire for parenthood; and it would seem to be the geneticist's obligation to supply the prognosis when the requisite information is available.

Very often prospective parents who are warned of a high risk of having severely defective progeny may thereby be saved from a good deal of tragic misery, either because (feeling that the risk is too great) they decide against having a child or because (being willing to proceed in spite of the risk) the impact of having an afflicted child is lessened by virtue of the forewarning. In either case the benefit of the prognosis has been primarily to the *individual family* concerned; in neither case is it likely to affect to any appreciable degree the genetic composition of the population. It is rather important to keep in mind the distinction here between problems of individual health and happiness and those of public welfare. Applications of genetic principles which may be definitely helpful in the former context may have little or no value as measures of population improvement.

Insanity (or *psychosis*), like the general category of feeblemindedness, includes a miscellany of conditions of different types and diverse causes. Whereas, in general, feeblemindedness may be regarded as reflecting simply a retarded or arrested intellectual development (roughly, a quantitative deficiency in intelligence), *psychoses* represent severe personality disorders often involving extreme behavioral eccentricities, excessive emotionality or total lack of normal emotional responses, and in some types, delusions and hallucinations. Some psychotic diseases (*dementias*) involve a progressive deterioration in intelligence; others are compatible with the persistence of intelligence of any level.

Psychoses may be conveniently classified as *organic* or *functional*. The former are characterized by the presence of discoverable physical abnormalities in the nervous system. At least one of the rarer organic psychoses, *Huntington's chorea*, has a simple Mendelian basis, being dependent on a dominant gene of which the pathologic effects, however, are not expressed until fairly late in life. Organic psychoses may also result from brain injury, from a number of poisons, and from syphilitic and certain other infections.

Functional psychoses are those without any discoverable organic basis. They include *schizophrenia* (often called *dementia praecox*), *manic-depressive psychosis*, and *paranoia*. Only the first two are very important from the standpoint of number of victims. Schizophrenia is characterized by a withdrawal from reality, so that the patient tends to live in a dream world of his own, behavior is purposeless and may be marked by giggling silliness or by extreme apathy, and there is often a progressive deterioration in intelligence. There is considerable doubt as to whether all conditions classified as schizophrenia constitute an entity attributable always to the same causes; it is quite possible that a number of diseases of different origin are included under this designation. Manic-depressive insanity is marked, as its name might suggest, by alternating periods of excited elation and abysmal depression. Some affected individuals are violent and destructive. Mild degrees of the condition, however, are compatible with satisfactory social adjustment, and borderline cases of good mentality are in some instances highly creative persons.

Our knowledge of genetic factors in insanity is approximately in the same state as our information on genetic components in the etiology of mental deficiency. There is no evidence for the implication of genetic factors in the toxic or syphilitic psychoses (which together constitute a sizable minority of psychoses as a whole), although this does not necessarily mean that genetic predispositions can be excluded. Schizophrenia has been studied rather extensively. The most elaborate research is that of Kallmann, who investigated 174 monozygotic and 517 dizygotic twin pairs, in each of which at least one member was schizophrenic, together with several thousand relatives of different degrees. Among the monozygotic twins, about 86 per cent were doubly affected (when a statistical adjustment for age of onset was made; 69 per cent without adjustment). Among the dizygotic twins, the (adjusted) frequency of doubly affected pairs was only 14.7 per cent, and the figure for sib pairs in which both members were affected was almost exactly the same, viz., 14.3 per cent. Fifty-nine of Kallmann's monozygotic pairs had been separated for a varying number of years (on the average, for 11 to 12 years) prior to the appearance of the disease in one twin; the average age at which they were separated appears to have been about ten. It is of interest to note that among the separated identicals the adjusted frequency of doubly affected pairs was somewhat lower than in those which had not been separated (78 per cent as compared with 92 per cent). The difference between the two frequencies must be regarded as only suggestive, however, since it falls short of being statistically significant. As in the case of feeblemindedness, the data strongly indicate that genetic factors are of etiologic significance (provided again the assumption is valid that the intra-pair environment is substantially as similar for a dizygotic as it is for a monozygotic pair), and at the same time they reveal that the determinants of the condition cannot be exclusively genetic. This is essentially all we can say about the roles of genetic and environmental factors in the development of schizophrenia; consequently, whatever limitations we found for the predictability of eugenic improvement through sterilization of affected individuals in the case of feeblemindedness would apply also to this disease. If anything, the probability of appreciable eugenic effects from sterilization in the case of schizophrenia is still smaller than in high-grade mental deficiency. Not only is the net fertility of schizophrenics reduced (it appears to be approximately 25 per cent less than for normal persons), but the majority of their children, about two thirds, are born before the onset of the disease in the parents.

Manic-depressive insanity has also been studied from a genetic standpoint, though much less extensively than schizophrenia. The limited data available point to conclusions essentially the same as those we have drawn from the schizophrenia material: both genetic and environmental factors are almost certainly involved, but their respective importance cannot be evaluated.

Epilepsy is a term applied to conditions characterized by the occurrence of various types of *seizures* which usually involve temporary loss of consciousness; in less frequent cases the patient retains consciousness during the seizures but is irrational. In the commonest variety of seizure loss of consciousness lasts but a few seconds and is accompanied by rhythmic twitchings, usually confined to the eyelids and eyebrows. In the less common, but more familiar (because more spectacular) variety, violent convulsions of the whole body occur during the attack. Seizures may occur almost daily or they may be experienced only at intervals extending up to several years. Epilepsy may appear as a consequence of brain injury or in certain instances of brain tumor. In the greater number of cases (sometimes collectively called idiopathic) no physical cause can be discerned.

One of the most tragic calumnies against any group of human beings is involved in the common superstition that epileptics as a class are degenerate or somehow a contemptible group Because brain damage which on occasion causes mental deficiency or psychosis may also result in epileptic symptoms, epilepsy is somewhat more common among the mentally deficient and the insane than in the general population. But the vast majority of epileptics themselves are neither mentally deficient nor psychotic, and the list of epileptics in the history of any nation would include many highly gifted and valuable members of society.

A few studies have been made on identical and fraternal twin pairs in which "idiopathic" epilepsy was present. The findings have about the same implications as results of the studies of this kind in mental deficiency and the psychoses, i.e., they indicate that both genetic and environmental factors are of causal significance. The investigations which give most promise of shedding light on the genetic factors of epilepsy, however, are those involving the analysis of "brain waves," as recorded by an electroencephalograph.

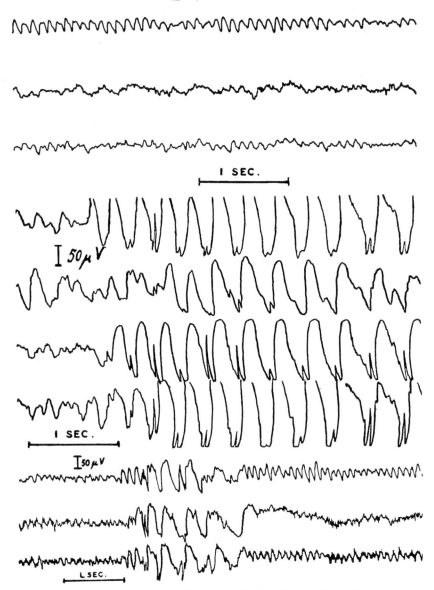

Fig. 29.4 Electroencephalograms (Tracings of Brain Waves). Upper lines, tracings from a normal person without epilepsy or cerebral dysrhythmia. Middle group of lines, tracings from an epileptic. Note the large spikes and waves, indicative of cerebral dysrhythmia. Lower lines, tracings from the mother of the epileptic. She did not have epilepsy, but the tracings show the presence of cerebral dysrhythmia, which might here be transmitted on the basis of a dominant gene, and to reflect a predisposition to epilepsy.

Electroencephalographic examination reveals that certain rather characteristic types of *cerebral dysrhythmia* occur in the brain-wave records of most epileptics (Fig. 29.4). Studies by Lennox and Gibbs in this country and by Harvald in Denmark have shown that these dysrhythmias are found also in roughly 15 per cent of persons who have never exhibited epileptic symptoms; *but they occur in about half of the close relatives* (sibs, parents, and children) of epileptics. The evidence to date indicates that the dysrhythmias in many instances have a genetic basis and that they are in some degree indicative of a predisposition toward the development of epilepsy. The predisposition can hardly be a very strong one, however. Not more than about 0.5 per cent of our population (that is, one person in 200) develops epilepsy; but, as we have seen, the cerebral dysrhythmias have a prevalence of approximately 15 per cent. Thus, epilepsy occurs in only about one person in 30 of those who have a cerebral dysrhythmia. Finally, although the available evidence points, as we have noted, to the implication of genetic factors in the etiology of epilepsy, it does not permit an analysis in terms of genetic mechanisms. Consequently, in the case of epilepsy, as for other conditions discussed in this chapter, we have no way of predicting the degree to which a sterilization program would be effective in reducing its prevalence.

We have now briefly discussed in the light of current genetic knowledge the five categories of defect for which sterilization has been most widely prescribed or recommended in existing legal statutes. What general conclusions can we draw regarding the eugenic implications of a sterilization program in the cases considered? In the first place, it has been seen that there is evidence, ranging from strongly presumptive to very nearly conclusive, that genetic determinants are to some degree involved in the etiology of conditions in all of these categories. We have also seen, however, that this is not sufficient to guarantee that sterilization can effect any appreciable change in the frequencies of relevant genotypes within a time span measured in human generations.

These considerations certainly give us no justification for a blanket denunciation of sterilization. They do suggest that the advocates of programs of negative eugenics have been insufficiently explicit in indicating just what results may reasonably be expected from the application of their programs, and perhaps that they have not altogether recognized the quantitative limitations of selective processes under various conditions. Our discussion should also suggest that there is no valid basis in genetic fact or theory to justify a blanket endorsement of sterilization programs, that negative eugenic proposals require careful *quantitative* scrutiny, and that each category of disease or defect proposed for sterilization must be judged on its own merits.

Finally, we have seen that considerations (humanitarian, economic, etc.) other than those which directly involve genetic principles may be relevant to programs which are ostensibly eugenic in their primary aims. Where this is the case the noneugenic implications of the program may have greater weight than its eugenic possibilities, and each must then be weighed against the other.

Positive eugenics, which was referred to earlier in this chapter (p. 461) can be discussed here with relative brevity, in large part because few of the proposals which have been advocated as positive eugenic measures can be analyzed in terms of genetic principles on the basis of our current knowledge of genetic mechanisms.

One reason for the difficulty in evaluating programs of positive eugenics lies in the fact that many of the terms in the proposals are not defined with sufficient precision to have much meaning to the geneticist. Thus, the general principle of positive eugenics lies in encouraging the reproduction of desirable genotypes, in contrast to the negative eugenic principle of concentrating on the discouragement of reproduction of undesirable genotypes. We are not concerned here with the exact specification of desirable and undesirable genotypes. *But it makes a great deal of difference at the outset whether the intention is to separate off the least desirable 5 per cent for example, and designate the remaining 95 per cent as desirable; or to separate off the most desirable 5 per cent and designate the remainder as undesirable.*

In the former case, any eugenic effects (in the sense of favorable alterations in relative genotype frequencies) which might be accomplished by increased fertility among the preferred 95 per cent of the population would, of course, be identical with the eugenic effects of a corresponding reduction in the fertility of the undesirable 5 per cent through sterilization or other measures of negative eugenics. Our earlier consideration of negative eugenics would lead us to suspect that such effects would be negligible. *They would certainly be negligible in comparison with the social and economic consequences* of the *general* rise in reproductive rate which increased reproductivity by *ninety-five* per cent of the population would entail, unless the rise were very small indeed. These consequences might be good or they might be bad. But in so far as they are likely to overshadow altogether any strictly eugenic effects of the measures which produced them, there would seem to be some question as to whether the term *eugenic* is an appropriate designation for these measures.

On the other hand, if it is intended to concentrate on stimulating the fertility of those having the *most desirable five per cent* of the genotypes, retaining the *status quo* (reproductively speaking) of the remaining 95 per cent, the effects on population growth as a whole would be insignificant. In this case, however, the problem of even approximately precise specification of genotypes looms rather large. It might not be too difficult to pick out, if not 5 per cent, perhaps 1 per cent, of genotypes in the population which we could generally agree on as at least "very undesirable." It would be quite impossible, however, to pick out *any* genotypes which could be designated as "most" or even "very" desirable. The simple reason for this is that although we have succeeded in identifying a reasonable number of individually rather rare genes which are responsible for gross and rather clearly undesirable effects, *we do not know of a single rare gene which produces desirable effects*. The normal alleles of all of the "undesirable" genes are of course desirable; but they all have frequencies of from 0.90 to 0.99 or above, and therefore could not be used for classifying an uppermost 5 per cent of desirable genotypes.

Now it is quite probable that the positive eugenics programs do not intend to attempt the partition of desirable and undesirable in either of the ways suggested above. The point is, as we have seen, that different methods of partitioning have very different implications, and it is essential that any realistic program which purports to be eugenic must therefore at least roughly indicate the partitioning that it proposes if it is intended that its effects should be susceptible of evaluation.

Other terms used by writers on positive eugenics also lack specificity and thereby confuse many otherwise lucid discussions. Among these is the frequently occurring expression "superior stocks" or "superior strains." It is not always completely clear whether the superiority relates to phenotype or to genotype; usually, however, genotypic superiority seems to be intended.

Now a reasonable acquaintance with the principles of gene-and-environment interactions during development should make it obvious that in general, the terms "superior" and "inferior" cannot be applied to genotypes in any meaningful sense *unless the environment in which they are to develop is specified*. A standard illustration of the point involves a comparison of Jersey cows, for example, which have been bred for high milk yield (*in Jersey*) with scrub cattle from the African bush. If animals of the two breeds are pastured on the Isle of Jersey, the Jerseys will yield enormously more milk than the Africans. If both breeds are put out in the African bush, the African cows will still yield milk, though in smaller quantity than on the Jersey pasturage; but the Jersey cows will cease to produce altogether and most of them will not even survive. Assuming that we have agreed to judge the breeds in terms of milk yield, it is clearly not possible to designate either as superior in any absolute sense. We can easily think of comparable illustrations in the human species. A man with a high degree of muscular coordination may be superior *as a surgeon* to a physician who has a genetically defective neuromotor organization; but the latter may be superior *as a diagnostician*. A sickly child, reared in a cultured atmosphere where there is sufficient wealth to afford him proper care may develop into a creative scholar of the first magnitude (as did Charles Darwin); the same child reared in a lumber camp, could very well be stamped as a weakling and a useless delinquent throughout his life.

Another objection to the phrases in question lies in the fact that the words "stocks" and "strains" are at best lacking in precision, and at worst they are actually misleading in their connotations. To the laboratory geneticist the terms imply *complete or very nearly complete genetic homogeneity*. Now genetic homogeneity is something which can be to a large extent measured, in man as well as in laboratory and domestic animals. The measurement is commonly expressed in terms of Wright's *coefficient of relationship* which gives the average probability, for pairs of animals chosen at random, that any given allele will be present in both of them through inheritance from a common ancestor. (It can also be defined as the average fraction of all loci occupied by identical genes of common origin in pairs of animals chosen at random.) When a geneticist refers to a *stock* of mice or a *strain* of Drosophila he usually qualifies the term by adding "isogenic" or "inbred by brother-sister mating for 20 generations," or else the qualification is understood. In strains of stocks in this sense the coefficient of relationship is unity or very near it.

To the stock breeder the terms do not imply nearly so high a degree of homogeneity, but they do suggest at least that there is uniformity with respect to a number of genetically determined characteristics such as pattern and configuration.

When the expression "superior stock" (or "inferior stock") is used in human context, the word *stock* almost certainly does not imply uniformity in genetically determined characteristics by which its members may be readily recognized. If the word has any precise meaning, therefore, we must suppose that it relates to some degree of genetic homogeneity; but if this is the case, the term requires some *quantitative* clarification. References to the current descendants of Jonathan Edwards or of the Darwin-Wedgwood families as a strain or stock can have little useful meaning unless some estimate is made of the degree of genetic homogeneity among them.

On the credit side of the ledger, it must be pointed out that writers on positive eugenics tend to be more aware of the distinction between phenotype and genotype than do the sponsors of negative eugenics (although, as we have just seen, they sometimes incline to overlook some of the immediate implications of this distinction). These writers favor numerous reforms (such as those quoted on p. 460) which they feel would minimize environmental inequalities. On the other hand (desirable though these reforms in themselves may seem to many) such measures are proposed not as ends in themselves, but as means to permit the more effective action of selective processes on the genotypic composition of the population.

To the thoughtful student of genetics, this may appear to be the long way around. The viewpoint of several representative geneticists on these matters is well expressed in an editorial summary of a recent symposium in which H. J. Muller, Th. Dobzhansky, M. Demerec, Philip Levine, Franz Schrader, and the senior author of the present volume participated.

"At the present level of genetic knowledge we cannot improve the genes with which we are born, and there is little we can do to determine which genes we pass on to our children. But we can improve the manifestations of our own genes and those of other persons so that the best possible phenotypes are produced. The control of the manifestation of human genes is, of course, possible only by proper manipulation of the environment. The implications as regards medicine, especially preventive medicine, are obvious. As Dobzhansky of Columbia University has put it: 'Medicine is the science of management of the human phenotype.'"

Here it is implied that the provision of conditions which would permit the optimal expression of existing genotypes is a worthwhile end in itself, and that if we can accomplish a general phenotypic improvement in this way, it is as good as any other. To some, this is an alarming proposition, because they fear that the human race may become genetically degenerate behind a façade of phenotypic improvement. The alarm would seem to be an unnecessary one, as witness the Jersey cow, genotypically "degenerate" in the sense that it does not even have the vigor to survive, much less produce, in natural conditions. The truth is, it does not live in *natural* conditions but, in the environment which has been devised for it, it is a superbly productive member of bovine society. The history of human social evolution has been in very large part one of learning to provide environments which will maximize social efficiency. It is to be hoped that this trend will continue.

If we are to provide such environments, the geneticist will have to assist in discovering what environmental factors are relevant in the expression of the various genes that have been identified to date. This will require further research into the mechanisms of inheritance, the mode of action of individual genes, and interactions among genes.

Perhaps the greatest task which confronts the geneticist today is the unraveling of the complexities of the exact hereditary and environmental influences which underlie the development and expression of human characteristics. Fortunately society is willing to encourage and aid those whose interests lie in this direction. It is to be hoped that more and more facts will be uncovered, and that with their discovery will come the willingness and the opportunity to use them to the fullest advantage for the human race.

PROBLEMS

29.1 About 9 per cent of all schizophrenics have parents one or both of whom ultimately succumb to schizophrenia themselves. Two thirds of the children of parents who develop schizophrenia, however, are born before the onset of the disease in either parent. Taking both of these facts into account, make an "empirical" prediction (similar to that attempted on p. 480 f. in the case of high-grade feeblemindedness) of the per cent by which you might expect the frequency of schizophrenia to be reduced from one generation to the next, if all schizophrenics were sterilized *immediately after diagnosis of the disease.*

29.2 It is readily shown (see Chap. 28), for most pathologic traits known to be contingent on single autosomal genes, that sterilization of all those who exhibit the traits would have negligible effects on the gene frequencies involved. The reason for this is that the genes determining the traits are either relatively *rare* recessives, or dominants of variable expressivity. It has often been suggested that a negative eugenic program directed against these conditions could be really effective if only we could identify and sterilize the normal carriers of the genes.

About how many persons would be subject to sterilization under such a program if we wished to apply it: (a) to "idiopathic" epilepsy, under the assumption that persons with cerebral dysrhythmia carry a gene which is manifested as epilepsy about 3 per cent of the time; (b) to juvenile amaurotic idiocy (assuming a population frequency of 0.0001 for the recessive homozygote); (c) to 15 or 20 different recessive conditions, each with a frequency of about 0.0001? Do your calculations suggest anything to you about the practicality of this kind of program?

29.3 The hereditary basis for mental traits has been much more difficult to establish than the hereditary basis for physical traits. Can you suggest reasons for this fact?

29.4 Give your answer to the question: "Is insanity inherited?" Is there a better method of stating this question? If so, how should it be stated?

29.5 It is sometimes said that if a certain character were conditioned by heredity, it could not be modified by the environment. Is this attitude justified? Discuss the statement in connection with mental traits.

29.6 Suppose that a certain mental trait seldom, if ever, appeared in more than one member of a family. Could it still be dependent upon hereditary factors? What sort of hereditary basis might be possible for such a trait?

29.7 Discuss the possible interactions of hereditary and environmental influences in the development of such a trait as musical ability.

29.8 Do you think the fact that the men in a family frequently follow the same vocation indicates the inheritance of a special ability along that line? What else might it indicate?

29.9 If you were studying the possibility of the inheritance of criminal tendencies, what would you want to know about the families besides their criminal records?

29.10 What is meant by "conditioned" behavior? Do human beings exhibit any behavior of this sort? How would such behavior affect studies of the inheritance of mental traits?

29.11 How has the study of identical twins aided the investigations of the genetic nature of mental traits?

29.12 Do you think that the mental traits of the members of a pair of fraternal twins would be more similar or less similar than those of ordinary brothers and sisters?

29.13 Suppose a friend of yours is in love with his cousin and wants to marry her. He comes to you for advice. What would you tell him?

29.14 Is there a sterilization law in your state? If so, how does it function? Are there adequate records available as to the success or failure of the plan?

29.15 If your state has no sterilization law, discuss the reasons for the fact.

In your opinion are these reasons adequate?

29.16 If possible, visit your state institution for the feebleminded. Observe what is being done for these individuals. Obtain the opinions of the officials of the institution as to the merits of the various suggested eugenic measures.

29.17 Visit if possible your state schools for the deaf and blind. How would suggested eugenic measures involving such individuals differ from those involving the feebleminded?

29.18 The Declaration of Independence states "We hold these truths to be self-evident, that all men are created equal . . ." Discuss this statement from the genetic standpoint.

29.19 What are some of the reasons which in your opinion account for the fact that at present the birth rate is relatively low among the educated classes?

29.20 Make a list of the genetic defects which in your opinion should legally prevent a person from marrying.

29.21 From the eugenic standpoint, what do you think are the effects of war?

29.22 Do you think that if adequate opportunities and training were provided for everyone, many of the apparent differences in ability between individuals would disappear?

REFERENCES

ANASTASI, ANNE, and FOLEY, J. P., *Differential Psychology*, Revised ed. New York, The Macmillan Co. (1949).

BLACKER, C. P., *Eugenics: Galton and After*. Cambridge, Harvard University Press (1952).

BURKS, BARBARA, in *The 27th Yearbook of the National Society for the Study of Education*, Part 1, 219. Bloomington, Ill., Public School Publ. Co. (1928).

Committee of the Amer. Neurological Assn. for the Investigation of Eugenical Sterilization, *Eugenical Sterilization*. New York, The Macmillan Co. (1936).

CORWIN, E. H. L. (ed.), *Ecology of Health*. New York, The Commonwealth Fund (1949).

DAVID, P. R., and SNYDER, L. H., *Genetic Variability and Human Behavior*. In *Social Psychology at the Crossroads*

(Rohrer, J. H. and Sherif, M., eds.). New York, Harper and Brothers (1951).

DOLL, E. A., in *Manual of Child Psychology* (L. Carmichael, ed.), Chap. 17. New York, John Wiley and Sons, Inc. (1946).

DUNN, L. C., AND DOBZHANSKY, TH., *Heredity, Race, and Society*. New York, The New Amer. Libr. of World Lit. Inc. (1946).

FREEMAN, F. N., HOLZINGER, K. J., and MITCHELL, B. C., in *27th Yearbook of the National Society for the Study of Education*, Part I, 103. Bloomington, Ill., Public School Publ. Co. (1928).

FREEMAN, FRANK S., *Theory and Practice of Psychological Testing*. New York, Henry Holt and Co. (1950).

GALTON, FRANCIS, *Essays in Eugenics*. London, The Eugenics Education Society (1909).

HAGGERTY, M. E., and NASH, H. B., *Jour. Educ. Psychol.* **15**:559 (1924).

HALDANE, J. B. S., *Heredity and Politics*. New York, W. W. Norton and Co. (1938).

HALDANE, J. B. S., *Human Evolution: Past and Future*. In *Genetics, Paleontology, and Evolution* (Jepson, G. L. et al., eds.). Princeton, Princeton Univ. Press (1949).

HARVALD, BENT, *Opera ex Domo Biologiae Hereditariae Univ. Hafn.* **35** (1954).

HOGBEN, L. T., *Genetic Principles in Medicine and Social Science*. New York, A. A. Knopf (1932); *Nature and Nurture*. New York, W. W. Norton and Co. (1933).

KALLMANN, F. J., *Heredity in Health and Mental Disorder*. New York, W. W. Norton and Co. (1953).

LANDMAN, J. H., *Human Sterilization*. New York, The Macmillan Co. (1932).

LEAHY, A. M., *Genet. Psychol. Monogr.* **17**:236 (1935).

LENNOX, W. G., *Science and Seizures*. New York, Harper Bros. (1941).

LEWIS, E. O. (ed.), *Report of the Mental Deficiency Committee* (Wood Report), Parts I–IV. London, His Majesty's Stationery Office (1929).

National Society for the Study of Education, 27th Yearbook, Part I: *Nature and Nurture, Their Influence upon Intelligence*. Bloomington, Ill., Public School Publ. Co. (1928).

National Society for the Study of Education, 39th Yearbook, Parts I and II: *Intelligence: Its Nature and Nurture*. Bloomington, Ill., Public School Publ. Co. (1940).

NEWMAN, H. H., FREEMAN, F. N., and HOLZINGER, K. J., *Twins: A Study of Heredity and Environment*. Chicago, Univ. of Chicago Press (1937).

OSBORN, F., *Practical Eugenics*. New York, Amer. Eugenics Soc. (1938); *Preface to Eugenics*, Revised ed. New York, Harper and Brothers (1951).

PENROSE, L. S., *The Biology of Mental Defect*. New York, Grune and Stratton (1949).

PRICE, BRONSON, and HALPERIN, S. L., *Amer. Jour. Ment. Def.* **45** (1940).

REED, S. C., *Counseling in Medical Genetics*. Philadelphia, W. B. Saunders Co. (1955).

ROBERTS, J. A. F., *An Introduction to Medical Genetics*. London, Oxford Univ. Press (1940).

ROSANOFF, A. J., HANDY, L. M., and PLESSET, I. R., *Psychol. Monogr.* **48**:1 (1937).

RUSK, R. R., in *The 39th Yearbook of the National Society for the Study of Education*, Part II, 269. Bloomington, Ill., Public School Publ. Co. (1940).

SJÖGREN, TORSTEN, *Hereditas* **14**:197 (1931).

SKODAK, M., and SKEELS, H. M., *Jour. Genet. Psychol.* **66**:21 (1945).

SNYDER, L. H., *Medical Genetics*. Durham, Duke Univ. Press (1941); *Bull. N.Y. Acad. Med.*, 2nd Series, **22**:566 (1946); Chapter V, *Human Heredity*. In Muller, Little, and Snyder: *Genetics, Medicine and Man*. Ithaca, Cornell Univ. Press (1947).

STERN, CURT, *Principles of Human Genetics*. San Francisco, W. H. Freeman and Co. (1949).

WHEELER, L. R., *Jour. Educ. Psychol.* **33**:321 (1942).

WOODWORTH, R. S., *Heredity and Environment*. New York, Social Science Research Council (1941).

INDEX

INDEX

Vinegar fly. *See* Drosophila.
Virus, 376, 401 ff.
Vitamins, 387
Von Gierke's disease, 391
VON TSCHERMAK, 35

WAGNER, 400
WARREN, 273
Wasps, 171, 338
WASSIN, 123
Watermelons, 60
WATSON, 363, 367
W-chromosome, 105
WEINSTEIN, 173
WELLHAUSEN, 293
WEXELSEN, 203, 210
WHALEY, 245
Wheat, 77, 200, 232
WHEELER, 472, 495
WHITE, 50, 154
Whitefish, 41
White forelock, 114
WHITING, 339, 347
WIENER, 189 ff., 196

WILSON, 50
WINTERS, 245
Wolf, 49
Wood Report, 476. *See* LEWIS, 494.
WOODWORTH, 470, 495
WRIEDT, 29, 34
WRIGHT, 221, 238, 245, 384 ff., 400, 457
WYSS, 400

X-chromosome, 92, 333
Xenia, 283
Xeroderma pigmentosum, 426
X-rays, 354 ff.

Y-chromosome, 93, 333
Y-chromosome inheritance, 423
Yeasts, 386, 391

Z-chromosome, 104 ff.
Zea mays. See Maize.
Zebu, 237
ZINDER, 414
ZIRKLE, 21
Zygote, 18